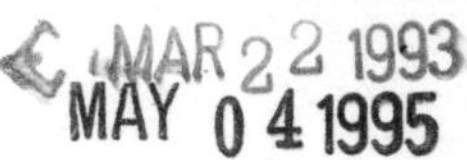

TEXT-BOOKS OF ANIMAL BIOLOGY

Books which have appeared in this series.

★

Edited by JULIAN HUXLEY

Comparative Physiology
by Lancelot Hogben

Animal Ecology
by Charles Elton

Life in Inland Waters
by Kathleen Carpenter

Vertebrate Zoology
by G. R. de Beer

The Development of Sex in Vertebrates
by F. W. Rogers Brambell

A General Zoology of the Invertebrates
by G. S. Carter

★

Edited by H. MUNRO FOX

Animal Evolution
by G. S. Carter

Parasitism and Symbiosis
by M. Caullery

Zoogeography of the Land and Inland Waters
by L. F. de Beaufort

Zoogeography of the Sea
by Sven Ekman

The Nature of Animal Colours
by H. Munro Fox and Gwynne Vevers

A GENERAL ZOOLOGY OF THE INVERTEBRATES

A GENERAL ZOOLOGY OF THE INVERTEBRATES

BY

G. S. CARTER

Fellow of Corpus Christi College
and Lecturer in Zoology
in the University of Cambridge

FOREWORD BY

JULIAN S. HUXLEY, F.R.S.

SIDGWICK AND JACKSON LIMITED
LONDON

First published in 1940
Second Edition in 1946
Third Edition (Revised and Reset) 1951
Reprinted 1957
Fourth Edition (Revised) 1961

MADE AND PRINTED IN GREAT BRITAIN BY WILLIAM CLOWES AND SONS, LIMITED
LONDON AND BECCLES

FOREWORD

LIFE is another name for the properties of protoplasm. Protoplasm is capable of self-reproduction; it metabolises, respires, excretes, it reacts to stimuli of various sorts, it moves, it mutates. In the course of evolution, it has become organised into various types of ultimate units. The most universal and the best organised of these is the cell: no animal organism exhibits a pre-cellular type of organisation.

Thus the first task of a writer on invertebrate zoology is to discuss the main properties of animal protoplasm and to describe the organisation of the typical animal cell. His next step will be to demonstrate the variety of forms assumed by free-living animal cells, the degree of size and complexity of which they are capable, and the types of organ capable of being differentiated within single cells. But it can be deduced on physiological grounds that the size and therefore the complexity of cells is strictly limited. Multiplication of nuclei within the single cytoplasmic boundary, perhaps in some cases followed by the subdivision of the whole into new separate protoplasmic units not strictly homologous with free-living cells; syncytial union of cells; simple colony-formation with eventual division of labour among the units; the formation of multicellular units of higher grade and differentiated from the start—these are some of the ways in which life attempted to overcome this basic limitation. The only fully successful method has proved to be the building of a single organism out of uninucleate cytoplasmic units, which, whether precisely homologous with free-living protista or not, are sufficiently similar to merit the same title of cells. Comparative anatomy and embryology make it reasonably certain that this step was taken twice in animal evolution—by the sponges on the one hand, by the true Metazoa on the other.

The interconnection of the units and their subordination to the whole organism seems to have been less in the sponges from the outset: in any event, this line never produced any highly integrated organisms.

The remaining invertebrate groups inevitably form the chief subject-matter of the invertebrate zoologist. The most basic question for him to ask about them must be this: how the unit of the organism and the specificity of its form is imposed on the constituent units and maintained throughout the changes of life-history and environment? On this point, studies in developmental physiology, regeneration, grafting, and experimental zoology in general have shed much light. Metazoan organisation is in origin dependent on "axial fields," affecting fundamental metabolic processes in a quantitatively graded way. An axial field appears always to possess a "dominant region," on the degree of whose activity depend the extent of the field and the subordination of its parts to the field's total unitary organisation.

Such axial fields appear to be general properties of protoplasm: a prime task of the invertebrate zoologist is to study their properties, the degree to which they can become specialised, and the limitations of their unaided activity. For instance, once a nervous system is established, this may, it appears, extend the limits of action of an axial field. It also introduces a new method of unification and co-ordination, as (by quite distinct methods) does the development of a blood-circulation and an endocrine system: and with increasing size of body, the nervous and circulatory systems may become the main or perhaps sometimes the sole agencies of co-ordination. Meanwhile, the development of complex skeletons, and of irreversible histological differentiation in general, may limit the effective action of axial fields, so that on the whole they will play a lesser part in higher organisms than in lower, in later than in earlier stages of ontogeny.

One type of field action, however, appears to be capable of continuing throughout life, namely the growth-field, regulating (in ways as yet unknown) the relative growth of different regions of the body. It is not even known whether the growth-field is the axial field expressing itself in another guise, or something of a wholly distinct nature. In any case, invertebrates afford much better material for studying both axial and growth-fields than do the higher vertebrates with their complex organisation and limited growth. Regeneration, bud-formation, differential resorption, dedifferentiation, and negative growth are also all much better exemplified in invertebrates than in vertebrates, and the study of these processes throws light on various points of their structure and life-history.

Summarised in the briefest way, the basic problem of the multicellular animal is the maintenance of organisation and of specific (or specifically changing) form. An analysis of the different methods needed for the maintenance of form at different levels of total size and complexity is not only of interest in itself, but sheds light on the very nature of the organisation found in various invertebrate groups, and its limitations.

Next comes comparative physiology with its study of different functions in different types of organisation and differing environments. The most fundamental aspect of this concerns the evolution of total efficiency. Some animal types are much larger and much more complex than others, capable of greater knowledge of the environment (or, if *knowledge* be too question-begging a term, of response to more extended and more varied experimental changes), of greater control over it, of greater self-regulation and independence. Such animals are rightly called higher, and their evolution may legitimately be called progressive. Comparative physiology studies the evolution of each primary function of protoplasm and enables us to understand the potentialities and limitations of various methods that have been adopted for securing progressive evolution. Thus vision by means of compound eyes, in spite of certain advantages (for instance the possible extent of the field of vision), appears to be inherently inferior in its potentialities to non-compound vision. Aërial respiration by tracheæ, while exceedingly efficient at small sizes, is useless for large organisms. A dead exoskeleton, with the consequent necessity of periodic moults, however obvious a device to start with, also becomes progressively less efficient with increasing size, as also does ciliary locomotion. A nerve-net cannot possibly give the elaboration of behaviour possible with a central nervous system. Hæmoglobin is in most ways a more efficient respiratory pigment than, say, hæmocyanin.

But, in addition to progressive levels of physiological organisation (which of course are reflected in levels of structural organisation), comparative physiology analyses the deviations of function which are possible in relation to differences in environment. Gut-parasites must be capable of periods of anærobic existence: sessile animals need different kinds of food-gathering mechanisms from those found in free-moving forms; the muscles which hold the valves of a lamellibranch shell closed must exhibit different properties of contraction from those subserving active locomotion in an insect or a squid; excretion within the closed microcosm of a shelled egg must make use of different chemical end-products from those got rid of in solution by a free-living animal's kidney. And each general plan of functional organisation will have different limits.

With the results of such studies to draw upon the ecology of organisms becomes clearer, and the limits of adaptive radiation set to different groups grows more intelligible.

Nor must life-history and behaviour be neglected. Larval organisation, as well as often shedding light on the evolutionary history of groups, has its functional meaning. Some larvæ are dispersal mechanisms, others feeding and growing stages, others a combination of the two. Parasites, just because they are parasitic, demand in general a higher degree of reproductive elaboration than free-living organisms. Insects will exhibit a different level and type of behaviour from echinoderms or mammals.

Studied in this way, the facts of invertebrate zoology take on a new significance. Instead of a bewildering procession of groups, each with its own elaborate details of structure to be memorised, the invertebrates reveal themselves as a series of major patterns of organisation, adapted in different ways to securing progressive advance, with different limits set to their ecological tolerance and their radiating specialisations.

Dr. Carter's is one of the few attempts that have yet been made to secure this mutual illumination of systematic zoology and general biological principles. The task is a difficult one, but for the new biological synthesis which is in the offing it is vital that it should be essayed. It is indeed fortunate that a zoologist so well equipped as Dr. Carter should have set himself to its realisation. I hope and anticipate that his book, keeping step with the rapid onward movement of zoology, will run into many editions.

JULIAN S. HUXLEY

March, 1940

PREFACE

This book is in no sense a text-book of invertebrate zoology. It has been written chiefly to meet the needs, as they seem to me, of the student in his first or second year at a university. He will have spent at least a year on animal biology and will be taking a course of descriptive zoology. There are many text-books of morphological zoology available for use with such a course, but it seems that the student also needs a book in which more general zoological problems are discussed, a book which can be read at the same time as his text-book. The present book has been written in the hope of filling this need. In writing it I have assumed some knowledge of animal biology and of invertebrate morphology. I have chiefly used the text-book on the Invertebrata by Borradaile, Eastham, Potts and Saunders, but any similar text-book would be suitable.

It is obvious that all the general problems of zoology cannot be discussed in a book of this size. Some selection was inevitable. I have selected mainly the questions which seemed of interest from the points of view of animal biology and ecology. These branches of the science, the study of animal life as we find it lived to-day both in the animal's own body and in the environment, are even now occupying a continually larger place in zoology, and their part is likely to become still more important in the future, as the need for knowledge and control of animal life is more keenly felt.

The outlook of these branches of zoology is necessarily organismal, and throughout the book this outlook has been adopted. They require a wide knowledge of comparative physiology and many other branches of zoology. It is this background of knowledge necessary for the biologist and ecologist that I have tried to summarise in this book. One large branch of biological knowledge has been entirely omitted. This is the science of heredity. I have omitted it, in spite of its admitted importance in all branches of zoology, because it has been well summarised in several recent books.

In discussing general questions such as those with which this book is concerned, it is certain that many views will be expressed which will need modification as the result of future work, and probably some with which many zoologists will disagree to-day. These are risks which must, I think, be taken. Discussion of such questions is not possible without these risks, and, if the purpose of a zoological course is to give a broad and consistent view of animal life, rather than a large body of uncontested fact, these questions must be discussed. If conclusions are always admitted to be tentative, to alter them in the light of later evidence is never difficult, for the student any more than for the professional zoologist.

My debt to many authors of previous books will be obvious. Some of these books are mentioned in the bibliography, where they are suggested for use in further reading. I wish especially to thank several friends who have helped me by reading the manuscript of many of the chapters. Among these are Prof. Sir J. Gray, F.R.S. (chs. II, III), Dr. L. A. Borradaile (chs. IV–VI), Dr. J. T. MacCurdy (ch. XXI and the part of ch. V on Behaviour), Prof. C. F. A. Pantin, F.R.S. (ch. XVI), Dr. J. A. Ramsay (chs. XII–XIX), Prof. R. J. Pumphrey (ch. XVII), and Dr. L. E. R. Picken (chs. IV and V). These friends have saved me from many mistakes, but the responsibility for the statements and views expressed is my own. I am also under a great debt of gratitude to Sir Julian Huxley, F.R.S., who has given me much help in writing the whole book and especially Part II.

I am indebted to these authors and publishers for permission to reproduce figures: to the *American Naturalist* for fig. 22; to Messrs. Edward Arnold & Co. for figs. 16 and 17, from E. A. Minchin's *An Introduction to the Protozoa*; to Messrs. Badger, of Boston, U.S.A., for fig. 39*b*, from H. S. Jennings's *Life, Death, Heredity, and Evolution in Unicellular Organisms*; to the *Biological Bulletin* for fig. 74; to the Editor of *Biological Reviews* for figs. 20 and 144; to Messrs. A. & C. Black, Ltd., for fig. 50*b*, from Lankester's *Oxford Treatise on Zoology*; to the Cambridge University Press for fig. 51, from *The Invertebrata*, by L. A. Borradaile and others, and for fig. 143, from J. Gray's *Ciliary Movement*; to the Challenger Office, Edinburgh, for figs. 55 and 56, from Murray and Pullar's *Survey of Fresh-Water Lochs of Scotland*, and for fig. 23, from H. B. Brady's volume on Foraminifera, in the *Reports of the Challenger Expedition*; to the Chicago University Press for figs. 58, 61, 62, 63, 65, 66, 69, from C. M. Child's *Individuality in Organisms*, for fig. 73, from his *Physiological Zoology*, and for fig. 160, from E. V. Conklin's *General Cytology*; to Messrs. Christophers for fig. 107, from E. D. Adrian's *The Basis of Sensation*; to the Columbia University Press for figs. 45, 46, 91, 92, from H. S. Jennings's *The Behaviour of the Lower Organisms*, and for fig. 161, from T. H. Morgan's *Experimental Embryology*; to Messrs. Doin, Paris, for figs. 84, 85, 86, from C. Champy's *Sexualité et Hormones*; to the Dove Marine Laboratory for fig. 82; to H. Eltringham, for fig. 138, from his *Senses of Insects*; to Messrs. W. Heffer & Sons, Ltd., for fig. 13, from T. S. P. Strangeway's *Growth and Differentiation of Tissue Culture*; to His Majesty's Stationery Office for fig. 76, from *Report on Crabs* (Ministry of

Agriculture and Fisheries), 1930, and for fig. 23; to the *Journal of Experimental Biology*, for figs. 108, 113–16, 120, 149; to the *Journal of Experimental Zoology* for figs. 4, 39*a*, 42, 43, 59, 67, 135, 159; to the *Journal of Genetics* for fig. 15; to the *Journal of Morphology* for fig. 7; to the Linnean Society for fig. 165; to the J. P. Lippincott Company, Philadelphia, for figs. 117, 123, 125, 156, from G. H. Parker's *The Elementary Nervous System*; to Messrs. Longmans Green & Co., Ltd., for fig. 106, from W. M. Bayliss's *Principles of General Physiology*; to the McGraw-Hill Book Company, Inc., New York, for figs. 127, 132, from R. E. Snodgrass's *Principles of Insect Morphology*; to Messrs. MacMillan & Co., Ltd., for fig. 38, from J. G. Kerr's *Zoology for Medical Students*, for fig. 129, from T. J. Parker and W. A. Haswell's *Textbook of Zoology*, and for fig. 136*a*, from the Cambridge Natural History, Vol. II; to the MacMillan Company, New York, for fig. 12, from E. B. Wilson's *The Cell in Development and Heredity*, and for fig. 145*b*, from B. U. Dalgren and W. A. Kepner's *Textbook of Animal Histology*; to the Marine Biological Association of the United Kingdom for figs. 28, 47, 77, 95; to Messrs. Methuen & Co., Ltd., for figs. 78, 79, 80, from J. S. Huxley's *Problems of Relative Growth*, and for figs. 89, 103, from V. B. Wigglesworth's *Insect Physiology*; to Messrs. Martin Nijhoff and to the *Archives Néerlandaises de Physiologies* for figs. 99, 100; to *Parasitology* for fig. 11; to the *Quarterly Journal of Microscopical Science* for figs. 25, 40, 52, 154, 155, 157, 158, 164; to the Ray Society for fig. 167; to the *Revue suisse de Zoologie* for fig. 33; to the Royal Entomological Society of London for fig. 140; to the Royal Society for figs. 26*a*, 53, 54, 96; to the Scientific Reports of Tohoku University for fig. 60; to the University of California Publications on Zoology for figs. 35, 36; to the University of Pennsylvania Press and to the Oxford University Press for fig. 109, from E. D. Adrian's *The Mechanism of Nervous Action*; to the Yale University Press for fig. 1, from E. B. Wilson's *The Physical Basis of Life*; to the Zoological Society of London for figs. 81, 152: to the Symposium of Society for Experimental Biology 6, 105, 1952 (J. M. Mitchison) for fig. 21; to the Journal of Experimental Biology 34, 306, 1952 (G. M. Hughes) for fig. 121; to the Journal of Physiology 124, 272, 1954 (J. W. S. Pringle) for fig. 148.

G. S. CARTER

CAMBRIDGE,
November, 1939

PREFACE TO THIRD EDITION

In this edition the text has been revised so as to bring it into agreement with recent work, and some of the figures have been redrawn. I have to thank my friends Dr. L. E. R. Picken and Dr. W. H. Thorpe for kindly helping me in the revision. I owe to Dr. Picken much help in the revision of Part I, and to Dr. Thorpe similar help in that of ch. XXI.

G. S. CARTER

December, 1950

PREFACE TO FOURTH EDITION

Many changes have been made in this edition in the light of more recent results, but the general arrangement of the book has not been altered.

G. S. CARTER

June, 1960

CONTENTS

PART IV SOME GENERAL PROBLEMS OF INVERTEBRATE ZOOLOGY

LIST OF PLATES

FIGURES IN THE TEXT

A GENERAL ZOOLOGY OF THE INVERTEBRATES

CHAPTER I

INTRODUCTION

THERE are some characters which are common to all, or almost all, animals and evident from everyday knowledge. These need no scientific investigation to establish their truth: they will be accepted by everyone as soon as they are stated. But the more obvious a fact is the easier it may be to overlook it; and a fact is not, by reason of its obviousness, unimportant. More usually the opposite is true; an obvious fact is often general and therefore fundamental. It is at least clear that these obvious facts about animals must be kept in mind in all zoological discussion, and conclusions must never be allowed to conflict with them. It will therefore be well to state the more important of them before we pass on to discuss the results of scientific investigation of invertebrate animals.

1. We know from ordinary experience that the animal body is, as a general rule, separate from other animal bodies, whether of the same or another species. The animal is, in fact, typically a separate individual. Like so many other statements about animals, this is not true without exception. Colonies in which the bodies of numerous individuals are united to a greater or less extent are known even to ordinary experience. And we sometimes find the bodies of two or more individuals united in species in which the individuals are normally separate—as, for instance, in Siamese twins. Multiple bodies of this type are known as monsters, and monsters not only occur naturally but can be obtained by several kinds of experimental treatment. Both colonies and monsters will be discussed in a later chapter (ch. IX), where we shall find that the separate individualities of the united animals are always to some extent retained. Here, we need only notice that the bodies of animals are *typically* separate from those of other animals. Multiple bodies are exceptional.

2. Throughout its life every animal retains its character as an independent individual, even though the substance of its body is constantly being renewed. This implies that within the body there is organised a system of physiological processes capable of maintaining

the life of the living substance and of providing the energy necessary for its various activities.

3. The animal is to some extent independent of changes in its surroundings. If these changes become too large, the animal dies, but, so long as they do not exceed a certain limit, it is able to adapt itself to the changed conditions and to continue its life.

4. The animal has a life-history. In all multicellular animals there is a period of development in which the body grows in size, and its structure increases in complexity from the apparent simplicity of the fertilised egg to the condition of the adult. Even after the adult condition is reached, structural changes continue—the body of the senile animal is different in form from that of the animal in the prime of its life.

We shall discuss later (p. 73) how far development of this kind occurs among the unicellular animals.

During its life-history the physiology of the animal as well as its structure changes. There is, for instance, during life, a continuous reduction in the activity of the tissues, which leads in the end to senescence. These, or similar changes, are characteristic of all animals, including most of the Protista, as we shall see, as well as other animals.

5. The animal can reproduce itself. It is thus able to provide for the indefinitely continued life of the species. Non-reproductive forms occur in some species (*e.g.* neuter ants and worker bees), but every species must contain reproductive individuals.

6. The body of every adult animal has a shape which is characteristic of the species to which the animal belongs. The specific form is not constant. It varies very greatly during the life-history. During development it alters continually, and we shall find that it is often capable of a certain amount of modification even in adult animals. But no one will deny that each species has a typical form. The almost complete constancy of the adult form is one of the most striking characters of the animal. But it is a character of the animal which has yielded very little to investigation. We are very largely ignorant of the causes which make the animal assume the specific form and maintain it.

Not only does the normally developing animal grow into the specific form of the species, but the animal body tends to regain the specific form when that form has suffered damage in any way. A lost part of the body tends to be regenerated. The regeneration may not be complete: it is usually less complete the more complex the body of the animal. But the tendency for it to occur is present in all animals. More than this, in many of the simpler animals a small piece of the body which has been separated from the rest will, provided certain conditions hold, remould itself into the specific form of the body from which it has been separated.

It seems to be a general property of the living matter of animals that any piece of it, if it is separated from other living matter, always tends to take on the form of the species to which it belongs. Only if the conditions in which the piece of tissue is living are very unlike those in which it normally lives, and the piece is itself very small (as in tissue-cultures), or if only a few of the tissues of the body are present in the piece, is this tendency absent.

7. Each animal species is defined not only in shape but also, more or less approximately, in size. The size of animals varies greatly from one type to another, and to some extent among the individuals of a single species. Nevertheless the mean size is determined more or less accurately for each species. We shall discuss later the reasons which prevent large variations in the size of the body from the mean of the species.

8. All animals are sensitive to changes in the surrounding environment and are able to react to them. These reactions, together with the continuous activities of the animal, constitute its behaviour. It is a general characteristic of the behaviour of all except the simplest multicellular animals that it is co-ordinated throughout the body of the animal. The animal behaves as a unit. When we come to consider behaviour in multiple bodies, such as those of colonies and monsters, we shall find that the behaviour is more complex in these exceptional animals.

9. Above all, our common experience shows us that the individual animal, however simple or complex its body may be, so long as it is not multiple, is the unit of life. This may be expressed by saying that the animal is an *organism*, a unit of living matter capable of continuous independent life as a member of the animal kingdom. The animal shows its unity as an organism in many ways, but perhaps most clearly in its specific form. A part separated from the animal body is no longer an organism. So long as it remains a part and does not regenerate into a whole animal, it cannot behave as an organism, nor has it the specific form of the species. Parts of the body may survive for some time after removal, but, unless they regenerate into whole bodies, they cannot live permanently and they cannot reproduce. A separated part is not an efficient member of the animal kingdom. It can only become such by regeneration.

Thus, the animal is not only a unit of living matter but also the smallest unit which retains the characters of the organism.

In so defining the animal as an organism, we must be careful not to allow our definition, consciously or unconsciously, to carry with it implications beyond those warranted by the facts. By calling the animal an organism we imply no more than that it is a completely functional living unit and that no smaller piece of animal matter is a living unit in the same sense. We do not make any statements about the nature of the organisation which exists within the animal. The question whether a *complete* mechanistic interpretation of the organisation of the animal is possible—that is to say, whether its organisation is at base of the same kind as the organisations we find in non-living matter, or whether we must demand for the animal some type of organisation entirely different in kind from anything outside the living body—is a very old question and one which is still disputed. But this question lies beyond the scope of our discussions. It is one of the objects of zoology to interpret as many as possible of the facts about animals on mechanistic lines, but the zoologist is not called upon to decide whether this attempt will ultimately be completely successful, so that the animal will be shown to be nothing more than a physical and chemical system. All he need say is that at present his success in making this attempt is by no means complete. There are many facts about animals which we cannot now express in terms of physics and chemistry.

Our definition of the animal as an organism implies no conclusions about the ultimate nature of animal organisation. The animal is an organism in the sense in which we have used the term whatever the nature of its organisation may be. It would remain an organism if, in the future, the mechanistic view was shown to be true. It would still be a living unit and the smallest living unit which retains its character as an organism.

As a result of this discussion of what common experience teaches us about animals, we may start our enquiry into the life of invertebrate animals with the following statements. An animal is an organism, the smallest living unit capable of permanent independent life; it possesses a body with a typical specific form; it is able to maintain its life in a changing environment, to react in various ways to the changes of the environment, and to reproduce itself; and, if multicellular, it undergoes a life-history consisting of development from the egg to the adult, and of life in the adult condition, followed by ageing and death.

PART I

PROTOPLASM AND THE FREE-LIVING CELL

CHAPTER II

PROTOPLASM

IN this chapter we shall discuss the chemical and physical characters of the living substance of which the animal body is composed. There are many features in the behaviour of living matter which are peculiar to it and cannot at present be explained as resulting from its physical nature. These we shall discuss in later chapters. But it cannot be questioned that living matter and the animal body which it composes behave as physical systems in some of their activities, and that, wherever they behave as such, the physical laws, such as the law of conservation of energy, are obeyed. In this chapter we shall consider living matter only as a physical system, subject to the same laws as non-living physical systems, in order to find out what type of non-living systems it most resembles.

"Protoplasm" is the name given to the ground substance of living matter. The term is an expression of the fact that living substance is very similar in many of its chemical and physical characters wherever it is found, but the use of this term for living substance in general must not be taken to imply that protoplasm is a single substance in the chemical sense. Protoplasm is not a single substance, but a highly organised and very variable system of substances, which is never the same in any two animals or in any two parts of one animal. We shall not discuss these variations in the chemical nature of protoplasm here. We shall deal not with the many special characters which protoplasm shows in the various forms of life, but with the universal characters of protoplasm, the properties which all protoplasm possesses as long as it is alive.

In the living animal body, protoplasm is organised into small masses or units known as cells. Whether the body contains one or many of these cells, the cells themselves possess structural features without which the life of the body cannot go on. Discussion of the organisation of protoplasm in the body must therefore include an account of its arrangement in the cell. This will be the subject of the next chapter. In these two chapters we shall cover the *essential* structure of the animal body as a living system, for many animals contain only one cell.

THE PHYSICAL NATURE OF PROTOPLASM

1. Protoplasm may appear completely structureless when it is observed with the microscope. The whole animal cell is never without structure; granules and vacuoles are present and the protoplasm is differentiated in various parts of the cell to form the cell organs. Even where the protoplasm is not so differentiated, it usually contains inclusions of various sizes (Plate I, Fig. 1). But the protoplasmic matrix in which the granules and vacuoles are contained is without any visible structure; and in some cells parts of the protoplasm may be without contained bodies of any kind. Optically the protoplasm is then entirely homogeneous. This is true, for instance, of the protoplasm of the pseudopodia of *Arcella* or *Difflugia.*

Thus, structure which is visible under the microscope is not an essential character of protoplasm.

2. One of the most obvious physical characters of protoplasm is that it is much more often liquid than solid. In some places in the cell at all times, and in other places at certain times during its life, protoplasm may be gelatinous. But there can be no doubt of the liquidity of the majority of examples of protoplasm. There can be no doubt, for instance, of the liquid condition of the flowing endoplasm of *Amœba* and of the protoplasm which flows out of a cell (*e.g.* a sea-urchin egg) when the surface of the cell is torn. Particles suspended in protoplasm can often be seen to be in Brownian movement, and this is only possible if the medium surrounding the particles is liquid.

3. The liquid basis of protoplasm is water. Water forms at least 75 per cent. of the substance of protoplasm by weight, and a droplet of water injected into protoplasm (*e.g.* into the endoplasm of *Amœba*) usually mixes completely and rapidly with the surrounding protoplasm. It is true that naked protoplasm sometimes does not mix with water when it comes into contact with it, as, for instance, when it flows out of the cut surface of a cell, but this is due to very rapid formation of a more solid layer on the surface of the protoplasm.

4. Protoplasm consists of a complex mixture of substances, some dissolved in its watery basis, others suspended in the water in the colloidal state. The substances in true solution include inorganic ions as well as more complex substances; the suspended particles probably contain the greater part of the complex constituents of the protoplasm. The size of the particles in non-living colloidal systems varies between 10 and 1000 Å *; it is probable that the colloidal particles of protoplasm also lie between these limits of size.

* Ångström unit (Å) $= 10^{-8}$ cm.

Although we cannot discuss here the nature of the colloidal state, something must be said of the evidence on which the belief that protoplasm is a colloidal system is based. This belief, which it is now impossible to question, is founded on the general similarity between the reactions of protoplasm and of non-living colloidal systems to changes in the condition of the medium in which the particles are suspended. The similarity is very widespread and only a few examples of it can be mentioned here.

(*a*) Many non-living aqueous colloidal solutions can be coagulated by heat, becoming irreversibly solidified. A familiar example of coagulation is the solidification of the albumen of a bird's egg when it is boiled.* Protoplasm also coagulates when it is heated, but the temperature at which coagulation occurs is lower than that required for the coagulation of albumen. Most animals die when the temperature of their protoplasm is raised to some point between 40° and 50° C. Their death is probably due to coagulation of parts of their protoplasm. Many animals die at much lower temperatures, but it is probable that death is then due to some other cause. Some animals can live at a higher temperature. Animals have been found living in hot springs at 65° C.

(*b*) Both protoplasm and colloidal suspensions can be coagulated by many chemical substances as well as by heat. The "fixation" of protoplasm which is carried out in preparing it for histological examination is simply coagulation by chemical means, and the usefulness of a chemical substance as a fixative depends on its power of coagulating the protoplasm with little change of structure.

Albumen solutions can be fixed in the same way as protoplasm and by the same chemical substances. Corrosive sublimate, potassium dichromate, formalin, and many other fixatives of protoplasm coagulate albumen as efficiently as they fix protoplasm.

(*c*) The stability of colloidal solutions is very sensitive to changes in the acidity and alkalinity of the medium in which the particles are suspended. This is true of protoplasm to an even greater extent. The protoplasm of the cytoplasm (p. 28) of animal cells has been found to be at *p*H 6·9, although granules and vacuoles included in the cytoplasm may be more acid or alkaline than this. The nucleus (p. 28) is often more alkaline than the protoplasm outside it. It has been found to be at *p*H 7·6 in many cells which have been investigated.† Any acid or alkali which is able to penetrate a cell has marked effect on its physiological activity, even though no change in the *p*H of

* The albumen of an egg, although produced by a living system, is a non-living colloidal solution, and therefore a suitable example to be considered here, but it must be remembered that this type of heat-coagulability is a property only of protein solutions, all of which are derived from living organisms.

† *Cf.* review by Chambers mentioned in the bibliography.

PLATE I

Figure 1. Fine structure of the protoplasm of a starfish egg; inclusions of various sizes in a hyaline matrix. (From Wilson.)

Figure 2. Spireme stage of a nucleus photographed with ultra-violet light. (After Köhler.)

Figure 9. (*a*) Intranuclear division figures without centrosomes in *Monocystis rostrata*. Only the nucleus and the neighbouring protoplasm is shown. (After Mulsow.) (*b*) Intranuclear division figures with centrosomes in *Collodictyum triciliatum* (Mastigophora). (After Bělăr.)

PLATE I

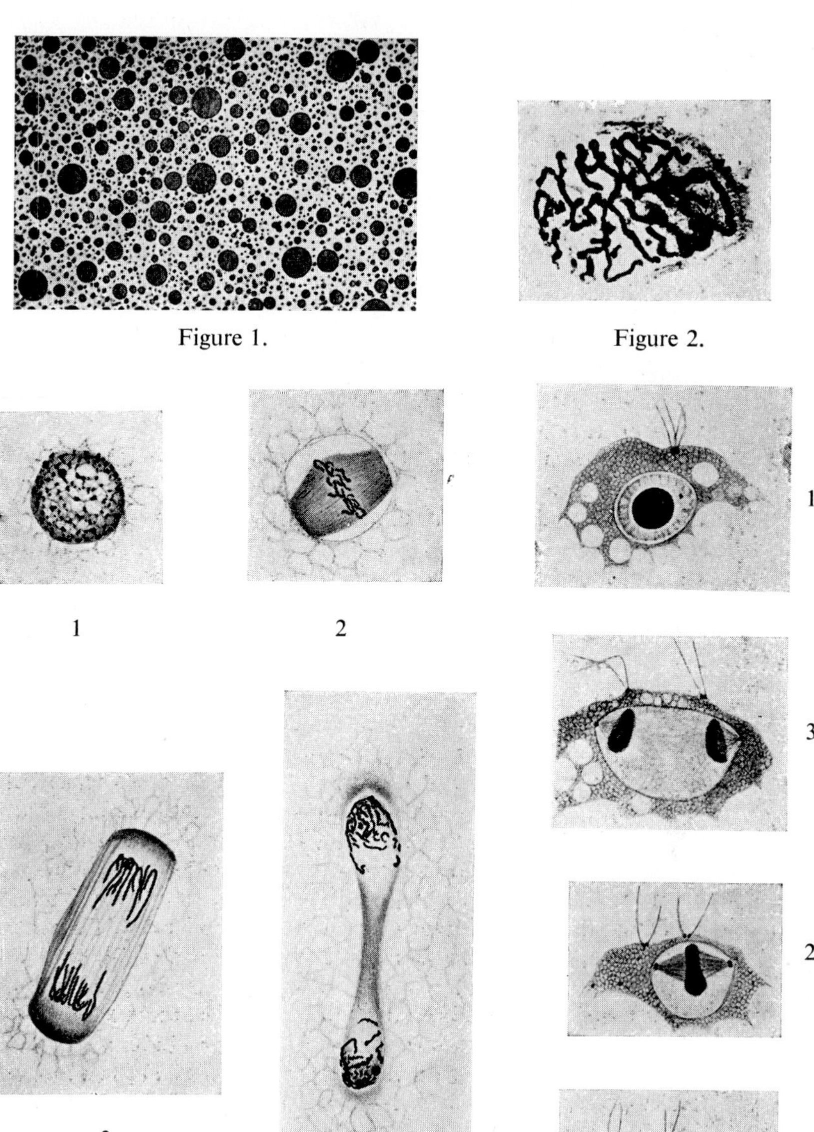

Figure 1.

Figure 2.

Figure 9*a*.

Figure 9*b*.

[*To face p.* 8.

the protoplasm can be observed. It is probable that the behaviour of protoplasm is sensitive to changes in its *p*H smaller than we are able to observe.

(*d*) Both protoplasm and colloidal suspensions are sensitive to alterations in the salt content of the medium. This effect is in some ways parallel to that of changes in the *p*H of the medium. Changes of *p*H are due to alterations in the proportions of H^+ and OH^- ions in the medium. The salts are ionised in the medium and so also give rise to charged ions. Multivalent ions bear charges in proportion to their valency. It is therefore to be expected, and is found to be true in general, that the greater the valency of an ion the greater will be its effect on the stability of colloidal solutions. This is also true of protoplasm.

Protoplasm is sensitive not only to the total amount of salt present in the medium but also to changes in the proportions of the various salts. Marine animals, for instance, can live in artificial sea-waters only if all the four most plentiful cations of sea-water (Na, Ca, K, Mg) are present in the media, and their condition is more normal the closer the proportionate concentrations of these ions in the media are to their concentrations in sea-water. The tissues of other multicellular animals also require the presence of all these ions in the media in which they are living. Similar phenomena are known in non-living colloids.

These are some of the resemblances between the reactions of protoplasm and of non-living colloids. There are many others. There are also many resemblances between protoplasm and non-living colloids in other features of their behaviour. Only one of these can be mentioned here. Protoplasm shows frequent and rapid changes from a more liquid, "sol," to a more solid, "gel," condition. In other words, the viscosity of protoplasm may vary greatly and rapidly. Similar changes of viscosity may occur in non-living colloids.

The viscosity of protoplasm can be measured in several different ways, perhaps most simply by measurement of the rate at which particles or liquid vacuoles move through it under the force of gravity. The measurement is made much easier when the gravitational force is increased by rapidly rotating the cells containing the protoplasm in a centrifuge. In this way the force of gravity can be multiplied several thousand times. The viscosity may also be measured by introducing small iron particles into the protoplasm and measuring the rate of their movement under a known magnetic force. Several other methods have been used.

The results of these experiments are not very consistent, probably because the viscosity of the protoplasm varies not only in different parts of the cell but also from time to time. It is probable that the viscosity of liquid protoplasm may be as low as three or four times that of water. This value has been obtained for the interior protoplasm of the sea-urchin egg. The interior liquid protoplasm of *Paramecium* has about the same viscosity.* Gelatinous protoplasm may be as viscous as a 1 or 2 per cent. solution of gelatine, the viscosity being about 30,000 times that of water.

We cannot here discuss the viscosity of non-living colloidal systems. It must suffice to say that they show variations of viscosity as great as those which are found in protoplasm, and that the viscosity of a system may alter, as a result of small changes in the medium, as greatly as that of protoplasm is found to alter from time to time.

Protoplasm is, then, a colloidal system which is generally liquid but may occasionally become gelatinous. But we can go a little further. Non-living liquid colloidal systems are of two kinds. These are:

1. Lyophobe colloids. In these the stability of the particles is maintained by repulsions between electric charges on their surfaces. These colloids are precipitated at the isoelectric point, where the charges become zero, and the stability therefore vanishes.

2. Lyophil colloids. In these the particles are hydrated, that is to say, covered with layers of molecules of the diffuse phase, normally water. These colloids are stable even at the isoelectric point, where the particles are not charged, their stability being due to the layers of molecules with which the particles are covered. On either side of the isoelectric point, however, they are sensitive to the concentrations of charged particles in the medium. The stability of the suspensions may be increased or decreased by changes in the concentration of such particles. These colloids are sensitive to cations on the alkaline side and to anions on the acid side.

This view of the difference between these two types of colloids is undoubtedly too simple to be accurate, but it is sufficient for our purpose.

All the evidence goes to show that the colloids of protoplasm are mostly, if not all, lyophil. We must therefore think of the protoplasmic colloidal particles as covered with layers of water molecules. The sensitivity of protoplasm to the concentrations of ions is no evidence against this view, since lyophil colloids are also sensitive to the concentration of ions when they are not at the isoelectric point, and the *p*H of protoplasm (*p*H 6·9) is on the alkaline side of the isoelectric point of its colloids.

* R. H. J. Brown, *Jour. Exp. Biol.*, xvii, 317, 1940.

THE ESSENTIAL STRUCTURE OF PROTOPLASM

Protoplasm consists of a highly complex arrangement of colloids. If evidence of the complexity of the colloidal system were needed, the very complex chemical processes which go on in protoplasm, often simultaneously, would provide it. Life would be impossible not only in a structureless fluid but also in a simple colloid.

It may be asked whether this complex colloidal structure can be made visible in protoplasm, in spite of the fact that the particles, and the units of the structure they compose, are too small to be seen with the microscope.

The presence of particles in colloidal systems can often be demonstrated with the ultramicroscope. In this instrument the object to be examined is illuminated with a powerful beam of light at right angles to the axis of the microscope. Ultramicroscopic particles, if they are present, appear as points of light, caused by scattering of the light at their surfaces. The presence of particles only 10–100 Å in diameter can be recognised in this way, but it is only the presence of the particles and not their shape which is observed.

Protoplasm, even if it appears to be entirely homogeneous under the ordinary microscope, almost always shows the presence of colloidal particles when it is examined with the ultramicroscope, but occasionally even the ultramicroscope fails to show structure in protoplasm unless the light is made so strong that it, or the heat waves which accompany it, are likely to damage the protoplasm. With such strong light we cannot be sure that the structure we see is not due to the damage done to the protoplasm.

The fact that the ultramicroscope does not always show structure in protoplasm must not be taken to imply that protoplasm is sometimes without colloidal structure. Particles will only be visible in the ultramicroscope if the light is scattered at their surfaces. If there is no scattering of the light, particles may be present, but the instrument will give no indication of their presence.

We may say that the evidence that protoplasm is a complex colloidal system is sufficient to show that it must have complex ultramicroscopic structure, and that the presence of this structure can usually be demonstrated with the ultramicroscope.

Accepting this, we may still ask whether protoplasm has any essential structure on a larger scale than this, and particularly whether there is any essential structure on a scale large enough to be seen under the microscope, and so for its form to be observed. The lower limit of size for microscopic vision is definite, varying only with the wave-length of the light used. With light of the visible spectrum, form cannot be clearly seen in structures less than about $0{\cdot}3\mu$ * in diameter.

* $\mu = 10^{-3}$ mm.

This will be the lower limit of size for the units of any visible structure in protoplasm.

It has already been stated that protoplasm often shows no structure when observed with the microscope. But does this mean that no structure can be present on a scale large enough to be seen with the microscope? May structure be present but invisible in the microscope? And, if so, can we make it visible by any form of treatment?

In order to answer these questions we must know what conditions must be fulfilled if an object is to be visible in the microscope. Objects will not be visible unless they differ from the medium with which they are surrounded in one of two ways. Either they are more or less transparent than the medium, when they will appear lighter or darker than the medium; and, if the transparency differences vary with light of different wave-lengths, their colour will differ from that of the medium. Or the light must be refracted at the surface of the object, when the outline of the object will be visible as a dark line.* No refraction at the surface will occur if the refractive index of the object is the same as that of the medium. If there is no difference in either transparency or refractive index between the object and the medium, the object will be invisible. An example of this is the almost complete invisibility of a piece of glass in a medium of Canada balsam.

So, it is by no means impossible that protoplasm should have an essential microscopic structure, although it sometimes appears homogeneous. It has been stated many times that such a structure is present in protoplasm. The structure described has been of many different kinds. It has been said by some to consist of an arrangement of granules in a liquid medium, by others of a similar arrangement of vacuoles, and by others again of a network of more solid fibrillæ in a more liquid matrix. Since protoplasm is often liquid and can flow, it is hard to see how the last of these types of structure is possible.

Many descriptions of protoplasmic structure have been founded on study of "fixed," *i.e.* coagulated, protoplasm. We shall consider in the next chapter how far we may accept the presence of structure in protoplasm after fixation as being evidence of the presence of similar structure in the living protoplasm. Here it need only be said that it is extremely dangerous to do so when the units of the structure under observation are near the lower limit of microscopic vision in size, as these supposed structures in protoplasm are. Also, many types of structure which have been described in fixed protoplasm may result in non-living colloidal systems (*e.g.* suspensions of albumen) from the action of the same chemical substances as are used in fixing

* Dark lines indicating surfaces where the refractive index changes become more evident when the "phase-contrast" or the "interference" microscope is used. *Cf.* Oster and Pollister *Physical Techniques in Biological Research*, Acad. Press, 1955, vol. 1; Bayliss, *Principles of General Physiology*, vol. 2, ch. 1, 1960.

protoplasm. Thus, there can be no doubt that these structures in fixed protoplasm are artefacts, resulting from the treatment which the protoplasm has undergone in its coagulation. Their occurrence in coagulated protoplasm must be due to lack of homogeneity in the unfixed protoplasm, but the fact that the structures occur in fixed non-living colloidal systems shows that the discontinuities from which they result are also present in the non-living systems. They must be regarded as the result of the colloidal structure.

Since the use of fixed protoplasm leads to deceptive results, we must demonstrate any essential microscopic structure in living, or at least unfixed, protoplasm, if we are to believe in its existence. But we have seen that protoplasm may appear structureless under the microscope, and the microscope is our only means of directly observing objects too small to be seen by the naked eye.* If we are to see essential structure in protoplasm, it would seem that the microscope must be improved as a means of observation.

1. The transparency of substance to light varies with the wave-length of the light. In the visible spectrum these variations give rise, as we have seen, to differences of colour, but they also occur outside the visible spectrum, and objects which show no differences in colour may differ in their transparency to ultra-violet or infra-red light. So, we may be able to display structure which is invisible with ordinary light by using light outside the visible spectrum. Ultra-violet light has been most frequently used for this purpose. Since ultra-violet light is of shorter wave-length than visible light, it can also be used to observe objects below the minimum size visible with the ordinary microscope. The method is theoretically simple, but it has many practical difficulties. The lenses of the microscope must be of quartz, for glass is opaque to ultra-violet light; and the object must be photographed, since the eye cannot observe light outside the visible spectrum. But more important than these difficulties is the fact that protoplasm is damaged by more than a very short exposure to ultra-violet light. It is not easy to be sure that any structures seen in the protoplasm are not produced by the damage.

Some cell organs, which cannot be easily seen with ordinary light (*e.g.* the spireme stage in the nucleus, Plate I, Fig. 2), show clearly when they are photographed with ultra-violet light. So far as the structure of protoplasm in general is concerned, the method has given negative results. No essential microscopic structure has been found by this method.

2. Protoplasm may be stained while it is still uncoagulated and

* By use of the electron microscope objects far too small to be seen in the light microscope can be demonstrated, and essential structure on a sub-microscopic scale is found to be present (p. 33).

alive. This is the principle of the *intra-vitam* stain. Many stains may be used to stain living protoplasm and they will often stain parts of the protoplasm more than others, so that we might hope to display structure in the protoplasm by staining it intra vitam. It is often objected to the use of this method that stained protoplasm is never healthy. This is probably true, but at least it is uncoagulated and the method therefore avoids most of the dangers of the use of fixed protoplasm.

Intra-vitam staining has never shown any essential structure in protoplasm. The method is of great use for study of the distribution of the cell organs, but has always given negative results so far as the essential structure of protoplasm is concerned.

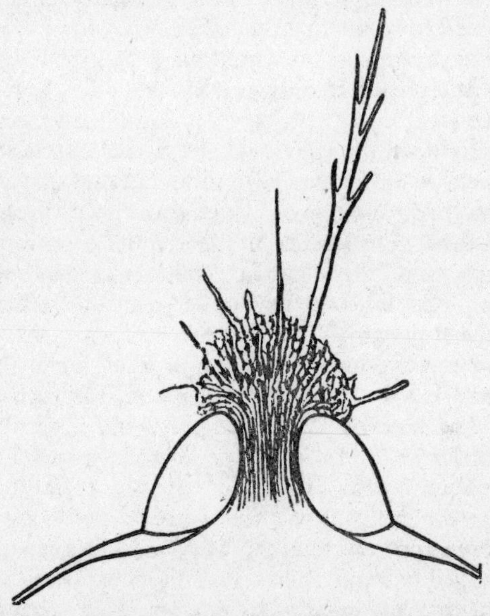

Figure 3. Fibrillar structure of the protoplasm at the mouth of the shell of *Gromia dujardinii*. (After Bütschli.)

3. Some other forms of treatment may produce visible structure in protoplasm which is normally homogeneous. Fibrillæ may often be seen in otherwise homogeneous protoplasm when it is subjected to pressure. This may occur naturally, *e.g.* in the protoplasm of Foraminifera, where it flows through the mouth of the shell (Fig. 3). Similar fibrillæ can be produced artificially by pressure. But much the same may be said of these fibrillæ as of the structures which appear in coagulated protoplasm—they can be produced in non-living, colloidal systems. Albumen gels subjected to pressure show fibrillæ of

this type. These fibrillæ must be the result of the ultramicroscopic, colloidal structure of the system, whether protoplasmic or non-living, but they do not show that protoplasm has a structure of a type different from that of non-living colloids.

Even if it were shown that all animal protoplasm has an essential microscopic structure, this could not be true of the protoplasm of all organisms, for many organisms are too small for visible structure in their protoplasm to be possible. The filterable viruses have a unit size which is often far below the limit of microscopic vision (down to 50 Å in diameter). It may, perhaps, still be questioned whether the viruses are truly alive, but there can be no doubt that the bacteria are alive and some of them are only just large enough to be visible (0·4μ). Visible structure is impossible in the protoplasm of these organisms. No free-living cell is as small as this. The smallest free-living cell (apart from the bacteria, which are not true cells, p. 23) is 2μ in diameter. This size is large enough to allow of visible structure in its protoplasm.

Thus, visible structure is possible only in the protoplasm of organisms larger than some of the bacteria. But we have seen that no essential visible structure has been demonstrated by any of the methods we have so far discussed in the protoplasm even of animal cells. And it has not up to the present been demonstrated by any other method. We must conclude that there is at present no reason to believe in its existence.

We may therefore define protoplasm as a complex colloidal system with ultramicroscopic structure which is necessarily far more complex than that of any known non-living colloidal system, but with, so far as we know, no essential structure large enough to be visible under the microscope (*cf.* p. 33).

THE SURFACE OF PROTOPLASM *

(*a*) *The Cortical Layer.* The outermost layers of protoplasm in a cell are usually more viscous than the interior, and the layer immediately below the surface is frequently gelatinous.† This layer is also to some extent elastic. These properties can be demonstrated very easily with microdissection needles, which are fine glass points moved by mechanical means in the field of the microscope and used for dissecting small objects such as an animal cell. When the outer layer of an *Amœba* (*i.e.* the pellicle) is stretched with the needle, its gelatinous character becomes obvious (Fig. 4). Its elasticity is shown by its return, which is not always complete, to its original form, when the force stretching it is removed.

* *Cf.* the review by Chambers and book by Bayliss in the bibliography.

† In some there may be a liquid layer immediately below the surface (sea-urchin egg, Chambers).

These surface layers are parts of the living protoplasm and therefore distinct from the cuticle and other hard, non-living secretions of the protoplasm with which the cell is often covered.

(*b*) *The Surface Membrane.* We have noted that protoplasm contains various substances in solution. The concentrations of these

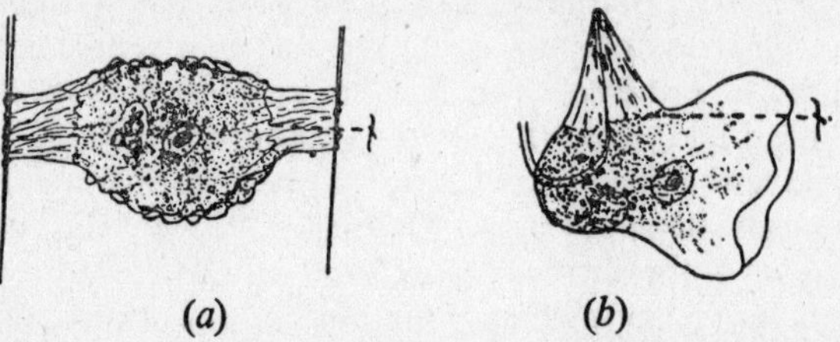

Figure 4. Dissection of the surface layers of *Amœba verrucosa* with micro-dissection needles.

(*a*) pellicle drawn out by two needles; (*b*) pellicle extended by hook-shaped needle; *f*, surface of the endoplasm. (After Howland.)

substances in the protoplasm is often very different from their concentrations in the medium outside the protoplasm. Protoplasm also contains many substances in solution which are not present in the medium.

As an example of the differences of concentration of substances in protoplasm and the surrounding medium, we may take the concentrations of inorganic salts. These are present in all protoplasm and in all natural media. The figures of Table I give the concentrations of several ions in human blood corpuscles and in the serum of the blood. Any other type of animal cell would give similar differences in the concentrations of inorganic salts in the protoplasm and in the medium outside it.

TABLE I

	Corpuscles per cent.	Serum per cent.
Na	0·065	0·335
K	0·38	0·02
Ca	0·004	0·01
Mg	0·0035	0·0025
Cl	0·20	0·36
Total solids . .	32·0	9·9

The differences in concentration vary in amount among the various ions. They are therefore not merely the expression of a difference in osmotic pressure. In fact, there is no difference of osmotic pressure, the greater proportion of total solids in the cells being due to the larger molecules of many of the constituents of the cells.

Other evidence shows that the salts in protoplasm are almost all ionised, *i.e.* present as charged ions. The surface of protoplasm therefore separates two solutions of dissolved substances which can remain indefinitely at different concentrations. In non-living systems membranes which do this are called semi-permeable. They must be impermeable to the substances which are at different concentrations on opposite sides of the membrane. Protoplasm is therefore surrounded by a semi-permeable membrane. This membrane is on the extreme surface of the protoplasm, and we shall call it the *surface membrane*. It is only a few molecules thick (50–100 Å) and is therefore invisible. It should be clearly distinguished from the much thicker gelatinous cortical layer which lies within it.

It is not possible to discuss the structure of the surface membrane in detail (*cf.* p. 43). Its structure is by no means fully known. It is unlikely, however, that it is of the same type as any known non-living semi-permeable membrane with which we are able to compare it. In non-living systems such membranes have no source of energy except that of the solutions on the two sides of the membrane. Such a membrane cannot, for instance, concentrate a dissolved substance against a rise of osmotic pressure. Either the substance will not pass through the membrane, when its concentration on the two sides remains indefinitely unchanged; or it will pass, when the concentrations become gradually the same on the two sides by diffusion across the membrane. There can be no increase of concentration on the side of the membrane where the concentration was originally greater.

It is by no means true that the protoplasmic surface membrane cannot concentrate substances against a gradient of osmotic pressure. To do so it must have some other source of energy besides that of the solutions on the two sides of it. It may be that energy ultimately derived from the food of the protoplasm can be used in the surface membrane, as we know it can be used in other parts of the protoplasm, *e.g.* in producing movement. If this is so, the surface membrane of protoplasm is obviously different in type from all known non-living semi-permeable membranes.

A few facts about the permeability of the surface membrane may be mentioned. They will serve to indicate other difficulties in the way of comparing it with non-living membranes.

1. The semi-permeability of the membrane disappears when the protoplasm dies. The salts and other dissolved substances then diffuse in both directions across the membrane until the concentrations on the two sides are the same.

2. The maintenance of the semi-permeability demands the presence of various ions in the medium outside the membrane. We have noted that many marine organisms cannot live permanently unless all the four cations Na, K, Mg, and Ca are present in the medium. It can be shown that their death is due to breakdown of the semi-permeability of the surface membranes of their protoplasm. Even

freshwater animals cannot live permanently in distilled water which contains none of these cations.

3. Water can undoubtedly pass the membrane in most types of protoplasm. In the simplest marine animals the osmotic pressure of the protoplasm is equal to that of the medium and varies with it when it is artificially altered, the animal shrinking or swelling until equilibrium is again reached. In freshwater animals the conditions are different. The osmotic pressure of their protoplasm is always greater than that of the medium. Either their surfaces are impermeable to water (as seems to be so in many freshwater eggs), or work must be done by the animal to maintain this difference (*cf.* p. 54).

Although the surface of the animal cell is normally permeable to water, it is not necessary that its permeability should be great. The thinness of the membrane and its large area compared with the volume of the cell (which results from the small size of the cell) make a slight permeability sufficient to account for the observed facts. In the sea-urchin egg the permeability of the surface membrane has been found to be not more than $1/10^5$ of that of a collodion membrane of the same thickness.

4. Some dissolved substances can pass through the membrane much more readily than others. Substances soluble in fats are found to penetrate into protoplasm more easily than most other substances. The fatty acids, acetic, butyric, etc., for instance, are fat-soluble, and enter much more easily than the mineral acids, hydrochloric, sulphuric, etc., which are not fat-soluble. This can be shown by staining the cell with a dye which changes colour as the medium in which it is dissolved becomes more acid. The speed with which the colour changes gives a measure of the rate at which the acid penetrates. The method is suitable for measuring the rate of penetration of the acid in spite of the fact that such dyes accumulate rather in vacuoles or granules in the protoplasm than in the protoplasmic matrix, the *p*H of which is not recognisably altered. The change of colour in the stained inclusions still indicates the penetration of the acid.

Many fat-soluble substances besides the fatty acids penetrate into protoplasm easily. Many narcotics, for instance, are fat-soluble, and readily pass the membrane (but their activity as narcotics is due rather to action on the properties of the surface than to their penetration).

Everywhere in the behaviour of the surface membrane the facts are more complicated than appears from this account. For example, the equilibrium of the animal cell with water is not accurately accounted for, even in marine animals, by supposing the surface membrane semi-permeable. If the cell is subjected to a large change of osmotic pressure, the loss or gain of water to the cell is less than a simple semi-permeable membrane would allow. Probably the nature of the membrane changes when the external medium is made to differ largely from that normal to the life of the cell. But even the few facts we have considered show the difficulty of comparing the surface membrane with any known type of non-living semi-permeable membrane. This is so even if we neglect the possibility that the surface membrane of protoplasm may be able to make use of energy. If we are to make a satisfactory comparison of the surface membrane with non-living membranes, we must find a non-living membrane which is impermeable to many ionised salts but which will allow water and fat-soluble substances to pass through it. At present we know of no simple non-living membrane with these properties. The ease with which fat-soluble substances penetrate into the cell makes it probable that fats play some part in the surface membrane. The membrane is probably complex. It is not unlikely that it has ultramicroscopic structure, parts being composed of one material and other parts of a different material, but we do not yet know definitely what its structure is, though some types of structure have been suggested (p. 43). It must not be forgotten (1) that the structure of the membrane probably alters from time to time with changes in the activity of the protoplasm, and (2) that the membrane is a part of the living protoplasm and may, like other parts of the protoplasm, be capable of using energy. If either of these suppositions is true, the protoplasmic membrane differs fundamentally from all non-living semi-permeable membranes.

(*c*) *The Electrical Properties of the Protoplasmic Surface.* If an electric current is passed through a medium in which inactive cells are floating, it is generally found that the cells pass towards one pole of the current, most frequently towards the anode. This movement is due to cataphoresis, and its occurrence shows that the cells bear a static surface charge, which is usually negative. This static surface charge remains after the death of the protoplasm. It is not surprising that the surface of protoplasm should become charged in this way, for a similar charge is found on the surface of small non-living particles, such as those of colloidal suspensions. But this must not be taken to imply that the cause of the surface charge of protoplasm is necessarily as simple as that of the charge on colloidal particles.

A phenomenon which is distinct from the static surface charge of protoplasm is the current which flows from a region of greater activity in the surface of protoplasm to one of less activity. This is known as the *bio-electric current*. It can be demonstrated by setting up a galvanometer with contacts on active and inactive parts of the protoplasm. It can be shown most easily in nerve (as an impulse passes along the nerve) and in muscle (during contraction), but it is apparently characteristic of all active protoplasm. In contracting muscle the potential difference may exceed 50 millivolts at its maximum. In contrast with the static surface charge, the bio-electric current disappears as the protoplasm dies.

We cannot discuss the causes of the bio-electric current. We can only note it as one of the characteristic properties of living protoplasm.

THE CHEMISTRY OF PROTOPLASM

During its life protoplasm obtains energy for its maintenance, growth, movements and all its other activities from chemical reactions which go on in its substance. These chemical processes together are usually called the metabolism of the protoplasm. In all of them the physico-chemical laws, such as that of conservation of energy, are obeyed. The regularity with which these complex chemical processes go on in protoplasm can only result from the character of its ultramicroscopic structure. We may not know the details of this structure, but we have a great deal of knowledge of the chemical substances which take part in the reactions of metabolism, of the nature of the reactions which occur, and of the manner in which their rate is controlled. We can only touch on the vast subject of the biochemistry of protoplasm here.

1. Analysis of protoplasm shows that the greater part of its solid constituents consists of the elements of which most of the organic compounds of carbon are composed—C, H, N, O. But many other elements—S, Fe, P, Cl, and others—are always present in protoplasm and are essential for its life. The cations Na, Mg, K, Ca are also essential, as we have seen. However, these facts tell us nothing of the manner in which the metabolism of the cell is carried on.

2. One group of substances, the proteins, are characteristic of living substance and of substances derived from it, but of no other material in nature. They always make up a large proportion of the weight of protoplasm. Carbohydrates, such as glycogen and sugars, and lipoid substances, oils and fats, are also always present in protoplasm in large quantities. The proportions in which these various substances are present differ greatly from one type of protoplasm to another. Typical results of analysis of the dry substance of protoplasm are given in the following table, but in all such analyses a large amount of material which is not the actual living substance of the protoplasm must be included. Reserve food material and excreta, for instance, are always present in protoplasm and must be included in the analysis. For these reasons too much weight should not be given to such analyses.

TABLE II

ANALYSIS OF THE DRY SUBSTANCE OF PROTOPLASM

	per cent.
Proteins	45
Carbohydrates	25
Lipoids	25
Other substances	5

3. Although the chemical reactions of metabolism are of the same kind as those of non-living systems, and although they obey the law of conservation of energy, reactions often proceed in metabolism at rates which are very different from their rates in non-living systems. Many reactions proceed much more rapidly in protoplasm than elsewhere. Glucose, for instance, is split up in protoplasm at a far more rapid rate than we can produce in the laboratory by using any reagent which could possibly be present in protoplasm. Many other examples of the rapidity of the reactions of metabolism could be given.

These differences between the reactions of metabolism and of non-living systems are differences of rate only. There are no modifications of the final products of the reaction. They are, in fact, differences of the type produced in non-living systems by the presence of catalysts. They result from the occurrence in protoplasm of a peculiar type of catalyst, the *enzyme*. Enzymes can often be extracted from protoplasm and their properties can be studied *in vitro*. They are probably often protein in chemical nature and almost always colloidal. They do not occur in non-living systems; they are formed in the protoplasm. They are sensitive to heat, their activity being almost always destroyed before the temperature reaches the boiling-point; and their action is very selective, each enzyme catalysing one or at most a few reactions. But protoplasm contains a large number of enzymes and very many of the reactions of its metabolism are catalysed. In metabolism a single substance often undergoes several successive reactions, each catalysed by an enzyme. Such chains of enzyme-catalysed reactions may, indeed, be said to be typical of the chemistry of protoplasm.

The mode of action of enzymes is believed to consist in attraction of the reacting substances to the surface of the colloidal enzyme particle. There the substances are brought into close contact, and perhaps also into some form of chemical combination with the molecules of the enzyme. The reaction occurs on the surface of the enzyme particle and the products of the reaction are then set free, the enzyme particle itself being unaltered by the whole process. Thus, enzyme particles, like other catalysts, may in theory catalyse an indefinite amount of the reacting substances, but some breakdown of the enzyme probably always occurs, and is replaced by new enzyme built up by the protoplasm.

There is no doubt that the surfaces of enzyme particles form a very important part of the ultramicroscopic structure of protoplasm, on which the progress of metabolism depends.

4. We will take as a single example of the chains of enzyme reactions in metabolism the oxidative reactions controlled by the cytochromes. These reactions are responsible for a large part, but not the whole, of the respiration of protoplasm. The cytochromes are substances which contain iron and are chemically related to hæmoglobin. They resemble hæmoglobin in the important part they play in respiration, but they are present in all animal protoplasm.

In the presence of oxygen and an enzyme, cytochrome oxidase, reduced cytochrome becomes oxidised and water is set free. The oxidised cytochrome then receives hydrogen molecules from reduced cell constituents and returns to the reduced condition. For this reaction catalysis by other enzymes present in the cytoplasm, the dehydrogenases, is required.

CH_2 oxidised H_2O

Dehydro-genases → cyto-chrome ← Cytochrome oxidase

C reduced $\frac{1}{2}O_2$

C—Cell constituent

The final result is that oxygen has been taken up from solution in the protoplasm (which it has reached by diffusion from the external medium) and the constituents of the protoplasm have lost hydrogen. Dehydrogenation of an organic compound is equivalent to its oxidation. Thus, the constituents of the protoplasm have become oxidised at the expense of oxygen derived from the external medium, that is to say the respiration of the protoplasm has been advanced.

We have similar knowledge of many other chains of reactions in metabolism, but of a great deal of metabolism we do not know so much. It is probable, however, that most metabolic processes involve similar chains of reactions, all catalysed by enzymes. The chains of reactions are often much longer and more complicated than the example given here.

CHAPTER III

THE ESSENTIAL ORGANISATION OF THE CELL

THE units, or cells, into which the protoplasm of animals is organised have essentially the same structure in all animals. Each cell consists of a mass of protoplasm with at least one visible organ, the nucleus, differentiated from the rest of the protoplasm. Every animal cell contains other organs besides the nucleus, but these other organs are often not visible to direct observation. Together these organs form the essential organisation of the cell, which we shall discuss in this chapter.

One or many cells may be present in the animal body. In the multicellular body, each cell is organised in essentially the same manner as the whole body of the single-celled organism. We may therefore consider this type of organisation as necessary for the life of animal protoplasm. A very similar organisation occurs in the cells of the great majority of the plants. But not all living protoplasm has this organisation, though in some forms which have not exactly this organisation there may be similar but perhaps simpler organisation. Thus in certain bacteria it has recently been shown* that a pair of dumb-bell-shaped bodies are present which are strongly stained by the dyes which stain the nuclei of animal cells. They also give a positive reaction to the Feulgen test (p. 26). These bodies are thought to be comparable to the chromosomes of the nuclei of plant and animal cells (p. 38). The organisation of the smaller viruses is probably even simpler than this.

The term "cell" is not obviously appropriate to this unit of animal protoplasm. The term was first used for the cells of the bodies of the higher plants, where the hard cellulose walls separating the cells are very obvious and first attracted attention. For such units the term was clearly appropriate. From this use the term was extended to the cells composing the bodies of multicellular animals, which are also separated from each other by intercellular walls, though these are far less conspicuous than in the plants; and thence it was extended to the free-living cells of the Protista.† Better terms have been suggested

* Robinow, *Proc. R.S.*, Bcxxx, 299, 1942.

† The distinction between the single-celled plants (Protophyta) and animals (Protozoa) is one which it is difficult to make logical. It is often said that all organisms containing chlorophyll are plants. Single-celled organisms containing chlorophyll are therefore often called Protophyta, and the many closely related

for the unit we are calling the cell—energid, protoplast—but the term "cell" is almost universally used. Since the only organisms we shall need to consider in this book are the multicellular animals and the Protista, we need not discuss whether the bodies of simpler organisms such as the bacteria and viruses should be called cellular, so long as we define the term "cell" as the unit into which the protoplasm of the Protista and of multicellular animals is organised, there seems no reason why we should not use the term.

The cell, then, is typically a unit of protoplasm containing a nucleus and some other organs to be defined later. But this definition must be extended if it is to cover all types of animal cell. The organisation of protoplasm is not always as simple as this. In some cells there may be many nuclei, *e.g.* in multinucleate amœbæ such as *Pelomyxa.* In some tissues of multicellular animals, cell walls are absent and the tissue is formed of syncytial masses of protoplasm with many nuclei (*e.g.* vertebrate muscle). Degenerate cells also occur, such as the red blood corpuscles of the mammals, which have no nuclei. But the definition covers all the more typical animal cells, which are not degenerate.

Before we go on to discuss the organisation of the animal cell, we must consider some questions concerned with the methods available for the investigation of the structure of the cell.

When we were discussing the fine structure of protoplasm (p. 12), we found the study of coagulated or "fixed" protoplasm to lead to false ideas of its structure. Here the question arises how far we may safely use fixed protoplasm in studying the structure of the cell. If it is permissible, there are many advantages to be gained from coagulating the protoplasm of the cell before we study its structure. Many of the cell organs are not easily visible in the living cell. Protoplasm cannot be kept for long in a fit state for study, unless it has been coagulated. Also, coagulated protoplasm can be cut into thin sections in which the structure of the cell organs can be seen much more easily than in the whole cell. These sections can be stained and the cell organs often take up the stains differently, so that their structure is still more easily seen. But it is clear that we must not rely on these methods unless we can be sure that the fixed cell gives a true picture of the structures in the living cell.

The cell organs are larger than the elements of the supposed

forms which are without chlorophyll are also frequently included in the Protophyta, for not all plants contain chlorophyll. But the organisation of these forms is very like that of many which are usually grouped as Protozoa. It is difficult to believe that the distinction is a natural one. It seems better for our purposes to use the term Protista for all single-celled organisms which have the complete organisation of the cell. Thus we shall avoid the necessity of distinguishing the Protophyta and Protozoa.

essential structure of protoplasm (p. 12), which are very close to the lower limit of size for microscopic vision. The larger a structure is, the less likely it is that artefacts due to alteration of the ultramicroscopic colloidal structure of the protoplasm will interfere with its appearance after fixation. For this reason there is less danger in using fixed material in the study of the organs of the cell than in that of the fine structure of protoplasm.

Nevertheless, it is dangerous to accept without further question the structures seen in fixed material as the same as those of the living cell. There are some precautions we may take to reduce this danger.

In the first place, we should make the fixation rapid, for experience shows that there is less chance of change in the structure if this is so. There is no difficulty in doing this, since the fixatives which histologists have found to be "good" all fix protoplasm rapidly.

Secondly, several fixatives, which should be as different from each other in chemical characters as possible, can be used in studying the same structure. We may fix the cell with mercuric chloride, osmium tetroxide, and formaldehyde, and compare the structure in protoplasm fixed by each of these fixatives. It is unlikely that all these fixatives will alter the structure in the same way. If we find that they all give the same picture of the structure of the cell, it will be safer to conclude that the structure is not altered by fixation.

It must be remembered that many fixatives will produce other changes in the protoplasm besides those due directly to its coagulation. For instance, fixatives containing a large percentage of alcohol may fix some of the cell organs excellently, but they will dissolve fatty substances out of the protoplasm (since fats are soluble in alcohol). They will therefore greatly alter the structure of organs which contain much fatty material.

When reasonable precautions are taken and the action which the fixative is likely to have on the protoplasm as a result of its chemical nature is allowed for, it is justifiable to accept results obtained from fixed material if the structures under investigation cannot be observed in unfixed protoplasm. But it must never be forgotten that there is always some danger of artefact when fixed material is used. Whenever possible, results should be confirmed by observation of living, or at least unfixed, protoplasm, and descriptions of cell structures can never be regarded as established beyond doubt until this is done.

On the whole, it is perhaps surprising how little distortion of the cell organs is caused by fixation used judiciously. Even structures not more than a few μ in size are often found to have been very little altered by fixation, when their structure is confirmed by observation of the living protoplasm. This has happened time and again in the study of the cell. However, in the following account of the structure of the cell, it will always be mentioned when structures are described which have only been seen in fixed material.

Some means can be used to increase the detail which can be observed in the living cell. These have been mentioned when we were discussing the structure of protoplasm (pp. 13 f.). Both ultra-violet light and intra-vitam stains have been useful in the study of cell structure. This is especially true of the intra-vitam stains. Many cell organs take up one or other of these stains, and can be seen in the living cell after they have been stained. Although the protoplasm is undoubtedly altered to some extent by being stained, the structure of the cell organs is not likely to have been much altered. Ultra-violet light has so far been less used. The phase-contrast and interference microscopes are also useful (p. 12).

When we describe the structure of the cell, we should include descriptions not only of the shape and arrangement of the cell organs, but also of their chemical constitution. This subject, which may be called the chemical morphology of the cell,* has recently been given considerable attention. The most direct method of studying it is to treat the cell with reagents which give well-marked reactions with the various cell constituents. For example, fats are stained black by osmic acid, and red by a dye named Sudan III; starch is stained black by iodine. The distribution of many other constituents can be mapped out by treatment with suitable reagents. These methods have been applied to one at least of the protein constituents of the animal cell. A method due to Feulgen, after whom it is named, is apparently specific for de-oxyribose-nucleic acid (sometimes called thymonucleic acid), the essential constituent of the nucleo-protein (p. 28) of the animal cell. By using this method the distribution of the nucleo-proteins can be examined accurately. Many other constituents of the cell may be identified, and their distribution studied, by their micro-chemical reactions. Even some enzymes—oxidative enzymes, phosphatases—may be so studied.†

In many of these microchemical tests the protoplasm is killed but not coagulated. In some it is also coagulated. If it is coagulated, we must use the same precautions as in studying the form of the cell organs in coagulated protoplasm.

THE ESSENTIAL STRUCTURE OF THE ANIMAL CELL IN THE "RESTING" CONDITION

By the resting condition of a cell is meant its condition when it is not undergoing the changes which precede and accompany division.

* Now often called cyto-chemistry.

† *Cf.* E. W. Dempsey and G. B. Wislocki, *Physiol. Rev.*, xxvi, 1, 1946.

We will consider these changes later. The use of the term "resting cell" must not be taken to imply that the cell is in any sense inactive between the divisions.

In Fig. 5 the essential structure of a typical, resting animal cell is shown diagrammatically.

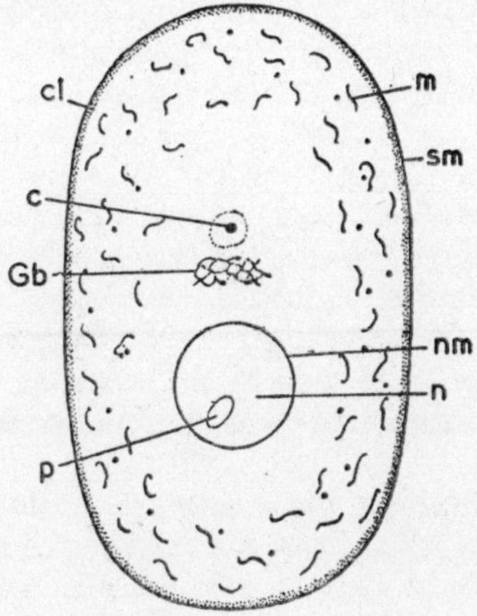

Figure 5. Diagram of the essential structure of an animal cell.

n, nucleus; *nm*, nuclear membrane; *p*, nucleolus; *sm*, surface membrane; *cl*, cortical surface layer; *Gb*, Golgi bodies; *c*, centrosome; *m*, mitochondria.

(*a*) *The Shape of the Cell*

We have seen (p. 15) that, although the greater part of the protoplasm of the cell is liquid, there is usually a surface layer which is more viscous than the interior and often gelatinous. If the whole cell were a homogeneous liquid, we should expect that its shape would be spherical, which is the shape of a liquid drop in a liquid medium. But the frequent presence of a gelatinous surface layer removes the necessity for this; a body with a solid surface layer may take on any shape. We find that cells may have many forms; they are often far from spherical.

The shape of cells is often determined by conditions outside their protoplasm. In the multicellular body the cells are usually deformed by the pressure of surrounding cells; and in many Protista the shape of the cell is determined by that of the hard external skeleton secreted by the protoplasm. In other Protista, movements of the protoplasm may deform the cell. It does so in *Amœba*.

Nevertheless, it is true that the animal cell tends towards a spherical shape. The cells of many of the simpler Protista do so. So also do many of the cells of the multicellular body if they are removed from the body, and so released from the pressure of their neighbours. The smaller the cell, the more marked this tendency is. This is to be expected, for the forces tending to make the cell spherical become relatively greater as the size diminishes.

(*b*) *The Nucleus*

No normal animal cell capable of long-continued life and division is without a nucleus (Fig. 5). The protoplasm of the nucleus has sometimes been found to be liquid in the healthy, undamaged state. It is so, for instance, in the echinoderm egg and in the irregular, lobed nuclei of the spinning glands of the silkworm. More often the nucleus is spherical or ovoid, and its protoplasm viscous. It may very easily become gelatinous when it is damaged. For instance, a nucleus removed from an *Amœba* is found to consist of a tenacious jelly, but this condition is a result of changes which take place during its removal. The nucleus of *Amœba* is liquid in the healthy cell. But in protistan cells the undamaged nucleus is sometimes gelatinous.

The chemical substances which differentiate the protoplasm of the nucleus (*nucleoplasm*) from that of the rest of the cell (*cytoplasm*) are the nucleoproteins to which we have referred already (p. 26). The nucleoprotein material of the nucleus is the substance which stains with such dyes as hæmatoxylin, though these dyes are not specific for it. It can be recognised by the Feulgen test (p. 26). It is especially characteristic of the chromosomes (see p. 38). It is only found in nuclear protoplasm and, if it occurs in the cytoplasm, as it sometimes does, especially among the Protista, the protoplasm containing it is derived from the nucleus. In the cytoplasm the bodies containing nucleoprotein are usually in the form of granules.

Bounding the nucleus and separating it from the cytoplasm is the *nuclear membrane*. In the vast majority of cells this membrane disappears during division, but at other times it is a definite structure and is solid. Its solidity is shown by the fact that, when deformed by a microdissection needle pressed against it, it then takes a form which could not be taken by a liquid surface layer (Fig. 6). If the membrane is punctured by the needle, the nucleus usually degenerates. It is possible, although we have no direct evidence on the point, that the nuclear membrane acts as a semi-permeable membrane between the contents of the nucleus and the cytoplasm, just as the surface membrane does between the cytoplasm and the external medium. Like other membranes of the cell it is shown by the electron microscope to be double (p. 33).

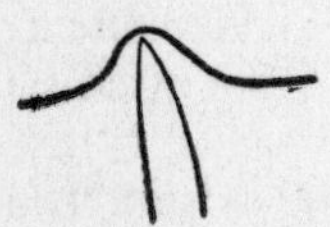

Figure 6. Reaction of the nuclear membrane to the microdissection needle.

In the majority of living cells the only obvious bodies within the nucleus are the *nucleoli*, spherical masses of protoplasm distinctly separated from the rest of the nucleoplasm. The nucleus may contain one or two (and occasionally more) nucleoli, but many nuclei are without them. There is evidence that the nucleoli contain a nucleo-protein distinct from that of other parts of the nucleus. They also contain an enzyme concerned in the metabolism of phosphates, phosphatase. They may play a part in the exchange of metabolic material between the nucleus and the cytoplasm outside it. They have been found to arise in association with certain of the chromosomes (p. 38).

There are some exceptions to the statement that the nucleoli are the only visible structures in the nucleus of the resting cell. In the nucleus of *Amœba*, for instance, a ring of bodies, the chromatin blocks, which contain nucleo-protein, can be seen lying near the surface of the nucleus. In many protistan nuclei there is a central mass of nucleo-protein, the *endosome*.

The nucleoplasm usually has no visible structure in the resting nucleus. A fine structure of a network of strands of a more solid substance passing through a liquid matrix has been described, but this has only been seen in the coagulated nucleus. Its presence in the living state is doubtful. By staining the coagulated nucleus the presence of nucleo-proteins can be demonstrated, chiefly near the surface of the nucleus. The presence of these substances and their aggregation near the surface may be accepted, but they have also been described from coagulated material as distributed in granules or small masses on the surface. It is much more doubtful whether this distribution can be accepted as true of the living nucleus.

Evidence derived from the hereditary functions of the chromosomes shows very clearly that they persist in some form between the division. They can be recognised by use of the electron microscope (p. 34).

(*c*) *Cytoplasmic Organs*

Of the many organs which may occur in the cytoplasm of a cell only a few are present in all, or most, cells. Since we are discussing the essential cell organs, we are concerned only with these few organs of the cytoplasm. Even of the organs discussed in this section, some have not been demonstrated in every animal cell. But the distribution of these organs in the animal cell is certainly very wide. We are probably justified in assuming that they or similar organs are essential to the life of the cell.

1. *The Surface Membrane and the Cortical Layer*. These are undoubtedly essential cell organs. We have discussed them in the section

dealing with the organisation of protoplasm. We need not discuss them further here.

2. *Mitochondria.* These are small bodies, either small rods or spheres, present in almost all animal cells. They are characterised by containing much lipoid material and by staining intra-vitam with a dye known as Janus Green. So stained, they are easily visible in the living cell. They are present in the cells of the multicellular body, except in such degenerate cells as the red blood-corpuscles of the mammals. They are also present in many—and perhaps all—protistan cells.

Mitochondria are not nuclear in origin, and do not contain nucleoprotein. They are sometimes scattered evenly through the cytoplasm, but in some cells they are collected in definite regions, either round the nucleus or in parts of the cell where active chemical metabolism is going on. They occur, for instance, near the base of the cilium in ciliated cells (Fig. 7), and where secretion is being formed in secretory cells. They are most numerous when the chemical metabolism of the cell is most active.

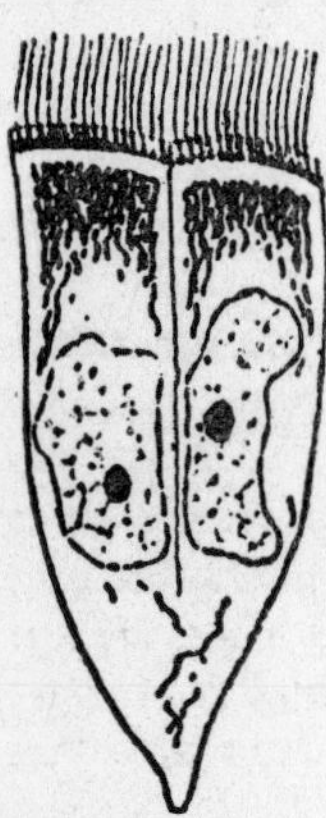

Figure 7. Collection of the mitochondria round the base of the cilia in a ciliated cell. (After Saguchi.)

3. *Golgi Bodies.* In all the cells of the multicellular body, unless they are degenerate, and in many, perhaps all, of the Protista,* there is found a system of organs in the cytoplasm to which the name "Golgi bodies" has been given after their discoverer. These organs are usually studied in fixed material, but their outlines and some of the details of their arrangement have been seen in the living cell. There is no doubt that the picture given by fixed material is a real one.

These bodies may be restricted to one area of the cell or scattered through the cytoplasm. When restricted, they usually lie near the nuclear membrane or between it and the seat of greatest chemical activity in the cell. They are scattered in cells in which the chemical activity is not orientated, *e.g.* in many eggs.

The Golgi bodies consist of tubes or spheres of various arrangement. In the living cell they may be continually changing in form. Often, they have an outer layer of lipoprotein material and an inner mass; the latter may be absent. It is possible that the inner substance may be the product of the activity of the outer layer.

4. *The Centrosome.* In the mitotic figure of dividing cells of the multicellular body (see pp. 34 ff.), the asters usually arise from small bodies at their centres, the centrosomes. These are spherical proto-

* P. P. Grassé and A. Hollande, *Arch. Zool. exp.*, lxxxii, 301, 1941.

plasmic bodies, often with a central granule called the *centriole*. The latter can be intensely stained with some nucleur stains but it does not contain nucleoprotein and is not nuclear in origin. Often a single centriole persists between divisions, and it is the division of this centriole which is the first visible sign of the approaching division of the cell. But the centriole can be formed *de novo* in some cells before division. From the centrioles the centrosomes grow out. When the Golgi complex is situated in a definite region of the cell, the centriole is often found at the centre of this complex, except during division.

Thus, in cells of the multicellular body, the centrosome, with its contained centriole, is a cytoplasmic organ. In the Protista it is often a nuclear organ but its relations to the nucleus and other cell organs are complex.

In the first place centrosomes (and centrioles) are often absent in protistan cells even at division. Their place at the poles of the division figure is taken by large areas of cytoplasm known as the *polar plates*. These show no central body (Fig. 8). Secondly, the whole division figure may be within the nucleus and this may be so whether the

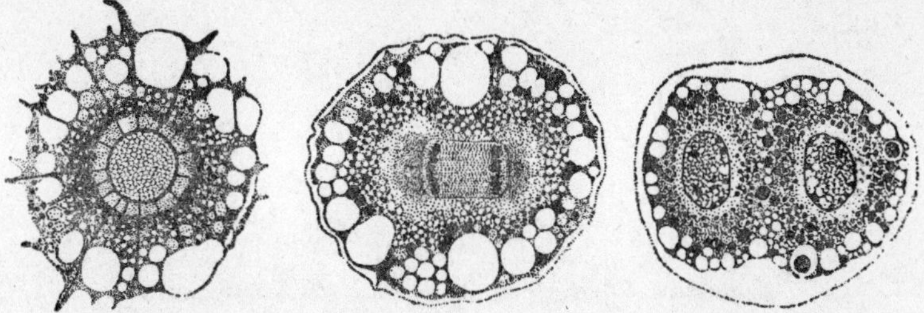

Figure 8. Division of the nucleus in *Actinophrys sol* (Heliozoa).
The division figure extends beyond the nucleus, but there are no centrosomes. (After Bělăr.)

centrosome is present or not (Plate I, Fig. 9, facing p. 8). The centrosome, if it is present, is then a nuclear organ; between divisions it is often within the nucleolus. In many other Protista there are cytoplasmic centrosomes, with centrioles, which persist between divisions (Plate II, Fig. 10*a* and *b*).

In many Protista the centrosome is seen to act between divisions as the basal granule of the flagellum (p. 61). This is clear in the division of some of the Flagellata (Fig. 11), where the basal granule becomes the centrosome at division. Plate I, Fig. 9*b*, facing p. 8, is an example of a division in which the basal granule does not act as the centrosome. Often the basal granule is connected with the nucleus by a fibril, the *rhizoplast*,* which perhaps indicates that the intranuclear position of the centrosome is the more primitive position, a

* Rhizoplasts also occur in the collar cells of sponges.

conclusion which is supported by the fact that the centrosome is often intranuclear in the flagellates, which are usually believed to be the most primitive Protista. But a rhizoplast is not always present. Whether there is a rhizoplast or not, there is sometimes (Trypanosomes and some Flagellata) near the centrosome a body (*kinetonucleus* (p. 58)) perhaps of nuclear origin.

There is some evidence that the basal granules of the cilia of cells of the multicellular body are also derived from the centrosomes. Basal granules are organs essential to the beat of the cilium or flagellum, and the centrosome seems to control the kinetic activities of the cell at division. So, in all its functions, this organ seems to be in control of kinetic activity in the cell.

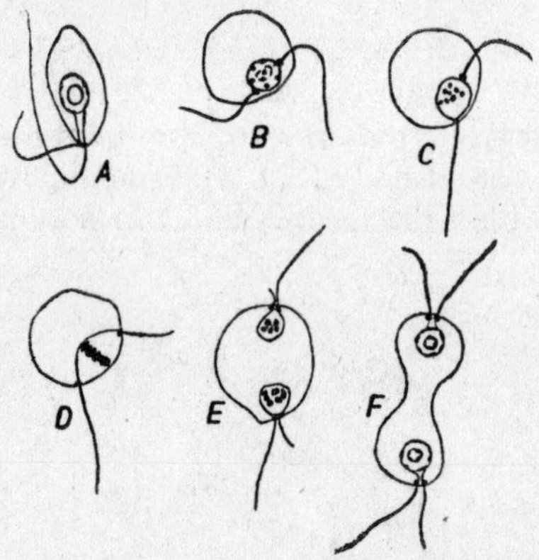

Figure 11. Division of *Heteromita* (Mastigophora).
The basal granules act as centrosomes in the division. (After M. Robertson.)

THE FUNCTIONS OF THE CELL ORGANS

(1) *The Nucleus.* The nucleus has other functions besides the well-known hereditary function of the chromosomes.

No animal cell, unless it is degenerate, is able to live permanently without nuclear material. But a portion of the resting nucleus is often sufficient to maintain the life of a part of a protistan cell. Parts cut from many protistan cells are able to grow and reproduce if they contain a part, and not too small a part, of the nucleus. In some of the Protista the fraction of the nucleus which is sufficient for life is small. Pieces of the ciliate *Stentor* have been found to be capable of indefinite life with only 1/64th part of the whole nucleus. Thus, the nucleus of the Protista cannot contain a single set of organs all of which are necessary for the life of the protoplasm. It is probably polyploid with many sets of the essential chromosomes.

The death of enucleate fragments of a cell is not always rapid. The

PLATE II

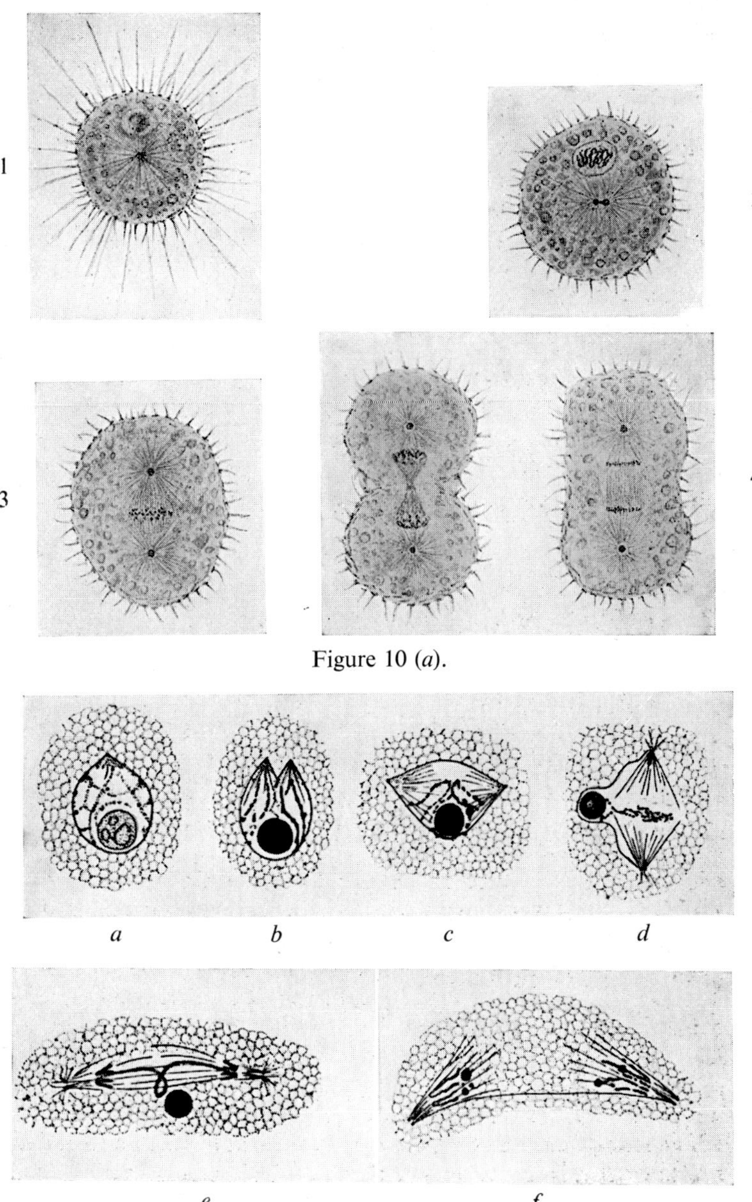

Figure 10 (*b*).

Figure 10. (*a*) Division of *Acanthocystis aculeata* (Heliozoa). (After Schaudinn.) (*b*) Nuclear division in the cyst of *Pterocephalus gracilis* (Sporozoa). Centrosomes just outside the nuclear membrane. During the division the large endosome is cast out of the spindle and degenerates. (After Leger and Duboscq.)

[*To face p.* 32.

order in which the various activities of the protoplasm are disturbed in such a fragment gives us some evidence of the functions of the nucleus in the normal life of the cell.

Regeneration and growth almost always cease when the cell fragment is removed from the influence of the nucleus. Enucleate fragments do not take on again the typical form of the species, as nucleate fragments may do. Nor are the organs of the cell normally regenerated. In one protistan cell, *Acetabularia*, a green alga, enucleate fragments have been found to regenerate lost organs. This exceptional case may be due to some influence of the nucleus already present in the cytoplasm before separation. Cytoplasmic division, usually abnormal, may occur in the absence of the nucleus,* but not mitosis.

On the other hand, the catabolic activities of the cell, those by which free energy is developed from the chemical energy of the cell constituents, may continue for some time in enucleate fragments. An enucleate fragment of *Amœba* forms pseudopodia, and the contractile vacuole, if it is present, continues to pulsate. Cilia and flagella may continue to beat so long as the parts of the ciliary apparatus which lie within the cell (p. 61) are undamaged. The contractile fibrils of the Protista, the myonemes (p. 66), may contract. Gradually, however, all these activities cease, and finally, often only after several days, the protoplasm dies.

The conclusions to be drawn from these facts are (*a*) that nuclear material is absolutely essential for the permanent life of the animal cell; (*b*) that it is immediately essential for growth, regeneration, and mitosis; but (*c*) that catabolic activities come to a stop more slowly in the absence of nuclear material. The nucleus is therefore primarily concerned with control of the anabolic rather than the catabolic activities of the cell. The ultimate breakdown of catabolic activities in enucleate fragments is perhaps mainly due to the absence of the normal activity of the nucleus in maintaining and regenerating the protoplasm which is responsible for these activities.

(2) *Metabolism and Sub-microscopic Structure in the Cell.* Recent work, mostly with the electron microscope, has shown that our inability to find any essential structure in protoplasm visible in the light-microscope does not mean that it is structureless on a smaller scale. The matrix of the protoplasm is organised in a reticulum (*endoplasmic reticulum*) of vacuoles and canaliculi, the vacuoles about $0{\cdot}15\mu$ across and the canaliculi $0{\cdot}05$–$0{\cdot}15\mu$ in diameter. Associated with this reticulum are small bodies (*microsomes*) of varying size ($0{\cdot}05$–$0{\cdot}15\mu$). Mitochondria have complex structure. They are surrounded by membranes, double as is the nuclear and the

* Harvey, *Biol. Bull.*, **71**, 101, 1936; Swann, *Symp. Soc. exp. Biol.*, **6**, 89, 1952.

cell membrane (p. 43), and the inner layer of the membrane is carried into the substance of the mitochondrium in numerous parallel folds. The morphology of the Golgi complex is less well known. The nucleus is also complex in structure and the chromosomes persist between mitoses as fine threads (*chromonemata*).

We cannot discuss these recent findings in detail here.* It is very probable that the sub-microscopic structure of the cell and its organs is essential for co-ordination of the long chains of chemical reactions of which metabolism is built up, perhaps largely by providing ordered arrangement of the enzymes. The mitochondria are believed to be the seat of most of the katabolic metabolism by which energy is released. The Gogli complex is also concerned in the control of metabolism.

MITOSIS

(*a*) *In the Cells of the Multicellular Body*

We will first consider mitosis, the process by which the nucleus divides, in the fully elaborated form which occurs in the cells of the multicellular body.

The course of a typical mitosis in this complete form is shown in Fig. 12. This figure is drawn from results obtained from fixed protoplasm, but most of the details of the process can be seen in the living cell. The process is continuous, but it may be divided into the following stages:

		mins.
1. Division of the centriole and migration of its parts to the poles of the nucleus. 2. Formation of the centrosomes around the centrioles and of the asters. Beginning of the growth of the asters. Appearance of the chromosomes as a gradually thickening spireme, which in the later stages of the thickening is formed of double threads. 3. Disappearance of the nuclear membrane and formation of the spindle.	Prophase	30–60
4. Collection of the chromosomes on the equatorial plate of the spindle.	Metaphase	2–10
5. Division of the chromosomes and movement of their halves to the poles of the spindle.	Anaphase	2–3
6. Re-formation of the nuclear membrane.	Telophase	30–130

Throughout the division, the asters, centred on the centrosomes, increase in size, until, in many cells, they fill almost the whole of the cytoplasm.

The times given in the last column of this table must not be taken as more than very rough estimates of the length of the various stages in a typical division. The speed of the division is variable, both as a whole and in its different parts. It varies with the temperature and

* *Cf.* De Robertis *et al.*, *General Cytology*, Saunders, 1955; Picken, *The Organization of Cells and other Organisms*, Clarendon Press, 1960.

other conditions as well as with the type of cell. The order in which the stages of the mitosis succeed one another is more constant, but even here some variation occurs. For instance, the nuclear membrane may disappear before the thickening of the spireme is complete.

In Plate III, Fig. 13, the division of a tissue-culture cell is shown as it appears in the living cell (a) and in coagulated material (b). It will be seen that much of the detail of the mitotic figure can be seen in the living cell. The division figure of this cell differs considerably from that shown in Fig. 12. For instance, the asters are not visible in the tissue-culture cell either in the living or coagulated protoplasm. They are probably absent in this type of division. They can be seen in many living cells of other types, as in the sea-urchin egg.

1. *Initiation of the Division.* We know very little of the causes which determine that division shall begin in a cell. Some experiments on a ciliate protistan *Frontonia* indicate one condition which seems to be important in this type of cell, and may be in others. In *Frontonia* it has been shown that there is a very rapid growth of the nucleus just before division, and that at that time the size of the nucleus increases in comparison with the size of the cytoplasm (Fig. 14). Before this rapid growth of the nucleus takes place, the division can be delayed by cutting off a part of the cytoplasm; after the growth, this has no effect on the course of the division. It seems that, in this cell at any rate, the proportionate sizes of the nucleus and cytoplasm have importance in controlling the oncoming of division. But there is no evidence that similar growth of the nucleus occurs before division in all animal cells, and it must not be assumed that the relative sizes of nucleus and cytoplasm control the initiation of division in all cells. We know nothing of the causes which initiate division in most cells.

2. *The Asters.* Microdissection has shown that there are large variations in the viscosity of the protoplasm in different parts of the asters. The protoplasm surrounding the centriole at the centre of the aster, *i.e.* that of the centrosomes, is relatively liquid. As a whole the aster is a more solid body than the rest of the cytoplasm. It can be moved about the cell with the microdissection needle.

3. *Formation of the Spireme.* It has been observed in an amphibian spermatocyte that, if the nuclear membrane is pricked with a microdissection needle, the spireme appears immediately although not previously visible in the nucleus. This has been thought to be evidence that a spireme was present before the membrane was pricked. If the nuclear membrane of the spermatocyte of the grasshopper, *Dissosteira,* is pricked in an early prophase of the division of the cell, the thickening and shortening of the spireme is greatly accelerated. It

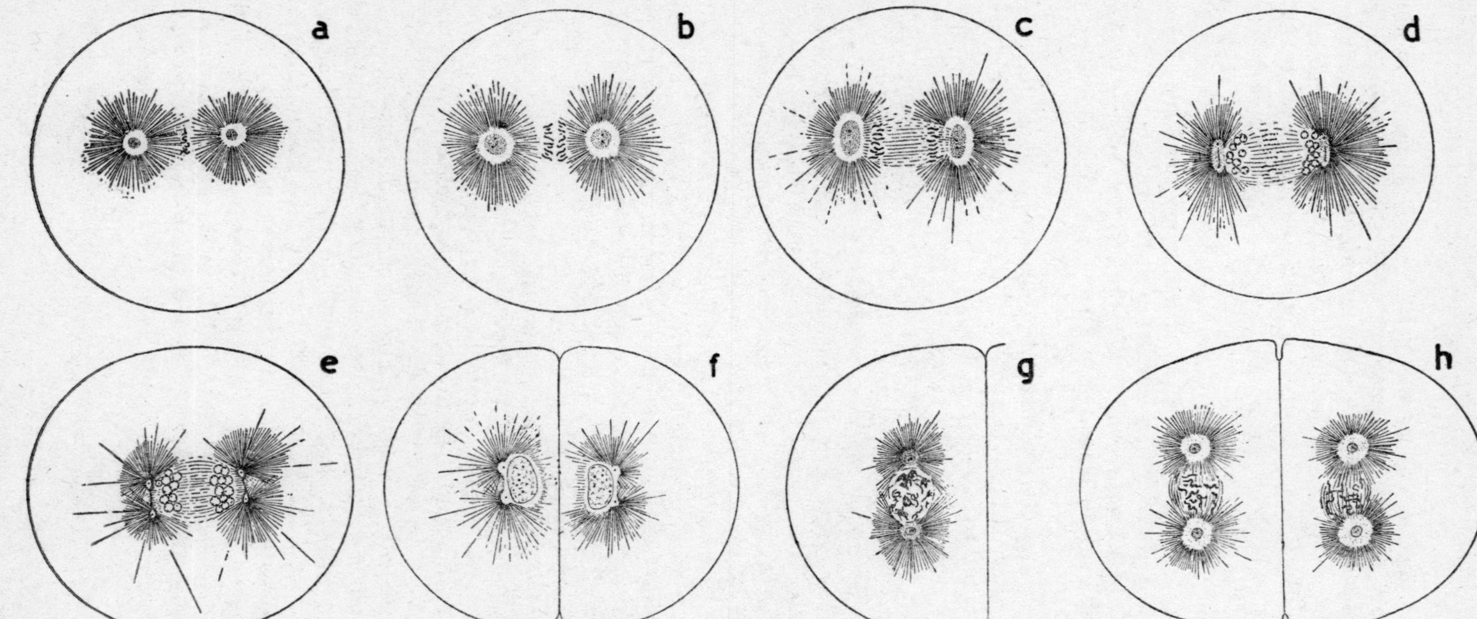

Figure 12. Course of mitosis during the first division of a sea-urchin egg and the beginning of the second. *a*, *b*, metaphase of first division; *c*, anaphase; *d*, *e*, *f*, telophase; *g*, *h*, prophase of second division. (After Boveri.)

would seem that the thickening of the spireme is associated with breakdown of the nuclear membrane, perhaps with the removal of the semi-permeable separation between the cytoplasm and the nucleoplasm which the membrane provides in the resting cell. It is probable that the spireme is never a single continuous thread. Throughout, it probably consists of the very elongate chromosomes, each as a separate thread. But the threads forming each chromosome cannot be distinguished in early stages of the spireme.

4. *Disappearance of the Nuclear Membrane*. It can be shown that the nuclear substance is not separated from the cytoplasm by any solid membrane after the nuclear membrane has disappeared. But this does not imply that complete mixing of the nucleoplasm and the cytoplasm takes place. It probably does not, although they cannot be distinguished after the disappearance of the membrane. It is probable that the original nucleoplasm forms at least the greater part of the substance of the spindle.

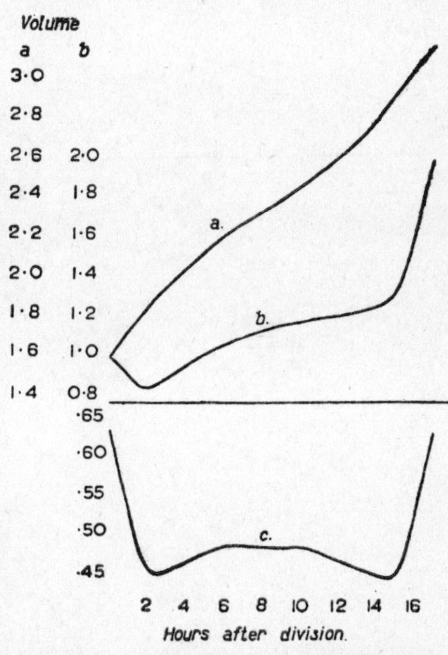

Figure 14. Growth of the cytoplasm (*a*) and nucleus (*b*) between two divisions in *Frontonia*. Changes in the proportion $\frac{\text{nucleus size}}{\text{cytoplasm size}}$ are given (*c*). (After Popoff.)

5. *The Spindle*. The spindle, though formed mainly from the nuclear protoplasm, extends outside the region of the nucleus. Its poles reach almost to the centrosomes. Its protoplasm is more solid than the cytoplasm. It behaves as a jelly when touched with the microdissection needle and can be moved about the cell as a whole. But its viscosity varies both in its different parts and during the course of the division. In tissue-culture cells the chromosomes have been seen to wriggle on the equatorial plate, which cannot be solid in these cells. It is probable that the equatorial plate is less solid than the rest of the spindle in all cells.

Fibres known as the spindle fibres have been described as attached to the chromosomes and passing from them to the poles of the spindle. These fibres have been seen in living material. It is believed that true fibres more solid than the surrounding protoplasm are present in the spindle, and it is thought possible that the chromosomes are drawn to the poles at anaphase by contraction of these fibres.

6. *The Chromosomes.* Both the threads of the spireme and the chromosomes into which they shorten are gelatinous bodies more

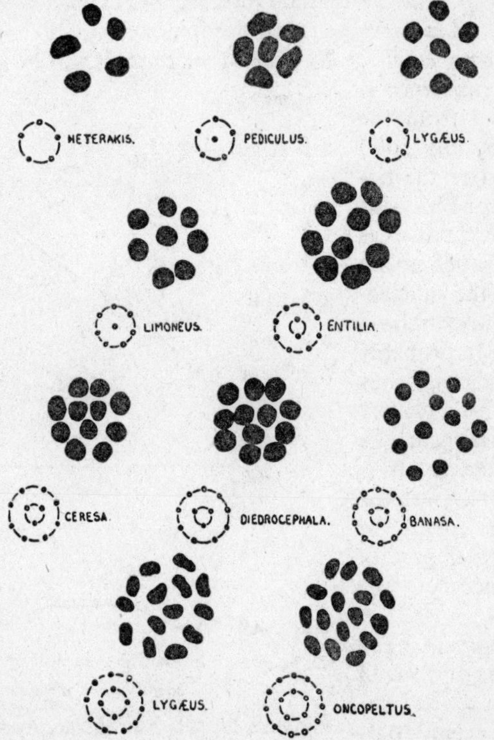

Figure 15. Arrangement of the chromosomes on the equatorial plate in several genera compared with the arrangement of similar numbers of floating magnets. (After Cannon.)

solid than the surrounding protoplasm. The spireme threads can be pulled out of the nucleus by means of the microdissection needle, and the chromosomes can be pulled away from the equatorial plate. A chromosome can be pulled apart by two needles inserted into its ends. The two halves separate as if they were composed of a stiff jelly. The minute structure of the chromosomes is complex. We have not space to discuss it here.

The chromosomes are arranged more or less regularly on the equatorial plate (Fig. 15). Their arrangement is very like that which

PLATE III

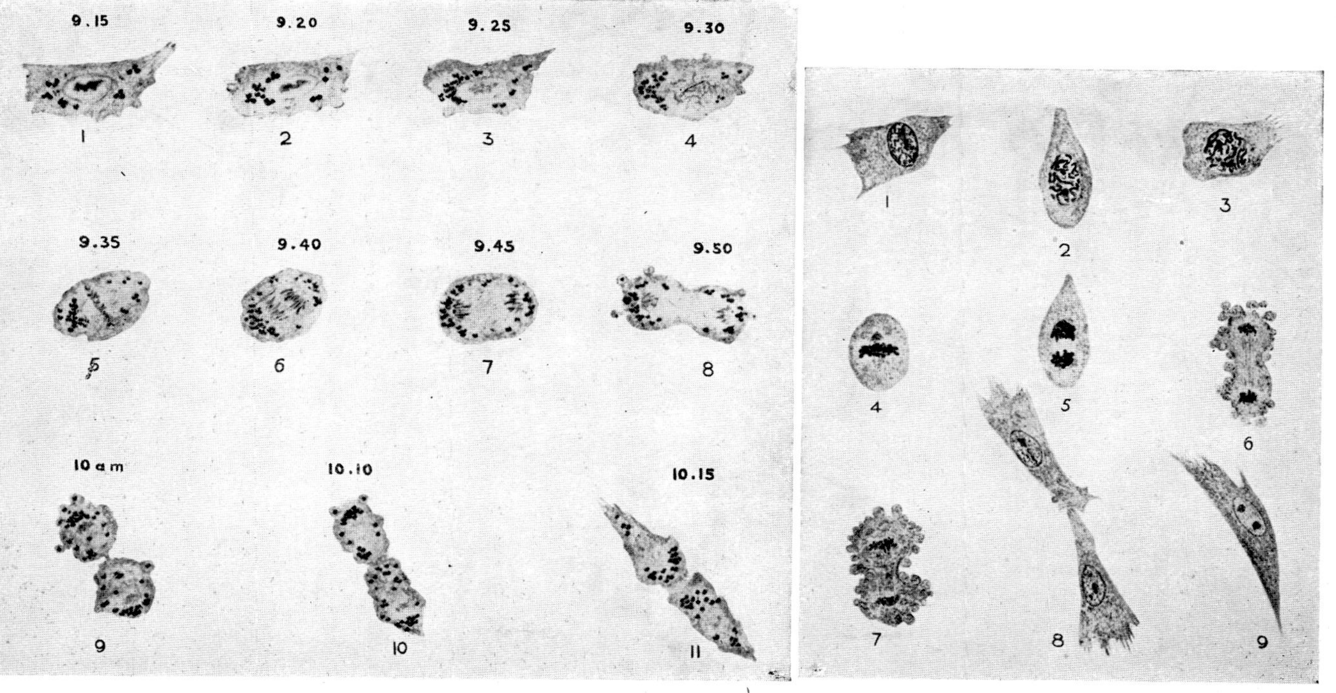

(*a*) (*b*)

Figure 13.

Figure 13. (*a*) Division of a tissue-culture cell as seen in the living cell. The times above the figures give the intervals between the corresponding stages. (*b*) Division of a tissue-culture cell as seen after coagulation and staining. (Both after Strangeways.)

[*To face p.* 38.

we should find in a physical system if they were attracted by some force towards the poles of the spindle and repelled by each other. It is the same arrangement as that of magnets floating with the same pole uppermost below a stronger pole of the opposite sign. This agreement holds whether the number of the chromosomes is few or many. But it must not be thought that this implies that there is any system of forces present in the spindle similar in arrangement to those between such magnets. More probably, the chromosomes while on the plate are repelled from the poles, not attracted to them.

The separation of the halves of the chromosomes takes place as if each half was either pulled by some force to one of the poles of the spindle or repelled from the other half of the chromosome. Either the ends or the middles of the chromosomes may separate first. The halves separate first at the position of a special organ in the chromosome, the *centromere*. This point is the position at which the spindle fibre is attached, and is in front as the chromosome moves to the pole. It may be that the force pulling the chromosomes to the poles is due to contraction of the spindle fibres.

7. *Reformation of the Nuclei.* During telophase the chromosomes may either become vacuolated, then less distinct, and finally disappear; or they may form a network rather like that of the spireme and then disappear. Finally the nuclei are reconstituted and the nuclear membranes reformed. It is not clear how far the original nucleoplasm forms the nucleoplasm of the daughter nuclei.

(*b*) *In the Protista*

Some of the Protista, especially many of the Heliozoa (Plate II, Fig. 10*a*, facing p. 32), have mitotic figures almost exactly similar to those of the cell of the multicellular body. In some Protista many of the details of the division figure cannot be recognised.

1. It has already been noted (p. 31) that the centrosomes may be within the nucleus in the Protista. The whole mitotic figure is then within the nucleus (Plate I, Fig. 9, facing p. 8) and the nuclear membrane never breaks down.

2. It has also been mentioned that centrosomes may be absent in protistan mitoses, and that their place is then taken by the polar plates, large areas of protoplasm at the poles of the figure (Fig. 8, p. 31). When this is so, the figure is often much simpler than in typical mitosis. For instance, in *Paramecium* (Fig. 16) the division of the micronucleus (p. 58) has been described as little more than a flow of the nuclear material to the two poles of the figure.

3. Bodies which resemble chromosomes are often present but much of the nucleo-protein often passes to the poles without forming chromosomes. In most cases the material which behaves in this way

is, at least in part, that of the endosome. Thus, even if chromosomes occur in protistan nuclei, they may not form the whole of the nucleo-protein.

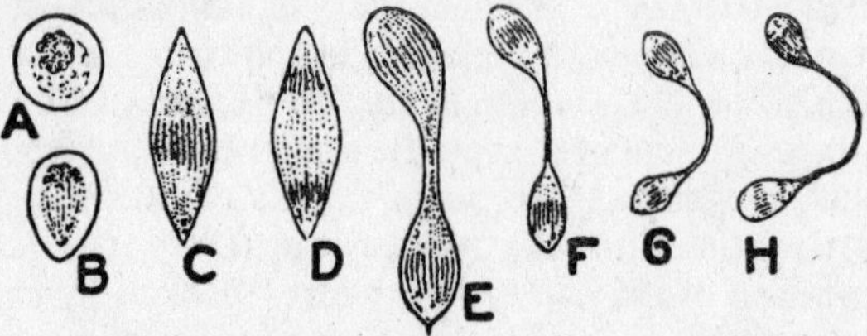

Figure 16. Division of the micronucleus in *Paramecium*. (From Minchin, after Hertwig.)

4. In some Protista (*e.g. Coccidium*, Fig. 17) the nucleus pulls apart without any recognisable division figure or chromosomes being formed. In some non-typical cells of the multicellular body division without mitosis may occur. It is known as amitosis. It also occurs in the division of the meganucleus of ciliates.

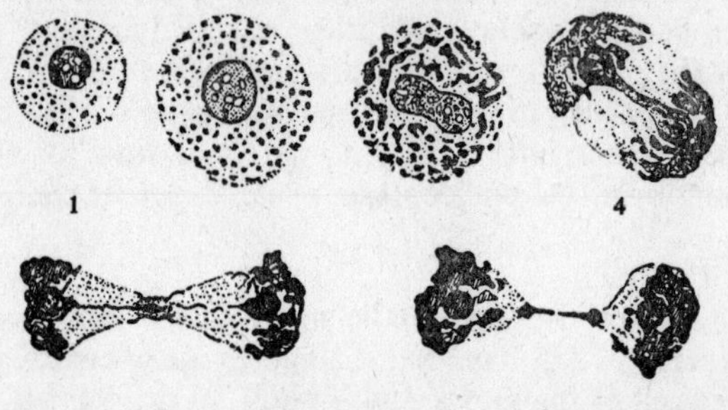

Figure 17. Division of *Coccidium* (Sporozoa). (From Minchin, after Schaudinn.)

Thus, in the Protista we find a series of forms of mitosis. The occurrence of these mitoses proves that the details of the metazoan mitosis are not essential for the life of the animal cell.

(*c*) *Theories of the Mitotic Figure*

So far we have considered the changes which occur during mitosis only as observed facts. We have made no attempt to explain how these changes are brought about. We cannot, in the present state of our knowledge, hope to reach a complete physical explanation of this or, indeed, of any other vital phenomenon. The visible changes in mitosis are even more complex than those in most other cell processes. They include movements within the cell, changes of viscosity, disappearance and formation of cell organs and many other changes. A complete explanation would have to account not only for these changes but also for their occurrence in a definite sequence. Mitosis is as good an example as we can find of the complexity of life within the cell. We must not hope for a complete physical explanation of it.

Nevertheless, in some vital phenomena it has been possible to determine certain of the physical processes which go on in the protoplasm during its activity. For instance, it has been possible to determine the electrical changes which accompany the passage of the nerve impulse down a nerve. Such results do not completely explain vital phenomena, but they may still be of great value.

It might be hoped that we should be able to arrive at some idea of the physical forces at work in the cell during mitosis. This hope is encouraged by the fact that many of the phenomena of mitosis strongly suggest that forces similar to those we find in physical systems are active in the cell at this time. The typical form of the astral figure is identical with that of the field of force found in many physical systems, *e.g.* that round two unlike magnetic poles. The arrangement of the chromosomes on the equatorial plate and their movements to the poles of the spindle also suggest some such system of forces. Also, the longitudinal organisation of the protoplasm in the spindle suggests that this protoplasm is in a state of strain (*cf.* pp. 37–8, and Fig. 3, p. 14).

Many attempts have been made to find a system of physical forces which might be supposed to act within the cell and to account for the observed facts of mitosis, but none of these attempts have been completely successful. The difficulty of finding any such physical system is greatly increased by the many abnormal forms of the mitotic figure which are occasionally seen, and often result in complete division of the nucleus. We are not here referring to the imperfect mitoses of the Protista, for these cannot be called abnormal, being the normal behaviour of these cells. But division figures which differ from the form of the figure usual in the type of cell being observed, and are thus abnormal, may occur. Astral figures with three or more poles are sometimes seen. In such cases the cells divide into as many daughter cells as there are poles of the astral figure, and the results of the division are abnormal only in the distribution of the chromosomes to the daughter cells. This is necessarily abnormal since the chromosomes divide normally and there are therefore not a sufficient number of divided chromosomes to give each cell its full complement. The occurrence of these multipolar astral figures and their apparently normal behaviour in the division of the cell makes it impossible to accept any theory of the mitotic figure which postulates forces of opposite signs at the two poles of the normal astral figure.

In some of the Sporozoa (Fig. 18), multipolar astral figures occur normally.

Again, in the division of the cell of the multicellular body, the centriole may fail to divide and a perfect but single and spherical aster is then formed (monaster). In divisions of this type the chromosomes are formed normally and divide, but their halves do not separate. A single nucleus is re-formed with double the original number of chromosomes. It would seem that an astral figure with at least two poles is necessary for separation of the chromosomes and division of the nucleus.

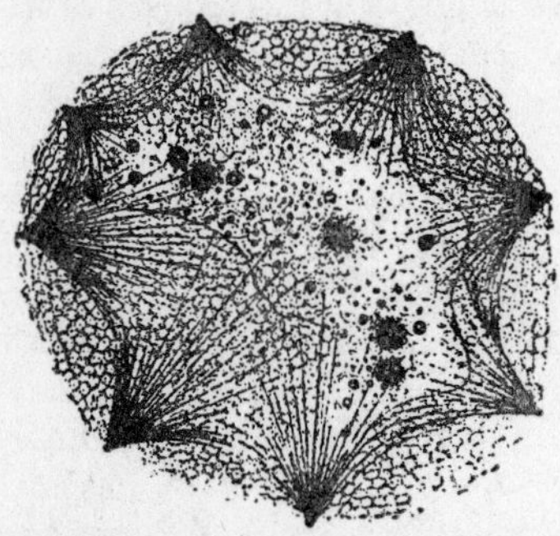

Figure 18. Multipolar division of *Aggregata jacquemeti* (Sporozoa). (After Moroff.)

We must leave the problem of the forces at work in mitosis at this point. For a discussion of recent theories on the subject, the reader may be referred to the book by C. D. Darlington (*Evolution of the Genetic Systems*). Even if we could define these forces we should still have to explain the causes of the many other changes which occur in the cell at this time.

THE CLEAVAGE OF THE CYTOPLASM

In a typical division of a cell of the multicellular body, the cytoplasm divides either soon after the chromosomes have reached the poles of the spindle, or during the re-formation of the nuclei. But cleavage of the cytoplasm does not necessarily follow mitosis. In some cells several divisions of the nucleus may occur without division of the cytoplasm. This often happens in spore formation in the Protista. The cytoplasm later divides into as many parts as the nuclei which have been formed. It also happens in other cells under experimental conditions, or when the cell is not healthy. A developing egg of a multicellular animal will often behave in this way. Cleavage must therefore be regarded as a phenomenon distinct from mitosis, although it normally follows it.

Often, no division of the cell occurs unless the nucleus is present, but it may (p. 33). The progress of cleavage is independent of the nucleus. In ciliates its progress has been shown to be associated with growth and multiplication of the cytoplasmic organs and especially of the ciliary structures.* Cleavage is a cytoplasmic rather than a nuclear phenomenon.

* E. Fauré Fremiet, *Folia Biotheoretica*, 3, 1948, p. 25.

The manner in which the division of the cytoplasm is brought about differs greatly from one type of cell to another. In a dividing tissue-culture cell or in *Amœba*, the two halves of the cell seem to pull themselves apart by the movements of the pseudopodia at their ends (Plate III, Fig. 13, facing p. 38). In the tissue-culture cell there is a curious, slow bubbling at the ends of the cell just before cleavage. This consists of extrusion and resorption of more or less spherical processes from the cell-surface. Its significance is unknown. In these cells we know little more than this about cleavage.

In many other cells the form during cleavage is determined by that of the hard secretions with which the protoplasm surrounds itself. This is true, for instance, of many shelled Protista, such as *Coleps* (Plate IV, Fig. 19).

The form of cleavage which has been most accurately studied is that of the echinoderm egg, a cell without pseudopodia or hard cuticle. The forms taken by the egg during its first cleavage are shown in Plate IV, Fig. 20.

Many theories to account for the form of the cleavage of the egg have been put forward. In earlier editions of this book it was suggested that repulsion between the growing asters at anaphase, and after it, caused the formation of the furrow, but this has lately been disproved by the observation that destruction of the asters at anaphase either by treatment of the egg with colchicine, a drug that destroys them, or by disturbance of the protoplasm within them by

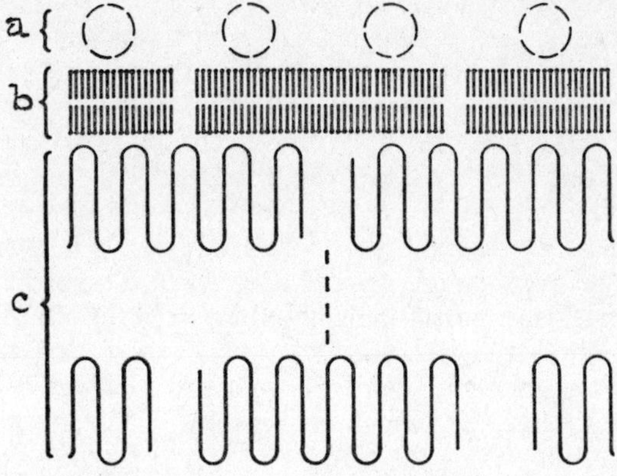

Figure 21. Model of the surface structure of a cell (mammalian red blood cell). *a*, outer layer of protein (20–50 Å); *b*, layer of orientated lipid molecules (40 Å); *c*, layer of coiled molecules of gelled protein (5000 Å). (After Mitchison.)

the micro-dissection needle does not prevent the cleavage from continuing, though the cleavage is then abnormal.

A recent theory depends on the probable structure of the surface layers of the egg (Fig. 21).* Within an outer layer of protein (*a*), the presence of which is not certain, there is believed to be a layer of orientated molecules of lipid (*b*) with scattered small holes in it, and within this again a much thicker layer of gelled protein (*c*) with the long molecules coiled, as shown in the figure, except that the coiling would not be in a single direction but in all tangential directions.

It is suggested that, in anaphase and later, a substance diffuses from the chromosomes and causes tangential expansion of the protein layer (*c*) on reaching the surface. This happens first at the poles since they are nearest to the chromosomes, but it extends towards the equator. The egg therefore first elongates, but as the equator is reached the expansion continues round the surface of the asters, and the furrow is formed between them. This is the only part played by the asters in the cleavage.

This theory probably accounts for the phenomena better than any previous theory, but it must not be assumed that the explanation is complete. The occurrence of cleavages in the absence of a nucleus (p. 33) is not explained.

Here in a simple cleavage we may, now or in the future, go some way in defining the physical forces which lie behind the changes of form we observe. Even in this example the explanation is not by any means complete: we have to postulate production of the active substance by the chromosomes, a vital activity which we cannot at present express in physical or chemical terms. We have here a good example of the part played by physical explanation in biology. The phenomena which we can state in terms of physics and chemistry lie on the surface of the vital activities: behind them are other activities, much less approachable. Perhaps, if we knew more of the ultramicroscopic organisation of protoplasm, we might go further in interpreting the activities of protoplasm on physical lines, for it is clear that it is this organisation which controls the vital processes in the cell. At present, although continued study extends physical explanation among the phenomena we observe in the organism, there are many vital phenomena which we have no immediate prospect of relating in any way to the facts of physics or chemistry.

* J. M. Mitchison, *Symp. Soc. exp. Biol.*, **6**, 105, 1952.

PLATE IV

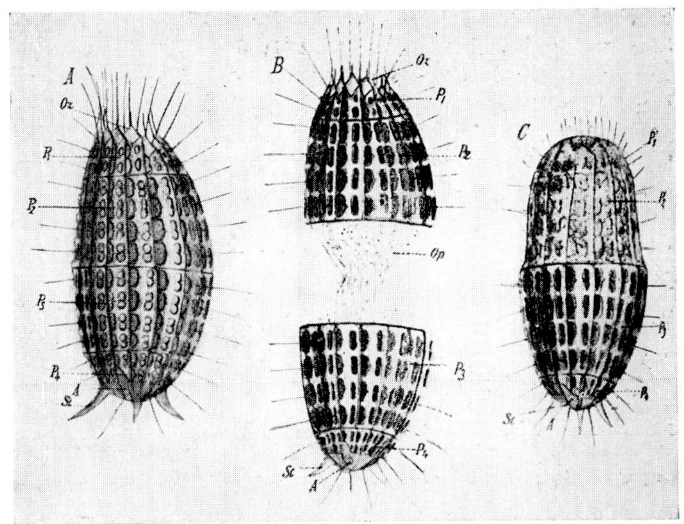

Figure 19.

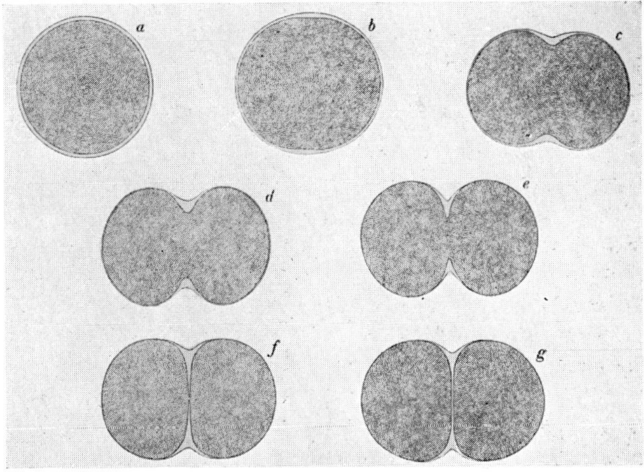

Figure 20.

Figure 19. Division of *Coleps hirtus* (Ciliata). *A*, resting cell; *B*, cell during division; *C*, daughter-cell forming new cuticle. (After Doflein.)

Figure 20. Division of the cytoplasm of an echinoderm egg. (After Gray.)

[*To face p.* 44.

CHAPTER IV

THE CELL AS A FREE-LIVING ORGANISM

WE may now leave consideration of the essential structure of the cell, and pass on to consider the elaborations of this structure which occur in the bodies of the single-celled organisms, the Protista.

It is characteristic of the Protista that their bodies should consist of single cells living independent, free lives throughout the whole of their life-history. Protista may be associated together to form colonies, sometimes with a certain amount of specialisation among the members of the colony, but they never form a true multicellular organism.* We shall discuss the distinction between colonies and multicellular bodies in a later chapter (p. 148). Free-living cells occur at certain stages in the life-histories of all organisms—eggs and spermatozoa—but the whole life-history is passed as a single cell only in the Protista.

The fact that the protistan cell often contains many nuclei (*e.g. Pelomyxa*, *Actinosphærium*) does not make the distinction between them and the multicellular animal difficult. The distinction lies in the fact that in the body of a protistan "whether there be one nucleus, or a few, or many, no nucleus has charge solely of a specialised part of the cytoplasm; whereas in other animals there are always many nuclei, each in charge of a portion of cytoplasm which is specialised for a particular function, such as contraction, conduction, or secretion." †

It is often said that it is more accurate to speak of the protistan body as non-cellular rather than as unicellular. This is so if the term "cell" has its original meaning (p. 23), one of the parts into which the multicellular body is divided. The protistan body, being not so divided, is then not cellular and may be called non-cellular. But if we define the cell, as we have done, as the unit of the organisation which all animal protoplasm possesses, the Protista are truly unicellular, for their bodies contain one, and only one, of these units.

It follows from the fact that the Protista are unicellular that the differentiated parts of their bodies, their organs, are intracellular,

* An exception to these statements is discussed below (pp. 110–11).

† Borradaile, Eastham, Potts, and Saunders, p. 10.

and not, as in other animals, often composed of many cells. These intracellular organs are often called "organelles," but they are as truly organs as are those of multicellular animals. It seems unnecessary to use different terms for the organs of uni- and multicellular animals.

We find a general tendency for the size of animals to increase throughout evolution. Protista are in general smaller than invertebrate multicellular animals, and invertebrates smaller than vertebrates. Even in many smaller groups there is often the same increase in size as evolution has gone on, *e.g.* in the fossil horses or elephants. It is true that there are many exceptions to the statement that evolution has been accompanied by increase in size. Some groups, such as the birds and many groups of insects, show no evolutionary tendency to increase in size. Some animals have evolved in the reverse direction, becoming smaller and not larger. Many insects and rotifers have become very small (down to 1/100 of an inch in length): they are in fact smaller than many of the Protista. Nor is it true that vertebrates are always larger than the invertebrates. Some invertebrates have reached large size—the Cephalopods may have a body length of 20 feet; and many fishes and frogs are smaller than some of the insects, which are not especially large invertebrates.

The facts are more accurately stated by saying that there is a range of size for each group of animals, outside which the sizes of the members of the group do not go, and that the mean of this range has become larger with increasing complexity of the body. In many groups the range of size may appear to be large. In present-day terrestrial mammals it extends from the size of a mouse to that of an elephant, a range of about 1 to 100 in length or 1 to 10^6–10^7 in weight. The range becomes even larger when we include animals which live in environments very different from those of the majority of the group. Aquatic animals are often larger than terrestrial, for heavy weight is of less importance in an aquatic environment. So, the whale is much larger than any terrestrial mammal, and the mammalian range of size is increased if we include it. Parasitic animals are also often large; some of the Sporozoa are very large Protista. But the more limited the group of animals we are considering, and therefore the more similar the organisation of the members of the group, the smaller is the range of size in the group. Even in a single species the individuals vary in size within a certain range (*e.g.* in a species of *Paramecium*, Fig. 22), but the range of size in a species is small compared with that in larger groups of animals. In *Paramecium* the range of variation in length is about 1 : 7.

There can be no doubt that the mean size has increased with increasing complexity of structure. In weight the range for the Protista is from 10 to 10^{-12} g.; for the invertebrates, 10^7 to 10^{-7} g.; and for the vertebrates, 10^9 to 10^{-1} g.*

Thus there is in evolution an association of large size with complexity of structure. It is not hard to understand why this association

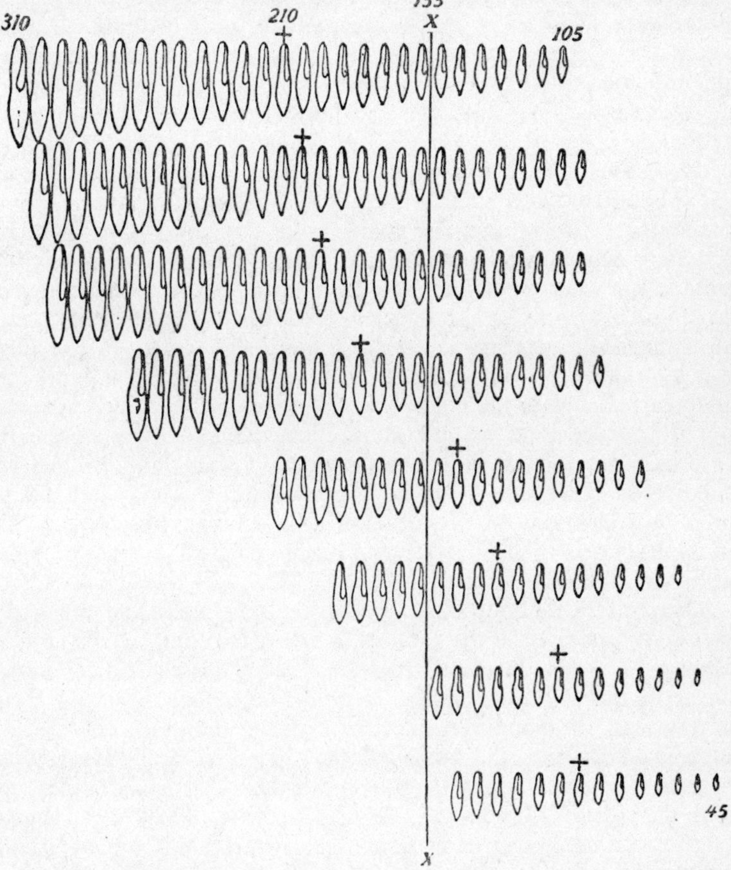

Figure 22. Size variations in eight families of a species of *Paramecium*. The vertical line gives the mean of the whole and the + signs the means of the family. (After Jennings.)

should exist. We will consider it for the present only in the free-living cells.

Many of the physical and chemical reactions on which the life of the cell depends are surface reactions. This is true not only of the reactions at the ultramicroscopic surfaces of the enzymes, but also

* Haldane and Huxley, pp. 276–80; see also Wells, Huxley and Wells, *The Science of Life*, pp. 624–30, for discussion of size in animals.

of the reactions at many larger surfaces, the intake of food and removal of excreta across the cell surface, transport across the nuclear membrane, etc. Protoplasmic chemistry, indeed, depends fundamentally on surface reactions.

As the cell increases in size, the volume of its protoplasm increases as the cube of its linear dimensions, but the area of those surfaces which are determined in number in the cell, such as the cell surface and the nuclear membrane, increases only as the square. It is true that surfaces which increase in number, not in size, as the cell grows—and all the ultra-microscopic surfaces probably belong to this class—will increase in area at the same rate as the volume of the cell, *i.e.* as the cube of the linear dimensions. Only the larger surfaces will increase more slowly than the volume. But the speed of a complex process is determined by the speed of its slowest component, so that metabolism must be slower for each unit of the protoplasm in the larger cell. The cell must therefore become a less efficient living mechanism if it gets larger without alteration of structure. The only way by which this result can be avoided is by the evolution of organs adapted to increase the efficiency of the metabolism. Such adaptations, both in Protista and multicellular animals, are extremely various. They include increase of surface by branching, folding or subdivision of organs, better circulation about the body and many other modifications. It is clear that, if an animal, whether uni- or multicellular, is to grow larger and remain efficient, it must become more complex in structure.

There can be no doubt that this association of large size and complex structure holds in the Protista. Some of the complex ciliates are among the largest Protista—*Bursaria* reaches a diameter of 3 mm. Some of the Foraminifera are larger—*Nummulina* may be 1 inch across—but these are very inactive Protista and can afford to be metabolically sluggish. Some of the Sporozoa (*e.g. Monocystis magna*) also reach a very large size, but this is probably associated with their parasitic habit and also with inactivity. Most of the flagellates have a much simpler cellular organisation than the ciliates, and are much smaller in average size. A simple type of cellular organisation is very generally associated with small size in the Protista.

This statement must not be taken to imply that all the Protista with complex structure are large. Some of the ciliates are small in comparison with other members of the same group. Some are as small as or smaller than many flagellates. But this does not invalidate the conclusion that complex structure is necessary if the body of an active protistan is to grow large. We have seen that many multicellular animals with complex structure are small—some of them smaller than the largest protistans. Complex structure does not prevent an animal becoming small in comparison with other animals of the same group, but it makes active life at a larger size possible. But complex animals cannot become indefinitely small; their complexity imposes a minimum size. Thus, the smallest vertebrate is larger than the smallest member of any other phylum.

It is by no means obvious at first sight why animals should tend to increase in size in the course of evolution. One, and perhaps the chief, reason for this tendency is the greater isolation from the changes of the external environment which larger size allows. We have seen (p. 16) that the life of protoplasm demands maintenance of conditions within it which are different from those in the external medium. In addition to this, the conditions in any natural environment alter continually, and it is valuable to the animal to be able to maintain the conditions in its protoplasm, and therefore its life, so far as possible unaffected by these changes in the external medium. Isolation not only from the permanent conditions in the external medium but also from the continual changes in these conditions is of value to the animal, so long as the necessary interactions with the environment, such as the uptake of food and the excretion of waste products, are maintained.

As the animal's body increases in size, the environmental conditions which are of most importance to its life will alter. Many of these conditions will be of less importance to the larger animal. For very small animals it is possible that Brownian movement is an important factor in disturbing their life. It may be so in the ultramicroscopic metabolism of all protoplasm, but only the bodies of the smallest organisms are affected as wholes by this factor. Again, small aquatic animals are carried about by currents in the medium; larger animals can resist the currents by their own activities. And, in terrestrial animals, capillary forces are only important to animals which are not larger than relatively small invertebrates, such as the smaller insects. A fly has difficulty in moving out of a drop of water owing to the surface forces of the drop; such forces do not hinder the movements of vertebrates. Also, as the animal becomes larger it can store greater quantities of reserve material which can be used to resist changes in its body that would otherwise be caused by changes in the environment. Its greater speed of movement will be of use to it in the search for food.

In these and many other ways the larger animal is better able to avoid or make harmless the changes of the environment, and this will be true not only of the physical environment but also of the animal's relations to other animals—its biological environment. It is true that some conditions become of greater importance to the animal's life as it gets larger—the force of gravity, for instance, in terrestrial animals—but these are probably only of sufficient importance to outweigh the advantages of increased size when the animal approaches the maximum size which it is possible for it to reach in the environment in which it is living.

THE ORGANS OF THE PROTISTAN BODY

1. SKELETAL STRUCTURES

The skeleton of the Protista consists of hard, non-living secretions of the protoplasm which serve for its support. Other supporting structures occur in many Protista. Pellicles, for instance, are surface layers of tough but living protoplasm. They cannot be included in the skeleton on the definition here given.

There are two types of skeleton in the Protista. The first type consists of horny secretions which cover the outer surface of the protoplasm and are thus external (Rhizopoda). Similar structures also occur within protistan cells. The central capsule of the Radiolaria is an example, but this, and all other such internal structures, are probably composed of living protoplasm. External horny skeletons are various in form and consistency. They include not only thick shells, such as those of many Sarcodina, *e.g. Arcella*, but also the very thin cuticles of many flagellates and other Protista. Shells and cuticles may be of various substances—of mineral material in an organic matrix as in *Arcella*, of cellulose, and of other materials. They often show elaborate structure, as in *Arcella*, determined perhaps by the form of the protoplasmic surface on which they are laid down. Sometimes foreign bodies are attached to them, as in the shell of *Difflugia*, which is made of sand grains embedded in the cuticular skeleton and arranged by the protoplasm so that they form a regular shell. In *Euglypha* the place of the sand grains is taken by plates of silica which are secreted by the animal. These are formed within the protoplasm and may therefore be regarded as a skeleton of the second type. They pass to the surface and are arranged to form the shell. Many types of foreign bodies may be used by Protista in the construction of their skeletons. *Difflugia* will use splinters of glass and other material. *Haliphysema*, a marine foraminiferan, uses sponge spicules, many of which are always attached to its cuticle. Owing to its large size and this habit, this animal was at first described as a sponge.

The second type of skeleton is always internal. It consists of crystalline inorganic material secreted within the protoplasm. The material is almost always either calcium carbonate (Foraminifera) or silica (Radiolaria), but it is said that in a few Radiolaria the crystals are of strontium sulphate. The crystals of this type of skeleton may be very small, and the skeleton is not then obviously crystalline (*e.g.* in many Foraminifera such as *Polystomella*). The skeleton may also be very close to the surface of the body (*Polystomella*), but it is always covered with protoplasm except in such forms as *Euglypha* where the crystals secreted within the protoplasm are passed to the exterior. Very complex forms may be made by the crystalline skeleton in the Radiolaria.

One of the most striking features of protistan cells is that we sometimes find among them forms similar to those which occur in non-living systems. Forms such as these are, perhaps, commoner in planktonic species than in others, possibly because the environment for planktonic animals is nearly the same in all directions and the forms of their bodies are less modified by irregularity in the environment. They can therefore show regularity which the bodies of other animals cannot show.

For example, some planktonic Foraminifera have forms similar to those of drops hanging in a medium of a lower specific gravity (Plate V, Fig. 23). Here it may be supposed that the shell is laid down round the body when its form is determined by physical forces and not by differences within the protoplasm. Many of the Radiolaria show forms which are similar to those of bubbles or drops. Mathematical forms occur in many animals, not always planktonic. In some bottom-living Foraminifera (*e.g. Polystomella* and *Nummulina*) the outline of the shell follows a logarithmic spiral, a mathematical curve of known properties. This shape would result if the chambers, which are added to the shell as the animal grows, were all of the same shape but increased regularly in size; and this seems to be the reason for the occurrence of this curve in the form of the shell. Here it is the regularity, or lack of complexity, in growth, which allows the mathematical form to appear. We find many other examples of the logarithmic spiral in biology, *e.g.* in the shell of molluscs and ammonites, and in the horns of ungulates, but it always has an explanation as simple as that of its occurrence in the shell of the Foraminifera.*

2. NUTRITIONAL ORGANS

All known types of nutrition occur among the Protista. Many flagellates possess chlorophyll and are holophytic, and chlorophyll also occurs in one rhizopod, *Paulinella*. Some flagellates and almost all the Sarcodina and Ciliata are holozoic. Parasitic forms are saprophytic, and free-living saprophytes are also common. Some Protista can feed in more than one of these ways: *Euglena* may be either holophytic or saprophytic.

Holophytic Nutrition. The chlorophyll of Protista with this type of

* For further discussion of mathematical form in animals the reader is referred to the book by D'Arcy Thompson (*Growth and Form*, 1942).

nutrition is, so far as we know, the same substance as that of the plants. The chlorophyll is usually contained in intra-cellular organs, the *chromatophores*, and not normally spread diffusely through the protoplasm. The chromatophores are well-defined bodies, sometimes with and sometimes without a definite wall, which divide at the division of the cell. Often there are present inside the chromatophores bodies of protein material, the *pyrenoids*, which appear to be the centres at which photosynthesis goes on. They, also, divide at division. The chromatophores are green in most groups of holophytic flagellates, but yellow or brown in the Chrysomonadina and Cryptomonadina and bluish green in *Paulinella*. The variations of these colours from the yellow-green of chlorophyll are due to the presence of other pigments which mask the colour of the chlorophyll.

The process of photosynthesis in Protista seems to be similar to that in plants. Most commonly the material produced by photosynthesis is either starch or paramylum, a substance related to starch but without the character of staining black with iodine.

Protista, like plants, may lose their chlorophyll if kept in the dark. This occurs in *Euglena*, which becomes saprophytic in the dark. The chlorophyll reappears when the organisms are returned to the light. In the dark the chromatophores shrink; they grow again on return to the light.

In some flagellates (*Euglena* under certain conditions, *Hæmatococcus*, etc.) a red pigment, *hæmatochrome*, occurs. This is related to chlorophyll and, probably more closely, to carotin, another pigment which occurs in plants. It is also closely related to the red pigment of the eyespot. It is not photosynthetic. In *Euglena* this pigment is developed when the environment is poor in nitrogenous food materials and phosphorus. It is spread diffusely through the cell in bright light and collected in the interior when the light is weak. It has been supposed to protect the protoplasm from the light of the blue and violet parts of the spectrum, which it absorbs.

Holozoic Nutrition. In holozoic Protista the food is captured in many different ways. We shall discuss some of the organs for the capture of food later (p. 66). Usually the food is surrounded by the protoplasm and enclosed in a food vacuole within the body (many Sarcodina, Ciliata). In some forms (*e.g.* Foraminifera such as *Polystomella*) it is digested outside the body by the protoplasm of the pseudopodia, which flow round it.

Digestion in the Protista can be most easily studied in the food vacuole, where the process can be watched throughout its course. This is not so in saprophytes, their food is liquid and diffuses at once through the protoplasm. They have no digestive organs of larger than ultramicroscopic size. For these reasons little is known of the process of nutrition in saprophytes, and most of our knowledge of protistan digestion is derived from study of the food vacuole. Our knowledge is therefore somewhat one-sided.

The food vacuole does not differ greatly in the Protista in which it occurs, but there are some differences of detail. Thus, the pseudopodia of *Amœba* in flowing round the prey enclose a good deal of water with it, but in some other Protista very little water is enclosed. In all food vacuoles, however, the food is in a watery medium and it is through this medium that digestion and absorption takes place. In *Amœba* the wall of the vacuole has been shown by microdissection to be a solid membrane. It is probably so in other Protista; presumably, it is semi-permeable. In many forms (*Amœba, Paramecium*) the food vacuoles are carried about the cell by the endoplasmic current. By this circulation the nutrition of the parts of the cell must be made more efficient.

The food of a holozoic protistan may be still alive after it has been enclosed in a food vacuole, or it may have been already killed, *e.g.* in the Heliozoa and Foraminifera, which kill their prey by some secretion of their pseudopodia as soon as it comes into contact with these organs. The prey of the Suctoria is also killed as soon as it touches their tentacles. Even if the prey is still alive when it is enclosed in the vacuole, it is soon killed, presumably by substances secreted into the vacuole.

We have some knowledge of the process of digestion in the food vacuole. Soon after the vacuole is formed, the fluid in it, in many Protista if not in all, becomes acid. This can be shown by introducing into the vacuole a dye which changes colour with variations in the acidity or alkalinity of the medium. It may be this acidity which kills the prey, if it is still alive when it is enclosed in the vacuole. The first part of digestion takes place in this acid medium, but, as digestion goes on, the acidity of the vacuole disappears and the fluid becomes alkaline. These changes are similar in sequence and extent to the changes in the acidity and alkalinity of the contents of the gut in the vertebrates, but there the different acidities occur in different spatial regions.

The Protista can certainly digest proteins. Proteolytic enzymes have been extracted from the cells of many forms, both enzymes of the pepsin type, which act in an acid medium, and of the trypsin type, for which the medium must be alkaline. Enzymes which convert carbohydrates into sugars have not so far been extracted, but it has been shown that the conversion occurs in some Protista (*Amœba, Pelomyxa*). It is not known that the Protista can digest fats, but fat globules are often present in the cells and it is difficult to believe that digestion of fat does not occur. Cellulose is digested by the flagellates which inhabit the gut of termites (*Trichonympha*). On the whole, it may be said that the digestive enzymes of the Protista are of the same type as those of multicellular animals, and that it is probable that enzymes similar to most of the enzymes of multicellular animals occur in the Protista.

The digested food is presumably absorbed through the wall of the food vacuole. Its fate beyond this is unknown. The undigested remains of the food are cast out in some forms at a permanent anus, in others anywhere on the surface of the body.

3. ORGANS OF OSMOTIC CONTROL AND EXCRETION

There are two functions in animal physiology which consist in removal of material from the tissues. These are excretion of the waste products of metabolism and control of the osmotic pressure of the internal liquids by expulsion of water. In some animals at any rate, these two functions are served by the same organ—the mammalian kidney performs both. We have here to consider how these functions are provided for in the body of the Protista.

Excretory material is poisonous if it is allowed to accumulate in the protoplasm. If the excretory products are relatively insoluble, they can be made harmless, although they still remain within the cell, by crystallisation, for crystals will be removed from the field of action of metabolism, which can only go on in a liquid medium. Crystals of many substances are found in the protoplasm of the Protista and some of these are of excretory material. Crystals of guanine, for instance, are said to be present in *Amœba*. Urate crystals occur in other forms.

Many excretory substances (*e.g.* ammonia, urea) are highly soluble and cannot be dealt with in the living cell by crystallisation. These substances can only be removed from the cell in solution, either by diffusion through the surface or by the action of an excretory organ.

The osmotic relations between the cell and the surrounding medium are still not very clearly understood, especially in cells living in media of low osmotic pressure, such as fresh water. Where the osmotic pressure of the medium is high (sea-water or the internal fluids of other animals) the osmotic pressure of the protoplasm is probably in all normal circumstances equal to that of the medium, and there is therefore no necessity to assume passage of water across the surface of the cell by osmosis. But in cells living in fresh water, osmosis into the cell is bound to take place if the surface is at all permeable to water, for the osmotic pressure of the protoplasm must be greater than that of the medium. (In some freshwater ciliates the internal osmotic pressure has been found to be equal to that of an 0·05 M salt solution.) We know that the permeability of the surface of a cell may be very low or even non-existent (p. 18), but the fact that we find in many freshwater Protista organs which expel water from the cell shows that, in these forms at any rate, water can enter the cell.* Their surface must be permeable to some extent. But it need not be assumed that all cells living in fresh water are permeable to water, nor that a cell which is permeable at times should be so always. If the cell is impermeable, osmotic control is not an obviously necessary function. It is so in freshwater Protista if their surface is permeable.

The only organ in the protistan body which seems adapted to perform the functions of excretion and osmotic control is the *contractile vacuole*. Many Protista are without this organ, and in them these functions must be carried out by the general surface of the cell.

There may be one or more than one contractile vacuole in the Protista which possess them. They always lie near the surface of the protoplasm, contract rhythmically, and expel their contents through the surface over them. At this position a pore is formed when the vacuole contracts. Such a pore may in some forms be permanently present. In some of the ciliates, such as *Paramecium*, the vacuole system is more complex; collecting ducts leading towards the vacuole are present. In *Paramecium* the vacuole and its ducts are said to lie in a spongy layer of protoplasm on the inside of the ectoplasm. The vacuole, in all Protista in which the point has been investigated, is surrounded by a layer of gelated protoplasm, and in some its wall has been shown by microdissection to be a solid membrane. In *Amœba* there is said to be no such membrane. Outside the wall of the vacuole there is a layer of lipoid material which behaves to chemical tests in much the same way as the material of the Golgi bodies. The mechanism of contraction is by no means completely understood. It has been supposed that the vacuole acts as a pump, the gelated protoplasm around it contracting actively at the time of discharge and driving the water through the surface, but it is improbable that this is true in most Protista. It has also been suggested that turgor of the protoplasm causes rupture of the surface at the pore when the vacuole reaches its maximum size, and that the vacuole is so discharged. This may be true in some forms, but it is improbable that it is the complete explanation in all contractile vacuoles.

There is little doubt that the water which fills the vacuole is actively secreted into it by the protoplasm. Where the vacuole has an osmoregulatory function, this is necessary, for the water must be secreted against an osmotic gradient, and energy must therefore be

* A small amount of water will be formed in the cell as one of the end-products of metabolism (p. 224), but this water will be so small in amount in the Protista that we can justifiably neglect it in considering their physiology.

used in the process. It has been shown that the activity of the vacuole reacts to poisons (*e.g.* potassium cyanide, which is known to inhibit a large part of the oxidative mechanisms of the cell) in much the same way as other cell activities such as the contraction of muscle or cilia. It is concluded that the production of energy by the mechanism of the vacuole is, at least in part, an oxidative process.

We have now to consider what direct evidence we have that the contractile vacuole serves the various functions which we have suggested it may serve.

Not much is known of excretion in the Protista. Uric acid is present in the protoplasm of *Paramecium*. It has not been recognised in the liquid content of the contractile vacuoles, probably because it is there too dilute owing to the great activity of the vacuoles of this animal. It can be shown that picric acid which has been injected into the body of *Amœba* is excreted through the vacuole. Picric acid has a strong yellow colour by which its presence can be recognised in the protoplasm and in the vacuole, which becomes strongly stained. It is not a natural excretory product, but the fact that it is thrown out of the cell by the vacuole may be thought to strengthen the probability that other chemical substances are excreted in this way. The *p*H of the excreted fluid in *Amœba* has been found to be *p*H 6·9–7·0, the same as that of the protoplasm.

It cannot be said that we have much direct evidence of the excretory function of the vacuole in the Protista, but that excreta must pass out through it in those forms which possess it can hardly be questioned—water driven out of the cell after passing through the protoplasm must contain excretory material. In so far, the vacuole must be an excretory organ. But it must not be forgotten that excretion takes place through the general surface of the cell in the numerous Protista which have no contractile vacuole. Even in forms in which the vacuole occurs much excretion may take place in this way.

More work has been done on the vacuole as an organ of osmotic control. Its occurrence is significant in this connection. It occurs in all but a few freshwater Protista—*Pelomyxa* is an exception; and it is absent in most marine and parasitic forms. It occurs, however, in certain marine ciliates and in certain parasitic forms, especially ciliates (*e.g. Nyctotherus* and *Balantidium*). In the sea-water Protista which possess a vacuole it is clear that the function of this organ is normally not that of osmotic control. Nevertheless, it has been shown that if certain of these forms are placed in diluted sea-water the output of the vacuole increases greatly and may reach eighty times its value in normal sea-water. This is what we should expect if the vacuole were controlling the osmotic pressure of the protoplasm. Similarly, if certain freshwater ciliates are placed in media of osmotic pressure higher than their normal medium, the output of their contractile vacuole falls. It has also been observed that freshwater Protista may lose their vacuoles when they are placed in sea-water and regain them when they are returned to fresh water. In one marine amœba (*Vahlkampfia*), which is normally without a vacuole, one has been found when the animal had been acclimatised to fresh water.

Together, all these observations provide fairly good evidence that the activity of the vacuole is in many forms controlled, at least partly, by the osmotic pressure of the medium. If we accept this evidence, it is hard to resist the conclusion that the vacuole has the function of osmotic control in many forms which live in media of low osmotic pressure. But it seems that this is not true of all freshwater forms. In *Amœba proteus* some evidence has been given that the output of the vacuole is not altered by raising the osmotic pressure of the medium. If so, it is not likely to be in control of the osmotic pressure of the protoplasm. Also, the output of the vacuole in this animal is small. A volume equal to that of the body is expelled in seven to ten hours, whereas in *Paramecium* the period is thirty to sixty minutes. But this might not be in conflict with a function of osmotic control if the permeability of the surface is low.

We may conclude that the contractile vacuole almost certainly acts as an organ of osmotic control in many freshwater Protista, but that it has not been excluded that other parts of the cell, and especially the surface, also take part in this control, even in cells which possess vacuoles. In *Amœba* and some other freshwater Protista, it is doubtful whether the vacuole controls the osmotic pressure. In freshwater forms which have no vacuole, either the surface must be impermeable to water, or the surface itself controls the osmotic pressure. In marine and parasitic forms the vacuole rarely needs to exert osmotic control in normal circumstances, but, in some forms at least, it probably may do so when the osmotic pressure of the medium is made abnormally low. Wherever it occurs, the vacuole must act as an excretory organ to some extent, but we do not know that the greater part of the excretory material of the cell passes out through the vacuole.

4. THE NUCLEUS AS A METABOLIC ORGAN

We have discussed in the last chapter the functions of the nucleus in the essential organisation of the cell, and especially its function in controlling the anabolic side of metabolism. In some Protista a part of the nucleus is structurally differentiated to serve this purpose. This is so in the Ciliata, where a part of the nucleus, the *meganucleus*, is set apart from the rest and appears to exercise only the metabolic functions of the nucleus. It apparently becomes worn out by its activity and is replaced from the micronucleus during conjugation (or autogamy—see below, p. 76). The latter is, so far as we know, inactive except at conjugation. The metabolic material of the meganucleus is called *trophochromatin*, the hereditary material of the micronucleus, *idiochromatin*. Besides its general control of anabolism in the cell, the meganucleus has been found competent to control regeneration in some but not all Protista.

The question whether these two types of nuclear material are distinct in other groups of Protista is one which cannot be said to be decided. There is some, but not conclusive, evidence for it (p. 76).

The distinction between the two types of nuclear material is not recognisable in most cells of the multicellular animals. There is, however, a phenomenon in the nematode *Ascaris* which may indicate a distinction of a similar kind. In the first divisions of the fertilised egg, parts of the chromosomes are cast off in all except the blastomeres which are to develop into the gonads. The chromosomes of the zygote have thick ends and a thinner centre (Fig. 24); it is the thicker ends which are cast off. Their material degenerates and disappears. Here, the germ cells retain the whole of the chromosome, the body cells only part of it. The phenomenon, although it seems to indicate a distinction between hereditary material and material used in control of body activities, is of a somewhat different type from the distinction between tropho- and idiochromatin in the Protista.

Figure 24. Form of a chromosome of the zygote of *Ascaris*.

It is possible that the bodies called the *kinetonucleus* of the trypanosomes and other flagellates may also be nuclear material, but recent evidence indicates that they are rather of the nature of Golgi material (p. 30). They occur in the cells near the base of the flagellum and apart from the nucleus. They are certainly not essential for the beat of the flagellum, for in a flagellate (*Bodo*) and in some trypanosomes, strains of the organisms have been found in which the kinetonucleus was missing. These strains lived for some generations but died out finally. Their flagella were able to beat normally. The functions of the kinetonucleus are very doubtful.

5. ORGANS OF RESPONSE

Protoplasm is irritable, that is to say it has the power of responding by alterations in its activities to stimulation caused by changes in the external environment. Since it is typical of animals that they possess the power of locomotion, it is natural that response to stimulation often takes the form of alterations in their locomotion. But this is not the only form of response. Changes in the shape of the animal and in the activities of its internal organs are familiar means of response.

Response to stimulation implies, first, reception of the stimulus and, secondly, co-ordinated changes in the animal's activities. Co-ordination is essential to response, for without it the actions of the animal would be meaningless. In considering response, we have therefore to consider three functions of the animal: reception of the stimulus, co-ordination, and the action of the organs by which the response is carried out. In multicellular animals, these functions are carried out by the receptor organs, the nervous system, and the effector organs. In the Protista, we have much less knowledge of the functioning of these organs, especially of those of co-ordination, but these three functions are provided for in their cells as in the bodies of multicellular animals.

(*A*) *Receptor Organs*

Localised sense-organs are scarce among the Protista. Eye-spots are well known in many forms, and some ciliates have immotile hairs and bristles which are very sensitive to mechanical stimulation and may also serve some chemical sense. These are almost the only sense-organs to be found in the bodies of the Protista.

Nevertheless, there can be no question that all Protista are sensitive to stimulation. In most Protista reception of stimuli is carried out by the unspecialised sensitivity of the general protoplasm. In *Amœba*, for instance, the whole surface is sensitive and there is no evidence of localisation of the sensitivity. In other Protista some parts of the surface may be more sensitive than others. Often the front of the animal as it moves is more sensitive, or the parts surrounding the mouth. The sensitivity of the protoplasm is unspecialised also in the wide range of stimuli to which it can respond.

The eye-spot in its simplest form consists of a small mass of pigmented protoplasm, often red or brown, without further visible differentiation. Eye-spots are undoubtedly sensitive to light, but it is not the pigment itself which is sensitive. In some Protista (*e.g. Euglena*) individuals have been found in which the pigment is missing, but in these individuals the region of the eye-spot was still sensitive to light. This fact does not prove that the pigment is functionless with regard to the sensitivity to light. It may increase the sensitivity by absorbing the light, or it may act (as it does in *Euglena*) as a screen shielding the light-sensitive protoplasm on one side. It is clear, however, that it is a part of the protoplasm near the eye-spot, and not the pigment, which is responsible for the actual reception of the stimulus.

Unless its functioning were modified by the arrangement of the body around it, a spherical eye-spot could be sensitive only to the presence or absence of light, and to its intensity. It could have no power of distinguishing the direction of the incident light. But even a spherical eye-spot will be most sensitive to light from the direction in which it is least shaded by other parts of the body. Directive sensitivity in eye-spots certainly occurs; it is necessary for the phototropic behaviour of many Protista (*e.g. Euglena*). It may be due either to the asymmetrical arrangement of the body round the eye-spot or to the shape of the eye-spot. In *Euglena* it is due to the pigment which is in the form of a cup surrounding the sensitive protoplasm, so that light from one direction only is effective in causing stimulation. In the more highly differentiated protistan eye-spots it is still more obvious that the organ is arranged to make directive sensitivity possible. For instance, in *Proterythropsis*, a dinoflagellate, the eye-spot has a lens and other differentiations (Fig. 25). It is clearly arranged so as to be sensitive to light from one direction more than from others.

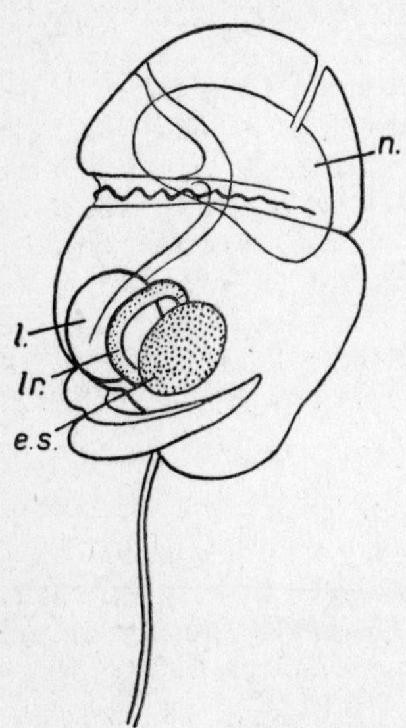

Figure 25. *Proterythropsis vigilans* (Dinoflagellata).

n, nucleus; *es*, eye-spot; *l*, lens; *lr*, dark ring round the lens. (After Marshall.)

(*B*) *Effector Organs*

We will here break the logical sequence and consider the effector organs before the means by which their activities are co-ordinated, about which much less is known.

(i) *Cilia and Flagella.* All organs of both these types are essentially similar in structure, and may be considered together. Cilia may be regarded as small flagella present in large numbers on the surface of a single cell. "Flagella" may also be numerous on a cell (*e.g.* in such flagellates as *Trichonympha*). It is difficult to find any real distinction between such flagella and cilia. In the Protista the term "cilium" is usually restricted to the organs of the ciliates.

Structure: Cilia and flagella are variously arranged on the surface of the cell, but we need not consider their arrangement. Cilia are often associated together to form more complex organs (*e.g.* membranellæ and cirri). Essentially these organs consist of fused cilia.

The structure of a cilium or flagellum, so far as we can see it in the microscope, is simple. Outside the surface of the cell the organ consists of a protoplasmic thread or lash, which is extremely thin (0·3μ in diameter) and normally shows no visible structure in the living state. There can, however, be no doubt that the lash possesses structure, for all the evidence goes to show that it is the lash itself which is contractile and that it is not moved by some means from the inside of the cell. Contraction of the types shown by cilia and flagella would not be possible in simple, undifferentiated threads.

Differentiation in the lash of the flagellum and cilium has been described, but these descriptions have mostly been from coagulated material. Both flagella and cilia have been described as consisting of a straight core with a straight or spiral sheath surrounding it. In dried material observed in the electron microscope a core (*axoneme*), sometimes of more than one fibre, and a sheath with several fibres running up it, have been observed.* These structures are very small and they are also the types of differentiation which might be expected to occur as artefacts in the coagulation of a body of the shape of the lash, or as the result of drying such a structure. Their real existence must be considered doubtful until they have been demonstrated in the living state. Lateral processes have also been observed attached to some flagella, when they are studied in the electron microscope.

Within the cell the cilium or flagellum is continued for a short distance into the protoplasm, and ends on a small, usually spherical, body, the *basal granule*, which we have seen in many cells to be either the same body as the centriole or derived from it (p. 31). Still farther within the cell, a fibre, the *internal fibre*, is often seen in coagulated material of ciliated cells. This fibre is attached to the basal granule and passes inwards into the protoplasm. It is not attached at its inner end to the nucleus, and is a different structure from the rhizoplast (p. 31). It has not been seen in living protoplasm, and it must be considered doubtful whether any true fibre is present in the living state. The appearance of a fibre in coagulated material might be an artefact representing longitudinal arrangement of the elements of the protoplasm in this region. Some evidence that the protoplasm is so organised in ciliated cells of multicellular animals has been obtained from uncoagulated material. The beat cannot occur unless the basal granule and, probably, at least a part of this modified protoplasm is attached to the cilium.

There are no other visible structures constantly present in the cilium or flagellum, or constantly associated with them.

* J. R. G. Bradfield, *Quar. J. Micr. Sci.*, **94**, 351, 1953.

Beat: In flagella, the beat is usually spiral or undulating; in cilia, it is usually pendular, *i.e.* from side to side, like a pendulum. Pendular beat may be entirely in one plane, or the tip of the cilium may describe an oval figure, passing from one side to the other of a median plane. In some large flagella (*e.g.* in *Peranema*) either a part or the whole of the flagellum may beat; often the base is immotile and only the terminal portion beats. In other flagella the form of the beat may alter from time to time. When the beat is pendular, it is different in form in the two directions. It consists of an effective beat in one direction, in which the lash is actively contracting, and a recovery beat in the opposite direction. The latter is, perhaps, purely elastic. The cilium is stiff in the effective beat and limp in the recovery beat. The beat of cilia which are arranged in rows is often metachronic, that is to say, the cilia beat rhythmically, each slightly out of phase with the cilia next to it in the row (*cf.* ch. XVIII, p. 293).

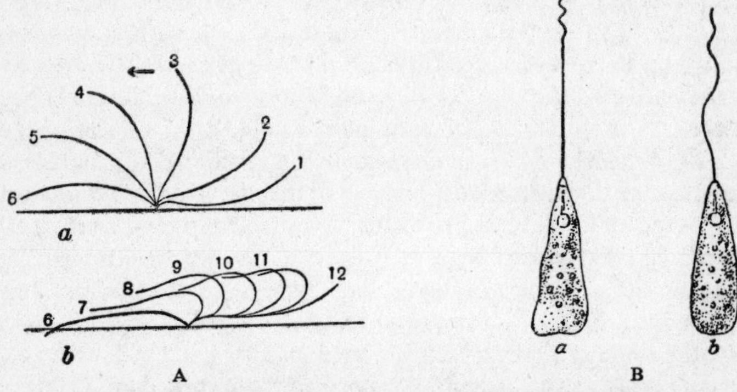

Figure 26. Types of movement of cilia and flagella.

A, pendular beat (the arrow gives the direction of the effective beat); B, spiral beat of a whole (*b*), and a part (*a*) of the flagellum of *Peranema*. (From Gray, *Ciliary Movement*, after Gray and Verworn.)

Lowndes* shows that the contraction passes up the flagellum from its base, so that an anterior flagellum cannot draw the body after it. According to him, long flagella, several times the wave-length of their contractions, do not directly cause the movement of the body. They are extended laterally and their beat exerts a lateral push on the body, causing it to gyrate spirally around the axis of movement. It then acts as a propeller driving itself forwards. A short flagellum, shorter than the wave-length, may itself gyrate round the axis of movement and act as a propeller.

Theories of the Mechanism of the Beat: The theories which have been put forward to account for the beat of cilia and flagella on

* A. G. Lowndes, *Proc. Zool. Soc., London,* **111**, 111, 1941; **113**, 99, 1943; **114**, 325, 1944.

mechanical lines are numerous. Many of these theories postulate some action within the cell and suppose that the lash is passively moved as a result of this action. As has been said, this is contrary to the greater part of the evidence. We have not space to go into this evidence here,* but we may discard any such theories. The observed forms of movement might result from contraction in a sheath of protoplasm surrounding a more solid non-contractile core, which is the structure suggested for the lash by study of coagulated and dried material. A uniplanar beat might result from contraction passing up one side of the sheath, and a spiral beat from contraction passing spirally up the sheath.

Physiological study of the cilium shows that its activity (in the cells of multicellular animals) reacts to changes in the external environment in much the same way as the contraction of muscle reacts. It has been concluded that the chemical processes involved in the production of energy for movement in cilia and flagella are similar to those in muscle.

(ii) *Pseudopodia.* (*a*) Axopodia: The pseudopodia of the Heliozoa, which are known as *axopodia*, are perhaps intermediate between flagella and the filamentous or lobose pseudopodia of the rest of the Sarcodina. The axopodium consists of a solid axial filament and, around this filament, a layer of liquid protoplasm, which is thick enough to be visible. The axial filament passes inwards into the cytoplasm of the cell and may end on a granule which, like the basal granule of the flagellum, can act in some forms as the centriole. In most of the Heliozoa (*e.g. Actinosphærium*) the axopodia bend in the capture of food, but execute no other movements except their extension and retraction. Some Heliozoa, however (*Artiodiscus* and *Acanthocystis*), can move by contractions of their axopodia, rolling on their points. The bending of the axopodium is apparently brought about by alterations in the solidity of the axial filaments and by contractions of the liquid protoplasm.

Axopodia may then, perhaps, be considered to be flagella in which the outer layers of the protoplasm of the lash have become thicker and the power of rhythmical contraction has been lost. This view is in accordance with recent views of the evolution of the Protista in which the Sarcodina are believed to have been evolved from flagellate forms.

(*b*) Filopodia and Rhizopodia: The remaining types of pseudopodium in the Sarcodina vary from the thread-like pseudopodia of

* The whole subject of the beat of cilia and flagella is discussed in more detail in the book by Gray (1928). Machin (*Jour. exp. Biol.*, **35**, 796, 1958) shows mathematically that the observed form of the beat can be accounted for only by contraction along its length and not by action at its base.

the Foraminifera and Radiolaria to the broad, lobose pseudopodia of the Amœbina. These organs are all used for the capture of food and many of them for locomotion. They seem all to depend on streaming of the protoplasm for their activity, but in other respects they behave very differently.

The pseudopodia of the Radiolaria (filopodia) are filamentous. They are said to possess an axial filament and to anastomose slightly. They are very difficult to observe, and little is known of their biology.

The rhizopodia of the Foraminifera Polythalamia are also filamentous. They anastomose strongly, forming a network of protoplasm round the shell. Wherever they come into contact with food, a small mass of protoplasm is formed by the anastomosed pseudopodia. The food is digested in this mass. The pseudopodia consist of a fine, cylindrical axis which is more solid than the surrounding protoplasm, but by no means so well defined as the axial filament of the axopodium. The liquid protoplasm of the outer part of the pseudopodium is granular and continually flows up and down the pseudopodium, often up one side of it and down the other. The cylindrical axis of the pseudopodium is not continued into the cytoplasm.

The means by which the streaming of the protoplasm of the pseudopodia is kept up are unknown.

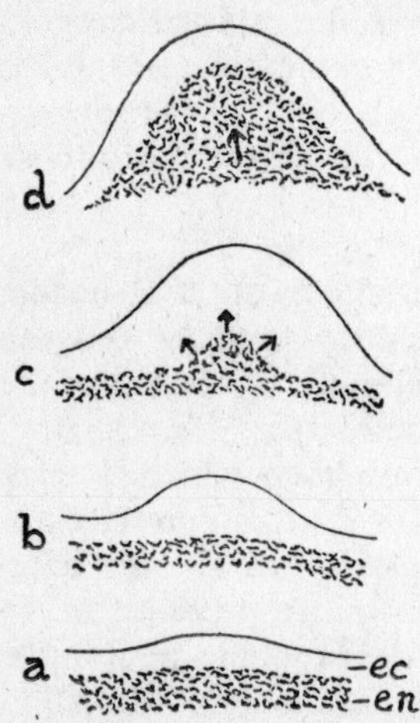

Figure 27. Formation of a pseudopodium in *Amœba proteus*.
en, endoplasm; *ec*, ectoplasm.

(*c*) Lobopodia: These, the lobose pseudopodia of the Amœbina and Foraminifera Monothalamia, have been the subject of many investigations. We can now reach a fairly definite idea of the manner in which the movements of some forms of the lobopodium are brought about.

In *Amœba proteus*, where the pseudopodia are formed at any point on the surface, the first sign of the formation of a new pseudopodium is a thickening of the ectoplasm (Fig. 27). This thickening proceeds for a short time, accompanied by no other visible change. Suddenly, some barrier between the endoplasm and the swollen ectoplasm seems to break down, and the granules of the endoplasm invade the ectoplasm. They flow into it until its thickness is reduced to little more than that over the rest of the surface. After this, the endoplasm flows continually into the pseudopodium producing its advance. Sooner or later the stream of endoplasm is reversed and the pseudopodium is withdrawn.

Amœba limax * is a marine amœba with only a single pseudopodium, which advances continually in the same direction. In this form it is possible to study the active, advancing pseudopodium much more easily than in the more complex *A. proteus*. In Fig. 28 a diagram of the movements of the protoplasm in the body of *A. limax* is given. The endoplasm is continually moving forwards, and it has been shown that new ectoplasm is continually formed from the endoplasm at the front end of the pseudopodium. The ectoplasm, as it is formed, gelates, so that the amœba advances through a tube of gelated ectoplasm. This tube remains stationary with reference to the substratum. The gelation of the ectoplasm increases as the endoplasm flows past it, until the hind end of the body is reached. There the ectoplasm is again liquefied and absorbed into the endoplasm.

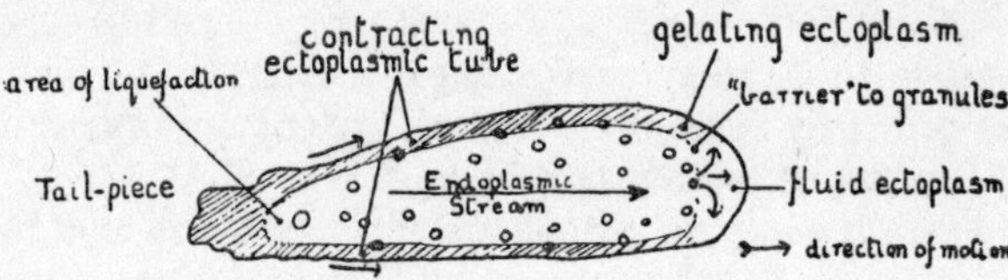

Figure 28. The movement of *Amœba limax*. (After Pantin.)

Thus it seems that pseudopodial movement of this type may depend ultimately on contraction of the gelated ectoplasm. In earlier sections we have seen that the movements of flagella and cilia and, possibly, the pulsations of the contractile vacuole in some forms are other expressions of this function of the protoplasm. So also is the contraction of a muscle fibre. It is interesting to note that pseudopodial movement in *A. limax* reacts to lack of oxygen, anæsthetics, and other changes in the environment in much the same way as the contraction of muscle reacts. It has been mentioned that there is a similar parallel between ciliary movement and muscular contraction (p. 63). It seems probable that in all these examples we are dealing with forms (not necessarily identical) of the same contractile mechanism. If so, this mechanism presumably lies behind the general contractility of protoplasm in all its forms.

In *A. proteus*, the swelling of the ectoplasm, which is the first stage in the formation of a pseudopodium, has been shown by microdissection to result from liquefaction, so that here, as in *A. limax*, the ectoplasm at the front of the pseudopodium is more liquid than that over the rest of the body. There may probably be other similarities

* It may be doubtful whether this form should be regarded as a true species.

between these two types of pseudopodium, but our knowledge is not sufficient to justify further discussion.

Many other types of protoplasmic streaming are not open to any such explanation as we have reached for that of *A. limax*. We can form no idea how the streaming of the protoplasm of the pseudopodia of the Foraminifera Polythalamia is caused, nor that of the cytoplasm of *Paramecium*. It is also doubtful whether all the types of movement in the amœbæ are at all similar to that of *A. limax* in their essential mechanisms. Some amœbæ, especially *A. verrucosa*, are said to roll over and over as they go forwards, the upper ectoplasm being continually carried on to the lower surface. Such movement, if it occurs, must be brought about in some entirely different manner. All we can say is that some types of pseudopodial movement and endoplasmic streaming have been shown to be due to contraction of the protoplasm similar to that which causes other types of motility in the cell.

(iii) *Myonemes*. These, unlike flagella, cilia, and pseudopodia, which are primarily locomotory organs, are effector organs of which the chief function is to alter the shape of the cell.

Many Protista which do not possess myonemes can alter the shape of their cells (*e.g.* flagellates such as *Euglena*). This is due to the general contractility of the protoplasm. The myonemes are the only formed organs in the protistan body with this function.

Myonemes occur in the Radiolaria, some Sporozoa, doubtfully in the trypanosomes, and, in their greatest development, in the Ciliata. They are contractile fibres, which may be likened to the muscle fibres of multicellular animals. They lie typically just below the surface of the cell and almost always parallel to the surface (*Stentor cæruleus*, Plate V, Fig. 29). In some of the ciliates they lie in hyaline canals in the ectoplasm (Plate V, Fig. 29). In Stentor they have been described as being cross-striated like the fibres of striped muscle. They also resemble muscle in their very rapid contractions. The contractions of undifferentiated protoplasm are much slower.

Practically nothing is known of the physiology of myonemes.

(iv) *Organs for the Capture of Food*. Very many of the effector organs of the Protista are used for the capture of food as well as for other purposes. Cilia and the various forms of pseudopodium are used for this purpose. We will not discuss their use as food-capturing organs here. The ciliary feeding mechanisms will be considered when we come to discuss filter-feeding in animals in general (ch. XIV). There are a few organs in the Protista which have, so far as is known, no other function than the capture of food. Of these the

PLATE V

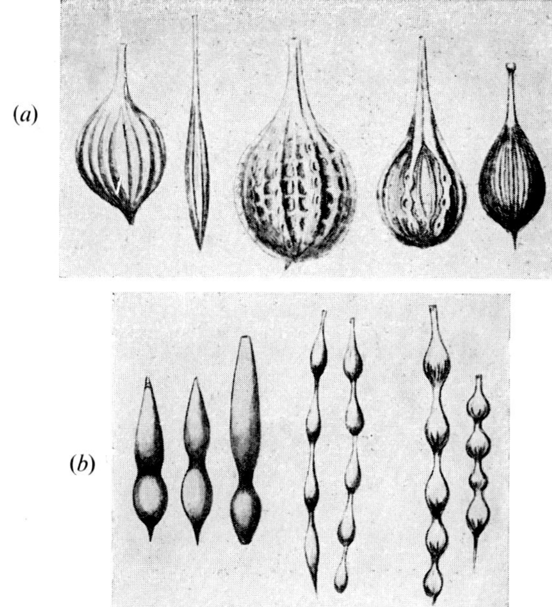

Figure 23.

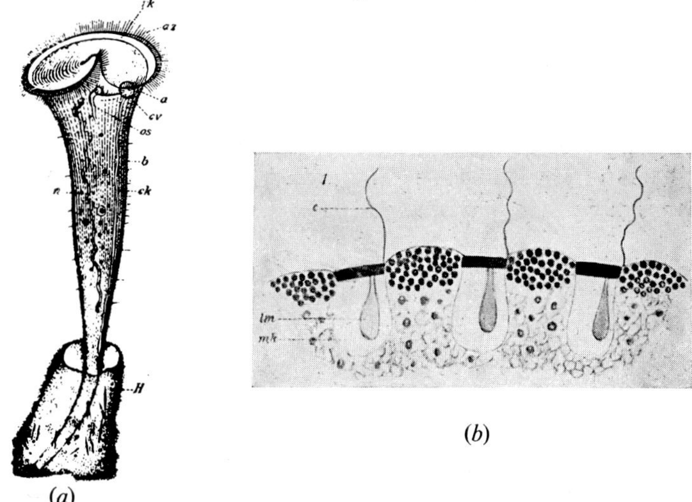

Figure 29

Figure 23. Forms of foraminiferan skeletons. (After D'Arcy Thompson.)

Figure 29. (*a*) Side view of *Stentor*; the myonemes are shown as thin lines running longitudinally along the body. (After Butschli.) (*b*) Transverse section of the myonemes *lm* and the canals in which they lie *mk*; *c*, cilium. (After Schroder.)

[*To face p.* 66.

tentacles of the Suctoria and the collar of the choanoflagellates are examples.

The Suctoria are a group of ciliates. They are holozoic, feeding on Protista, chiefly on other ciliates. Their bodies bear numerous, fine, rod-shaped processes of the protoplasm which have swellings at their ends (Fig. 30). These are the tentacles. In many species each tentacle is hollow, a fine tube passing up its length from the terminal swelling to the body of the cell. When the tentacles come into contact with the prey, the swelling adheres to it, and, presumably, a toxic substance is secreted, for the prey is soon killed. The tentacle then pierces the body of the prey, by some means not understood, and the internal protoplasm of the prey is sucked up the tube of the tentacle into the body of the suctorian. The protoplasm can be seen passing along the tube of the tentacle. It has been said that, at an earlier stage of the feeding, protoplasm can be seen passing out from the suctorian body through the tentacle into the prey, and that it is drawn back later. This is not certainly established.

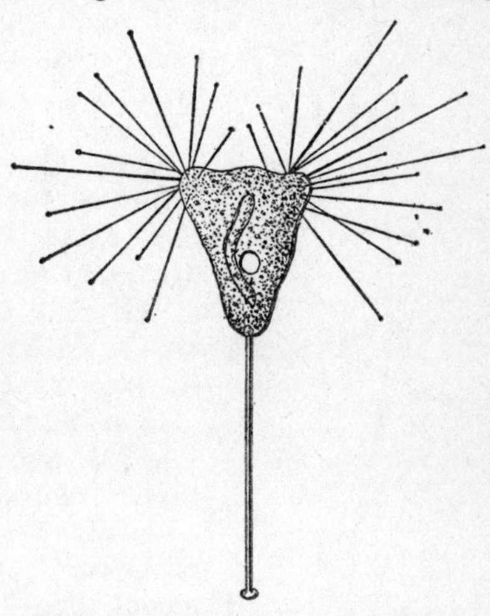

Figure 30. *Podophrya mollis*, Suctoria. (After Saville Kent.)

The collar of the choanoflagellate cell is a thin, transparent, protoplasmic cylinder surrounding the base of the flagellum (Fig. 31). Small particles are driven against the collar by the currents set up by the beat of the flagellum. They stick to its protoplasm and can then be seen to glide down the collar to the cell, where they are enclosed in a food-vacuole and digested. A similar method of feeding occurs in the collar-cells of the Porifera, though the details of ingestion are different.

(v) *Explosive Organs.* More than one type of explosive organ occurs among the Protista. The trichocysts of the Ciliata and the pole-capsules of the Neosporidia are organs of this type.

Trichocysts are normally arranged in the ectoplasm close beneath the surface (as in *Paramecium*, Plate VI, Fig. 32), but they are, in some ciliates at least, formed in the endoplasm and passed later into the ectoplasm. When unexploded, they are spindle-shaped bodies each with a fine hair-like projection which reaches the pellicle. At explosion, the trichocyst lengthens into a long and thin cylindrical body, most of which is outside the pellicle. The exploded trichocyst often bears a cap-like swelling at its distal end.

The function of the trichocysts is still in dispute. In some of the forms which possess them, they may be defensive organs. The threads are said to be toxic in some species, and to paralyse any protistan which comes into contact with them. But there is no evidence that the trichocysts of *Paramecium* and many other genera are toxic. It has been suggested that they may be defensive in that, when they have been exploded, they cover the body with a felt of threads. It seems hardly likely that this is an important function. They are certainly adhesive in *Paramecium* and are used to anchor the body to solid material in the environment.

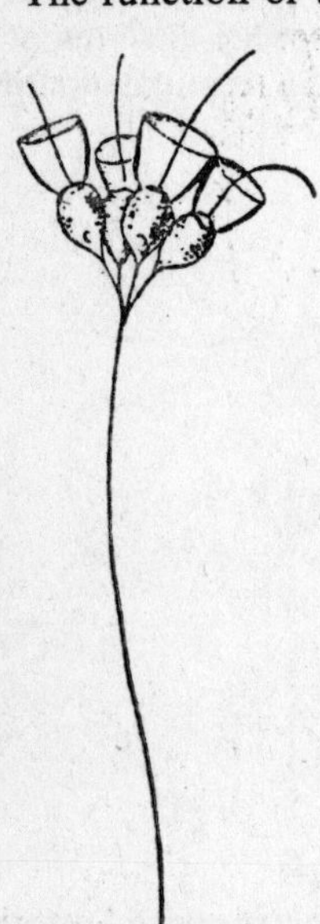

Figure 31. *Codosiga pyriformis*, Choanoflagellata. (After Saville Kent.)

In at least one ciliate (*Legendrea*, Plate VI, Fig. 33), the trichocysts are organs for the capture of food. In this animal, batteries of trichocysts are borne at the ends of processes of the cell. Normally, these processes are short, but at times they are greatly extended. This seems to happen when the animal is hungry and searching for food. The trichocysts are exploded when the prey comes into contact with them. They bear drops of liquid at their tips, and these may be toxic.

Some ciliates bear rods, known as *trichites*, in the region of the mouth. These are shot out into the prey and serve to hold it fast.

The *pole-capsules* of the neosporidian spore (Fig. 34, *cf.* Fig. 51, p. 111) are organs which resemble the nematocysts of the Cœlenterata in structure. They are rounded bodies, containing within them a coiled thread which can be shot out. They explode when the spore comes into contact with the tissues of its host and serve to fix it to the tissues.

(C) *Organs of Co-ordination*

Co-ordination is a necessary function of all organisms, but in the great majority of the Protista no distinct organs of co-ordination have been found. Without doubt, most of the co-ordination in protistan cells is carried out through the undifferentiated protoplasm. We shall

PLATE VI

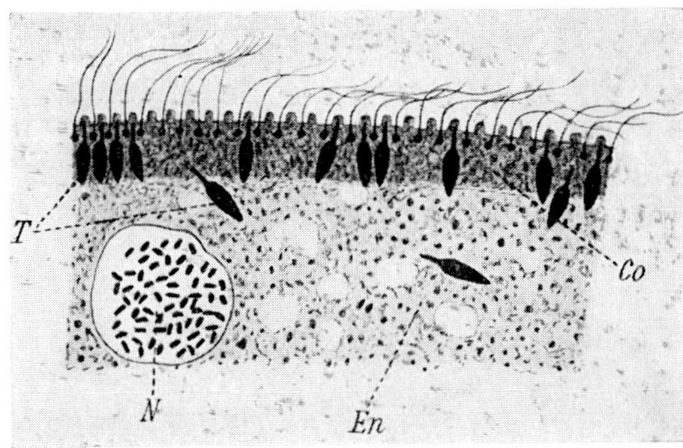

Figure 32.

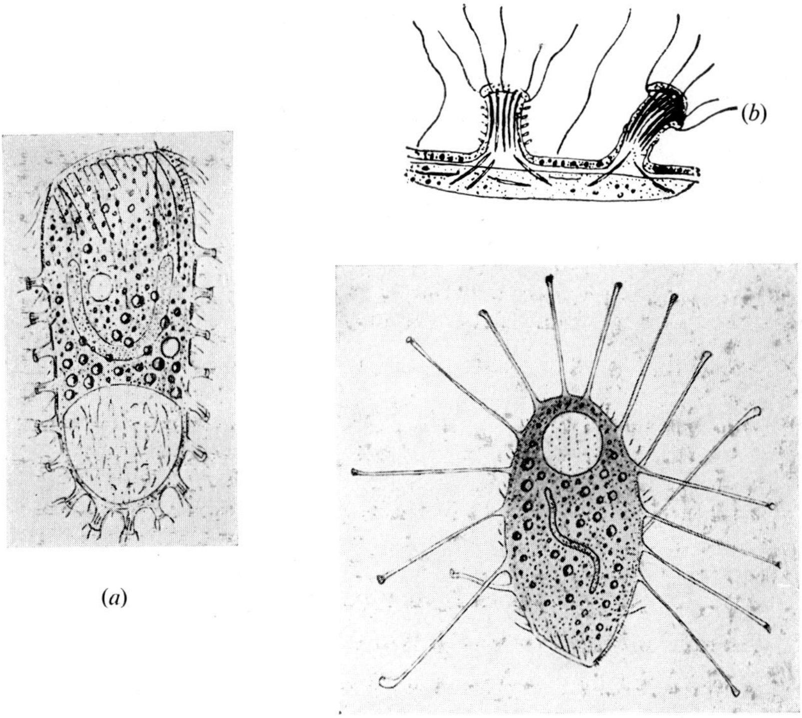

(b)

(a)

(c)

Figure 33.

Figure 32. Section of the surface of *Paramecium* showing the arrangement of the trichocysts *T* and their origin in the endoplasm *En*; *Co*, ectoplasm; *N*, food vacuole. (After Maier.)

Figure 33. *Legendrea bellerophon:* (*a*) normal condition; (*b*) papillæ with trichocysts; (*c*) condition when in search of food. (After Penard.)

[*To face p.* 68.

see in a later chapter (ch. XVI, p. 262) that, in the multicellular body, stimulation may be carried about the body through the protoplasm of the cells, and not always along differentiated nerves.

Fibres which have been thought to have a co-ordinating function have been found in the cells of some ciliates, but not in other Protista. The arrangement of these fibres in *Euplotes* is shown in Fig. 35. In this animal some of them (*a.c.f.*) seem to control the movements of the cirri, complex organs formed of fused cilia, which are the chief locomotory organs of the animal. This view of the function of these fibres is supported by their arrangement, ending on the cirri and radiating from a central organ, the *motorium*, which is believed to be a centre of co-ordination; and by the results of microdissection experiments in which the fibres were cut. It was then found that the movements of the cirri supplied by the cut fibres lost their co-ordination.

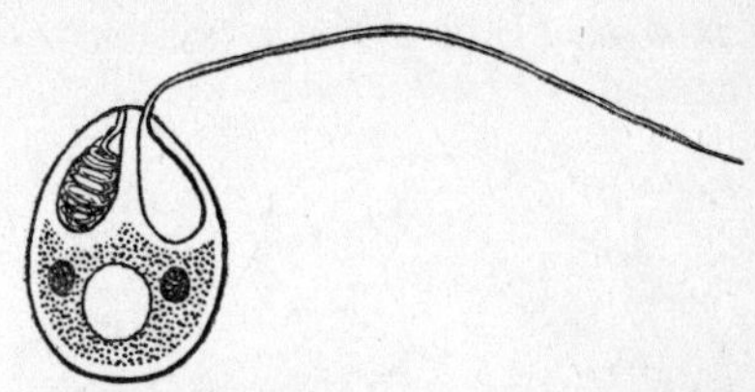

Figure 34. A spore of the Cnidosporidia with unexploded and exploded pole capsules. (After Doflein.)

The evidence of the co-ordinating function of these fibres can hardly yet be accepted as conclusive. Similar fibres are found in many other ciliates (Plate VII, Fig. 36). No other organs of co-ordination are known in the Protista.

6. ORGANS OF THE PROTISTAN BODY: CONCLUSION

In this account of the organs of the Protista, we have seen that organs may be formed in their cells to carry out most of the functions performed by the organs of the multicellular body. Some organs which are frequent in multicellular bodies do not seem to occur in the Protista, secretory organs for instance; and organs of all the different functions are not formed in every protistan body. It is clear that the protoplasm is able to carry out many of its essential functions by other means, presumably by organs which are ultramicroscopic in size. But the physiological needs of the protistan body are similar to those of the multicellular body; and sometimes the manner in which these needs are satisfied is similar in both. We see this, for instance, in the metabolism of digestion and of contraction.

The development of the organs is most advanced in those Protista which are believed to stand at the top of the tree of protistan evolution, the Ciliata. Indeed, we have not discussed at all fully the complexity which the protistan body sometimes attains—by no means all the organs of the protistan body have been described. This is illustrated by Plate VII, Fig. 36, in which the structure of *Diplodinium*, one of the more complex ciliates, is shown. The complexity of the body is almost equally great in such flagellates as *Trichonympha*, which stand at the top of another line of protistan evolution. We know very little of the functions of much of the complexity shown in the body of *Diplodinium* or of *Trichonympha*. But, if we compare the

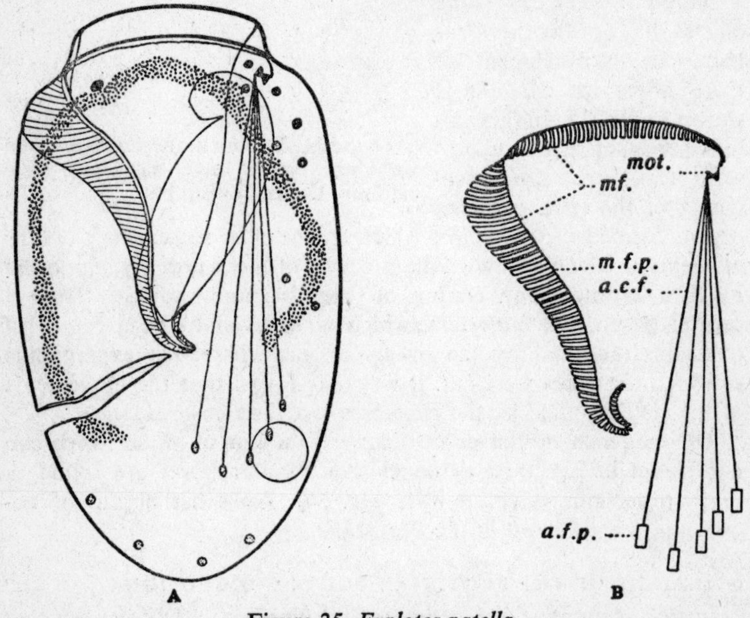

Figure 35. *Euplotes patella*.

A, general diagram of an individual with a lateral cut; B, isolated neuromotor apparatus. *acf*, fibres to the anal cirri; *afp*, plates below the anal cirri; *mf*, fibres to the membranellæ; *mfp*, plates at the base of the membranellæ; *mot*, motorium. (After Taylor.)

structure of the bodies of these animals with that found in one of the simplest flagellates, we see that, however complex the ultramicroscopic structure of protoplasm may be even in the simplest cell, in visible structure there has been almost as great an increase of complexity in the evolution of the Protista as in that of multicellular animals.

PLATE VII

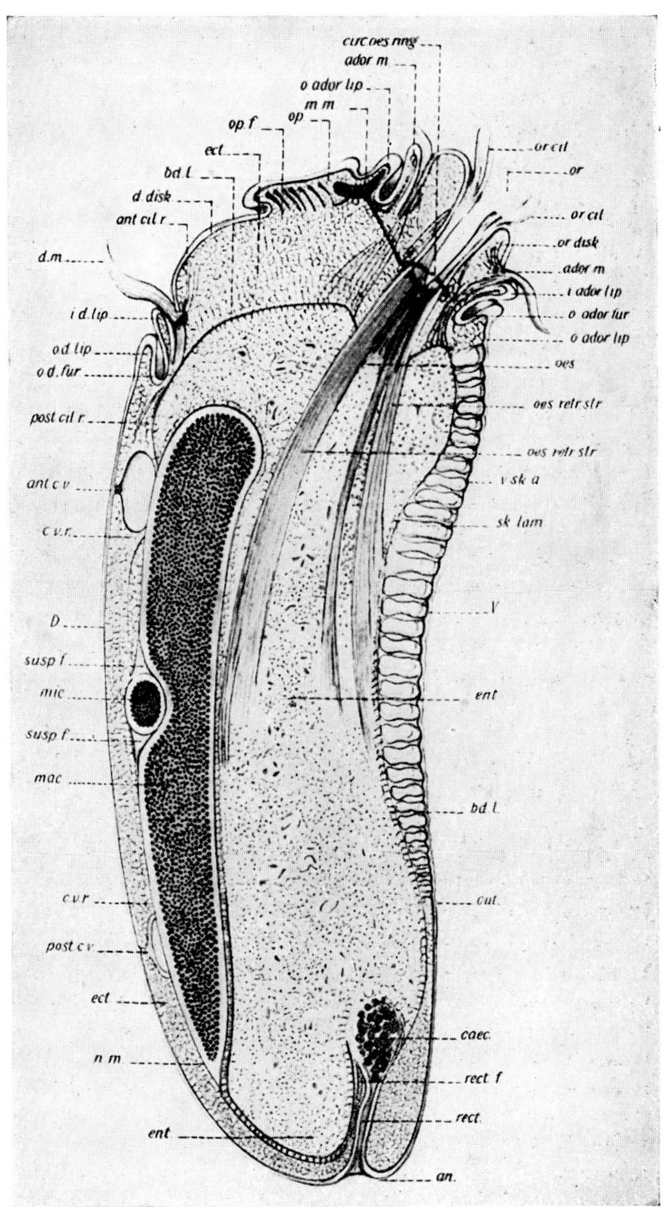

Figure 36.

Figure 36. Structure of *Diplodinium caudatum*: *or*, mouth; *ect*, ectoplasm; *ent*, endoplasm; *mac*, macronucleus; *mic*, micronucleus; *ant c.v.*, *post c.v.*, anterior and posterior contractile vacuoles; *rect*, rectum; *an*, anus; and many other structures. (After Sharp.)

[*To face p.* 70.

CHAPTER V

THE CELL AS A FREE-LIVING ORGANISM: THE LIFE-HISTORIES, BEHAVIOUR, AND ECOLOGY OF FREE-LIVING CELLS

I. THE LIFE-HISTORIES OF THE PROTISTA

THE life-histories of the Protista are extremely varied. The purpose of this section is not to give a systematic account of the various types of life-history which occur in the group, but to discuss some of the many questions of general interest which are raised by these life-histories.

The life-history of a protistan cannot be compared directly with that of a multicellular animal. The latter passes through a series of changes from the egg to senility, in which a single body develops the adult structure, lives for a certain time as an adult, and finally dies. The protistan life-history includes a series of divisions and, very often, conjugations (or syngamies). These follow each other sometimes in a definitely prescribed order, sometimes in irregular sequence, until the cells reach their original condition and the life-history is repeated. Each division is a reproduction, so that the period from one reproduction to the next is that between any two of the divisions in the life-history. It is this period, not the whole life-history of the protistan, which is comparable to the life-history of the multicellular animal. We find the protistan type of life-history in multicellular animals only when successive generations of the animals differ from each other, as in the hydroid and medusoid generations of many Cœlenterata, and the sexual and asexual generations which occur in several other groups of multicellular animals (p. 334).

Further, there is a development comparable to that of the multicellular animal, from the egg to the adult, in only a few protistans. The structure of a protistan cell is reorganised to a greater or less extent at each division. But this process of reorganisation is much more comparable to the remodelling (or regeneration) of a separated piece of a multicellular body into the whole specific form (ch. VIII) than to the development of the multicellular animal from the egg to the adult. In development much more happens than is required for the assumption of the more complex form of the adult. Larval organs are formed and later lost, and the course of development is

PLATE VIII

Figure 37. Bud formation in a suctorian.

a, animal with internal buds; *b*, one of these buds; *cv*, contractile vacuole; *n*, meganucleus; *n'*, micronucleus; *s*, buds; *st*, place where the stalk will be formed. (After Bütschli.)

Figure 53. Food reserves in *Daphnia*.

a, deposition of fat in the body cavity when sexual eggs are being produced; *b*, deposition of a substance similar to glycogen in the carapace when the reproduction is asexual. Fat is shown as vacuoles, the glycogen-like substance as solid granules. (After Geoffrey Smith.)

Figure 54. Forms of the carapace of *Simocephalus*.

a, normal; *b*, fed on *Chlamydomonas*. (After Agar.)

PLATE VIII

(*a*) (*b*)

Figure 37.

(*a*) (*b*)

Figure 53.

(*a*) (*b*)

Figure 54.

[*To face p.* 72.

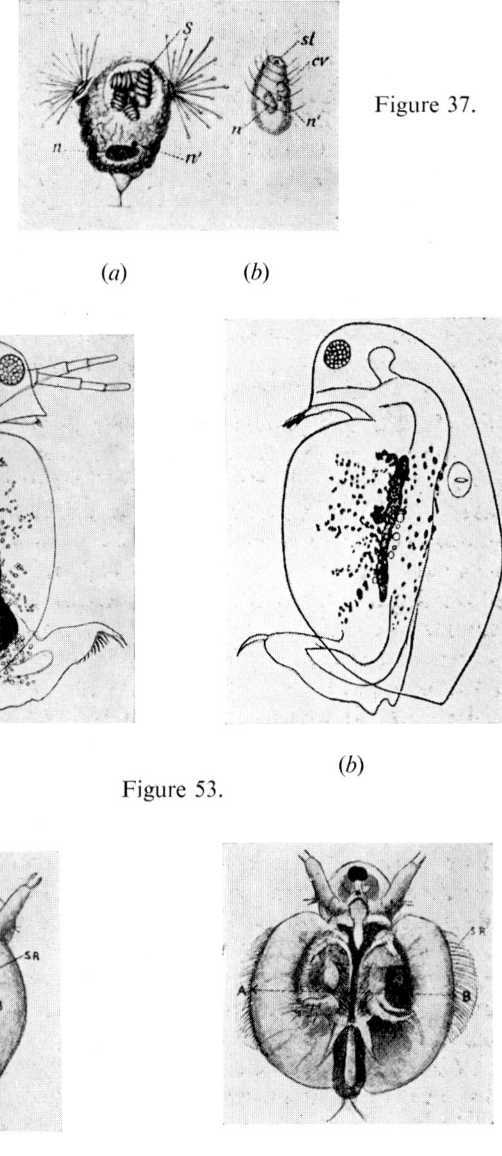

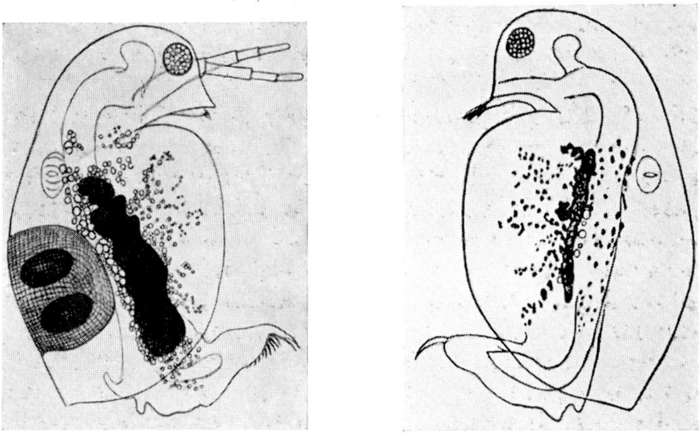

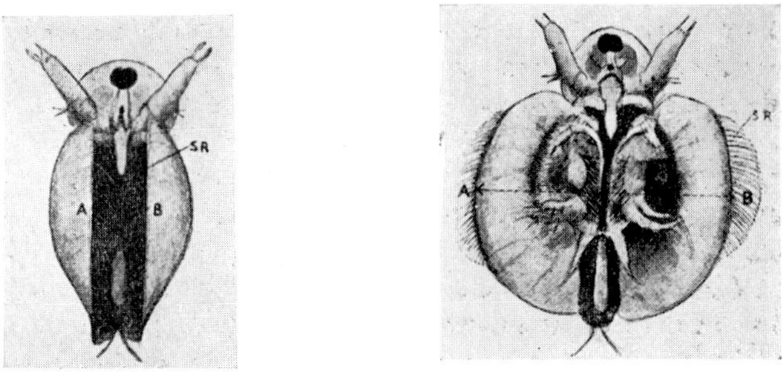

determined in part by the evolutionary history of the animal and not by the organism's own needs. Development is more than a modelling of the body into the adult form, whereas both the regeneration of a separated part of the multicellular body and the reorganisation of a protistan cell is, so far as we can see, no more than this.

Something which is apparently of the nature of true development occurs in a few of the Protista. The Suctoria (see above, p. 67, and Fig. 30) reproduce by forming buds, often in cavities in the interior of their bodies (Plate VIII, Fig. 37). These buds possess cilia, and are much more like other ciliates in structure than the adult Suctoria are. If the Suctoria are modified ciliates, as is generally believed, we have here an example of ancestral characters in early stages, which is one of the most important features of true development. Similar phenomena occur in a few other Protista.

1. THE SIMPLEST LIFE-HISTORIES OF THE PROTISTA

The simplest life-history which it is possible to imagine for the free-living cell would be a series of divisions, each identical with the last, and each regularly following a period of cell growth.

The trypanosomes have a type of life-history which is only slightly more complicated than this (Fig. 38). Their life-history is a series of divisions without syngamy or conjugation,* but the form of the body varies from one part of the life-history to another, in association with the position of the parasites in the bodies of its two hosts.

The life-history of *Amœba proteus* is also very simple. No syngamy is known, so that the life-history is again nothing more than a series of divisions. But at times the nucleus divides repeatedly without cleavage of the cytoplasm, and the nuclei so formed become each surrounded by a small mass of protoplasm. These bodies are then set free as amœbulæ. Encystment of small nucleated organisms also occurs in the life-history of *A. proteus*. Here, the complication of the life-history consists in variation of the type of the division.

It may be asked whether we can say anything of the reasons which determine that division shall occur in the protistan cell. We have already seen (p. 35) that in some cells the nucleus grows disproportionately immediately before division, but this may be looked upon rather as an antecedent of division, perhaps even as an early stage of the division process, than as a cause of division. We need to know why the nucleus starts to grow rapidly at these times.

We know very little of the biological causes which lead to division. Clearly, the cell divides as a result of physiological changes in the condition of the protoplasm that have occurred since the last division.

* Conjugation has been described in T. congolense (Fiennes, *Nature*, **156**, 390. 1945).

But we know very little of these changes. Some of them must almost certainly be due to the growth in the size of the cell that has been going on. We have seen (p. 48) that change in size will alter the rates of many of the processes of the physiology of the cell. This is certainly not the only cause of division in animal cells, for division occurs

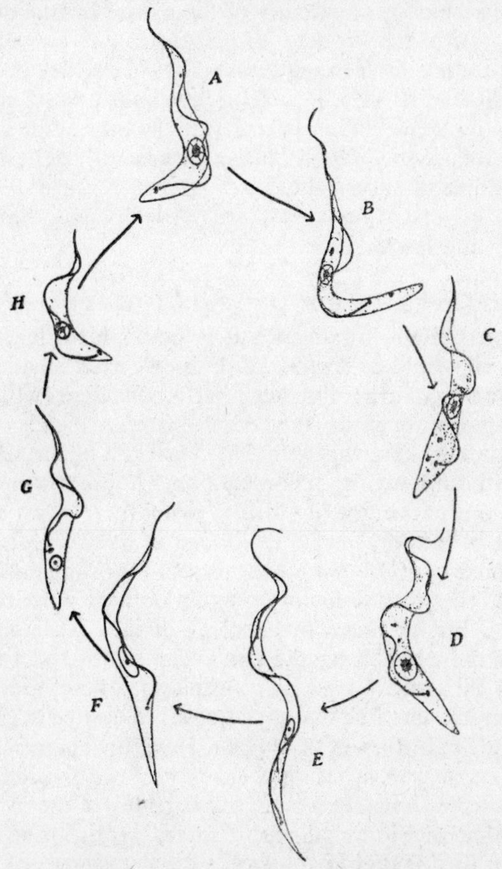

Figure 38. Life-cycle of *Trypanosoma gambiense*.

A, type ingested by the tsetse fly from the mammalian host; B, C, D, successive types from the intestine of the fly; E, from the proventriculus; F, G, H, from the salivary glands. (From Graham Kerr, after M. Robinson.)

in cells which are not growing larger (*e.g.* in the egg cells of multicellular animals).

It is obvious that reorganisation occurs in the cell during its division.* New cytoplasmic organs are formed in at least one of the

* E. Fauré Fremiet, *Folia Biotheoretica*, 3, 25, 1948.

daughter cells, and the nuclei are reconstituted. This reorganisation may be an important function of the division. Possibly it becomes necessary as a result of the loss of efficiency which seems always to accompany continued life in protoplasm.

Thus, it may be that division is a reaction to loss of efficiency in the cellular metabolism, due both to increase of the size of the cell by growth and to decay of the protoplasm. Even if these are true causes of division, it is very probable that there are others.

2. SYNGAMY, CONJUGATION, AND ENDOMIXIS

Not many of the life-histories of the Protista are as simple as those of the trypanosomes and *Amœba proteus*. In many protistan life-histories the series of divisions is broken sooner or later by the occurrence of one of the processes of syngamy or conjugation. A third process, autogamy, is in some ways similar to these. It is probably rare in the natural life of the organisms but it occurs in laboratory cultures. We shall consider these processes in this section.

(*a*) *Syngamy* and *Conjugation*, which may be regarded as a modified form of syngamy occurring in the ciliates, both consist essentially of the union of two nuclei to form the nucleus of a single cell. In syngamy two cells unite and their cytoplasm fuses as well as their nuclei. In conjugation (*e.g.* in such a form as *Paramecium*) a nucleus from one cell migrates into the other, typically without a recognisable amount of cytoplasm. It is the union of the nuclei which is the essential feature of syngamy and conjugation, not fusion of the cytoplasm.

In many Protista it has been shown that the nuclei, before uniting in either syngamy or conjugation, undergo two or three preparatory divisions, which strongly recall the meiotic divisions that precede syngamy in the gametes of the multicellular body. In the Protista it has been possible to determine that the number of the chromosomes is reduced from the diploid to the haploid number during these divisions only in some of the ciliates, in which the chromosomes are exceptionally large.* But one of these divisions is probably a reduction division in most of the Protista. They may, therefore, be regarded provisionally as meiotic divisions. On the other hand, in a few of the Sporozoa it has been shown that a reduction division occurs immediately *after* the fusion of the nuclei at syngamy, and that the nuclei are haploid for most of the life-history. It has been suggested that this may have been the primitive condition, and that

* Clear evidence of genes behaving in a Mendelian manner has been found in *Paramecium* (*Cf.* Beale in the Bibliography). For this meiosis is necessary.

the suppression of the haploid phase in animal life-histories is secondary.

In the ciliates, which possess a meganucleus differentiated from the micronucleus, conjugation has another obvious result, in addition to the fusion of the nuclei. The meganucleus breaks down immediately before conjugation. It is replaced after the fusion of the nuclei from material derived from a micronucleus, which is always one of the products of the division of the fused nuclei, the zygote. One function of conjugation in the ciliate is, therefore, replacement of the meganucleus by nuclear material from the zygote. This function should be distinguished from that of the union of the nuclei.

In other Protista there is no separated meganucleus, but there is some evidence that their nuclei contain material of two different kinds, and that these kinds of material differ in the same way as the material of the mega- and micronuclei (tropho- and idiochromatin, p. 58). It is possible, but not yet established, that syngamy produces in the single nuclei of other Protista the results which follow in the ciliates from replacement of the meganucleus. We shall discuss later what these results are. The course of nuclear reorganisation at conjugation in *Paramecium aurelia*, which has two micronuclei, is shown in Fig. 39 (*a*).

(*b*) *Autogamy*. If conjugation is prevented in species of *Paramecium* and some other ciliates, by culturing the animals singly so that they have no chance to meet, a process of reorganisation of the nucleus within a single individual often takes place (Fig. 39 (*b*)). This process was first described as that known as *endomixis*. It has now been shown* that the true course is that here given (*autogamy*), though endomixis may perhaps occasionally occur.

In both endomixis and autogamy, since the reorganisation is within a single body, there can be no fusion of nuclei from two individuals. In both these processes, as in conjugation, the macronucleus breaks down and the micronuclei divide twice (A–C), one division being probably meiotic. In autogamy two of the eight micronuclei so produced then fuse again and the others degenerate (D). The fused nucleus divides and one product of the division goes to each of two individuals into which the body now divides (E). The meganucleus and two micronuclei of each individual are formed from division products of the micronucleus received at the first division (F–H).

Endomixis differs from autogamy in that there is no fusion of micronuclei at stage D, so that, if one of the preparatory divisions is meiotic, the nuclei of the new individuals should be haploid.

* *Cf.* the book by Beale in the bibliography.

Perhaps, the diploid condition is regained later by division of the chromosomes and not the nucleus. Endomixis is in any case rare and, indeed, only doubtfully occurs.

It is said that in autogamy the new macronucleus may in some species occasionally regenerate from parts of the old macronucleus.

Conjugation and autogamy are of essentially the same type in other ciliates as in *P. aurelia*, but the details of the process vary.

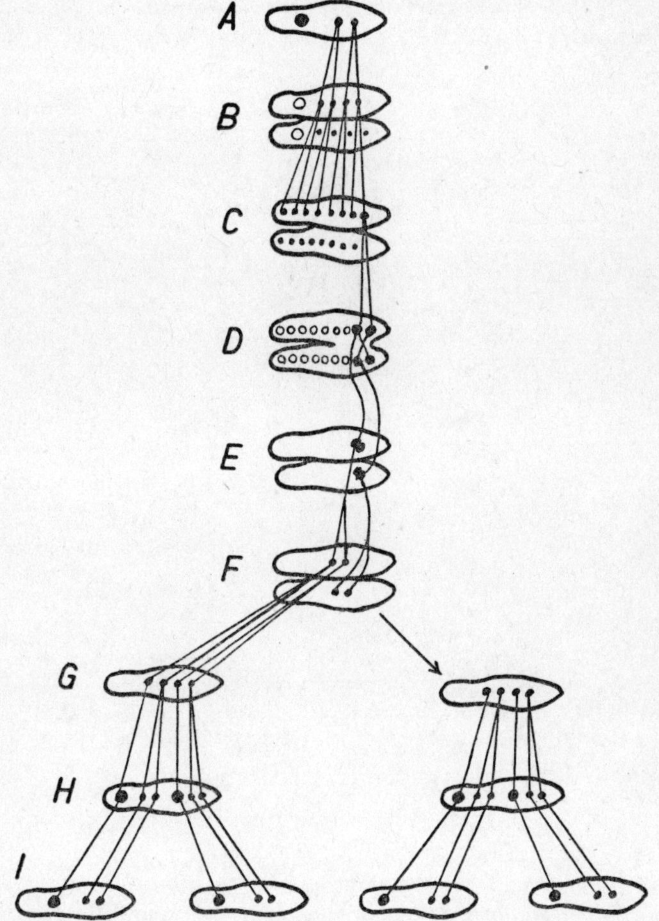

Figure 39 (*a*). Conjugation in *Paramecium aurelia*. (After Woodruff and Jennings.)

Thus, autogamy resembles conjugation in:

1. The replacement of the meganucleus from micronuclear material.

2. The possible occurrence of reduction in the number of the chromosomes.

The obvious difference between autogamy and conjugation is that union of nuclei from different individuals occurs only in conjugation. There is therefore recombination of the hereditary material only in conjugation. This difference is discussed further below (p. 80).

In both processes the meganucleus is reorganised. We have seen that reorganisation of the nucleus occurs at division (p. 74), but the reorganisation at conjugation and autogamy seems to be a much

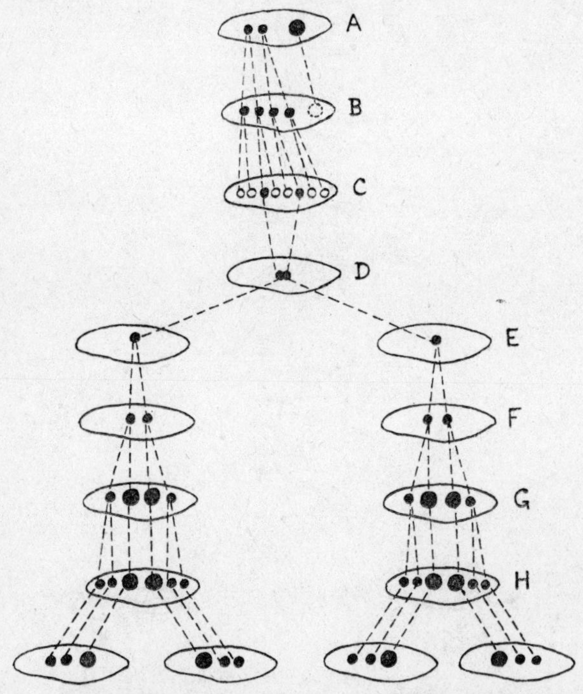

Figure 39(*b*). Autogamy in *Paramecium aurelia*.

more fundamental process. During conjugation and autogamy in the ciliates (and perhaps also at syngamy in other Protista), the trophochromatin is replaced from micronuclear material. We have no evidence that a similar replacement of one type of chromatin by the other occurs at division. There the reorganisation of the nucleus cannot be more than replacement of the organs of the nucleoplasm from nucleoprotein material in general.

We have thus in protistan life-histories two distinct cycles, the division of the cell and the processes of syngamy, conjugation or autogamy. These last three processes resemble each other in many of their fundamental features, though not in all. Nevertheless, they may be considered different forms of the same process. We shall see that these two cycles are distinct also in their functions in the organism.

The distinction between the division cycle and these three processes is not falsified by the fact that certain divisions, the meiotic divisions, seem to form an essential part of the processes of conjugation, and, perhaps, of autogamy and syngamy, and are therefore necessarily associated with these processes. Where these divisions are true meiotic divisions, they are distinct from normal divisions, since reduction occurs in them. The distinction which it is important to make is between the normal divisions and the processes by which the trophochromatin is replaced.

Nor is the distinction falsified by the fact that rapid division of the cell usually follows syngamy, conjugation and autogamy. This is the result of the changes in the condition of the cell which these processes cause.

The function of the division cycle is obvious: it is increase in the number of the individuals, *i.e.* reproduction. That of the conjugation cycle is less obvious. This cycle is often called "*sexual reproduction*" since, as we have seen, it is associated with rapid division. But the conjugation cycle is not itself an increase in the number of the individuals, and therefore not reproduction of any kind. Nor is it in general associated with sexual differences. The term "sexual reproduction" is inaccurate when applied to the Protista and should be discarded. We have to enquire what is the function of conjugation and syngamy, and why they occur in the life-histories of animals.

In the life-histories of most of the Protista, replacement of the trophochromatin is by syngamy or conjugation; autogamy does not normally occur. The division cycle alternates with either syngamy or conjugation. The alternation may be regular as in *Polystomella*, in which a generation which gives rise to gametes alternates with one that reproduces by division without syngamy. More frequently, it is irregular: the division cycle is repeated through an indefinite number of divisions and the sequence is only occasionally broken by a syngamy or conjugation. The latter type of life-history occurs in many ciliates (*e.g. Paramecium*) and is characteristic of many groups of the flagellates, especially of the Phytomastigina. An example is shown diagrammatically in Fig. 40, in *Copromonas*.

Since syngamy occurs occasionally in these life-histories, it may be supposed to occur when the physiological condition of the organisms is in some way different from what it is at other times. We must therefore consider what is known of the physiological conditions which lead to syngamy or conjugation in cultures of animals such as these. We may also ask what are the changes which result from these processes.

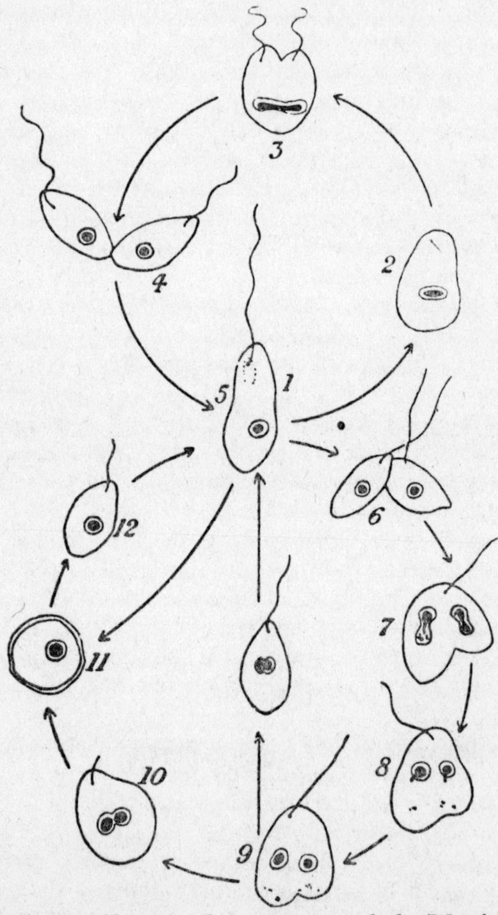

Figure 40. Life-cycle of *Copromonas subtilis* (Mastigiphora).
1, normal form; 2–4, division cycle; 6–10, syngamy; 11, encystment; 12, liberation of active animal from the cyst. (From Graham Kerr, after Dobell.)

Let us take the second of these questions first. There are two distinct changes in the condition of the cell which we might expect to follow from the processes of syngamy and conjugation as we observe them.

1. We have seen that, in the ciliates and probably many other Protista, reduction of the number of the chromosomes to the haploid

and subsequent return to the diploid number occurs at syngamy or conjugation, in just the same way as we know it to occur in multicellular animals. This must result in rearrangement of the hereditary material. Most of the general features of the organisms, such as their size or shape will be the result of the action of a large number of genes rather than of a single gene. When this is so, rearrangement of the hereditary material will cause great increase in the variability of the animals, for many new combinations of hereditary material will be formed. This will often be useful in enabling the animal to survive unusual conditions.

If the nucleus is reduced from the diploid to the haploid condition before autogamy as it is before conjugation (and we have seen that this is likely), there will be *some* rearrangement of the hereditary material at autogamy, but it will affect only those characters for which the original nucleus was heterozygotic. Some, though not all of these will become homozygous when the sister nuclei fuse. Other characters will be in the same condition after autogamy as before it. And, in autogamy, in contrast to conjugation, no new characters will be brought in from another nucleus. The rearrangement of the hereditary material will therefore be much less at autogamy than at conjugation.

Thus, autogamy, like syngamy and conjugation, may be expected to increase the variability of the animals, but syngamy and conjugation should be more effective in increasing variability. In these respects endomixis will resemble autogamy.

2. We have seen that in the ciliates both conjugation and autogamy result in renewal of the metabolic material of the meganucleus: and that it is possible, but not proved, that metabolic material is renewed at syngamy in the nuclei of other Protista. We should therefore expect that in the ciliates, and possibly also in other Protista, these processes would result in increase in the efficiency of the metabolic material, and therefore of the metabolism of the cell as a whole. This result should show itself in increased metabolic activity in the organisms.

We have now to enquire whether there is any evidence that these results do in fact follow syngamy, conjugation, and autogamy.

The times at which syngamy or conjugation occur in cultures of Protista provide some evidence of the functions of these processes. In cultures of flagellates, syngamy is rarely seen so long as the culture is healthy and multiplication is rapid. It often occurs at the end of a period of rapid growth, when the food supply of the culture is falling off and other conditions are becoming unfavourable for the growth of the animals. It may be followed by encystment. When the animals hatch from their cysts, they again divide rapidly, if they are then placed in a favourable culture medium. Thus syngamy follows a period of rapid growth and precedes another such period, sometimes with an intervening period in which the animals are encysted. It would clearly be appropriate that the metabolic activity of the cell should be increased at such a time.

The means which have been found to induce conjugation or syngamy in cultures of Protista provide some further evidence. If a culture is allowed to go stale until division has become slower, and conjugation or syngamy does not then occur, these processes can frequently be induced by taking a sample of the organisms from the culture and introducing them into a new and more favourable medium. The organisms in the sample undergo conjugation or syngamy, and they then multiply rapidly in the new medium. Here, also, these processes precede a period of active division, and occur at a time when increased metabolic activity would be of value to the organism. These results do not however *prove* that syngamy and conjugation have the effect of increasing the division rate, for the increase which is observed might be due to the more favourable conditions in the new medium.

Most of the experimental investigations on these questions have been carried out with a special type of culture known as the "isolation culture." In these cultures single individuals of the species being investigated are kept separately, and the products of division are separated after each division. Thus, syngamy or conjugation is prevented. Except in *Paramecium*, autogamy can be recognised because it only occurs during encystment; in *Paramecium* a careful watch has to be kept for it. If it occurs, the cultures are set aside, unless it is desired to study the effects of autogamy. By these means long-continued division without syngamy or conjugation can be studied. Also, since each culture is derived by division from a single individual the results cannot be complicated by hereditary variations in the organisms, for at division the arrangement of the hereditary material is not altered. When it is desired to observe the effects of syngamy or conjugation, two animals are put together and allowed to unite, if they will.* Throughout, any effects of the medium becoming stale, or the food in it becoming exhausted, are avoided by renewal of the medium daily.

The features of the behaviour which are most often studied in these experiments are the variability of the animals and the division rate. The latter is taken to be a measure of the growth of the animals and therefore of the metabolic activity or "vitality." Ciliates have been

* For recent work on the "mating types" of *Paramecium*, within which conjugation will not occur, see R. F. Ewer, *Sci. Progress*, **36**, 450, 1948, and the book by Beale in the bibliography.

most often used in these experiments, but Protista of other groups have also been used.

The results which these experiments have given may be summarised as follows:

1. There can be no doubt that conjugation or syngamy increases the variability of a culture of Protista. The range of variability has been compared in several characters between animals which have recently conjugated or undergone syngamy, and animals from parallel cultures in which these processes have not taken place. Several species have shown increased variability. The characters of each of the ex-conjugants are retained through the divisions until another syngamy or conjugation occurs, so that the variability of the whole culture is maintained.

The evidence that autogamy causes increased variability is much less complete. Whether it does so or not must be regarded as undecided. It has been found in *Paramecium aurelia* that a large proportion of the animals die during autogamy. This also happens during conjugation and syngamy. It may perhaps be interpreted as evidence for increased variability, only the more favourable variations surviving.

2. Certain protistans of each of the groups Flagellata, Sarcodina, and Ciliata have been kept in isolation cultures without syngamy, conjugation, or autogamy for many—often more than a thousand—generations, and have shown no loss of vitality (Fig. 41).

Thus, it seems that life for indefinite periods without syngamy or conjugation is possible, even in some Protista in which these processes normally occur. We already know that it is possible in Protista which have simple life-histories such as those of *Amœba* and the trypanosomes.

In other Protista the division rate in isolation cultures has been found always to fall off after a time, and the animals have finally died (Fig. 42).

It has been suggested that the division rate falls off in cultures of these organisms because the conditions of the culture are not sufficiently favourable. With better conditions there might have been no fall in the division rate. It is not certain whether this is so or not. We do not yet know whether indefinite life without conjugation or syngamy is possible for all Protista, though we already know that it is possible for some. A point in favour of the belief that the decline in the division rate is due to the cultural conditions is the observation that cultures in which the conditions are kept constant often decline and die, while others in which the cultural conditions are occasionally altered may survive. It appears that changes in the conditions in which the animals are living prevent (in some unknown manner) the fall in the division rate. If so, the cultural conditions must control the fall in the division rate, at least in certain circumstances.

3. That life for long periods without conjugation or autogamy is possible in some ciliates is shown very clearly by the results of

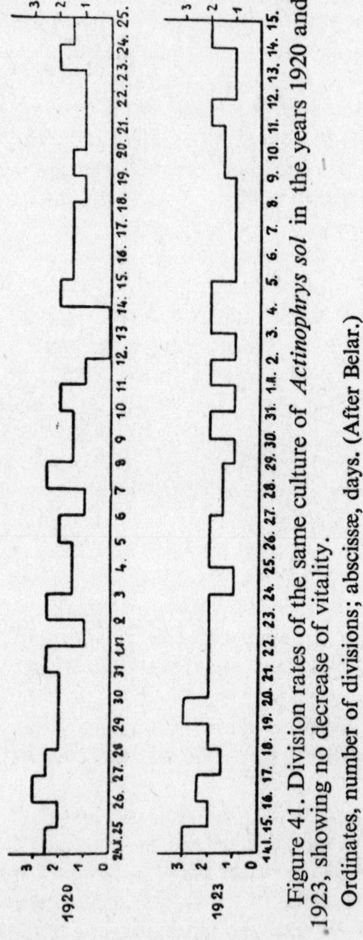

Figure 41. Division rates of the same culture of *Actinophrys sol* in the years 1920 and 1923, showing no decrease of vitality.

Ordinates, number of divisions; abscissæ, days. (After Belar.)

culturing some abnormal individuals of a ciliate, *Oxytricha hymenostoma*. These individuals had no micronucleus, and yet they were cultured for three hundred generations. The division rate, however, fell off. A similar race of *Paramecium caudatum*, also without micronuclei, has been kept for nearly two months. Neither conjugation or autogamy is possible in these races.

4. *Paramecium aurelia* and *P. caudatum* have been kept for very

many generations in isolation cultures without conjugation or fall in the division rate. One culture of *P. aurelia* was continued for 11,700 generations, and the animals were dividing as rapidly at the end as at the start. But the cultures differed from those already mentioned in that the division rate in them showed more or less regular

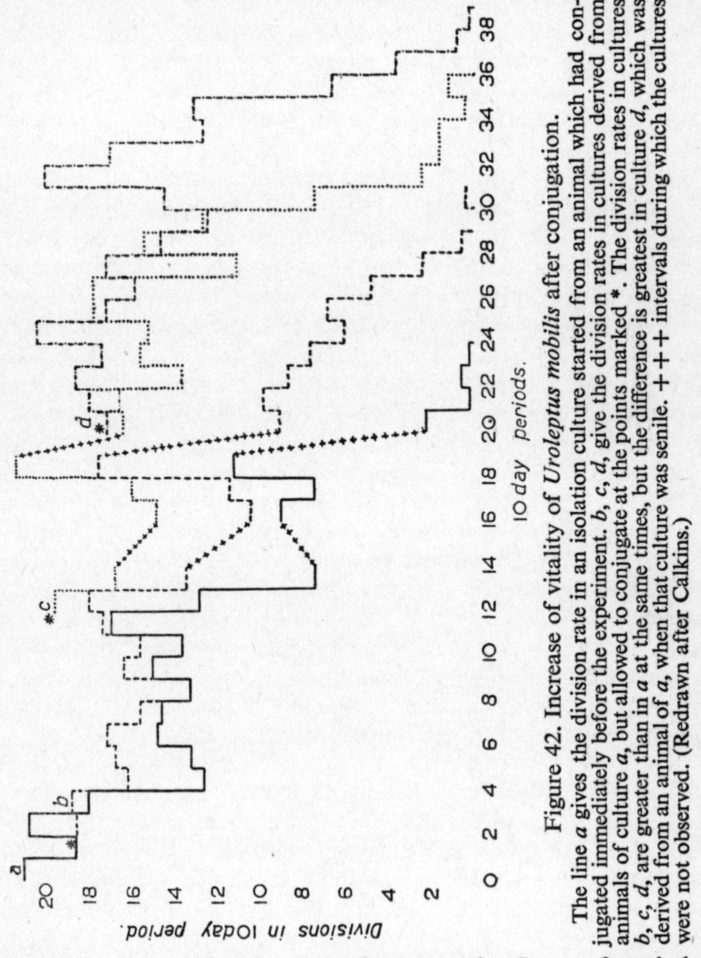

Figure 42. Increase of vitality of *Uroleptus mobilis* after conjugation.

The line *a* gives the division rate in an isolation culture started from an animal which had conjugated immediately before the experiment. *b*, *c*, *d*, give the division rates in cultures derived from animals of culture *a*, but allowed to conjugate at the points marked *. The division rates in cultures *b*, *c*, *d*, are greater than in *a* at the same times, but the difference is greatest in culture *d*, which was derived from an animal of *a*, when that culture was senile. +++ intervals during which the cultures were not observed. (Redrawn after Calkins.)

fluctuations in a cycle of one to three months. It was found that autogamy occurred in them when the division rate was at its minimum, and that the rate rose after autogamy. At first sight it seems that we have here good evidence that autogamy increases vitality, but it has been suggested that the fall of the division rate before autogamy may be itself a result of the oncoming of autogamy. If so, autogamy would not have any real revitalising effect on the culture; it would merely have produced a temporary fall and, later, a compensating rise of the rate. But in one other ciliate (*Didinium*) it has been clearly shown that autogamy does directly increase vitality. It may occur in that species without a fall of the division rate immediately preceding it.

5. Animals which have been kept in isolation cultures, and have reached a low level of vitality, usually show increased vitality after they are allowed to unite in syngamy or to conjugate (Fig. 42). The improvement is not always large enough to increase the vitality to its value in earlier stages of the culture. Occasionally, no increase of vitality is observed, and there may sometimes even be a lower vitality after conjugation or syngamy than before it. It is, however, much more common for the vitality to be increased.

It has been suggested that this usual increase of vitality after conjugation or syngamy may be a result merely of the increased variability which we know these processes to cause, and not an independent effect. With greater variability in the animals, some will have higher vitality than the culture had before syngamy or conjugation, and it is suggested that these are selected, the less favourable variations dying out. On the whole, the results are against this interpretation. Deaths during conjugation or syngamy are certainly numerous, but the increase in vitality is too great and it is observed in too great a proportion of the experiments for it to be the result of the increased variability alone. In the species which have been investigated, conjugation or syngamy appears to have a real revitalising effect, and this effect is independent of the increased variability which these processes also cause. It cannot be denied, however, that some of the increased vitality which is found after conjugation and syngamy may be due to the greater variability of the animals at these times.

Thus conjugation and syngamy, in some species and probably in all, have both the effects which seemed probable at the start of our discussion. Autogamy probably increases the vitality of a culture, though clearly not to the same extent as conjugation. We may also conclude that these two effects are, to some extent at least, independent.

We can say much less of the causes which initiate conjugation or syngamy in the normal life of the animals. These processes seem to be the reaction of the animal to conditions in which rapid multiplication and, therefore, high vitality are valuable. Probably also the increased variability is valuable, since it provides the culture with a proportion of favourable variations.

On the evidence which has been given it is tempting, and probably justifiable, to correlate the two distinct effects of conjugation and syngamy with the two chief changes we observe in the cells at this time, *i.e.* to suppose that the increase in variability is a result of the union of the nuclei, and the revitalisation of the cell a result of the replacement of the metabolic nuclear material. There is further evidence in favour of this correlation. In one ciliate (*Uroleptus mobilis*) it has been shown that increased vitality may result from conjugation even when union of the nuclei is prevented. These animals conjugate by uniting the body only at one end (Fig. 43). By cutting the body near the point of union before the nuclei had passed over, nuclear fusion was prevented. The meganucleus had degenerated and was replaced in the regenerating organism. The animals were found to show the increased vitality which is characteristic of ex-conjugants. This could not have been due to fusion of nuclei from the different individuals, which did not occur. It is hardly possible that it was due to reduction of the chromosome number, which occurred here as it does in normal conjugation. It seems much more likely that it was due to renewal of the metabolic material in the meganucleus.

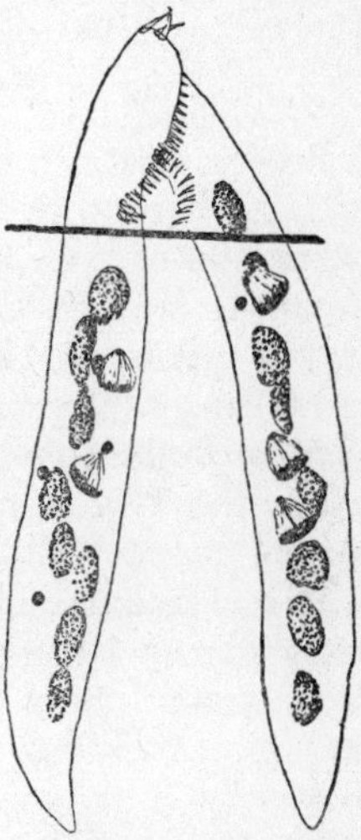

Figure 43. Conjugation of *Uroleptus mobilis*. (After Calkins.)

It is possible that autogamy occurs in these experiments; it may be that the nuclei of the resulting individuals are formed by fusion of products of division of the original nucleus. There is no evidence of this, and it is equally likely that they are formed directly from the original nuclei without fusion. The experiments do not allow us to decide between these alternatives. But whichever alternative is true it is clear that there was no transference of nuclear material between the individuals and that the increased vitality that was observed could only have been due to nuclear reorganisation in each individual. The experiments therefore give grounds for the belief that re-vitalisation is produced by replacement of the metabolic chromatin.

Autogamy has been found in other Protista besides the ciliates. It is known in *Actinosphærium* and has been described in some amœbæ and in the Neosporidia. In *Actinosphærium*, a uninucleate cell is formed by division of the normal multinucleate individual. This cell encysts and divides within the cyst. The nuclei of the two cells so formed undergo a process of meiosis. The cells then fuse and their nuclei unite to form a zygote.

There can be no more rearrangement of the hereditary material here than in *Paramecium*. The occurrence of this process, probably in several groups of the Protista, suggests that syngamy has other effects besides the rearrangement of the hereditary material. We may conclude that the most important of the effects of autogamy is to increase the vitality of the cell.

3. VARIATIONS OF THE BODY FORM IN THE PROTISTA DURING THE LIFE-HISTORY

Protoplasm, so long as it is alive, is a continually changing system, and it is therefore to be expected that the form of the cell, which is an expression of the condition of the protoplasm, should change continuously during the life of the organism. We have found it necessary to ascribe the cause of the reorganisation of the structure of the cell during conjugation and division to these, at present undefined, changes in the condition of the protoplasm. Here we must consider a few other types of change in the form of the cell which occur during the life-histories of the Protista.

In multicellular animals the most obvious changes of form in the body during its life-history are the changes which make up the development of the animal. In very few of the Protista, as we have seen (p. 73), is there development of the kind which occurs in the multicellular animal. In the Protista the life-history is made up of a series of interdivisional periods, and we find, as we should expect, that the form varies in the different interdivisional periods. We have already seen examples of this in the simple life-histories of the trypanosomes. The changes of form become much greater in the more complex protistan life-histories, such as those of the Sporozoa, *e.g.* *Monocystis* or *Plasmodium*. There is little more that can be said about these changes of form than about those which occur during division and conjugation. We know that they must be due to changes in the constitution of the protoplasm, but we are quite unable at present to define these changes.

It may be noticed, however, that some of these changes of form are associated with other types of change in the cell. A well-known example of this is the difference in form which we sometimes find between individuals of the same species which reproduce sexually and asexually. The macro- and microspheric forms of *Polystomella* give an example of this association. Another example is the very frequent differentiation of gametes into the two types which are called male and female. This differentiation is not universal in the Protista; the gametes of many species are indistinguishable in structure, and the syngamy is then called isogamous. But the differentiation occurs in all the larger groups of the Protista and must have arisen several times in their evolution.

This differentiation, when it occurs, is always between one type, the "female," which tends to become large and inactive, and a second type, the "male," which is smaller and more active. No other type of differentiation between gametes occurs either in the Protista or in multicellular animals. This is perhaps not surprising, for the differentiation which does occur is obviously appropriate for the functions which the gametes have to perform. A large body is necessary for storage of the food required for the zygote, and activity, in one gamete at least, is necessary to ensure syngamy. Activity and a large body containing much food material do not readily go together in organisms, and it is therefore easy to see that specialisation of the gametes, each to serve one of these needs, will be of advantage.

The differentiation of the gametes into the types which we have called male and female raises the question of how far we may speak of sex as occurring in the Protista. In multicellular animals the terms male and female were originally used to distinguish the individuals which produce the two types of gamete. From this use the terms were extended by analogy to the gametes produced by these individuals. Differentiation between the gamete-producing individuals is extremely rare among the Protista. It occurs only in a few Sporozoa (*Cyclospora*). In the original use of the terms we can only speak of the sexual difference between male and female as occurring among the Protista in these forms, but, since the differentiation between the two types of protistan gametes is so like that between the male and female gametes of multicellular animals, it seems justifiable to use these terms to distinguish the types of protistan gametes. It is more doubtful whether we should extend the terms, as is sometimes done, to cases where no true, independent gametes are formed, *e.g.* to the conjugation of ciliates such as *Paramecium*, where the motile nucleus is sometimes called male and the immotile female. Neither nucleus in such conjugation is an independently living cell, as all true gametes are. The use of the terms male and female for these nuclei originated from the theory, which may probably be true, that conjugation such as that of *Paramecium* was evolved from a condition in which free gametes were formed.

In spite of the differences in body form which occur so commonly in the protistan life-history, the constancy of the form at any one stage of the life-history is as striking a feature of the Protista as it is of multicellular animals. We can describe a multicellular animal from its structure at any one of many stages during its life-history. So, also, a protistan can be described from the structure of its body in the different stages of *its* life-history. But this constancy of the body form at each stage of the life-history is no more absolute in the Protista than we shall later see it to be in multicellular animals (ch. VII). The form alters to some extent (as we should expect) with changes in the physiological condition of the animal, and with the changes in the external environment which produce physiological changes within the animal. The body may vary in the same species both in size (Fig. 22, p. 47) and structure. Structural variations are greatest when the physiological changes are greatest, especially when the body becomes unhealthy. They are very noticeable, for instance, in a culture of *Paramecium* which has been prevented from conjugating for a long time.

II. THE BEHAVIOUR OF THE PROTISTA

By the behaviour of an animal we mean the whole of the actions which together constitute its activities as an organism. Each species has its own behaviour, adapted for satisfying its own needs. Activity may be, and very often is, continuous—a flagellate or a ciliate may swim continuously for a considerable time—but the behaviour of an animal is not only its continuous activity; it includes also the *changes* of activity which all animals exhibit.

Behaviour, since it includes changes in activities, necessarily postulates the power of response to stimulation, and therefore necessarily the possession of a system of response consisting of receptor organs, co-ordinating mechanism and effector organs (p. 58). In the multicellular animal the term "reflex" is used for simple forms of response in which stimulation is conducted through a nervous arc from the receptor to the effector organ (ch. XVI). Though in the Protista there is no nervous system, and the stimulation is conducted through the general protoplasm or, in a few forms, perhaps through special intracellular fibrils (p. 69), the response system is functionally so similar in them to the reflex arc in the multicellular animals that it seems justifiable that we should regard these responses as of the same type in both groups of animals. Nevertheless, it must not be forgotten that there are no structures in most Protista comparable to the nervous arcs of multicellular animals.

In the multicellular animals, at least the simpler types of behaviour may be regarded as purely automatic, that is to say determined entirely by the nature of the stimulation and the physiological condition of the animal, and not modified by the will or any other mental function. In the Protista and in the simpler multicellular animals, we have no reason for believing that any but automatic behaviour occurs.

Protistan behaviour includes several types of response. In the free-moving forms the greater part of the behaviour, and that part which is most easily studied, is the locomotory behaviour by which their movements about their environment are determined. We shall consider mainly the locomotory behaviour of the Protista, but it must be remembered that this is not the whole of protistan behaviour. The manner in which food is caught and ingested is also part of the behaviour of the organisms; in sessile species this may be the most obvious part of the behaviour. There are still other types of behaviour, *e.g.* the contraction into an immobile form, sometimes with encystment, which Protista often show when the environment is unfavourable.

Even the bacteria have behaviour of a simple type. If a drop of liquid containing a noxious substance, such as a strong acid, is introduced into a culture of bacteria, it will be found that they do not enter the drop; they remain outside it and collect farther and farther from it as the substance dissolved in the drop diffuses into the medium. Conversely, bacteria are found to accumulate in regions where the conditions are more favourable than in the rest of the environment.

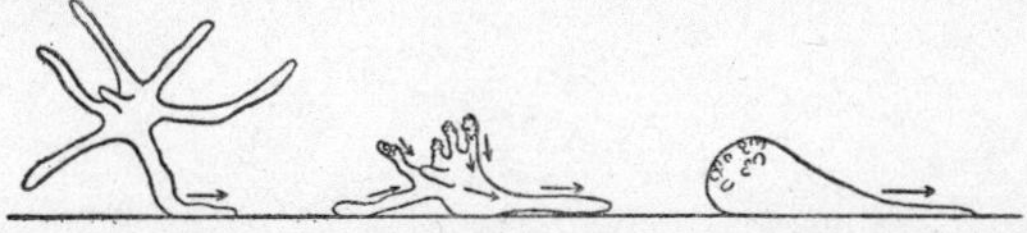

Figure 44. Forms of the body in Amœba as it comes into contact with a solid surface and moves along it. (After Jennings.)

Protista are organisms on a higher level of complexity than the bacteria, but the behaviour of the simplest Protista is not more complex than that of bacteria. The simplest and smallest flagellates will, like the bacteria, collect in favourable regions of their environment and move away from unfavourable regions. They show no other types of response. They have in fact only a single response for stimuli of all kinds. We shall consider the nature of their response later.

In many of the more complex Protista we find that the organism is able to respond in more than one way to stimulation. Some of the larger flagellates (*e.g. Euglena*) can alter the shape of their bodies as well as the beat of their flagella. *Amœba proteus,* when in contact with a solid surface, can react by protruding and retracting lobose pseudopodia, by forming large numbers of small amœbulæ and, in persistently unfavourable conditions, by encystment. When it is floating freely in the medium, it puts out pseudopodia of a shape very different from the broad, lobose pseudopodia which it forms when attached to a surface (Fig. 44). The pseudopodia of a floating

Amœba are long and finger-like, as if the animal were searching for contact. This is another, different method of response. An example of still more complex behaviour in a protistan will be mentioned later (pp. 95–6).

Nevertheless, the most obvious difference between the behaviour of the Protista and that of multicellular animals is the much smaller number of types of response which the former possess. Protista may possess more than one type of response, but they never have many.

Almost always the behaviour of a protistan (or any other organism) leads to results which are of benefit to its life, that is to say the behaviour of the organism is adapted to its needs. Sometimes the reaction leads directly to the beneficial result. The protrusion of a pseudopodium in *Amœba* towards a particle of food is stimulated by water currents set up by movement of the prey, which must be active.

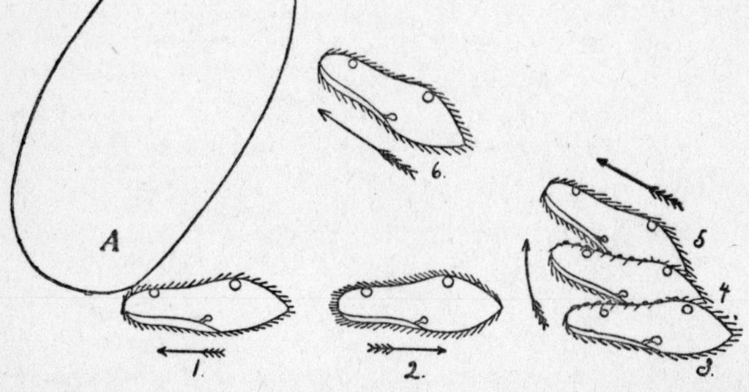

Figure 45. The reaction of *Paramecium* to unfavourable stimulation. The animal is stimulated at 1; 2–6, successive positions. (After Jennings.)

Amœba dubia has been shown to react to inanimate objects if these are artificially moved so as to imitate the movements of a living organism,* but not if they are immobile. The reaction results in approach to the food. The result is direct and immediately understandable. But this is not always so in protistan behaviour. A more complex type of behaviour is the normal reaction of *Paramecium* to unfavourable stimulation, which also leads to the beneficial result—in this case removal from the position of stimulation—but much less directly. We will next consider this reaction.

When a *Paramecium* meets unfavourable stimulation in the course of its normal continuous forward movement, it reacts in the manner shown in Fig. 45. The reaction consists of (1) a reversal of the animal's movement, so that for a short time it moves backwards; (2) a turning of the long axis of the body through an angle of about 30°; and (3) resumption of the forward movement in the new direc-

* Schaeffer, *Trans. Tennessee Acad. Sci.*, 1912–13.

tion. The result of the reaction is that the animal passes at a little distance from the position at which it was stimulated. Such a reaction does not necessarily remove the animal from the source of stimulation; it would do so much more efficiently if the body were turned through 180° instead of 30°. But the reaction is repeated as often as the animal is stimulated, *i.e.* until it has moved out of the unfavourable region of the environment. This result is sure to occur eventually.

Animals with this type of behaviour also collect in favourable regions of their environments. In passing out of such a region they are stimulated by coming into contact with the unfavourable conditions outside it, and perform their reaction. Thus, they can enter the favourable region but they cannot leave it.

Behaviour of this type is very common among the Protista. It is known as "*trial-and-error*" *behaviour*, and the reaction is called a "*shock reaction*" (or *phobotaxis* *). It should be noted that stimulation is caused only by a deterioration and not by an improvement of the surrounding conditions. The animal is stimulated, and the response occurs only when it passes into less-favourable regions of the environment.

We must contrast with locomotory behaviour of this type the behaviour of *Amœba* when it puts out a pseudopodium towards a particle of food. The latter type may be called *directive behaviour* (or *topotaxis* *), for it appears that the direction in which the pseudopodium is put out is determined by the direction from which the stimulation comes. Any behaviour in which the direction of the response is determined by some feature of the stimulation is directive.

We have, then, two types of locomotory behaviour in the Protista —directive and trial-and-error behaviour. Both occur among the Protista; we must discuss how widely distributed each of the types is.

Many of the flagellates show trial-and-error behaviour. It is probable that, in many species, the behaviour by which they collect in regions of favourable conditions is of this type. In some of them at any rate it is definitely so. In one flagellate (*Chilomonas*) it has been shown that when the organism is stimulated it responds with a shock reaction in which the body is turned to one side, probably by unequal beat of the flagella towards the two sides of the body. The movement is then continued in the new direction. The response is therefore very similar to that of *Paramecium*, though simpler. As in *Paramecium*, avoidance of unfavourable conditions or collection in favourable conditions is attained by an indefinite number of repetitions of this response.

* The term "taxis" is used for any orienting reaction of an animal. Phobotaxis is derived from the Greek φοβος, fear or flight. Topotaxis is from τοπος, place or position (from which the stimulus comes).

Many flagellates, however, show what seems to be directive behaviour in response to some types of stimulation, especially in responses to incident light. Colonies of *Volvox*, for instance, will move towards the incident light if it is not too strong, and away from it if its strength is above a well-defined maximum. They do this by turning the anterior side of the colony (*i.e.* the side which is always in front in their movement) either towards or away from the light and then proceeding in the new direction. However, it has been shown that the turning of the colony to or from the light is due to changes in the direction of the beat of the flagella of the separate members of the colony. These changes are in reality the result of shock reactions produced in each member of the colony by illumination from a side. The altered beat of the flagella results in turning the colony so that its anterior side is again directed towards the light. Here the apparently directive behaviour is the product of a large number of shock reactions.

Comparatively few types of response have been studied accurately—very few with the exactness with which the behaviour of *Volvox* has been studied. It may be that most responses which appear to be directive, when the movements of the organisms are first observed, will prove to be trial-and-error behaviour when the responses of the individual organisms are examined carefully. This seems the more probable since directive behaviour implies appreciation of the direction from which the stimulus comes, and therefore requires a better developed receptor system than trial-and-error behaviour.

Nevertheless, there are some examples of what may be true directive behaviour among the Protista, besides that of *Amœba* mentioned above. *Paramecium* and some other ciliates are said occasionally to show directive behaviour, in place of their normal trial-and-error behaviour. *Euglena* and some other flagellates are also said to show both trial-and-error and directive behaviour in their responses to light. The usual behaviour of *Euglena* has been clearly shown to be due to shock reactions.

With the continuous activities of the organisms, these two types of response make up the whole of the locomotory behaviour of the Protista. In one respect at least the two types are similar. It is clear in both types of behaviour that the nature of the response is determined by the features of the organism's reflex system and not by the nature of the stimulus. In all shock reactions the stimulus is no more than the trigger which sets off the response. And this is equally so in directive behaviour such as the protrusion of a pseudopodium in Amœba.

Since many of the Protista show several distinct types of response, we may next enquire what are the conditions that determine the type of response which shall follow a given stimulus. It is to be expected that the nature of the stimulus will often decide the type of the response. This is so. *Paramecium* discharges its trichocysts in response to several types of especially harmful stimulation (chemical stimulation, pressure, etc.). Less harmful stimulation leads to the shock reaction. Often, however, the behaviour of Protista may change while the stimulation is kept constant. The change in behaviour can then only be due to physiological changes within the body of the organism. This aspect of protistan behaviour is well illustrated by the behaviour of the ciliate *Stentor rœselii.* The behaviour of this protistan will also give us an example of non-locomotory behaviour in the Protista.

Stentor rœselii (Fig. 46) is, when expanded, a trumpet-shaped animal, sessile within a tube of mucus, which it forms for itself. It possesses myonemes, arranged longitudinally along the surface of the trumpet from its base to its distal end. By these myonemes it can contract inside its tube into an ovoid shape. Also, the whole protoplasm is contractile, but its contractions are much slower than those of the myonemes. The animal possesses a mouth near the edge of the disc at the distal end of the trumpet, and the disc is surrounded by a ring of cilia, which beat continuously while the animal is expanded and draw a current of water over the animal. Particles in this current are passed into the mouth. The current is therefore primarily a feeding current.

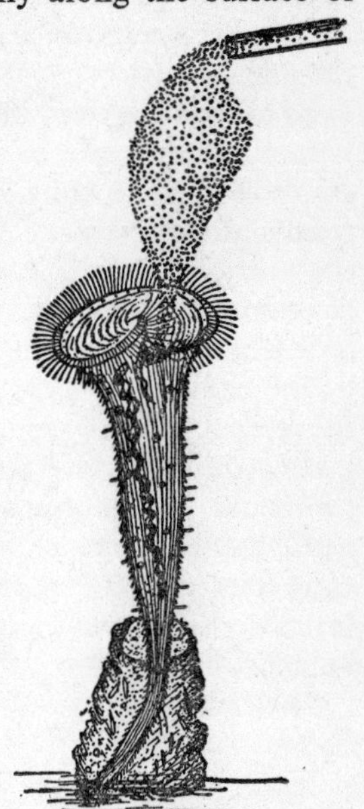

Figure 46. *Stentor rœselii,* stimulated by introduction of particles into its feeding current. (After Jennings.)

The animal can be stimulated by introducing particles of some non-toxic substance, such as carmine or Indian ink into the feeding current in front of the disc. If the stimulation is not strong, there is for some time no response. After a time, however, the animal will respond by bending the body slowly to one side. This is a response of the general protoplasm and is not due to contraction of the myonemes. If the stream of particles is small, this first response may result in the animal being no longer stimulated, but continued stimulation leads to the body being bent several times in different directions. If this is still unsuccessful in avoiding the stimulation, the type of the response suddenly alters. The cilia at the disc stop and possibly reverse their beat for a very short time, so that particles near them or on the disc are thrown away. This again is repeated several times and is then replaced by a third response, a sudden and rapid contraction into the tube, produced by contraction of the myonemes. After about half a minute the animal re-expands. Further stimulation results in repetition of the contraction into the tube. Finally, after one of these reactions, the animal contracts violently two or three times within the tube, the attachment of its base is broken by these violent contractions, and it swims away and forms a new tube in another position.

Thus, in the behaviour of this protistan we find a preliminary period during which there is no response, and, after this, four distinct types of response. Each of these types of response is entirely different from the others, but the character of each of them bears no obvious relation to the nature of the stimulus, and is clearly determined by the animal's responsive system. The stimulus is maintained constant throughout the behaviour, so that the changes to which the alterations of the behaviour are due must be changes within the body of the animal. They must be produced within the body either as direct results of the accumulation of the stimulation, or as secondary results of the responses to the stimulation. We do not know which of these alternatives is true. Such a series of responses bears great resemblance to the chain reflexes which form an important element in the behaviour of multicellular animals (ch. XXI).

The behaviour of *Stentor rœselii* illustrates another point. When the animal is first stimulated there is for some time no response. Later, though the stimulation continues unaltered, the animal responds. Thus a stimulus may be summative. If it is too slight to cause immediate response, its effect may be summed up so long as it continues, and the animal will respond after a time. We shall find this also to be characteristic of the reactions of the multicellular animals.

This account has not covered the whole of the behaviour of *Stentor rœselii*. For instance, when swimming freely, it reacts with a shock reaction very like that of *Paramecium*. Its behaviour is exceptionally complex for a protistan, but we have no reason to think that it is otherwise exceptional. We do not know of so long a chain of responses in other Protista, but there is no doubt that the reactions of many species alter with change of their condition. The response in other Protista is partly determined, as it is in *Stentor rœselii*, by internal conditions in the animal.

So far we have considered only the observed facts of protistan behaviour. We have not considered how the response is organised in the body of the organism, except that it has been said that the nature of the response is determined by the characters of the animal's responsive system and not by the nature of the stimulation. Before we leave the subject, one theory of the organisation of the response must be considered. This is Loeb's "local action theory of tropisms." *

According to this theory a directive response of an organism is due to direct action of the stimuli on the receptor organs in the various parts of the body. These each respond in proportion to the strength of the stimulus which reaches them and pass on the stimulation in the same varying strengths to effector organs with which they are each in communication. The total response of the organism is the sum of the various responses of the effector organs. It is thus supposed to be made up of separate responses of the parts of the body, and not to be a unitary response of the body as a whole. Sometimes the response is supposed to be due to direct effect of the stimulus on the effector organ, which is itself supposed to act as a receptor organ.

A directive response of a ciliate would on this theory be due to greater activity of the cilia on one side of the body and less activity on the other side, these differences of activity being due to differences in the stimuli which reached the two sides. In the case of a light stimulus the differences of stimulation would be caused by shading of one side by the protoplasm of the body. The alterations in the activity of the cilia on the two sides would result in the body being turned until the cilia on both sides were equally stimulated, which would normally be when the body was directed either towards or away from the light. Similarly, a directive response of a flagellate with two flagella would be due to unequal stimulation of the flagella.

A response so built up of responses of symmetrical parts of the body is called by Loeb a "*forced movement*" or "*tropism.*"

Such a theory is clearly inapplicable to any but directive response, and we have seen that most of the locomotory behaviour of the Protista is not directive. Also, when the organ receiving the stimulus is single, it can only apply if we assume that different parts of this organ are differently stimulated. It has been shown, for instance, that the single eye-spot in the flagellates is sensitive to light and it is difficult to believe that it is not the receptor organ for this stimulus. It is very unlikely that its different parts are stimulated differently, though this certainly occurs in multicellular organs such as the eyes of the higher animals. But unless parts of the eye-spot are differently

* This theory has been stated in many different forms. The theory is here given in Loeb's original form. Essentially similar views were put forward by other biologists before Loeb, but in recent times he has been the chief proponent of these views.

stimulated, the reactions of flagellates to light cannot be tropistic, even when they are directive. Again, the theory does not apply to the protrusion of the pseudopodium of an *Amœba* towards food, or the bending of those of *Actinosphærium*, for, though these are reactions of parts of the body, the whole animal is not necessarily oriented by these movements. A tropism as it is defined on this theory is a response of the whole organism.

The theory was first proposed for the behaviour of bilaterally symmetrical multicellular animals, to which it is much more easily applied. It is clear that it is not true of by far the greater part of the behaviour of the Protista. Those examples of protistan behaviour which have been most carefully studied have almost all been found to be single responses of the whole organism and not tropisms. Colonial behaviour, such as that of *Volvox*, is certainly built up of the separate actions of the cells forming the colony, but the behaviour of each of the separate cells is not tropistic.

There are, however, some examples of protistan behaviour which are at least compatible with the tropistic theory. An *Amœba* has been described as following another *Amœba* for considerable distances and finally catching it and feeding upon it. This may readily be tropistic behaviour, caused by differential stimulation of parts of the surface of the *Amœba* by stimuli emanating from the organism being chased. Directive behaviour in ciliates, if it occurs, may possibly be tropistic, though it is hard to believe that this is so in animals such as *Paramecium* which revolve rapidly on their long axis as they move. The differential stimulation of the cilia which, on the tropistic theory, should be responsible for the turning response of the animal, must be reversed in such animals at very short intervals.

The behaviour of the Protista which is most clearly tropistic is their response to the stimulus of an electric current passing through the medium. If a *Paramecium* is lying across the direction of a current when it is first turned on, it turns until its long axis is in line with the direction of the current, and its head towards the cathode. It then moves forward towards the cathode or backwards towards the anode according as the current is weak or strong. The turning into line with the current can be clearly shown to be due to different effects produced by the current on the cilia on the two sides of the body, and is in fact tropistic. But the electrical stimulus is entirely artificial, and it is by no means clear that the behaviour it calls forth is of the same kind as any type of the natural behaviour of the organisms. For this reason we need not discuss responses to electrical stimuli further here.

Summarising the preceding account of protistan behaviour, we may state the following conclusions:

1. The most striking character of the behaviour is the small number of types of response which a protistan can carry out.

2. Locomotory behaviour may be either "trial-and-error" or directive. Both types occur, but trial-and-error behaviour is more common and many types of apparently directive behaviour are probably due to unrecognised shock reactions.

3. The behaviour almost always consists of reactions of the organism's whole responsive system; the tropistic theory is applicable to at most a very small part of protistan behaviour. The stimulus sets in motion the animal's own responsive system, and the nature of the response is determined for each species by the characters of this system.

4. When a protistan has more than one type of response, the type which follows any given stimulus is determined in some cases by the nature of the stimulus and in others by the physiological condition of the animal.

5. In at least one protistan, *Stentor rœselii*, several different types of response follow each other during continuous, constant stimulation. The change from one type of response to another is here due to physiological changes within the organism.

6. Stimuli which are too weak to produce immediate response may be summated to produce one later.

III. THE ECOLOGY OF THE PROTISTA

The problems with which ecology deals are extremely complex. This is as true of the ecology of the Protista as of that of any other group of organisms. Each species differs from all other species in the environmental conditions which are necessary for its life, in its food requirements, and in the enemies which it has to defend itself against or to avoid. In every environment the conditions which are important for the life of the fauna and flora are very numerous and of many of them we know very little; and almost every environment, even if it is small and self-contained, contains numerous species of animals and plants which interact upon each in very many different ways.

Also, our knowledge of ecology is very imperfect. Naturalists have observed the behaviour of animals for a long time, but ecology in its modern sense, the attempt to interpret the life of organisms in terms of the conditions of their physical and biological environments, is a young science, and one in which progress has not up to the present gone very far.

For these reasons, it should not be surprising that in most ecological work we are forced to study each environment and the species of its fauna and flora separately, and to leave the framing of general ecological conclusions to a later stage in the development of the science. Ecology is, in fact, still mainly in the descriptive stage of its development. Therefore, since we are not interested in the details of the ecology of particular species of Protista, we will confine the discussion of this section to a few general remarks about their distribution and the environmental factors which seem to be of greatest importance in controlling it.

The distribution of the protista is very wide. Many genera and even species of Protista are found all over the world. Protista occur wherever there is a watery medium for them to inhabit. The presence of water is almost the only condition which limits the distribution of the group as a whole; the other conditions of natural environments are rarely outside the possible range for protistan life. Protista are found in the sea, both at the surface and at great depths, in brackish and fresh waters, in soils, and in the internal liquids and the protoplasm of other organisms, both animals and plants. In temperature their range extends from the waters of lakes which are frozen for the greater part of the year and in which the temperature never rises above the freezing-point by more than a few degrees, to the waters of hot springs, up to a temperature of 65° C. for holozoic forms and still higher for holophytic forms. Some blue-green algæ have, indeed, been found growing in water at 93° C. In general the range of conditions is smaller for holozoic than for holophytic Protista, in spite of the fact that the latter need light. Holozoic forms demand the presence of organic food in their environment, whereas the holophytic forms feed on inorganic compounds and are often able to live where the concentrations of their food-substances are extremely low.

A watery medium is necessary for active protistan life, but it is not necessary for them during inactive stages of their life-history. Encystment occurs very generally in the life-histories of free-living Protista; the species which live in fresh waters are almost all able to encyst. And protistan cysts are in general able to withstand any desiccation which is likely to occur in nature. The encysted condition is also a very general means of distribution. Cysts are readily carried about in the air; it has been found that an average sample of air contains between two and three protistan cysts per cubic metre. But, in spite of the large number of air-borne protistan cysts, it is improbable that many species are distributed in this way. Protistan cysts adhere readily to solid objects—they are always to be found, for instance, on dried grass—and the cysts of most species are probably more often carried about with the object to which they are attached.

From the point of view of their ecology, Protista may be classified in many different ways. The general features of their habitat give obviously appropriate classifications. They may be divided into marine, brackish, and freshwater forms, pond and lake forms, etc. Those forms which require the presence of calcium in their environment may be separated from those which do not and are therefore found in the waters of volcanic rather than limestone regions. Again, katharobic Protista are those which live in the clean waters of springs and streams, and oligo-, meso-, and polysaprobic forms demand in this order increasing concentrations of the organic products of bacterial decay in their environment, though they may be holozoic. Many other characteristics of the environment may be used for ecological classification of protistan floras and faunas.

In many environments the conditions change with time either rhythmically or in a single continuous sequence. The change of conditions may be determined either outside the environment, as in the seasonal changes of many natural environments, or by changes in the conditions within the environment itself. A good example of an environment which shows a single sequence of changes is a hay-culture. This is also as simple an environment as can be found. It will serve to illustrate some of the main features of protistan ecology.

The culture is formed by simply placing hay or dried grass in water. The first stage in the development of such a culture is decay of the hay by bacterial action. In the course of this decay many organic substances are released into the medium. Soon Protista appear, derived from cysts present on the hay. They succeed each other in a regular sequence. The more saprobic forms appear first, for the organic products of bacterial decay are then plentiful. These are mainly flagellates (*Monas*, *Oicomonas*, *Bodo*). They are followed by the less saprobic forms (ciliates such as *Colpidium*, *Stylonychia*, *Paramecium*, and rhizopods such as *Amœba*). During the development of the culture many other conditions are altering besides the concentration of the products of decay. Many conditions of the physical environment are changing, and with the succession of organisms the biological environment of each species alters. The appearance of many species in large numbers is largely controlled by the biological environment, especially by the presence in the culture of suitable food. Thus, we find that most of the Protista which appear early are saprophytic, feeding on the dissolved products of the decay. The later species are almost all holozoic, feeding on the species which have appeared earlier, the ciliates mainly on bacteria, *Amœba* mainly on flagellates and ciliates. The appearance of each species of holozoic organism is determined by the presence of the particular organisms which are its chief food.

This simple environment illustrates two general principles of ecology:

1. If any organism is to live and increase rapidly in an environment

both the physical and the biological conditions must be suitable. The holozoic organism is dependent on the presence of other organisms in the environment, and the saprophytic organism on the products of the activities of other organisms. Only the holophytic organism can ever be independent of its biological environment, and the occurrence of holophytic organisms is often controlled by changes in the physical conditions of the environment brought about by the activities of other organisms.

2. Even in so simple an environment as the hay culture, we find the organisms forming sequences in which each organism feeds on the earlier members of the sequence and is itself the food of later members. Such a sequence is called a *food-chain*, and such food-chains are characteristic of the fauna and floras of all natural environments. The earliest members of a food-chain must be either bacteria or plants, for they alone are able to live independently of other organisms; the later members of the chain are usually the larger and more complex holozoic organisms. In many environments the food-chains are very complex. Several organisms may form a single chain, and a single organism may take part in several chains, itself feeding on several organisms and being the food of several others.

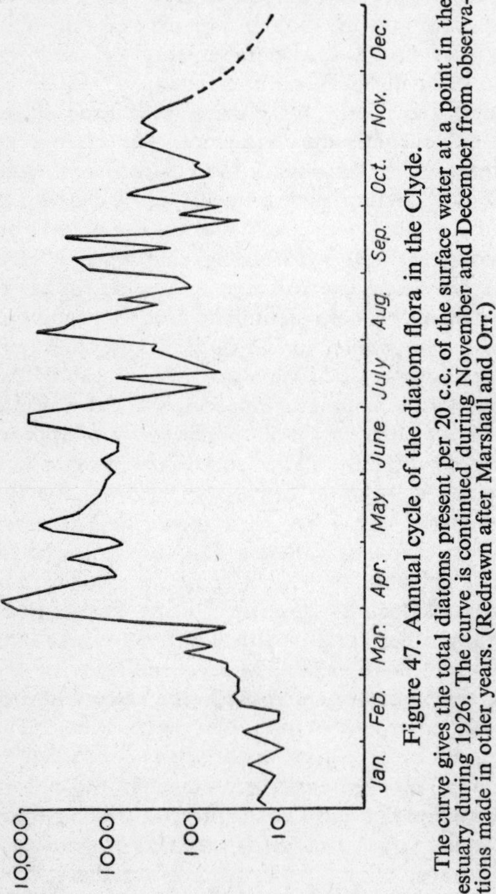

Figure 47. Annual cycle of the diatom flora in the Clyde.

The curve gives the total diatoms present per 20 c.c. of the surface water at a point in the estuary during 1926. The curve is continued during November and December from observations made in other years. (Redrawn after Marshall and Orr.)

A complete investigation of even so simple an environment as a hay culture is impossible. The physical conditions are too numerous and the interactions of the flora and fauna too complex. It is clearly still less possible to investigate larger environments completely. But in all environments something can be done towards working out the interactions of the organisms and the effects of some of the physical conditions on their life. Ecological investigations have these objects.

A very common difficulty in such investigations is the extreme sensitivity of the organisms. Their life is frequently controlled by changes in the physical conditions which are only just above—and probably often below—the limits of our present methods of measurement. This has been very evident in investigation of the ecology of the sea. The curves of Fig. 47 show the abundance of the total flora of diatoms in the surface waters of the Clyde at different times of the year. It will be seen that the diatom flora is most abundant during the spring and summer months, especially the earlier months of the spring, but that it shows very large variations during these months. It has been shown that the abundance of the diatoms is controlled to some extent by the amount of inorganic food material in the environment, and especially of phosphates and nitrates. But the amount of these substances in the water at any time is very small. During the summer months, in the surface waters of the Clyde, the phosphate content varies between 0 and 60 mg. per cubic metre (*i.e.* 0–60 parts per 10^9), and the nitrate content is only slightly greater. These concentrations are only just measurable.

Freshwater Protista are as sensitive as marine Protista to minute changes in their environment; and the freshwater environment is as complex and far more variable than the marine. Freshwater ecology is therefore at least as difficult a subject as marine ecology. We have less knowledge of it because far less work has been done on the fresh waters. But it seems that the same general principles control the distribution of organisms in both types of environment. In both the occurrence of the organisms is controlled partly by the physical conditions and partly by the occurrence of other organisms.

We have not space to discuss here the many special environments of the Protista. One of these, the parasitic environment, will be discussed in relation to invertebrate animals in general in ch. XXII.

PART II

THE MULTICELLULAR BODY

CHAPTER VI

THE MULTICELLULAR ORGANISATION OF THE BODY

In considering the Protista, we saw (pp. 46 ff.) that complexity of structure enables some of them to reach a much larger size than the simpler members of the group, and still to remain active. It was mentioned that the largest active protistan has a diameter of about 3 mm. (*Bursaria*), but that sluggish Protista may reach a diameter of an inch (*Nummulina*).

There are some animal cells of greater size than any free-living protistan. Nerve-cells, for instance, may reach a length of several feet in the largest vertebrates; and the eggs of birds, which are single cells until they start their development, may be very large. Fossil birds' eggs are known with a capacity of two gallons (Æpyornithidæ). These cells owe their ability to live at such large sizes to one of two reasons. Either, as in the nerve-cell, their shape is very different from the round or ovoid shape of the typical animal cell, and for this reason the proportion between the surface of the cell and the volume of its protoplasm remains large (p. 48); or all except a small part of the volume is filled with inactive food material, as in the egg of the bird.

The free-living cell cannot afford to adopt either of these means to make life at a large size possible. For efficient free-living life it must remain active, and a cell largely filled with inactive food material is not capable of active free life. Also, the conditions of free-living life make bizarre shapes, such as that of the nerve-cell, impossible. Complexity of structure has allowed some increase in the size of the active, free-living cell, but it seems that there are very definite limits to the size which can be attained by these means. Protistan cells have not been able to exceed these limits.

If, then, in the course of evolution, the size of the organism was to increase beyond the limit of size for the free-living cell—and we have noted (p. 49) the general tendency for increase in size in evolution, a tendency which can only mean that increase of size is very often of value to the organism, so long as the efficiency of its life can be maintained—some other means had to be found to allow efficient life to go on at a larger size. In the evolution of both plants and animals, this problem was solved by the development of a multicellular body. The living substance of the body became divided into small masses, the cells, each within its own enclosure, the cell-wall. These cells of the multicellular body have each essentially the same organisation as the free-living cells of the Protista. On the average, they have a diameter of about 10μ, a size which is equal to that of many of the simpler Protista. Each cell, with this organisation and size, is able to carry on its essential metabolism efficiently within its own protoplasm, and the multicellular body can increase in size far beyond the maximum size of the free-living cell by increase of the number of cells within it.

If the only conditions controlling size in the multicellular body were those which we have so far discussed, there would be no obvious upper limit to the possible size of the multicellular body. But this is not so. As size increases, other controlling conditions come into play, such as the need for efficient transference of food and other substances about the body, for efficient co-ordination, support, and so on. These needs become less easily satisfied as the body gets larger, and although increased complexity of organisation has, during evolution, greatly increased the maximum size of the multicellular body, there must always be a limit to the size which it can reach.

Reduction of size raises almost equally difficult problems in the efficient working of the multicellular body. The body cannot become indefinitely small.

The control of size in the multicellular body will be discussed further in a later chapter (ch. XII). Here we need only note that the evolution of multicellular organisation was the greatest step in the evolution of animals towards attainment of greater size. It was very probably the drive towards a greater body-size that led to the evolution of this type of organisation. This is true in spite of the fact that not all multicellular animals have evolved in the direction of large size (p. 46).

The multicellular body is composed of many cells, but it is more than a mere agglomeration of cells. The animal has a unique organisation which extends over the whole body and shows itself most clearly in the single, unique specific form. It is in fact an organism (p. 3). We shall discuss the nature of this unique organisation of the multicellular body in the following chapters. But, it must be emphasised here that this organisation makes of the multicellular body something more than an agglomeration of separate cells bound together by non-living matter between them.

Even from the morphological point of view the multicellular body is not a simple agglomeration of cells. In the body the cells are all in communication with each other through the internal liquids of the body—blood and lymph in the more complex animals and less well-defined liquids in the simpler animals. These liquids form an internal environment for the body (ch. XII). Through them part of the co-ordination of the body is carried out. In addition to this, very many of the cells in the multicellular body are in direct protoplasmic connection with the cells near them. Some tissues are even syncytial, *i.e.* with no cell walls separating the protoplasm controlled by each of the nuclei. Some epithelia and the striped muscle fibres of the vertebrate are syncytial. In other tissues the cells are connected with each other by narrow protoplasmic bridges which pass across the inter-

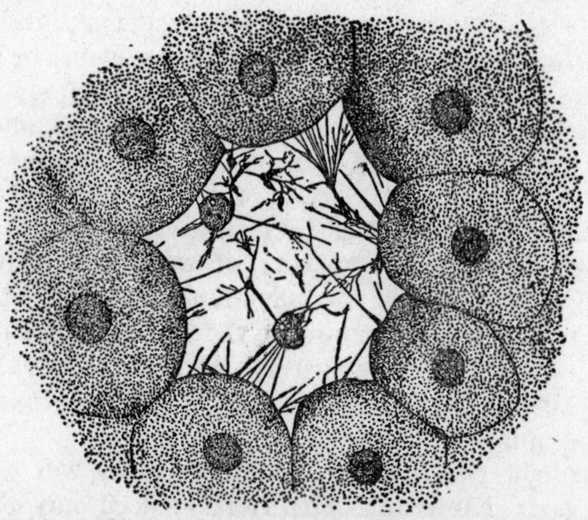

Figure 48. Protoplasmic bridges between the blastomeres of a blastula of the starfish, *Asterias*. (After Andrews.)

cellular spaces. These bridges can be most easily seen between the blastomeres of very young embryos (Fig. 48), but they are present throughout life in many tissues. They cannot be recognised in all tissues, however, and it is probable that they are not present in all. They are most clearly absent where the cells are surrounded by thick layers of secreted material, as they are in some supporting tissues, such as cartilage, but even in these tissues the secretions are laid down round protoplasmic bridges or networks between the cells, which later break down.

Then, again, the organisation of the body may be to some extent independent of the size of the cells that compose it. In polyploid larvæ of the Amphibia (in which the cells contain a higher multiple of the haploid number of chromosomes than 2), the cells are larger than normal, but the size of the body and its organisation may be nearly normal.

It is even true that organisation may occur in complete absence of cell division. This is well shown in larvæ treated with KCl. In these larvæ the egg nucleus does not divide and no cell walls are formed, but differentiation of some of the organs of the normal larva occurs in the undivided protoplasm. Such larvæ have been observed in a marine annelid, *Chætopterus* (Fig. 49). They became arranged as a body very like a blastula and covered with cilia. They could swim by the beat of the cilia. Even the distinction between ectoderm and endoderm appeared, Fig. 49*b*. Not all the differentiations of the normal trochophore appeared in them, but they had some differentiation and this is enough to show that organisation is possible in an undivided body.

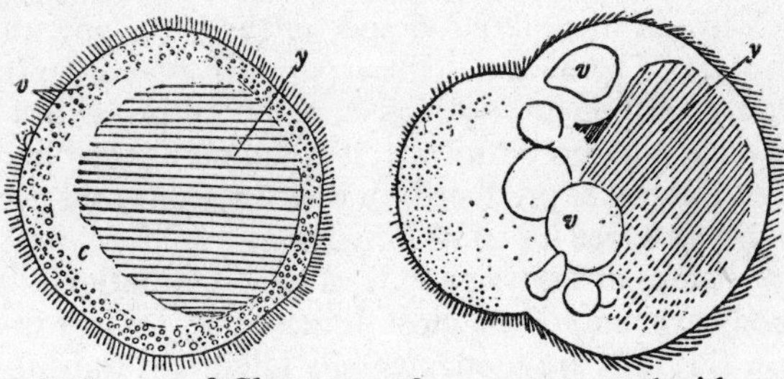

Figures 49. Larvæ of *Chætopterus* from eggs treated with potassium chloride.
***v*, vacuoles; *c*, cavity; *y*, undivided yolk. (After Lillie.)**

Facts such as these indicate that it is much more justifiable to look upon the multicellular body, so far as its functioning as a living organism is concerned, as a single mass of protoplasm divided by internal partitions into smaller masses, which we call the cells, rather than as an agglomeration of separate and independent cells. This view is also in much better agreement with the character of the multicellular animal as a single, independently living organism, with an indivisible specific form. But, as we shall see (p. 111), this does not necessarily exclude the possibility that the multicellular body was evolved from a colony of protistan cells. We must distinguish the physiological and evolutionary views of multicellular organisation.

In the sponges (Parazoa), the character of the body as a single mass of protoplasm is less clear than in other multicellular animals. The sponges probably had an evolutionary origin entirely distinct from that of the rest of the multicellular animals (Metazoa), and we shall consider them separately later (ch. XIX).

It may be thought that the behaviour of the cells of the multicellular body in tissue cultures makes such an interpretation of the body impossible. In tissue cultures the cells separate and, although it is possible that they may still be connected by protoplasmic bridges between them, they seem to live and behave as separate organisms. But this is no real objection to the view of the multicellular body that has been put forward here. These facts merely imply that the cells, when they have been separated from the body, are capable of independent life as organisms. They are good evidence that the cells retain the potentiality of the complete metabolism which is necessary for independent life, but they do not show that, while they are still in the body, they are independent cells rather than parts of the whole protoplasm of the body.

It is true that there are some cells in the multicellular body to which it is not easy to apply the interpretation of the multicellular organisation which has been suggested. This is especially true of the cells which live in the internal liquids of the body, and above all of the amœbocytes. These seem to live separate lives as organisms within the body, and, although they lack some of the properties of organisms—they do not reproduce in most animals—they may best be regarded as free cells, produced by division from other cells of the body, but living a free life in its liquids.

These questions of the real nature of the organisation of the multicellular body are among the most difficult that we find in the study of animals. But they are fundamentally important to us if we are to attempt to understand the life of the multicellular animal. This at least can be said. The multicellular animal is as much an indivisible organism as a protistan, and its body shows the unity of its organisation in many characters but especially in its unique specific form. It is easier to realise the possibility of this unique organisation in the body if we think of it as a single mass of protoplasm rather than as an agglomeration of cells. And, as we have seen, the facts of the structure of the multicellular body favour the first of these possibilities rather than the second.

Although the structure and behaviour of the multicellular body forces us to this view of its organisation, it is still true that it is often very difficult to distinguish the single animal organism from colonies, which are formed by agglomeration either of free-living cells or of multicellular bodies, and which, therefore, one would think, cannot have the unique organisation which the multicellular body possesses. In the simpler colonial forms there is not much difficulty in distinguishing the colony from a single organism. The individuals of the colony are often all alike and capable of independent life if they are separated from the colony. If we separate a *Tubularia* polyp from the colony it will live indefinitely, reproduce and in all ways behave as an organism. Later it may form a new colony by asexual reproduction.

But if the members of the colony become differentiated, the distinction is much less easy and sometimes impossible to direct observation.

Among the Protista, the series of colonial forms in the group to which *Volvox* belongs give us a good example of increasing organisation in the colony. In *Pandorina* and *Eudorina* the colony is a simple group of cells, but in *Volvox* it has become much more organised. The colony of *Volvox*, in fact, possesses, as a whole, many of the properties of an organism. It has definite form with distinct anterior and posterior parts, it reproduces as a colony, and to some extent it behaves as a single whole (p. 94). There is also some differentiation between its parts; the sexual cells, for instance, are formed at the side of the colony which is posterior as it moves.

The organisation of colonies of multicellular organisms is sometimes carried even further than this. Anyone who saw a siphonophoran colony, such as *Vellela* or *Physalia*, for the first time would regard it as a single multicellular organism. The parts of these colonies are greatly differentiated and the colony behaves as a single unit. It is certain that some at least of the polyps could not live an independent life after separation from the colony. Many of them have lost some of the organs essential to free life; some, for instance, are without mouths. It is only our knowledge of the comparative morphology of the cœlenterates that shows us that these are colonies, formed of numerous polyps, each of which should, by analogy with other cœlenterates, be an independent organism.

It seems that we must admit that there is a general tendency for colonies of organisms to take on the characters which we find in single organisms. This may be called a tendency to individuation in the colony. We need not here discuss whether the individuation in the forms we know to have arisen as colonies ever becomes complete—whether, for instance, we should regard the siphonophoran as an individual organism or as still a colony. But there can be no doubt that this tendency towards individuation is a general feature of animal colonies.

The existence of this tendency towards individuation in animal colonies makes it seem probable that the multicellular body was evolved from a protistan colony in which the individuation became complete, so that the colony became an organism. It is not always admitted that the multicellular animal was evolved from free-living cells at all similar to our modern Protista, but, even if we assume that it did arise from some such form, there are two ways in which the evolution might have occurred. These are:

(1) By the individuation of a protistan colony. There is a

considerable amount of evidence which seems to favour this.

Some protistan colonies resemble the multicellular body much more closely than the colony of Volvox does. Most of the dinoflagellates are typical, free-living protistan organisms, but one group, the Catenata, contains some forms which are colonial. In *Haplozoon* each cell buds off numerous cells which remain attached to the mother cell. These cells in some species form a chain; in other species they form an elongated mass several cells thick (Fig. 50), which is not much less organised than the bodies of some of the simplest multicellular animals (*e.g.* some of the Mesozoa, Fig. 50). There is even differentiation in a *Haplozoon* colony between the original cell and the cells which are budded off from it. After a time, however, the cells of the *Haplozoon* colony break free and live independent lives.

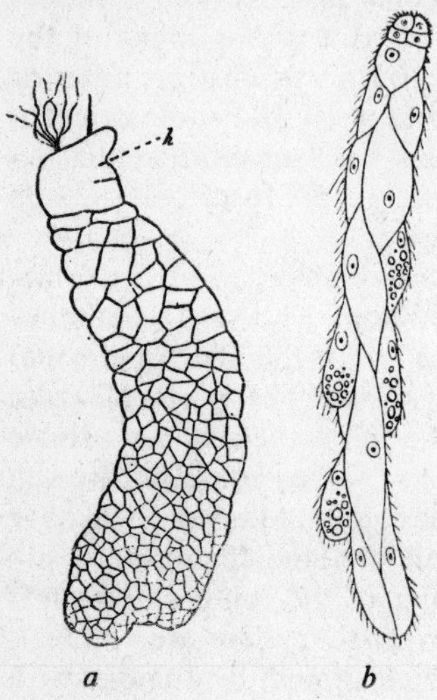

Figure 50. (*a*) *Haplozoon macrostylum*; *h*, original cell. (After Huxley.) (*b*) *Dicyema typus*, a mesozoan. (After Benham.)

The ease with which the tissues of the multicellular body can break down into separate cells in tissue cultures and also under experimental conditions in the laboratory (p. 153), and the ability of the cells to live independent lives when so separated, may perhaps be considered evidence for the colonial origin of the body. The bodies of sponges can be broken up very easily into separate cells, and the same is true, to a somewhat less extent, of hydroid polyps. Since it is probable that sponges and other multicellular animals arose separately from free-living cells, the sponge body may have had a colonial origin whether the bodies of other multicellular animals arose in this way or not. But it is clear that a colonial origin is by no means impossible for all multicellular bodies.

(2) The second manner in which the multicellular body may have arisen supposes no colonial stage intermediate between it and the free-living cell.* Protistan cells with many nuclei are common. These are not multicellular bodies because their protoplasm is not divided into differentiated parts each under the control of one of the nuclei (p. 45). But if, in such a protistan cell, the protoplasm became divided and its parts differentiated, we should have a body which

* *Cf.* Dobell, *Arch. Protistenk.*, **23**, 269, 1911.

would be indistinguishable in the type of its organisation from the multicellular body of the higher animals. In one group of the Protista this does actually occur. In the Cnidosporidia the organism at certain stages of its life-history forms within itself complicated reproductive bodies called spores (Fig. 51). Each of these consists of a layer of protoplasm on the outer surface under the control of two or three nuclei and forming a case, one or more nematocyst-like pole-capsules each with a nucleus, and a mass of protoplasm with one or more germ nuclei. All these parts are differentiated from each other in structure. The spore is set free and acts as an organism.

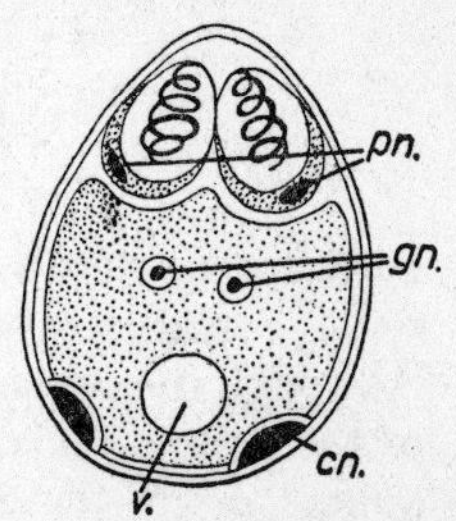

Figure 51. Cnidosporidian spore.
v, vacuole; *cn*, nucleus of case; *gn*, germ nuclei; *pn*, nuclei of pole capsules. (After Borradaile.)

There is no real difference between the organisation of this spore and that of the multicellular body. It is true that the spore is formed only at one stage of the life-history of an organism which, for most of its life-history, is a typical, one-celled protistan. But this is unimportant from our present point of view. We have in this spore multicellular organisation among the Protista.

In the cnidosporidian spore we have a very clear illustration of the second manner in which the multicellular body may have been evolved. It is possible that the multicellular body was formed by internal division and differentiation in the body of a single protistan. The cnidosporidia are an extremely specialised group of parasitic Protista, and there is clearly no possibility that such a group could have given rise to the multicellular animals. This is not suggested. If the multicellular body arose in this way, the cnidosporidian spore and the multicellular body would be examples of parallel evolution.

This method of origin of the multicellular body postulates no complete individuation of a body which was originally colonial and not that of a single organism. But, as we have seen, we have evidence that a tendency to individuation does occur in colonial animals. This is therefore not a sufficient reason for rejecting the colonial theory. The ease with which the multicellular body breaks down into its constituent cells and the fact that a tendency to individuation does occur in animal colonies makes the colonial origin probably on the whole the more likely of these two paths of evolution. The uncentralised arrangement of the nervous system in the simplest multicellular animals—the nerve net (p. 244)—may be thought another argument in favour of the colonial origin. But the alternative origin, by internal division of a single cell, can certainly not be excluded at present.

CHAPTER VII

MAINTENANCE OF FORM IN THE MULTICELLULAR BODY

In this chapter we shall discuss the conditions which are necessary for the maintenance of specific form in the multicellular body. Although the constancy of the specific form is a very striking feature of the animal body, this constancy is not complete. In multicellular animals as in the Protista (p. 88), the specific form varies to some extent among the individuals of a species. We are not here concerned with the changes of form which occur during the life-history of each individual, for the specific form should rather be defined as the whole series of forms which make up the life-history than as the form at any one stage of the life-history. It should, however, be noted that these changes extend through the whole life-history and not merely through the period of development. The body of the old animal differs in form from that of the young adult and from that of the animal in the prime of its life. If we are to compare the specific form of individuals of the same species, we must compare them all at the same period of the life-history.

Even when we do this, we find in every species variations in the specific form of the individuals. One is taller or shorter than another, the colour varies and the forms of parts of the body vary. All these are variations in the specific form. In many of these characters the individuals vary continuously about a mean form which is in most circumstances constant for the species, or, if the species is divided into a number of distinct races, for each race. These variations are due partly to variations in the hereditary constitution of the individuals and partly to varying action of the environment upon them during their life-histories. Many other abnormalities of form, which do not vary continuously in this way about the mean form of the species, are also due to the action of the environment. An individual may lose a limb by some accident, or the development of a part may be abnormal owing to some environmental condition.

We shall not be concerned in this chapter with any of these types of variation in the specific form. We shall discuss only two more general questions concerning the specific form of animals. These are: (1) whether the specific form is maintained in all conditions in which the cells and tissues of the body are able to live, and (2) whether the mean form of the species, around which the forms of the individuals vary, can be modified by any changes within the animal's body which are not changes in the hereditary constitution of the animal.

The answer to the first of these questions can be given without hesitation. It is unquestionably true that the cells and tissues of an animal body may continue to live in conditions in which the specific form of the body is entirely lost. Tissue cultures give us one example of this, and cancerous tissues another. In both these conditions the cells live and grow actively but the control of growth which is necessary for the maintenance of the specific form is absent; the growth, in fact, is "uncontrolled." * In tissue cultures the tissues also break down. The cells lose most of their differentiations ("dedifferentiate"), and live and grow separately and individually except in so far as their growth may be influenced by the presence of other cells of the culture in their neighbourhood—the extent of this influence of the cells upon each other is very little known. Uncontrolled growth may continue in tissue cultures for much longer than the life-history of the species. Both in cancerous growths and in tissue cultures the forms of the cells differ from the normal form, and in cancerous growths, at any rate, the metabolism of the cells is abnormal. All these facts show that in both these conditions the cells are in a very different state from their normal state in the body. They are alive and can grow, but their growth is uncontrolled and the specific form is lost.

The alterations which occur in the tissue culture cell are often largely reversible. If the cells are returned to the environment of the body, they will sometimes "redifferentiate" and form structures similar to those from which they were originally derived. Thus, separate dedifferentiated cultures can be made of the intestinal epithelium of the chick and of the mesenchyme cells which occur near or in the epithelium. If, now, cells from both these cultures are placed in the lens cavity of another chick, they will redifferentiate into hollow structures, the walls of which have many of the characters of intestinal epithelium—they are epithelial, and typical gland cells are present. This occurs only if both types of cell are introduced into the lens cavity, but this point is not important from our present point of view. The medium of the lens cavity is part of the internal liquids of the body, and by replacing the cells in this medium we have returned them to an environment very much more like their natural environment than the environment of the culture is. This return is followed by the cells regaining much of their original structure. These facts

* Controlled growth can also be obtained in tissue cultures. Growth of this type is much more like that in the body and the form of organs and tissues is retained. We are not here concerned with this type of growth.

indicate that the abnormal form and growth of the cells of tissue cultures are due to the abnormal environment in the culture. We do not yet know accurately what are the differences between the two environments which cause these differences in the behaviour of the cells.

Cancerous growths and tissue cultures are not the only conditions in which the cells of an animal body may continue to live although the specific form of the body is lost. The whole bodies of some of the less highly organised invertebrates have been found to lose their specific form and dedifferentiate to shapeless masses of cells in unfavourable conditions of many different kinds. Lack of oxygen, the

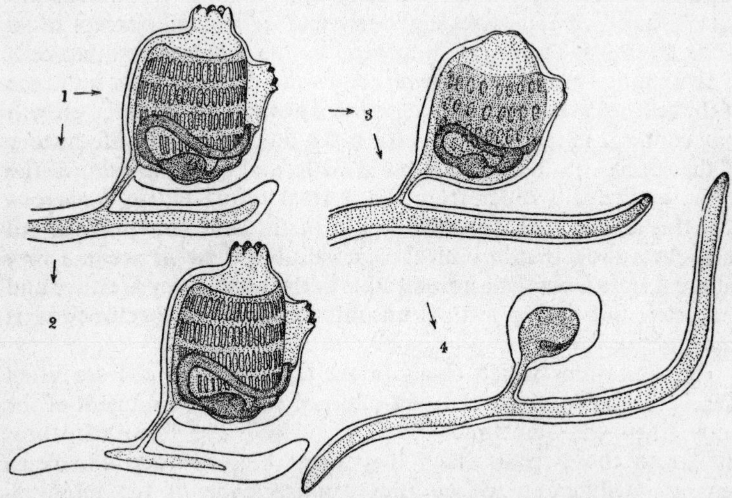

Figure 52. Dedifferentiation in an ascidian, *Perophora*.

1, normal zooid isolated from the colony; 2, maintenance of the zooid in favourable conditions; 3, 4, dedifferentiation and resorption in slightly unfavourable conditions. (After Huxley.)

presence of poisons in high dilution, and too high a concentration of the excretory products of their own metabolism have all been found to produce this result. Sponges, coelenterates, echinoderm larvæ and ascidians (Fig. 52) show this dedifferentiation. Both the general shape of the body and the visible differentiation between the cells of the different tissues are lost. But the cells remain alive and in some animals, especially in colonial forms such as the ascidians, the form can be regained if the environmental conditions again become favourable.

It is therefore clear that more is required for maintenance of the body form than for the life of the cells. Investigation of the nature of the conditions which lead to dedifferentiation has not yet gone far. So far as we know, almost any condition in which the life of the tissues is not healthy may have this result. We cannot say more than that maintenance of the specific form demands that the tissues should be in a normally healthy state.

It should not be surprising that dedifferentiation has been observed only in the simpler animals. In the bodies of the more complex animals, hard secretions of the protoplasm are laid down to form the skeleton. Even though the tissues were to dedifferentiate, these hard parts would prevent complete loss of the body form. Also, as the complexity of its body increases, the animal becomes more and more isolated from the external environment (p. 49). Conditions within the body are determined more closely and are altered less by changes in the environment. Parallel with the increasing isolation goes a tendency for the range of conditions in which the tissues can live to become narrower. The tissues of the more complex animals are not subjected in their normal life to so wide a range of conditions as are those of simpler animals and have lost the power of surviving in a wide range of conditions. When the more complex animals are placed in conditions which would produce dedifferentiation in simpler animals, they, first, offer greater resistance to the changes within the body which are necessary before dedifferentiation can occur, and, secondly, if this resistance is broken down, they die before they dedifferentiate.

It may be noted here that loss of structure in an animal body occurs in many other circumstances besides those which lead to complete dedifferentiation of the specific form. In the normal development of many animals larval organs which have been developed are later lost, and we shall find examples of similar loss of structure in the course of regeneration. This loss of structure in one or more of the organs of the body consists in dedifferentiation of the tissues, followed by reduction of their size and destruction. It may be called *resorption*. It is probably true that resorption and the dedifferentiation of the whole animal body are related processes. In the dedifferentiation of *Perophora* the organs disappear at different rates—the atrium and the pharynx early, and the heart, the epicardium and intestine much later. The disappearance of the organs in turn may be regarded as resorption. Dedifferentiation of the whole body may be thought of as resorption which extends to all the organs of the body as a result of its unhealthy condition, so that the whole specific form is ultimately lost.

In both resorption and the dedifferentiation of a whole body, the structure of the body is lost. In this feature they are distinct from simple *negative growth*, which is merely reduction in the size of the body. Many of the simpler animals, *e.g.* planarians or sea-anemones, may be caused to grow smaller by starvation. Often the animal can be reduced to a size which is a small fraction of its original size. Even insect larvæ, such as those of beetles, which are simple in structure (perhaps secondarily simplified), may grow smaller during starvation. But in such negative growth there is not necessarily loss of the structure of the body. The animal becomes smaller, but it retains all its organs at a smaller size, and its reduced structure is still that normal to the species. Dedifferentiation will set in later if the starvation leads to the body being unable to maintain itself in the healthy state necessary for the maintenance of specific form.

We must therefore distinguish (1) negative growth (reduction in the size of the body); (2) resorption (loss of structure in one or more organs, which may lead to their disappearance); and (3) dedifferentiation of the whole body (complete loss of specific form).

We can now pass to the second of the two questions which were proposed at the beginning of this chapter. We know that the mean specific form can be modified by changes of the hereditary constitution. Can it be altered by changes of other kinds in the conditions within the body or in the environment outside it? We know that the form alters during the life-history. Can the form at each stage of the life-history be modified? We are here concerned with *changes* in the structure of the body, not with the loss of structure which occurs in dedifferentiation. During the life-history changes of form are largely brought about by differential growth (both positive and negative) of the parts (ch. X), resulting in extreme cases of negative growth in resorption. Modifications of the specific form will be the result of alterations induced in these differential growth rates during the life-history.

That abnormal physiological conditions in the body may produce changes of its specific form is most obviously true in the vertebrates, where our knowledge of the physiology of the animal is most detailed. In the vertebrates the physiological conditions which have the most marked effects on the form of the body are changes in the secretions of the endocrine glands. The stunted, dwarf cretin is produced by subnormal secretion of the thyroid in early life; the acromegalic giant by over-production of one of the secretions of the anterior pituitary; and the differences of form in the two sexes are the result of differences in the internal secretions of the gonads. Similar phenomena occur in some of the higher invertebrates. In some insects the moult immediately before the adult instar, which is associated with large changes in the form of the body, is known to be correlated with changes in the secretion of glands within the body, much as metamorphosis in the Amphibia is associated with increased concentration of the thyroid secretion in the body.

In many other invertebrates physiological changes of one kind or another, not necessarily endocrine, are associated with changes of the body form. In *Daphnia* the reserve material is laid down as fat in the body cavity when sexual eggs are being formed, but as a glycogen-like substance in the carapace when the reproduction is asexual (Plate VIII, Fig. 53, facing p. 72). The case in which the sexual eggs are set free (ephippium) is a modified part of the carapace and its formation constitutes a definite change in the form of the body, so that we have here an example of a change of metabolism associated with change of form. Similarly, in the locust (*Locusta migratoria*) the migratory and sedentary phases, which differ in form as well as in habit, are associated with differences in the reserve food material in the body. The stores of fat are much more plentiful in the sedentary form. Another cladoceran, *Simocephalus*, gives us an example which is probably parallel to that just quoted in *Daphnia*. Normally in this animal, the ventral edges of the carapace fit together (Plate VIII, Fig. 54, facing p. 72), but when the animal is fed on the green alga *Chlamydomonas* the shape of the carapace is altered so that its ventral edges bulge apart. There can be little doubt that the difference in the food produces some physiological difference in the body, and that the change in shape is associated with this difference.

In these examples we only know that the change in form is *associated with* the physiological changes. Except in the last moult of insects, we have no proof that the physiological changes are the immediate cause of the change of form. We cannot have this proof until we are able to produce the physiological changes in more than one way, and to observe whether they are always followed by the change of form. But this has been shown to be true of some changes of form produced by endocrine changes, both in the vertebrate and in the last moult of insects. It seems at least probable that the other changes of form in these examples are direct results of the physiological changes which are associated with them.

Many of the physiological changes in the examples which have been given are caused ultimately by changes in the external environment. In *Daphnia* production of sexual eggs occurs when the animals are living at a low temperature or crowded, asexual eggs when the temperature is high or the animals are isolated. In the locust the appearance of the migratory phase is favoured by crowding and by other environmental conditions. In *Simocephalus* the nature of the food is an environmental condition. We can therefore say that changes in the external conditions may lead to changes in the form of an animal.

There is, indeed, much more evidence that this is so. Many other examples are known in which changes in the external environment produce changes of form, but in most of these examples we have no direct evidence that the physiology of the body is altered by the changes in the external conditions. Thus, the young larva of an echiuroid worm, *Bonellia viridis*, develops into a male if it settles on the proboscis of an adult female, and into a female if it does not. The sexual difference in form is extremely great in this worm. It is produced by some influence, probably a chemical secretion, of the proboscis of the female. But we have no knowledge of any physiological changes within the larva which are associated with the determination of sex. There are more instances in which the neighbourhood of other individuals of the same species influences the sexual differentiation. One such is in the gastropod mollusc, *Crepidula plana*, the slipper limpet. The young limpet normally settles on the shell of an older individual and so a chain is formed. As a member of the chain, the limpet is at first non-sexual and then passes through male, hermaphrodite, and female phases. If it fails to settle on an older limpet, the male and hermaphrodite phases are omitted and the animal passes directly from the non-sexual to the female condition.

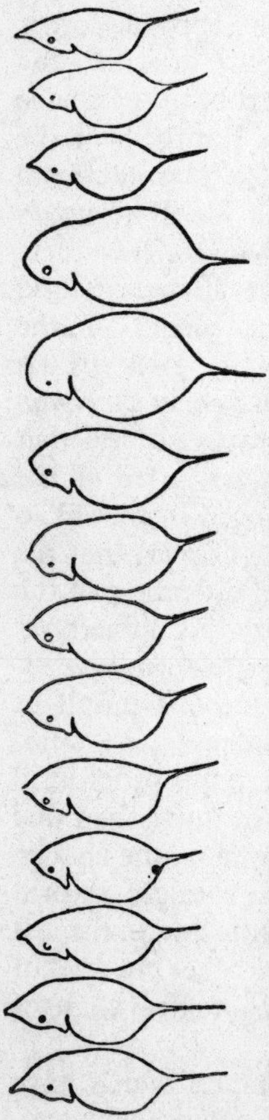

Figure 55. Variation of the form of the body in *Daphnia hyalina* from the same lake during the year. The series runs from August on the left, to August on the right. (After Wesenburg-Lund.)

Other conditions of the environment may have equally striking effects on the form of the body in animals. In *Daphnia hyalina* (Fig. 55) the process on the front of the head, known as the helm, varies in shape with the mean temperature of the environment, being longer and more pointed in the warmer environments. Summer and winter forms differ in many animals (*e.g. Ceratium*, a dinoflagellate, and *Bosmina*, a cladoceran, Fig. 56). All these effects may either be due to direct action of the temperature or to some indirect action of it, *e.g.* to differences of the food supply in the environments at different temperatures.

Another, very striking, example of change of form produced by changes in the external environment is that of the brine-shrimp, *Artemia salina* (Branchiopoda). This animal inhabits evaporating pools of sea-water, environments in which the osmotic pressure is liable to large variations. The form of the body is found to alter with changes in the osmotic pressure of the environment (Fig. 57). The abdomen is longer in proportion to the length of the thorax in environments where the osmotic pressure is relatively high, and many details of the form of the abdomen vary with the osmotic pressure. These changes are so distinct that the different forms were at one time described as a different species. In *Artemia* it is also possible to compare the effects of changes in the external environment with those of changes in the genetic constitution of the species. Polyploid races of *Artemia* have been bred (*i.e.* races in which the chromosome number is not $2n$ but some larger multiple of n). These races have been found to react to changes in the osmotic pressure of the medium in a way which is similar to that in which the normal animal reacts but not identical with it. The form of the species is modified by changes in either the genetic constitution or the environment: the specific form at any moment is the result of interaction of all these factors.

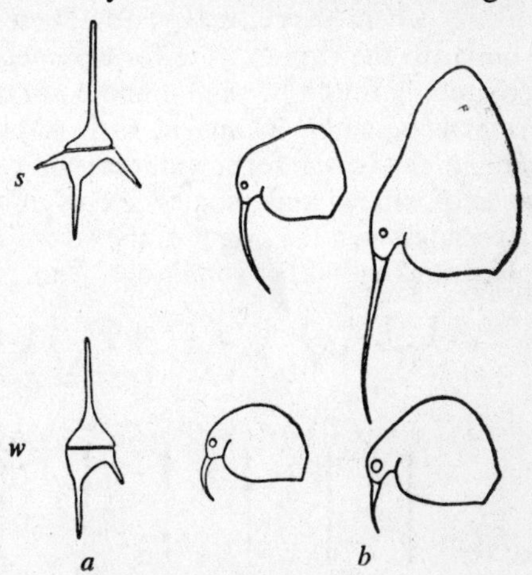

Figure 56. Summer and winter forms in *Ceratium* (*a*) and *Bosmina* (*b*); *s*, summer; *w*, winter. (After Wesenburg-Lund.)

That there is a close relation between the effects of genetic change and those of abnormal environment is very clearly shown by experiments such as those of Goldschmidt,* in which insects were exposed to abnormally high temperatures for short periods during their development. This resulted in abnormalities, presumably due to disturbance of developmental processes taking place at the time the heat was applied, and the abnormalities were very similar to those which had previously been known to be caused by mutation. Abnormalities simulating the effects of mutation but caused by abnormal environmental conditions have been called *phenocopies*.

Many other examples of change in the form of the body associated

* R. Goldschmidt, *Physiological Genetics*, 1938, pp. 10 ff.

with differences in the environmental conditions could be given. Coral colonies vary greatly in their form with the amount of their exposure to wave action. Colonies of the same species may be delicately branched tree-like forms in sheltered positions, and compact masses where they are exposed. These variations of form are very similar to the variations in form associated with external conditions commonly found in plants; and coral colonies more than any other animals resemble plants in their habit of growth. Sponges show similar changes in form with external conditions. Again, the appearance of winged and wingless forms in aphids has been shown to be associated with the extent of the crowding of the animals on the food plant, and with other conditions. And, in bees the differences between

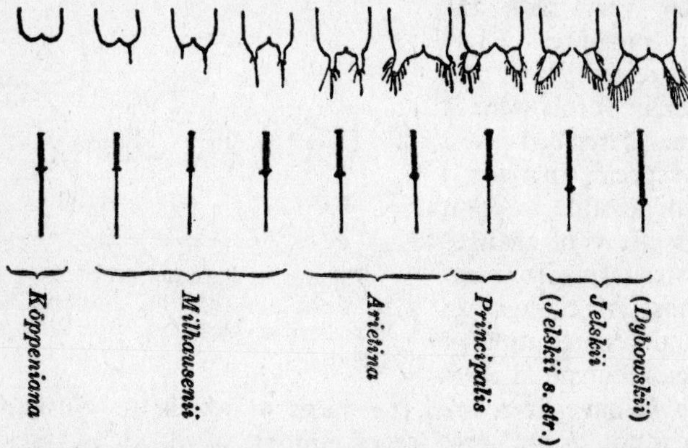

Figure 57. Variation in the body form of *Artemia salina*.

The salt content of the medium decreases from left to right of the figure. At the top, forms of the end of the abdomen in the various environments. In the second line, proportions of thorax (dark) to abdomen (light) in the same environments. Below, the names of the species under which these forms were formerly described. (After Abonyi.)

the worker and the sexual female are determined by differences in the food of the larva.

The discussion of this chapter has shown that the specific form of an animal is not completely constant, even though the hereditary constitution remains constant. In some animals form may alter as the constitution of the living substance is altered by physiological changes within the body, in others with undefined changes in the body produced by environmental changes. We must regard the specific form at each moment as an expression of the constitution of the living substance at that time. If all the tissues become unhealthy (as in dedifferentiation or cancer), or are living in a very abnormal environment (as in a tissue culture), the specific form of the body may be entirely lost.

Nevertheless, it must be emphasised that the mean specific form at each stage of the life-history varies very little in by far the larger number of animal species or races, except as the result of changes in the hereditary constitution of the animal. Changes in the mean specific form due to other causes occur in only a small minority of animals. This can only mean that the specific form is determined mainly by the hereditary constitution, and it is the constancy of the hereditary constitution of a species or race that determines the constancy of the specific form.

CHAPTER VIII

THE AXIAL ORGANISATION OF THE BODY AND REGENERATION

THE animal body is an ordered arrangement of parts, each of which has a determined place and shape. So much is evident. We are usually able to recognise certain general features in this arrangement. There is an anterior-posterior "axis," called the "axis of polarity," about which the parts are almost always arranged symmetrically, most frequently in radial or bilateral symmetry. In most animals there is an anterior region, the head, in which the sense organs are more numerous than elsewhere, and in which the mouth lies. And so on.

In spite of these recognisable features in its arrangement, the morphological organisation of the body is in the main simply an ordered arrangement of the parts of the body. It is an arrangement based on qualitative, not on quantitative, differences between the parts; numerical differences play no part in it.

In this chapter we shall discuss whether any other type of organisation can be recognised in the animal body as a whole, and, especially, whether we can recognise any organisation based on quantitative differences between the parts.

THE AXIAL GRADIENT OR FIELD

If a planarian is placed in a medium containing a poison at a concentration which is just strong enough to kill the tissues (*e.g.* 0·001M potassium cyanide), the tissues are not killed at the same rate in all parts of the body. The ectoderm is destroyed first, since it is the first tissue reached by the poison. If we watch its destruction, we find that the cells break down first at the anterior end of the body, and that a wave of destruction passes over the body from the anterior end (Fig. 58). The poison must reach the ectoderm in all parts of the body at the same time, since the whole of the surface is in contact with the external medium. The results we observe therefore show that there is in the ectoderm a region of maximum susceptibility to the poison at the anterior end and that a *gradient* of susceptibility extends backwards over the body from this region.

A *susceptibility gradient* with a maximum in the anterior region of the body has been found in animals of very many groups. Protista, cœlenterates, platyhelminths, annelids, and many other animals show it. It has been found even in undivided eggs (Amphibia, and many other animals), where the animal pole is the region of maximum susceptibility. It is apparently a general feature of animal organisation, certainly in the simpler animal bodies and possibly in the bodies of all animals.

It is important to note that this gradient of susceptibility occurs in tissues which are, as nearly as may be, identical in appearance over the whole body. If we had only found that cells of different types are destroyed at different rates by the poison, the observation would be far less interesting. Cells vary in their morphological and physiological characters, and it is to be expected that some would be more

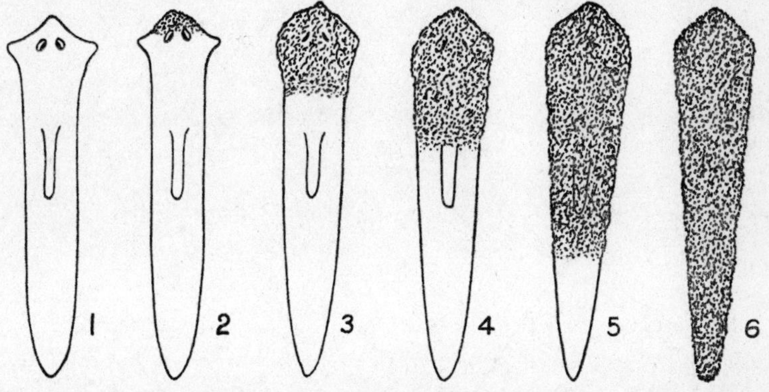

Figure 58. Progressive destruction of the ectoderm in a planarian treated with 0·001M KCN.

susceptible to poisons than others. But the gradient exists in the ectoderm of a planarian, which is very similar in all parts of the body. It is true that no tissue is precisely the same in structure over the whole body of an animal. The ectoderm, for instance, in a planarian contains more sense-cells at the anterior end of the body and differs in other ways in its various parts. But there is no reason to think that these structural differences are the cause of the differences in susceptibility which we observe. It is rather to be expected that the rate of destruction of the cells would vary with their general physiological activity. The more active the metabolism of a cell, the more rapidly it should react with the poison and be destroyed. Some confirmation of this is provided by the observation that increase of temperature (up to the optimum for the animal's life) increases the rate at which the tissues are destroyed. There can be no question that increase of temperature raises the physiological activity of animal tissues. The susceptibility also decreases as the animal grows older, and we shall see that there is a continuous decrease of physiological activity in the tissues of the body during the life-history (ch. XX).

The *arrangement* of the susceptibility gradient is not altered by change of temperature or during the life-history of the animal.

However, it is not necessary for us to discuss further the physiological basis which lies behind the susceptibility gradient. Its physiology has not been fully worked out and must be regarded as still uncertain. Here, we only need to remark that a susceptibility gradient with a maximum at the anterior end of the body is, so far as we can see at present, characteristic of the organisation of the animal body.

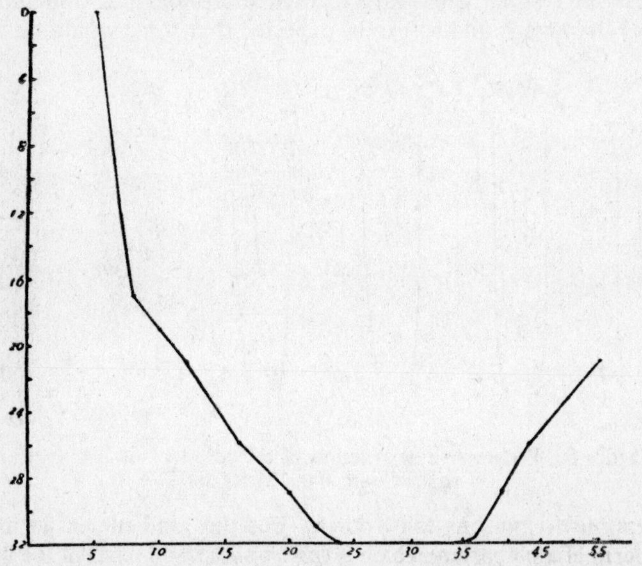

Figure 59. Susceptibility gradient in a species of *Dero* (Oligochæta). Ordinates, time in minutes before the tissue is destroyed; abscissæ, segments of the body. (After Hyman.)

There are some animals in which the distribution of susceptibility is not as simple as a single gradient from head to tail. This is so in many of the annelids, in which there is usually, besides the normal gradient, a reversed gradient in the posterior part of the body (Fig. 59). In the annelids new segments are formed at the posterior end of the body, and, as we shall see later (pp. 137–8), the normal single gradient is usually modified in regions where active growth is going on. It may be that these reversed gradients are associated with the active growth of this part of the body, as we shall see other types of reversed gradients are (p. 137). They are peculiar to the annelids, and they do not invalidate the rule that the animal body has normally a single gradient with a region of maximum susceptibility at the anterior end. Even where the gradient is more complex an anterior-posterior gradient is always present.

If susceptibility to poisons were the only character by which the gradient system of the body could be displayed, the grounds for believing in this organisation would be weaker than they actually are. It might well be thought dangerous to argue from the manner in which tissues die under the influence of poisons to their organisation in life. In the great majority of experiments on the gradient system

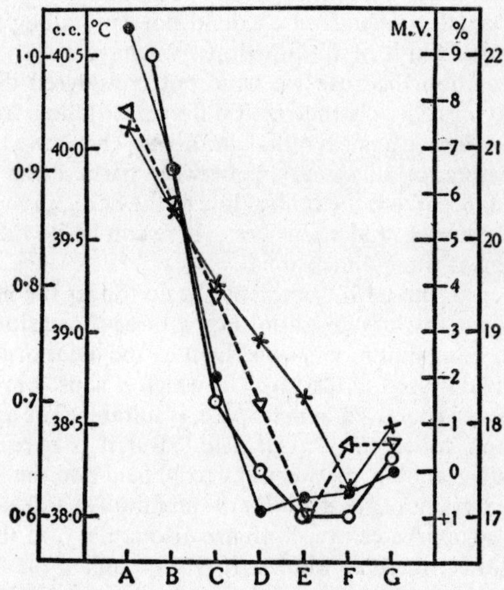

Figure 60. Gradients of various physiological characters in an oligochæte (*Pheretima*).

o–o and outer left scale, oxidisable substance.
x–x and outer right scale, solid content.
▽–▽ and inner left scale, temperature at which the body shortens when exposed to heat.
●-● and inner right scale, electrical potential in millivolts.
(From Huxley and de Beer. After Watanabe.)

poisons have been used to display the gradient, but other characters of the tissues can also be used. In Fig. 60 gradients in four physiological characters in the body of an oligochæte, *Pheretima*, are shown. The distribution of each character shows not only the usual anterior-posterior gradient but also the reversed gradient of the annelid. There can be little doubt that the same organisation is displayed here as in experiments with poisons (Fig. 59). If so, we have broader grounds for accepting the gradient system as characteristic of the organisation of the body.

So far we have spoken of this gradient as a gradient of susceptibility. If the distribution it displays is not confined to the susceptibility of the tissues to poisons, we need a wider term. It is usually called the "*axial gradient*," since it follows the anterior-posterior or polarity axis of the animal.

We have, also, so far regarded this gradient only as a one-dimensional gradient along the axis. But the body is a three-dimensional structure and the organisation within it must also be three-dimensional. The axial gradient must extend not only along the axis but also outwards from it in all directions. We have not so far met this radial distribution, because we have not considered differences in susceptibility or other characters at different distances from the axis. But there is evidence of such radial gradients. They have been demonstrated, for instance, in planarians between parts of the ectoderm at different distances from the central line of the body, in the developing limbs of vertebrates, and elsewhere. There can be no doubt that the axial gradient is three-dimensional.

This being so, the term "gradient" is no longer the most suitable we can find for this organisation. For a three-dimensional distribution around a maximum position, such as the axial organisation is, the term "field," used in the sense in which it is used in speaking of the field of force round a magnetic pole, is suitable. The axial gradient may be better called the "*axial field*." But it is necessary to emphasise that the analogy between the axial field and the field of force of a physical system is that both are quantitative three-dimensional distributions round a centre. Both are also unitary, in the sense that distortions affect them as wholes. It is not implied that there is any similarity between the vital processes which produce the axial field, whatever these processes may be, and physical forces. This is clearly not so.

The axial field is a quantitative organisation within the body and thus differs from the morphological arrangement of the parts, which is qualitative. We have therefore found an organisation of the kind for which we set out to look at the beginning of this chapter. The fact that several characters of the tissues are distributed along the gradients of the axial field suggests that we must attribute the cause of this distribution not to any one of these characters of the tissues but to some underlying organisation which controls the distribution of all of them. We shall find further evidence in support of this view (pp. 136, 157), but we have at present no idea of the nature of this underlying organisation.

REGENERATION

Much light is thrown on the characters of the axial field by the facts of regeneration, the process by which the body returns to its specific form when that form has been disturbed by loss of a part. It is hardly surprising that knowledge of the manner in which the specific form is regained should help us to understand the organisation of the body in its normal, complete state.

All animals possess the power to regenerate, but the extent of the regeneration which can occur becomes less as the evolution of the structure of the body proceeds. In the simpler multicellular animals the whole body will regenerate from a small part—an eighth or less—of the body, but even in the simplest animals there is a lower limit to the size of the piece which will regenerate. In the adults of the higher vertebrates only very small parts of the body are regenerated, such as parts of the skin or of muscle. This decrease of the power of regeneration during evolution is undoubtedly partly due to reduction of the ability of parts of the body to survive long enough for regeneration to take place: small parts of the more complex bodies cannot survive. But this is not the whole explanation, for, even if a complex body survives the loss of a part, it often remains incomplete. There is a definite loss of the power of regeneration as evolution proceeds, and this loss is not wholly due to increasing complexity of the body. Amphibia have greater power of regeneration than mammals, and the newt than the frog. These differences can hardly be associated with differences in the complexity of body structure. In general, it is true that the more primitive the structure of an animal, the greater is this power of regeneration. We can say little more than this.

The process of regeneration varies considerably with the extent of the damage which has been done to the body. When a small part has been lost from the body of either a simple or a complex animal, the specific form is regained by growth of the tissues in the neighbourhood of the damage. Some dedifferentiation takes place in the cells of the tissues near the damage, and a pad of "regeneration tissue" is formed over the damaged surface, partly composed of cells from these tissues and partly of undifferentiated, "reserve" cells which migrate to it from parts farther within the body. This pad of tissue then proceeds to grow and becomes moulded into the form of the lost parts by differential growth. Each part of the regenerating tissue grows at a rate appropriate to form the organ into which it is to regenerate, at the size appropriate to the specific form of the body. The result is that, when regeneration is complete, the specific form is exactly regained. We have here controlled growth of just the same kind as that which preserves the specific form in the animal growing normally, but there is the difference that the growth of the regenerating tissues is much more rapid than that of tissues in undamaged parts of the body. Clearly conditions of some kind within the body control the growth-rates of the parts of the regenerating tissue, just as they control the growth of parts in the normal body.

The growth-rate of the regenerating tissue as a whole is determined by the amount of growth necessary for the return to the specific form; the smaller the part removed the slower is the rate of growth of the regenerating tissue. This can be well seen in the regeneration of parts removed from the tail of an earthworm—regenerating growth is more rapid the larger the part of the tail which is cut away. Here again it is clearly the conditions within the damaged body as a whole which are controlling the course of regeneration. The growth is controlled, and controlled so as to result in return to the specific form.

While the regenerating tissue is undergoing this differential growth, it becomes redifferentiated into the various tissues necessary to form the organs to be regenerated. The course of this redifferentiation has been worked out more clearly in the vertebrate than in the invertebrate. It has been shown in the vertebrate that the regenerating pad is at first undetermined with regard to the form of the organs it will produce. If at this stage it is removed and grafted elsewhere, it will form organs appropriate to its new position—a tail-bud grafted on the cut surface of an amputated limb will regenerate a limb. As regeneration goes on, the type of the tissues to be regenerated becomes determined. If the bud is removed at this stage to another part of the body, it will form only the organs which would have been formed in its original position. In normal development there is a similar gradual determination of fate in the various parts of the body. This gradual determination in development, occurs in invertebrate as well as in vertebrate development, and it seems probable that determination is gradual in regeneration in invertebrates as well as vertebrates.

As a general rule, the tissue which forms any organ in regeneration is derived mainly from similar tissue in the parent body. Ectoderm is usually formed from cells which were originally ectodermal, endoderm from endodermal cells. But this is not always so. The mesoderm in the regeneration of oligochætes is said to be formed from ectoderm, and there are other cases in which one tissue in the body may give rise to other tissues in regeneration.

Regeneration of small parts of the body is, then, brought about by increased but controlled growth of the regenerating tissues and by their redifferentiation. By these means the specific form is regained. In some animals the course of regeneration is modified by other features of the organisation of the animal. In the arthropods the presence of a hard cuticle prevents complete regeneration until the next moult. A pad of regenerating tissue is usually formed at the seat of the damage—for instance, at the damaged surface of a limb which has been lost—and this pad may grow. But the limb is not completely regenerated until the animal has moulted at least once. This type of regeneration occurs in the Crustacea, the Arachnida, Myriapoda, and some insect larvæ.

Abnormal regeneration, in which the organ regenerated is different in form from that which was lost, also sometimes occurs. A striking example of this occurs in a prawn, *Palæmon*. If the whole eye-stalk of this animal, and the optic ganglion within it, is cut away, an antenna-like organ is regenerated. In mantids an amputated antenna has been found to regenerate as a leg. We cannot discuss these cases here. We shall meet other examples of regeneration which do not produce return to the normal specific form (pp. 135, 137). It need only be noted that these examples of abnormal regeneration are exceptional. They do not invalidate our general conclusions.

In the regeneration of the whole body of one of the simpler invertebrates from a small part of the body, reorganisation of the tissues plays a much larger part than in the regeneration of a small part which has been lost. A small piece separated from a body cannot grow as a whole during the regeneration, for the loss of most of its organs prevents its feeding. It lives on its reserves of food, and therefore decreases in total size. Nevertheless, the tissues near the cut surfaces grow actively at the expense of the other parts of the body. The lost organs are regenerated by differential growth of these tissues in much the same way as the lost organs are regenerated when a small part of the body is removed. Many of the old organs remaining in the piece may be taken over into the regenerated body, but others may be resorbed (p. 115). They lose their structure and disappear and new organs are formed to replace them. The shape of the new body is remoulded by differential growth out of the whole of the tissues of the piece. Even the organs which are taken over are altered in size to fit the new body. Reorganisation extends to the whole piece, not only to the new tissue formed by regeneration, as it does in the replacement of a small part of the body.

Thus, regeneration, wherever it occurs, consists of three processes which go on partly simultaneously and partly successively in the remaining tissues. These are (1) formation of a mass of undifferentiated tissue by loss of differentiation in the tissues near the damage and by migration of other cells to this position; (2) redifferentiation of this tissue into the various tissues which it is to form; (3) reorganisation of these tissues, and, if the damage is large, of other parts of the body, into the specific form by differential growth negative as well as positive. In different types of regeneration the extent of each of these processes varies.

The regeneration of a whole body from a small part of it is often distinguished from other types of regeneration and called "*reconstitution.*" But it, as much as any other form of regeneration is a return to the specific form. Since this is so, and since the processes of change in the body are so similar in all the forms of regeneration, it seems best to use the one term for this phenomenon wherever it occurs.

Other phenomena occur in the animal body which probably at base involve the same process as regeneration. Both the redifferentiation of a body which has lost its specific form by dedifferentiation, and the formation of a bud (ch. IX) are processes in which the specific

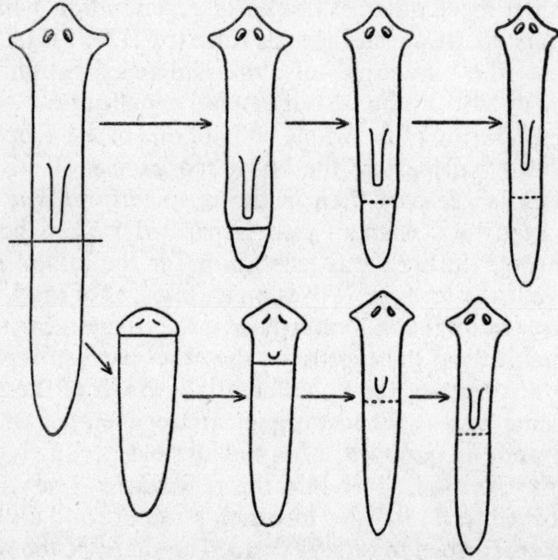

Figure 61. Regeneration of anterior and posterior parts of a planarian.

form is attained by direct reorganisation of the tissues. They are probably similar in essentials to the process of regeneration. All these processes are essentially different from the normal development of an animal from the egg to the adult (ch. XX).

Regeneration of large parts of the body in the simpler invertebrates throws much more light on the general organisation of the body than the more restricted regeneration of the higher animals. We shall consider here only the facts of regeneration in the simpler animals.

If a planarian is divided into two parts by a transverse cut near the centre of the body, the anterior half will regenerate a tail and the posterior half a head (Fig. 61). In both pieces most of the organs that remain are taken over into the new body. The anterior half grows directly backwards and forms a tail with the missing organs. At the same time its anterior regions are decreasing in size (by resorption), so that the whole is reorganised into a smaller planarian of the size appropriate to the total amount of tissue in the piece. In the posterior half the first new organs to be formed are the most anterior, those of the head. The missing organs between the head and the cut surface of the piece are formed later. Reorganisation of the whole into a body of the appropriate size goes on continuously, as in the posterior half.

There is thus a clear distinction between the processes of regeneration in the two pieces. Regeneration of the anterior half towards the tail proceeds directly; in the posterior half the head is first regenerated and the parts behind it later. This distinction between anterior and posterior regeneration holds for all pieces of a planarian body, whatever their original position, so long as they are able to regenerate completely.

If a planarian is divided by a transverse cut nearer the head or the tail, the course of regeneration is similar to that of a half of the body, provided that the smaller piece is large enough to regenerate.

A piece cut out of the middle of the body of a planarian by two transverse cuts will regenerate a whole body, again if it is not too small. A new head is formed at the front end of the piece, and a tail at its hinder end. The course of regeneration at each end is similar to that in the two halves of the body.

Regeneration of much the same type as that in the planarians has been observed in polyps of the cœlenterates. The whole of a polyp of *Tubularia*, for instance, will regenerate from a part, and regeneration at the anterior and posterior surfaces obeys the same rules as in pieces of a planarian. In the polyp the mouth region plays the part of the head of a planarian, and is regenerated before the organs between it and the anterior cut surface of the piece. In some of the annelids the course of regeneration appears to be different from that in these groups; it will be considered later (p. 139). For the present we shall only discuss regeneration of the type found in the cœlenterates and planarians.

There are several points to be noted in the regeneration so far described.

(1) The axis of polarity of the regenerated body is, in normal regeneration, always along the same line and in the same direction as that of the body from which the piece was taken. In a piece of a planarian body, a head is regenerated at the front, and not at the side or back of the piece. In some exceptional examples of regeneration this is not true. Environmental conditions may produce unusual regeneration in which it does not hold. Thus, if a piece of a polyp of

the hydroid *Corymorpha* is weakened by being treated with 2–2·5 per cent. alcohol, the original organisation of the piece is lost by de-differentiation. If the piece is returned to normal sea-water and laid horizontally, a new head is formed on the side of the piece (Fig. 62). On the other hand, if the piece is not weakened by treatment with alcohol, or is held upright when it is returned to sea-water, the regeneration is along the original axis of polarity. Here it is clear that environmental conditions have determined the axis along which regeneration occurs in a piece in which the original organisation was destroyed. We shall discuss later some examples of regeneration along the original axis of polarity but in the reverse direction (pp. 137–8).

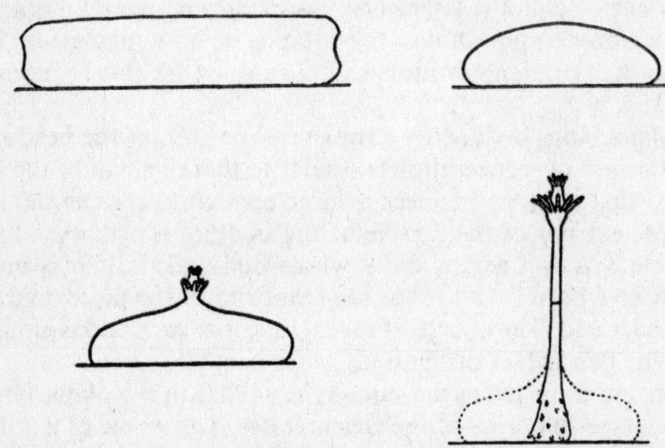

Figure 62. Regeneration of Corymorpha at right angles to the original axis of polarity. (After Child.)

(2) In regeneration at either end of a separated piece more posterior organs are regenerated only if more anterior organs are already present, either by being in the piece at the time of its separation or by having been regenerated. The head alone is an exception to this rule. In short pieces there is sometimes no regeneration of a head, and in such pieces the parts between the head and the anterior face of the piece are not regenerated. But the regeneration on the posterior face of such a piece may be normal.

These facts may be shortly stated by saying that anterior organs are dominant to posterior in regeneration, and that therefore the head is dominant to all the rest of the body. We may say that the head region has a "*field of dominance*" which extends over the body. In the examples of regeneration which we are here discussing, this field of dominance of the head appears to control the reorganisation of the body, for unless a head is present the new organisation cannot be complete; only parts which are already present in the regenerating piece and parts posterior to them can be organised. We shall see later that this dominance of the head in regeneration is probably not true of all animals (p. 139).

(3) The field of dominance of the head is normally exactly co-extensive with the tissue of the regenerating piece. The regenerated body is organised to fill the available tissue and each organ is of the size appropriate to take its place in a body of the size which the amount of tissue in the piece allows. The regenerated body is normal in specific form.

This is so in normal regeneration, but, again, not under all experimental conditions. If a separated piece of a planarian is treated with a narcotic during its regeneration, a smaller head than the normal is formed (Fig. 63, A), and the other organs, *e.g.* the pharynx, are not only smaller than the normal but closer to the head. In fact, only a small part of the body at the anterior end is organised under the influence of the head: most of the body is outside the field of dominance.

Narcotics lower the physiological activity of tissues, and we may conclude that the extent of the field of dominance varies with the physiological activity. In confirmation of this, when the activity of the tissues is raised by allowing the regeneration to occur at a higher temperature (so long as the temperature is not above an optimum), the regenerated head and other organs are larger (Fig. 63, A, *f*).

Experiments with narcotics give some further results. If pieces of a planarian are treated with a narcotic at concentrations somewhat higher than those required to reduce the size of the field of dominance, imperfect heads are formed. These may have only one central eye or no eye; the tentacles may also be absent (Fig. 63, B). When these imperfect heads are examined, it is found that the imperfections consist in the absence of a region in the front part of the head. The size of this region increases with the concentration of the narcotic and therefore with the reduction in the activity of the tissues. With higher concentrations the formation of a head may be entirely inhibited.

It seems that a certain level of physiological activity is necessary in the tissues if regeneration is to proceed. Further, this level is highest for the tissues at the front of the head and decreases from this region backwards.

The same close correlation between the physiological conditions of the tissues and the ability to regenerate is shown in experiments in which the minimum size of the piece of a planarian body that will regenerate is determined. It is found that the minimum size is larger in the presence of narcotics than when the tissues are normally active.

The less active tissues can only regenerate in the more favourable conditions of the larger piece.

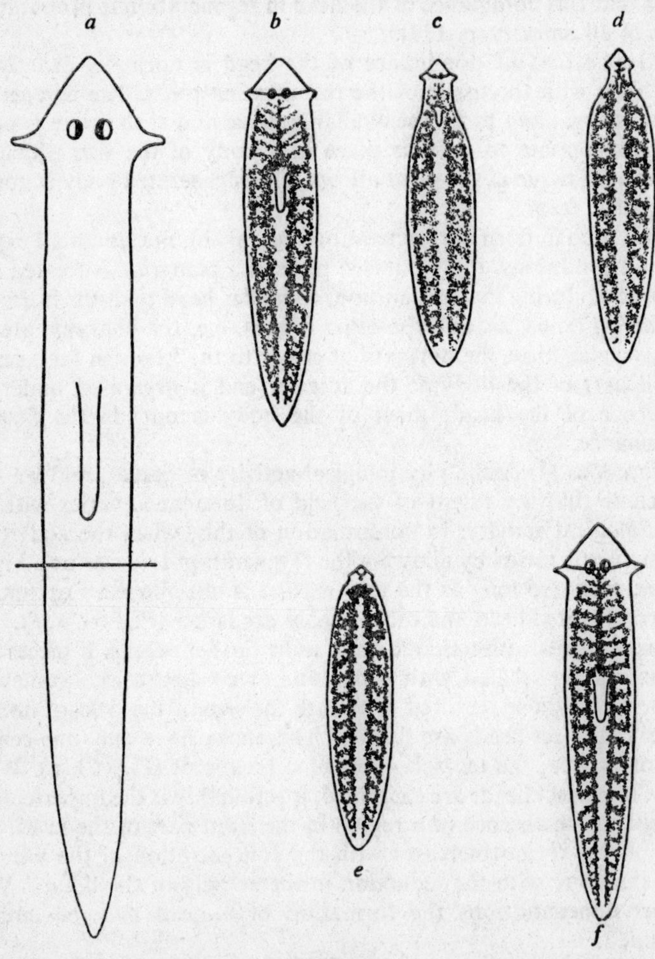

Figure 63 (A). Regeneration of pieces of a planarian treated with narcotics.

Reduced field of dominance of the head. *b*, normal regeneration of the part behind the transverse line of *a*; *c*, *d*, *e*, regeneration with increasingly reduced field of dominance; *f*, increased size of the organs when regeneration occurred at a higher (optimum) temperature. (After Child.)

That the power of a centre of dominance to organise the whole of a body depends to some extent on the size of the body is shown by the facts of bud-formation. Buds (*cf.* ch. IX) may be looked upon as parts of the body which have become free from the dominance of the head region, and have developed a new organisation of their own. In planarians and some other animals buds are almost always formed at the posterior end of the body, in the region at the greatest distance from the head. If a piece is cut from a planarian body which has already produced buds so as to include a part of the original body and some of the buds, it may become organised under a single centre, the separate organisations of the buds being suppressed, although they have been already formed. This has been shown in *Stenostomum grande* (Fig. 64). The head region in the separated piece which is best developed (*i.e.* that of the most posterior of the buds present in the piece, p. 136) becomes anterior by resorption of the organs which were in front of this head region. This is true of the head regions of the most anterior buds and of any other organs present. The whole piece becomes organised under the centre at the anterior end (Fig. 64, *b*, *c*, *d*). The separated piece is of the appropriate size to form a single body and becomes so organised. Later, as it grows, the piece will divide to form new buds (*e*, *f*). Clearly there is here correlation between the size of the piece and its organisation as a single body.

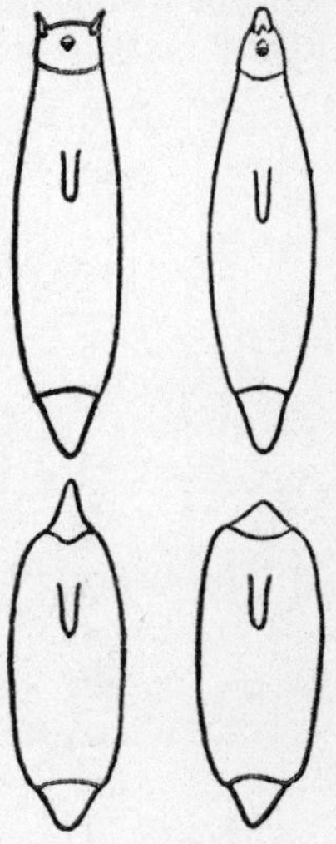

Figure 63 (B). Regeneration of pieces of a planarian treated with narcotics. Abnormally reduced heads with higher concentrations of narcotics. (After Child.)

Regeneration in the cœlenterates gives results precisely similar to those given by regeneration of planarians except that reversed regeneration (p. 137) is much more frequent in the cœlenterates. We may sum up the conclusions we have reached:

1. In these groups, more anterior parts are dominant in regeneration to more posterior parts. This dominance centres in the region of which will be the new head. Unless this centre is formed, or is already present, complete regeneration is impossible. From this centre a field of dominance extends over the body and is normally co-extensive with it. The strength of the dominant influence decreases as we pass farther from the centre. If the body is large, or the axial organisation weak, a part of the body may lie outside the field of dominance.

2. The ability to regenerate is closely correlated with the physiological activity of the tissues. A higher level of activity is necessary for regeneration at the front end of the body than elsewhere. The extent of the field of dominance of the head is also correlated with the physiological activity of the tissue.

In its distribution over the body the field of dominance of the head region recalls the axial field. Both extend as quantitatively distributed fields over the body and both have their dominant regions in the head. Also, as we have seen (p. 124), there is some reason to think that the distribution of the axial field is correlated with the physiological activity of the tissues, as is the power of regeneration. There

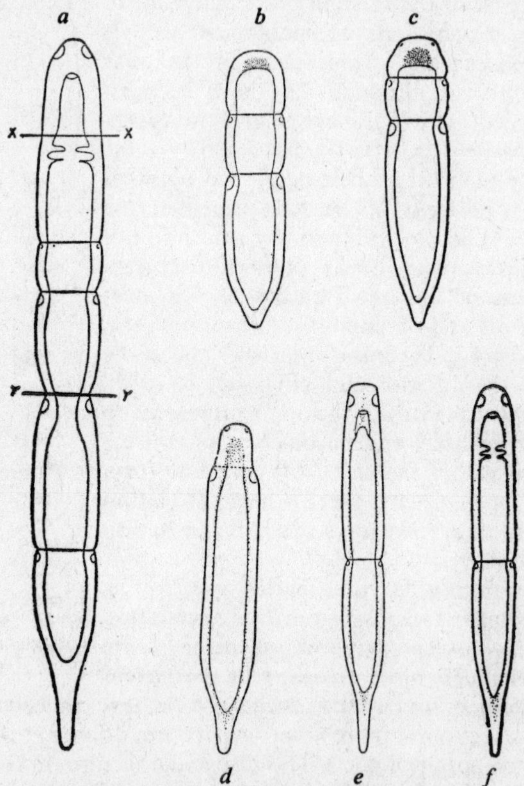

Figure 64. *Stenostomum grande.*

b–f, regeneration of the part between X–X and Y–Y in *a*. *b–d*, resorption of the heads of all except the most anterior bud and inhibition of formation of a head at the anterior surface of the piece. *e–f*, formation of a new bud at the posterior end of the regenerated piece. (After Child.)

can be very little doubt that the two systems are related, and, if so, very little doubt also that they are both expressions of a single underlying organisation, which we may call the "*axial organisation.*"

Since we have found this organisation to control regeneration in two large groups of animals, the planarians and cœlenterates, and since regeneration is the return of the body to its specific form after damage, it would seem very probable that this organisation plays some part in the maintenance of specific form in the normal, undamaged body. We do not know at present how it does so, and, as we shall see, it is certainly not the only system which controls the specific form (p. 155). But at least it is clear that we must think of the animal body as containing an axial organisation of the type we have defined and as normally containing only one such organisation. In discussing buds and monsters (ch. IX) we shall find further evidence that the axial organisation has some control over the specific form.

There are some facts of abnormal regeneration in planarians and cœlenterates which throw further light on the organisation of the body. For example:

If a very small piece is cut off the front end of a planarian by a transverse cut, a reversed head and not a tail is sometimes formed on the posterior face of the piece (Fig. 65). Formation of a reversed head on a posterior cut surface occurs much more readily in pieces of cœlenterate polyps (*e.g. Tubularia*, Fig. 66). It occurs in planarians only when the separated piece is very small, but in *Tubularia* pieces which contain a whole polyp and part of the stem may regenerate a reversed head. In such pieces this type of regeneration may even be more frequent than normal regeneration, which would here consist in formation of a stolon at the cut surface.

Figure 65. Reversed heads in *Planaria*. (After Child.)

If our conclusion that the axial organisation controls specific form is correct, a new centre of this organisation must have been formed in these pieces near the posterior cut surface, for a new specific form is developed in this region. This new centre must have established a reversed field in the posterior part of the piece. The question arises why this new organisation should have been established. There can be no doubt that the activity of the tissues in the neighbourhood of a cut is increased; repair is active in this region and this necessitates active division and growth of the tissues. It clearly follows that the raised activity of the tissues near the cut will give rise to a new area of maximum activity in this region. Since, in the normal body the head is believed to be a region of maximum activity, it is suggested that a new centre of the axial organisation is formed as a result of the formation of this new region of maximum activity. It is true that increase of the activity of the tissues near the cut must occur in all separated pieces and that in planarians reversed heads only occur on short pieces cut from the front end of the body. It must be supposed that the original axial field is able to inhibit the formation of new organisation in all except these short pieces, just as we saw the heads of buds in *Stenostomum* may be inhibited. It would seem that this inhibition is less strong in the cœlenterates than in the planarians, since reversed regeneration is much more frequent in the cœlenterates. It is true also that, in bud formation, the new head is most frequently formed at the posterior end of the body, *i.e.* at a distance from the original head, whereas in these short pieces of a planarian the reversed head is very close to the original head, and yet is not inhibited. We might expect the inhibition to be very strong in tissues close to the old centre of dominance. But it must also be remembered that the tissue which forms the reversed head was adjacent to the head in the original body and therefore probably similar to it in organisation and

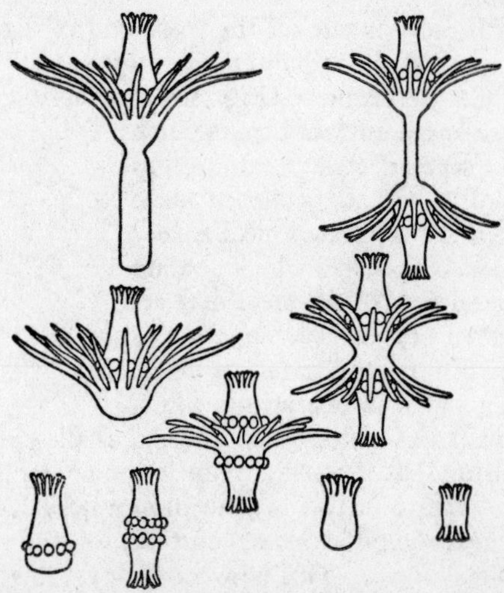

Figure 66. Reversed organisation in pieces of *Tubularia*.

The biaxial pieces are regenerates from the pieces shown to the left of each of them. (After Child.)

in physiological activity, if we may accept the gradient as associated with a gradient of activity. It may be for these reasons that a new head in this region is less easily inhibited.

However this may be, the formation of new heads on the posterior faces of these pieces gives us further evidence that high activity in the tissues is associated with the anterior regions of the axial field, for the activity of the tissues in this region as a result of the damage cannot be doubted.

We have not discussed by any means all the facts of regeneration in animals. So far we have considered only the regeneration of planarians and cœlenterates. We have chosen these facts because it is in them that regeneration displays the arrangement of the axial organisation clearly. In other animals regeneration is not so closely correlated with the arrangement of this organisation. As an example of regeneration of the latter type, we may take the regeneration of an annelid *Sabella*, in which the course of regeneration in separated pieces has been worked out carefully.

In *Sabella* a piece taken by transverse cuts from the middle region of the body ("thorax," Fig. 67) will, like a similar piece of a planarian body, normally regenerate a head at its front end and a tail at its hinder end. But the dominance of the head in the regeneration is by no means clear. Parts between the head and the cut surface may be regenerated at the same time as the new head is formed, or even, in exceptional cases, when the head never regenerates at all. Also, parts near the cut surface at the posterior end of the piece may regenerate to form organs belonging to more anterior parts of the body without the formation of a head in this region. Both these results are in disagreement with the rules which we have found to govern regeneration in planarians and cœlenterates. It would seem that the axial organisation does not control the regeneration of the body in these separated pieces of *Sabella*. The physiological condition of the tissues at the cut at the time of regeneration plays some part in the control of the regeneration, but it has been shown to be not the only controlling condition.

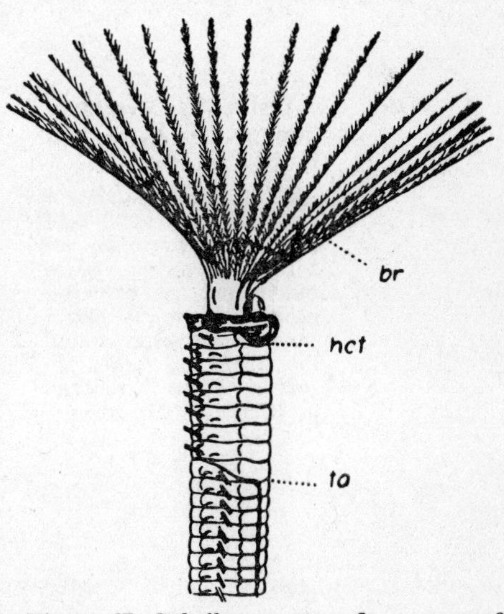

Figure 67. *Sabella pavonina*, front part of the body.

br, branchiæ; *hct*, junction between head and thorax regions; *ta*, junction between thorax and abdomen. (After Berrill.)

There is also evidence that in some animals special tissues may control the regeneration of large parts of the body. If the anterior part of an earthworm is cut away, the presence of the nerve-cord in the cut surface is apparently necessary for regeneration of the lost parts. The nerve-cord may be cut away from some segments immediately behind the anterior surface of the piece (Fig. 68), and regeneration then takes place from the cut end of the nerve-cord. The segments from which the nerve-cord has been removed degenerate.

These facts do not invalidate the conclusions we have drawn from the regeneration of planarians and cœlenterates. The facts of regeneration in those two groups are important for the evidence they give of the existence and distribution of the axial organisation in the body. The fact that in some animals regeneration seems to be controlled in other ways does not disprove the importance of this

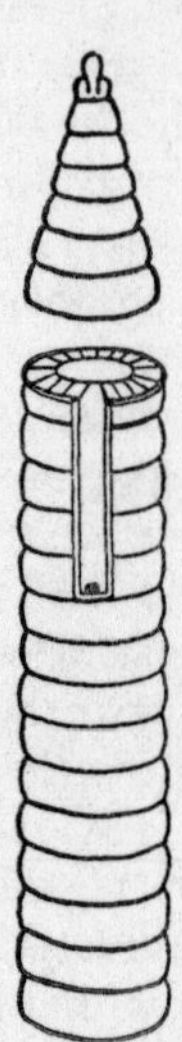

Figure 68. Regeneration from the nerve-cord in the earthworm.

If the front end is cut away and the nerve-cord cut out of a few of the remaining segments, as in this figure, the body regenerates from the nerve-cord, the segments without the nerve-cord being absorbed. (From Huxley and de Beer, after Morgan.)

organisation in the control of regeneration in planarians and cœlenterates. Nor does it weaken the evidence of the distribution of this organisation in the body which is provided by the facts of regeneration in these groups. If the axial field exists in the body, it is certainly an important part of the organisation of the body as a single whole, although other types of organisation may be superadded in more elaborate organisms; and, since it controls regeneration in at least some animals, it is hard to resist the conclusion that it is concerned in the control of specific form.

CHAPTER IX

BUD-FORMATION, MONSTERS, ETC.

BUD-FORMATION

THE formation of buds is one of the methods by which animals reproduce asexually (ch. XX). A part of the body becomes set apart to form the bud, and is then reorganised, while still attached to the parent body, into the specific form of the species. Usually the bud grows actively during its reorganisation. This reorganisation is a remoulding of the tissues by differential growth similar to that which occurs in regeneration (p. 127). Except in colonial animals the bud sooner or later separates from the parent and leads an independent life. Reproduction has taken place.

The formation of buds is a very common method of reproduction in most of the groups of the simpler invertebrates. It becomes less common as the body becomes more complex. It occurs very rarely, if at all, in many of the higher invertebrate phyla (Mollusca, Arthropoda). It does not occur in the vertebrates, but is common in two groups of the Chordata, the Tunicata, and the Pterobranchia. In general, the ability to reproduce by buds becomes reduced in the course of evolution, just as the power of regeneration is reduced. Probably, the large modifications of form which bud-formation necessarily demands would be incompatible with the life of a complex and specialised animal body.

Bud-formation is essentially the same process wherever it occurs, but the details of the manner in which the bud is formed vary greatly. In some of the simplest multicellular animals (*e.g. Hydra*) buds may be produced on many parts of the body, but in most animals the region of bud-formation is more restricted. Sometimes the buds are formed in special organs, such as the gonothecæ of the Hydrozoa. In different animals almost any part of the body may be the region of bud-formation, but it is most frequently at the posterior end. It is in that part of the body in the planarians and most annelids. In the simplest types of bud-formation in these groups, the whole hinder part of the body becomes organised as the bud and then separates. This is often called "fission": it differs from the formation of a bud on the surface of the body in that the tissues of the animal dividing by fission are originally organised and not an undifferentiated outgrowth. Fission may also occur in embryos, where it is known as polyembryony or twinning (ch. XX). Sometimes, as in *Planaria dorotocephala*, p. 143, the buds may themselves divide before they separate, so that a chain with the youngest bud at the posterior end of the chain is formed. In other planarians (*e.g. Stenostomum*, Fig. 64, p. 136) and in annelids, a zone of growth, *i.e.* a mass of actively growing tissue, is formed near the tail, and the buds arise one after the other by the growth of this zone. The arrangement of the buds on the zone of growth varies. A single bud may be formed at a time, and, if more buds are formed before the first separates, a chain is again formed, but here with the youngest bud at the front of the chain. In one annelid, *Trypanosyllis*, several buds are formed alongside one another on the zone of growth. In other annelids buds arise from parts of the body which are not at the posterior end. In *Syllis ramosa* they are formed on the dorsal cirri of the parapodia.

The specific form of the bud is usually, but not always, identical with that of the parent body. Imperfect buds, in which some of the organs are missing, are formed in some animals. Thus, the buds of *Syllis ramosa*, which remain attached to the parent and so form a complex branching body, have imperfect heads. Sometimes, again, the form of the bud differs from that of the parent in being another modification of the specific form of the species. This is so in the cœlenterates. The medusa, which is formed as a bud on the polyp colony, is very unlike the polyp in form, but both are best regarded as modifications of the one specific form (ch. XX). A similar example occurs in the annelids, where the buds often have functional genital organs and the parent bodies are non-sexual. The structure of other organs (*e.g.* the parapodia) may also differ between the parent and bud (heteronereis and heterosyllis). Bud-formation is always a re-organisation into some modification of the specific form, but not necessarily into the same modification as that of the parent body.

In at least one case, however, only a part of the specific form is formed from each bud. This is in *Diplosoma*, a tunicate, in which group bud-formation reaches what is perhaps its extreme development among animals. When the body of *Diplosoma* is about to divide asexually, two or three separate buds are formed in different parts of the body. Each of these buds reproduces the parts of the body from which it arose, and between them they form a complete new set of organs. The animal then divides so that each of the products of the division contains a complete set of organs. There is the further complication that the parent body itself divides in this division, part of each new animal being formed from the parent body and part from the buds. We do not need to consider the process in more detail. It is enough to notice that even here bud-formation consists in a re-organisation of the tissues into the specific form, although a whole body is not formed in each bud.

In this example we are passing rather far from such simple examples of bud-formation as the fission of a planarian. The buds of *Diplosoma* are reproductive buds, for they lead to division and reproduction of the animal. The fact that the new specific form is not developed from a single bud does not prevent us from regarding the example as one of reproductive bud-formation.

We pass entirely away from reproductive bud-formation when we come to phenomena in which the organs within a single body are reorganised in the course of its life history. Organs are sometimes formed during development from undifferentiated masses of tissue, called "buds." They may perhaps rightly be called "organ-buds," but are not reproductive. The "imaginal buds" of the insects are such. They grow at pupation and replace many of the organs of the larval body, which are resorbed. Similarly, in the metamorphosis of the echinoderms the adult rudiment replaces the larval organs by new tissues formed by its growth. In these examples much reorganisation goes on in the body, as it does in bud-formation, but no new organism is produced—it is not a process of reproduction, as bud formation is. It may well be that the processes of reorganisation in bud formation and metamorphosis are similar in their fundamental nature, but in this respect at least they are distinct. Reorganisation at metamorphosis passes on through examples in which the replacement is less general (*e.g.* in the metamorphosis of the tadpole) to normal development, in which, also, new organs are often formed and larval organs resorbed. There, it will not be suggested that the phenomenon is one of bud-formation.

If an animal (*e.g.* a planarian) which is forming buds is treated with dilute KCN, a maximum of susceptibility is found at the front end of each bud, where a head is forming. In Fig. 69 the susceptibility gradient along the body of a *Planaria dorotocephala* with a chain of developing buds is shown. Each bud shows a maximum of susceptibility at its head and a gradient over its body. The youngest bud (the most posterior, p. 142), has the highest susceptibility among the buds and the shortest gradient.

We have seen that the susceptibility gradient is probably one of the expressions of the axial organisation, which plays a large part in the control of the development and maintenance of the specific form. In the bud a new susceptibility gradient is developed, and a new specific form. We are therefore forced to the conclusion that a new axial organisation is formed in the bud. In fact, we must conclude that the tissues of the bud have become isolated from the control of the axial organisation of the parent body and have developed in themselves a new axial organisation, just as a new axial organisation develops in a separated piece of the body of a planarian. In the bud the isolation is functional only; the bud remains attached to the parent body during its reorganisation, and is not spatially separated from it. We have seen (p. 113) that isolation from the control of growth necessary for the maintenance of specific form occurs in cancerous tissues. This may also be a related phenomenon.

We know very little of the causes which lead to the isolation of the tissues of the bud. In discussing regeneration in pieces of a planarian body which had been rendered physiologically inactive by treatment

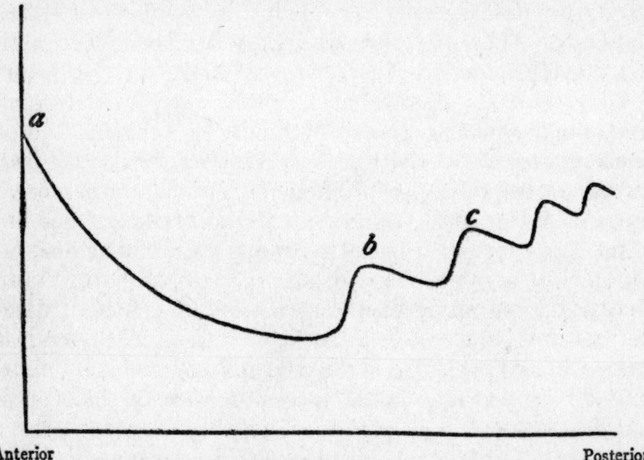

Figure 69. Susceptibility gradient in *Planaria dorotocephala*.

Ordinates susceptibility; abscissæ, polarity axis. *a*, head of the animal; *b*, *c* heads of the buds. (After Child.)

with dilute narcotics (p. 133), we found that a weakened centre of dominance might be able to organise only a small part of the piece—the field of dominance failed to cover the whole of the piece. Something of the same kind seems to happen in many examples of bud-formation. We have seen that buds are often formed as the body grows large, and more frequently at the posterior end of the body than elsewhere. It seems that with the decrease of physiological activity which accompanies increase of size, and with the increasing distance of the tissues from the centre of dominance, the axial organisation fails to cover the whole of the body and a part becomes isolated as a bud. In confirmation of this, it has been found that, when the activity of the tissues of a planarian is reduced by treatment with narcotics or by low temperature, buds are formed nearer the front of the body than normally.

These reasons will not cover the initiation of all types of buds. In many animals, such as *Syllis ramosa*, buds are formed on parts of the body which are not the most distant from the head. We found reasons to think (p. 137) that the reversed heads on the posterior faces of short pieces of a planarian were formed as a result of stimulation of the activity of the tissues by the damage. If this is so, we might expect a new centre of the axial organisation to be set up—and a bud to be formed—wherever in the body the activity of the tissues is raised sufficiently. In *Hydra* and *Corymorpha* it has been found that damage at some point of the body often results in the formation of a bud at that point. This may be due to stimulation of activity in the tissues at the point of damage (p. 137). It is also interesting, as confirming the general conception of the axial organisation which we have developed, that in one species of the Hydrida (*Pelmatohydra oligactis*) damage of the tissues results in bud-formation much more frequently if the head is cut off at the same time as the tissue is damaged. The inhibitory action of the head region (p. 135) is thus reduced and a new organisation is more easily formed. Cutting off the posterior end of the body has no such effect.

However, even if bud-formation is the result of increased activity of the tissues at the place where the bud is formed, we have no knowledge of the stimulus which produces this increased activity at certain places in the normal life of the animal. We have also no knowledge of the relation of many types of bud, *e.g.* the incomplete buds of *Diplosoma*, to the axial organisation. Our knowledge of bud-formation is very incomplete, but it seems that we can safely say that in some animals, and more often in the less complex animals, parts of the body may become isolated from the axial organisation—as a result of causes which are at present largely unknown—and that when a part becomes so isolated it develops a new axial organisation in itself and becomes organised as a bud.

MONSTERS AND COLONIES

A monstrous body is one which differs from a normal body in that the organisation of its specific form is markedly different from the normal. Monsters may be of many kinds. Some differ from the normal in the size of the parts, *e.g.* micro- or macrocephalic monsters; others in the number of the organs—vertebrate monsters with supernumerary limbs or a reduced number of limbs are well known. In this section we shall consider only those monsters in which the body can be shown to be composed of the bodies of two or more individuals incompletely united. Siamese twins are a well-known example of this type of monster. In monsters of this class some parts of the two bodies must be distinct—otherwise the body would be giant and not monstrous. Colonies are not monsters, although in them the bodies of the members are united to a greater or less extent, for the union in a colony is normal to the species.

In these double monsters the union of the two bodies may be very slight or almost complete. All intermediate conditions occur between two animals united by a small portion of the body to others in which the monstrous condition is shown by doubling in only a small part of the head or tail.

Monsters are always pathological and occur only rarely in nature. They have, however, been found even in complex animals (*e.g.* two-headed snakes). They can be produced in many different animals by several types of experimental treatment. In planarians a double monster may be obtained by the simple method of dividing the body at the head end by a longitudinal cut extending a short distance down the body (Fig. 70). If the divided parts are prevented from re-uniting, each forms a separate head and the body behind the cut remains single. This is a monstrous body.

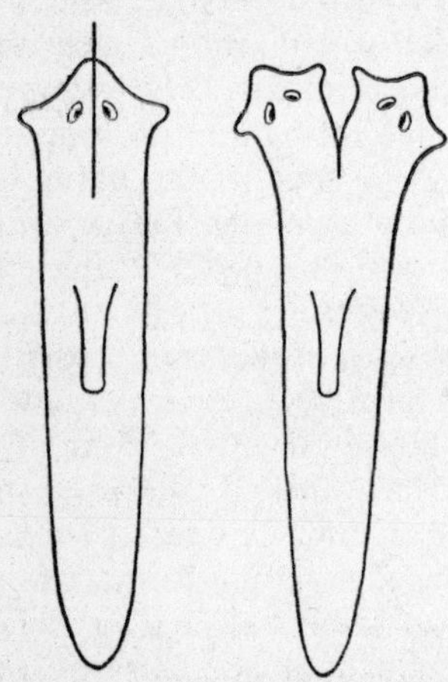

Figure 70. Monster formed in a planarian by a longitudinal cut in the head region.

Monsters with a single tail and two heads may be formed in several groups of animals by partially separating the blastomeres of the dividing egg. The best-known experiments of this kind have been carried out on the egg of a vertebrate, the newt. If a thread is tied round a newt's egg in the plane of the first division, double-headed monsters (often called "Janus-headed") are produced. The two bodies are united farther back in the dorsoventral plane of symmetry. The extent of the separation of the two bodies varies with the tightness of the thread. All conditions from two completely separated bodies, through monsters with two heads and one tail, to a single undivided body may be produced. Among the invertebrates, similar monsters have been obtained by interference with the early segmentation divisions in annelids (*Tubifex* and *Chætopterus*) and echinoderms (*Patiria*, a starfish). In all these monsters the double body is produced by independent development of the partially separated blastomeres, the independence of the development being more or less complete in the various examples of monstrous body.

Monsters can also be formed by uniting parts of two originally separate bodies. This can be done very simply in the eggs of the echinoderms. The segmenting egg is surrounded by the transparent gelatinous layer (hyaline layer) which holds the blastomeres together. This layer breaks down and disappears in calcium-free sea-water, but it is reformed when the eggs are replaced in normal sea-water. If two eggs in an early segmentation stage are first treated with calcium-free sea-water, and then returned to normal sea-water, and held together, the hyaline layer becomes continuous over them both. They develop as a body which may be either a giant or a monster. It is a single, giant body if the axes of polarity of the two eggs were parallel and in the same direction while they were held together; it is monstrous if the axes were at an angle to one another, or parallel but in opposite directions. These experiments are in reality examples of grafting two pieces of animal tissue together, a subject which we shall discuss in the next section. They are mentioned here because they result in the formation of monstrous bodies.

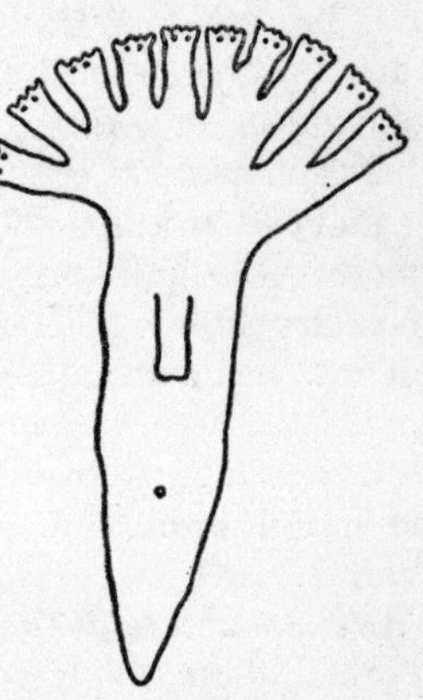

Figure 71. Multiple monster in *Dendrocœlum lacteum*. (From Huxley and de Beer.)

Very complex monstrous bodies may be formed in the planarians by making numerous cuts across the edge of the original body (Fig. 71).

We have seen that a single axial organisation is present in the normal animal body. It is to be expected that the multiple bodies of monsters would contain multiple axial organisations, separate where the bodies of the monster are separate, and united where they are united. This is, in fact, so. In double-headed monsters a centre of the axial organisation can be recognised in each head by examination of the susceptibility of the tissues to poisons; and the axial gradients become united in the single posterior part of the body. In monsters with other types of arrangement, the axial organisations are always multiple where the organisation of the body is multiple, and single where it is single.

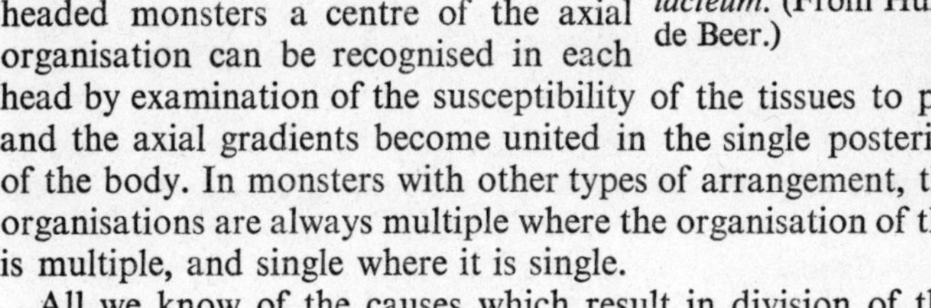

All we know of the causes which result in division of the axial organisation in a monstrous body is that such division may be produced by incomplete division of the tissue (as in the newt's egg) or by incomplete union (as in echinoderm eggs).

The plane of union of the two bodies in a monster is often one of the planes of symmetry of the body. This is not always so—echinoderm eggs may be united with the planes of symmetry arranged in any way. It is most common in monsters formed by interference with the early blastomeres. It is in such monsters, and probably always, rather a result of the way in which the monster was formed than a necessary condition for the union of two bodies to form a monster. The planes of symmetry in an animal body are often determined by the planes of the first few segmentation divisions. In the newt's egg the first division plane is the dorsoventral plane of the resulting animal, and the fact that the monsters are united in this plane is a result of the fact that the thread was tied in the plane of the first division.

Colonial animals resemble monsters in that the bodies of more than one individual are united in them. In colonies the union is often by the posterior end of the body, and frequently by an inactive stolon or stock, but in some colonies (*e.g.* in some of the colonial tunicates) large parts of the bodies of the members of the colony may be united. When the axial organisation of a colony is investigated by the method of susceptibility to poisons or by study of regeneration, it is found (in all colonies which have been examined) that each member of the colony has a centre of the axial organisation at its head and that the gradients from these centres fuse where the bodies of the individuals are united. The existence of a separate centre in each member of a colony appears, for instance, in the experiments on the regeneration of *Tubularia* polyps which we have discussed (p. 138). Colonies, therefore, resemble monsters in the arrangement of their axial organisations as well as in being composed of the united bodies of more than one individual. Some modifications of the typical arrangement of the axial organisation occur in colonies. There is a centre of the axial organisation at the growing point at a free end of the stolon from which the polyps arise in a hydroid colony. This centre is weak as compared with the centres at the heads of the polyps, and it is perhaps for this reason that it may not produce a polyp in this position.

GRAFTS

To graft two pieces of living tissue together is to cause them to unite so that they live and grow as one body after union. A small piece of tissue may be grafted into the body of an animal or plant of any group. Such a graft unites with the other tissues and is absorbed into the organisation of the body. Grafting of this kind is used commonly in the cultivation of plants and in surgery. A piece of skin, for instance, from another part of the body may be grafted over a wound. In some of the vertebrates (*e.g.* the Amphibia), larger organs such as limbs or gonads may be grafted. If the grafting has been successful, the grafted organ in time becomes provided with the nerves and blood-vessels necessary for its growth. If the graft is unsuccessful, the grafted tissue dies and is usually absorbed. The larger the grafted organ is, and the older the tissues of the host and the graft, the longer the body takes to accommodate the graft and the less likely it is to survive.

In many invertebrates, and the lower vertebrates (tadpoles), large parts of two bodies may be grafted together. Undamaged ectodermal epithelium will not usually unite with tissue held against it, but if two cut surfaces are held together, they will often adhere and the tissues on the two sides of the cut surfaces unite across the cut. Tissues of *Hydra* will join in this way if held together for a few minutes; in others of the simpler invertebrates (*e.g.* planarians) the surfaces must be held together longer to ensure union, but usually for only a few hours. Often the histological structure after junction of the tissues shows no trace that union has taken place. It is as true of grafting as of all other forms of reorganisation in the animal body—regeneration, bud-formation—that the simpler the body of the animal the greater its power of reorganisation.

Nevertheless, even in such highly evolved invertebrates as lepidopterous insects grafting is possible. Parts of pupæ have been grafted together, and the united organism has emerged as an imago. But here the union of the organs of the body was not complete.

As a general rule, the closer the character of the grafted tissue is to that of the normal tissue at the position of the graft the greater are the chances of successful grafting. Grafts from the host's own body survive more readily than grafts from another individual of the same species; and the nearer a graft is to its normal position in the body the more likely it is to be successful. Interspecific and even intergeneric grafts are sometimes possible, but are more difficult than grafts within a single species. In earthworms parts of the bodies of two different genera have been united (*Lumbricus* and *Allolobophora*). Different species of *Hydra* have been united. In tadpoles parts of the body in two species have been united and the resulting animal has metamorphosed.

When the piece of grafted tissue is small in comparison with the size of the host body, the organisation of the body is unaltered by introduction of the graft. But grafting experiments in which large parts of two bodies are united may result in considerable reorganisation. Such experiments give us another opportunity of studying the axial organisation of the body. By uniting different parts of the body we can make combinations of every kind, and can observe how the body reorganises itself. An example of these experiments has already been mentioned, the union of echinoderm eggs which produces monsters (p. 147). Many other grafting experiments result in the formation of monsters.

Pieces of the body of *Hydra* have been grafted together in a long series of experiments by a number of investigators. The subject has, in fact, been investigated for as long a time as any other subject in experimental biology. The first experiments were made by Trembley in 1763. Many zoologists have dealt with the subject since Trembley's time, some within recent years. Almost every possible combination has been made.

After two cut surfaces of *Hydra* have been caused to unite by being held together, no reorganisation of the body occurs for some time. The union becomes complete and the complex body lives for some time—often several days—unchanged. But later, in many cases, reorganisation occurs. This delay in the appearance of the reorganisation is important in its bearings on the interpretation of the whole process, for it shows that the reorganisation is not a direct result of the changes which occur at the time of union. It is rather the result of the conditions within the body after the union has taken place.

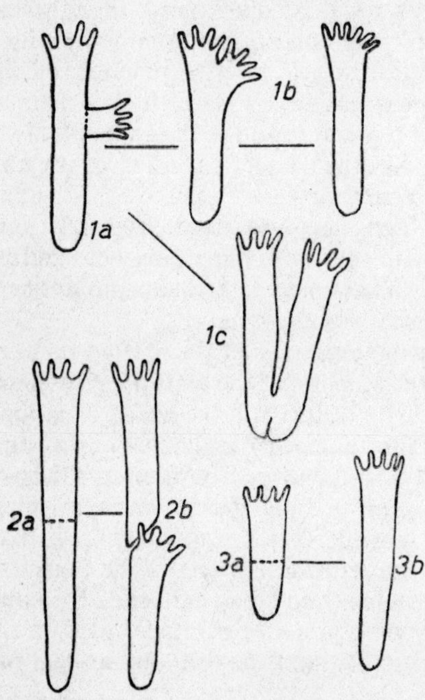

Figure 72. Results of grafting experiments on *Hydra*. (After Morgan.)

These experiments on *Hydra* give results which are exactly those we should expect from the knowledge we have gained of the axial organisation. In cœlenterate polyps such as *Hydra* the centre of the axial organisation is in the region of the mouth, and from this centre the organisation extends over the body. Therefore, if graft and host each contain a mouth, the axial organisation in the united body is double; the body is, in fact, monstrous. This is so, for instance, if a graft of the anterior part of the body is inserted on the side of a *Hydra* (Fig. 72, 1*a*). But monsters rarely persist in *Hydra*; almost always either the two axial organisations unite, or the body divides into two halves each with one of the organisations. This happens with grafts such as that of Fig. 72, 1*a*. Either the two heads unite by resorption of the tissue between them (1*b*), or the single tail is divided between the two heads and the halves separate (1*c*), these processes of reorganisation taking place, as usual, some days after the graft was inserted. Division of the body and its separation into two parts may occur in any combination in which the axial organisation is double, even if one of the organisations does not contain a head. For instance, when front and hind parts each of which is more than half the body (2*a*) are united, the axial organisation is double, for the front surface of the hind part is farther up the axial organisation than the hind surface of the front part. In the reorganisation the two parts separate at the point of junction. A new head is formed on the hinder part (2*b*). But, if the hinder part is shorter than that which was cut away from the front part, the axial organisation in the united body is single, and no separation occurs (3*a*, *b*). Many other results may be obtained. They are all in agreement with the conceptions of the axial organisation of the body which we have formed. A small graft in *Hydra*, as in other animals, may become united with the body of the host without reorganisation, whatever the arrangement of its axial organisation. It must be supposed that the axial organisation of the host is then able to overcome the axial organisation of the graft, and to impose on the graft its own organisation.

That a graft may organise tissues of the host body is shown by the results of some of these experiments on *Hydra*, where part of the host body separates and is organised under the control of the head in the graft (1*c*). It is shown equally clearly in experiments on the hydroid *Corymorpha* (Fig. 73). A piece of tissue inserted into the side of a polyp results in the formation of a head at the position of the graft, the head being formed partly from host and partly from graft tissue.* In these experiments it was found that the head is larger and its formation more rapid if the tissue to be grafted is taken from near the head of a polyp (Fig. 73, *d*, *e*).

The organising power of a graft is shown even more clearly in experiments on the planarians. In a planarian body, a head region may be grafted in reversed position near the tail (Fig. 74). The graft contains a centre of the axial organisation, and the organisation in the united body is therefore double, one organisation, that in the tail region, being reversed. The body is monstrous, but monsters in planarians, in contrast with *Hydra*, usually persist. In the reorganisation, the host tissues near the graft are organised under the influence of the reversed organisation. That this is a true reorganisation of the tissues in this part of the body is shown not only by the fact that new organs are formed in these tissues (*e.g.* a pharynx), but also by

* The formation of a head in the grafted tissue in these experiments may be due to damage at the place of the graft, just as a bud may be formed in *Hydra* at a place where the tissue is damaged (p. 145).

considerable independence of behaviour in the new organisation. The head in the posterior region of the body may be seen turning from side to side independently of the behaviour of the anterior head region.

In considering regeneration and bud-formation we have been forced to conclude that the centre of the axial organisation controls the organisation of the rest of the body. The results of the present section add the conclusion that tissues which were originally under the control of one centre may become organised under another

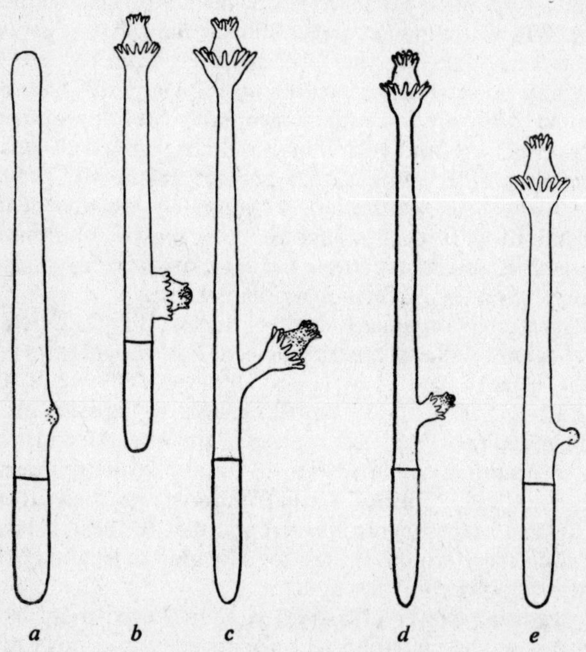

Figure 73. Induced heads in *Corymorpha* formed under the influence of grafts.

a–c, growth of the head when the grafted tissue is taken from near the head of a polyp; *d–e*, growth of two heads with grafts from farther down the polyp. Graft tissue stippled. (After Child.)

centre introduced into the body. Reorganisation in the grafted body is very similar to that in bud-formation. In both phenomena a new centre of the axial organisation is produced in an animal body—here by introduction from the outside, in bud-formation spontaneously. In both grafting and bud-formation the result of the formation of the new centre is that some of the tissues of the body are organised under its influence.

RESTITUTION

Union of two or more separated pieces of tissue of more or less the same size, to form a single body, is often called "*restitution.*" We have already met some examples of this phenomenon. It includes some cases of grafting; the union of two halves of a *Hydra* to form a single body (Fig. 72, 1*b*) is clearly an example of this phenomenon. So, also, is the formation of a single giant body from two echinoderm eggs which have been joined with their axes of polarity parallel and in the same direction. Echinoderms are not the only animals in which giant bodies can be produced by fusion of eggs. Similar giants have been formed in animals of several groups (vertebrates, nemertines, etc.). Giant larvæ are also known to occur naturally in nematodes (*Ascaris*); it is probable that they arise from united eggs.

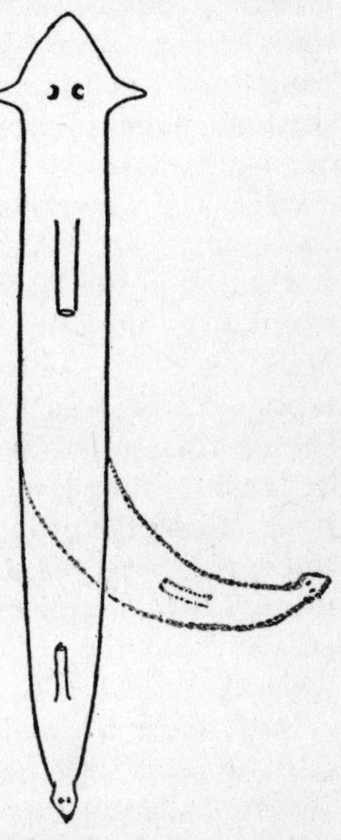

Figure 74. Grafted head in *Planaria* with reversed orientation. (After Santos.)

More complex examples of restitution are known. The process may occur in masses of tissue formed by the union of a large number of separate pieces. Even separate cells may unite and form a single body. The blastomeres of echinoderm eggs may be separated by being placed in calcium-free sea-water (p. 147). The hyaline layer which holds the blastomeres together breaks down and the blastomeres fall apart. They are normally contained within the fertilisation membrane which surrounds the egg after fertilisation at some distance from its surface, but if this is removed, they lie entirely free in the sea-water. Blastomeres of the two- or four-cell stages, when separated in this way, will, if they are returned to normal sea-water, develop into small but perfect larvæ. But, if several blastomeres are allowed to come into contact with each other at the time of their return to normal sea-water, they will sometimes unite and form a single, perfect larva. Since the blastomeres can develop separately, they must have, or at least be capable of forming, each a separate axial organisation. In fact, the existence of an axial gradient can be demonstrated even in the unfertilised echinoderm egg. After the union a single axial organisation must replace the separate organisations of the blastomeres.

A somewhat similar example of restitution can be observed in sponge tissue. The body of many sponges (*e.g. Sycon*) can be broken down into small masses of cells by being passed through gauze or crumbled between the fingers. Most of the cells are not killed by this treatment. They lie, at first singly or in small groups, in the medium, but they are soon collected into larger groups by the activities of the amœbocytes, which wander about among them. The other cells adhere to the surface of the amœbocytes, and so are brought together into these larger groups. If a group contains most of the types of cell which occur in the sponge body (which has far fewer types of cell than the bodies of most multicellular animals), the cells of the group arrange themselves into layers similar to those of the body of the sponge. The group then grows and takes on again the specific form of the sponge. The circumstances here differ somewhat from those of restitution in the blastomeres of an echinoderm egg. We have here restitution from cells derived from an adult body, and in the sponge body, as in the bodies of other multicellular animals, most of the types of cell are unable to modify themselves into other types. It is for this reason that most of the types of cell of the sponge body must be present in the group of cells if it is to grow into a perfect sponge body. Where the proportion of the various types of cell in the restitution group is very far from the normal, abnormal bodies are formed. Groups with a large excess of collar cells and few dermal cells form vesicles with the collar cells on the outside and not enclosed in flagellate chambers as in the normal sponge (ch. XIX).

Both in the echinoderm blastomeres and in the groups of sponge cells we must suppose that the axial organisation is either weak or absent in the separated pieces of tissue, and that, for this reason, it can be replaced by a single organisation in the united mass. We met another example of the replacement of a weakened organisation by a new system in the regeneration of horizontal pieces of *Corymorpha* which had been treated with dilute alcohol (p. 132).

The occurrence of restitution implies that there is a tendency for a single axial organisation to replace more complex systems in single masses of animal tissue. The existence of monsters and colonies shows us that, in the animal body, this tendency does not always result in the suppression of all but one of the axial organisations present; and in bud-formation we find that a second organisation may be developed spontaneously. Nevertheless, the tendency seems to exist. It is most marked and effective (1) where the complex organisations are weakly developed—as is presumably true in separated blastomeres and small masses of sponge cells; (2) where one of the organisations is much smaller than another—as in a small piece of tissue grafted into a much larger body; and (3) where the axial organisations are parallel and in the same direction—as in the united eggs which produce giant larvæ.

"ORGANISERS"

In the development of the Amphibia it has been shown that the earliest stages in the differentiation of some of the organs occur only if certain other organs are present in the neighbourhood of the differentiating organs. The best-known example of this is the action of the chorda-mesoderm (*i.e.* the tissue which has been rolled inwards over the blastopore lip and lies, in the gastrula, on the dorsal side of the archenteron), in causing the formation of neural tissue in the ectoderm above it. Unless the chorda-mesoderm lies under the ectoderm, neural ridges do not form. And, if pieces of the chorda-mesoderm are grafted under the ectoderm in abnormal positions, neural tissue is formed over the grafts, provided the ectoderm is in a suitable "competent" condition (*i.e.* provided the larva is of suitable age and certain other conditions hold). This invaginated tissue is therefore able to cause the formation of the ridges in the ectoderm. It has been called an "*organiser*."

It has been shown, however, that the chorda-mesoderm causes the formation of the neural tissue, not directly, but by instigating the ectoderm to produce them. The formation of the neural tissue is due to the inherent properties of the ectoderm, and the chorda-mesoderm merely sets in action the power of the ectoderm to produce them. It is therefore better to speak of the action of the chorda-mesoderm as "*evocation*" rather than as organisation .

The evocating power of the chorda-mesoderm has been said to be due to production of a chemical substance within it, and the ectoderm to respond to the presence of this substance as it diffuses into it from the chorda-mesoderm. Dead chorda-mesoderm will produce the effect. Tissue killed by boiling is still effective but not if it is heated to 150° C. It was concluded that evocation is caused by a chemical substance set free by the evocating tissue, which is destroyed at 150° but not at 100° C.

This evocation of the formation of the neural tissue is not the only action of the chorda-mesoderm in causing differentiation in the larva. We shall return to other actions of this tissue later.

Evocation of this type may probably be frequent in the bodies of animals. It is possible that control is exerted over the development of much of the structure of the body in this way. A second example of evocation in amphibian development is the evocation of a lens in the ectoderm by the tissues of the eye. Here again grafting of the evocating tissues below the ectoderm in abnormal positions results in the formation of the organs above them. Very probably the ectoderm responds to some chemical stimulus derived from the tissues of the eye, but we know nothing of the chemical nature of this stimulus.

Few examples of evocation are known to occur among the invertebrates, but we must not assume for this reason that it is uncommon among them. One undoubted example occurs in sea-urchin development. The adult rudiment is evoked in the larva by part of the cœlome, the hydrocœle, which lies beneath it. If a supernumerary (right) hydrocœle is formed, a second rudiment develops above it. The size of the rudiment is correlated with the size of the hydrocœle, and experimental disturbance of the position of the hydrocœle results in the rudiment being formed above the hydrocœle in its altered position. This evidence leaves no doubt that we are here concerned with evocation, but the nature of the evocating stimulus is unknown.

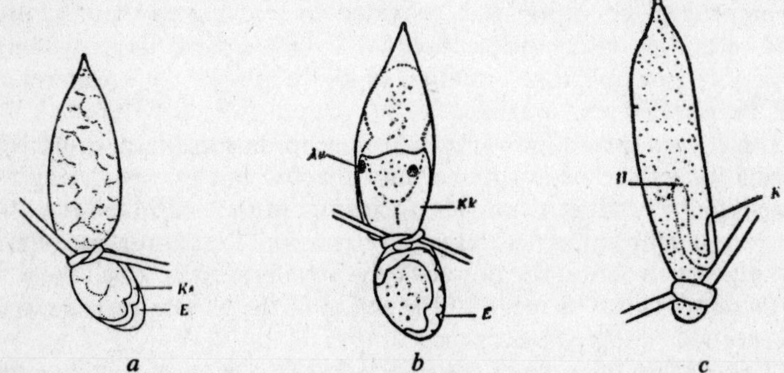

Figure 75. Development of constricted eggs of the dragon-fly, *Platycnemis*.

(*a*) no development in egg constricted tightly in front of the organising region; (*b*) development in loosely constricted egg; (*c*) development in egg constricted behind the organising region. (After Seidel.)

Evocation is also known to occur in the development of the insects. In the dragon-fly egg there is a region just in front of the posterior end of the egg which must be in communication with the rest of the egg if any part of the egg is to develop (Fig. 75). This region can be isolated from the other parts of the egg by constricting the egg with a thread tied round it in front of the evocating region. No development then takes place. But if the constriction is so loose that communication is still possible, all parts of the egg develop. And if the constriction is so far back that it is behind the evocating region, development is normal. Probably the evocating region produces a chemical substance without which other parts of the egg cannot develop, and diffusion of this substance through the egg is prevented by the constriction. If the egg is constricted during later development—when this substance would presumably have already diffused through the egg—development continues normally on both sides of the constriction. It seems, then, that we have here another example of evocation, but this example differs from those we have previously considered in that here all the tissues of the developing animal respond to the stimulus, and not only certain of them.

The concentration of a chemical substance diffusing from a tissue will decrease as the distance from the tissue increases. The evocating influence must therefore be exerted in a field round the evocating tissue, just as the influence of the axial organisation extends in a field round the centre. Since chemical fields of this type exist in the body, and are effective in controlling the development of structure, it may be asked whether all organisation in the body, and especially the axial organisation itself, may be brought about by chemical fields of this type.

Here we may refer again to the amphibian organiser. As we have seen, it evokes the formation of neural ridges, and this evocating power may be due to production of a chemical substance. But this is not the whole of the reaction. Not only are the neural ridges evoked but their parts become differentiated and arranged in a definite pattern giving the form of a normal nerve cord. It is not possible to believe that this organising (or as we may better call it '*individuating*') function is the result of the simple spread of an evocating substance outwards from the evoking tissue in a diffusion field. It must have some other cause, probably in the neural ridges themselves. It is exerted in a field in the region of the evocation, but we have no knowledge of the physico-chemical nature of this field. Its action is of precisely the same type as the action of the axial organisation in controlling the arrangement of the organs in the body as a whole. We may call such organising fields "*individuation fields*."

It seems, then, that we must think of two types of organisation of the body: (1) evocation by means of chemical diffusion fields, whereby tissues are instigated to produce structures; and (2) individuation by fields of unknown physical nature, whereby the arrangement of the tissues and the structures they will produce is determined. The amphibian organiser has both an evocation field and an individuation field; the axial organisation is so far as we know only an individuation field, though it is also probably correlated with the distribution of physiological characters in the tissues; and the organiser of the dragon-fly egg probably gives rise only to an evocation field. In the next chapter we shall consider yet another type of organisation in the body, that of the growth gradients. This is the *means* whereby much of the structural differentiation which results from these two types of field, and probably other unknown types of organisation in the body, is produced in the tissues.

CHAPTER X

GROWTH AND THE FORM OF THE ANIMAL BODY

THE term "growth" is here used to include both increase and decrease of size in the animal body. The growth may be called positive when the size is increasing and negative when it is decreasing.

Strictly, only change of size in the mass of the living protoplasm of the body should be called growth, but it is difficult to devise a method by which the true growth of the body, in this sense, can be measured. Both the weight and length of the body are often used as measures of its growth, but neither of these gives us an accurate measure of the true growth. Change of weight will differ from the true growth when the body is laying down or using up inactive reserve materials which are not part of the living protoplasm; change of the length fails as a measure of the growth when the length of the body is determined by the size of structural features laid down early in the life-history, or when the shape of the body is altering markedly. Nevertheless, if we take precautions to avoid these obvious sources of error, change in either length or weight will give us a fairly accurate estimate of the growth of the body, and they are the only means by which we can easily reach such an estimate. Growth in weight and length are closely related. So long as the form does not alter appreciably, the weight of the body is directly proportional to the cube of its length. Where the change of form may be neglected, as it often may when we are dealing with adult animals, both give similar results as estimates of growth.

Change in size and in form go on side by side throughout the life-histories of animals. During development this is obvious; the animal grows continuously and develops the complex structure of the adult at the same time. It is true that the rate of growth in different periods of the development varies greatly. The growth-rate is slight during the initial stages, when the animal is living on the stores of yolk in the egg. As soon as feeding begins growth becomes rapid, but from that time onwards the growth-rate, measured as a proportion of the size of the whole animal, falls off continuously. In some animals, for instance in the mammals, the rate falls to zero soon after the adult condition is reached, but it does not do so in all, or even in the majority, of animals. In most animals (many fishes among the vertebrates and most of the invertebrates except the insects) growth continues at a decreasing rate throughout the adult period. In such animals the curve of growth is, in fact, parabolic (Fig. 76); the growth-rate continuously approaches a zero value but never reaches it.

It is chiefly in terrestrial animals that growth ceases when the adult condition is reached. The probable reason for this is that the conditions of terrestrial life, and especially the greater weight of the body in air, exert a much stricter control on the size of the animal than the conditions in an aquatic medium. If the animal takes on a flying habit

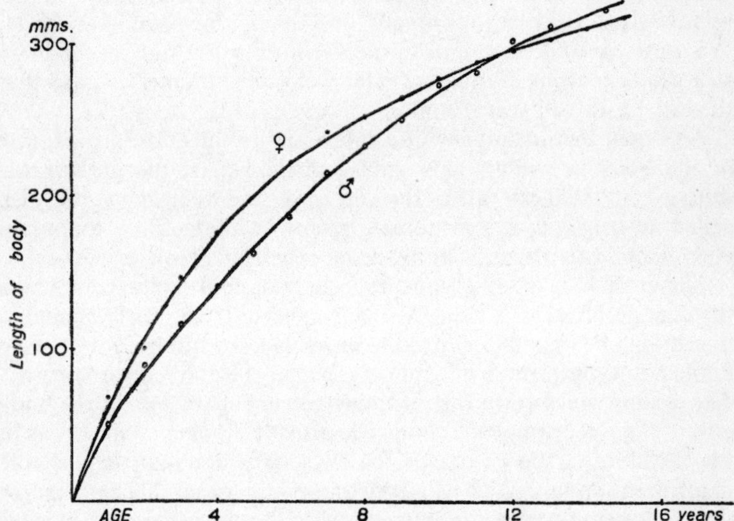

Figure 76. Growth curves of male and female lobsters. (After Elmhirst.)

birds or insects) the control becomes even stricter than in other non-aquatic modes of life. Large variations in size are much more dangerous for a terrestrial than an aquatic animal, for much the same reasons that the total size of the body may be larger in aquatic animals (p. 46). A more or less constant mean adult size must be regarded as an adaptation to terrestrial life. But not all terrestrial animals cease to grow as adults. Some reptiles and many terrestrial invertebrates grow throughout their life-histories.

Even in animals which cease to grow larger when the adult condition is reached, the size of the body is not entirely constant during any part of the life-history. Slight variations both in size and form occur as the animal becomes older. These variations are usually small during middle life, but increase again as the animal becomes senile. As man grows old, he usually decreases slightly in height and still more in weight. It is only in such animals as the insects, where the adult body is determined in size by the hard external skeleton, that no change in size occurs in the adult. Thus, growth, either positive or negative, is a characteristic feature of all stages of the life-history of animals. Throughout the life-history it accompanies change of form.

This association of growth with change of form suggests that the two are closely related, and this is true. Most of the change of form which occurs during the life-history of an animal is produced by differential growth of the parts of the body, one organ or part of an organ growing faster or slower than another, and faster or slower than the body as a whole. These differential growth-rates alter the relative sizes of the various organs, and so alter the form of the body. We must conclude that during the life-history not only is the body as a whole growing at different rates from time to time, but also that the rate of growth varies among the organs of the body.

An organ that is growing at a rate equal to the mean growth-rate of the body is said to have *isometric* growth. If the growth-rate differs from the mean rate of the body, it is said to be *allometric* (also called heterogonic, dysharmonic), positively allometric if the organ is growing faster than the body, negatively if it is growing slower.

The growth of many organs, especially in adult animals in which the change of form is slow, if not isometric, is so nearly isometric that it may be impossible to show that it is not entirely so. But, even in the adult, the growth of some organs may be markedly allometric. The organs which form the secondary sexual characters of the body give us a good example of allometric growth. In many animals, as in the vertebrates, the young of the two sexes are indistinguishable in form, the organs which will form the secondary sexual characters in the adult being equally developed in both sexes. Males and females become different in form by unequal growth of these organs in later development and sometimes during adult life. This growth is allometric in at least one of the sexes.

The size of the abdomen in the crabs is a typical secondary sexual character. The abdomen is very much broader in the female than in the male, and the large size of the female abdomen is reached by strongly positive allometric growth. The growth of the abdomen in the female pea-crab, *Pinnotheres pisum*, is shown in Fig. 77. The figure shows very clearly that the abdomen grows faster than the body.

The growth of the abdomen in the crabs may be used to illustrate some other characters of allometric growth. In Fig. 78 the breadth of the abdomen in the two sexes of another crab, *Carcinus mænas*, the shore-crab, is plotted against the length of the carapace, which is taken as the convenient measure of the growth of the body. The abdomen being here, as in the pea-crab, a secondary sexual character, its growth differs in the male and female. The smallest crabs are indistinguishable in sex, but, in all crabs larger than this, the abdomen

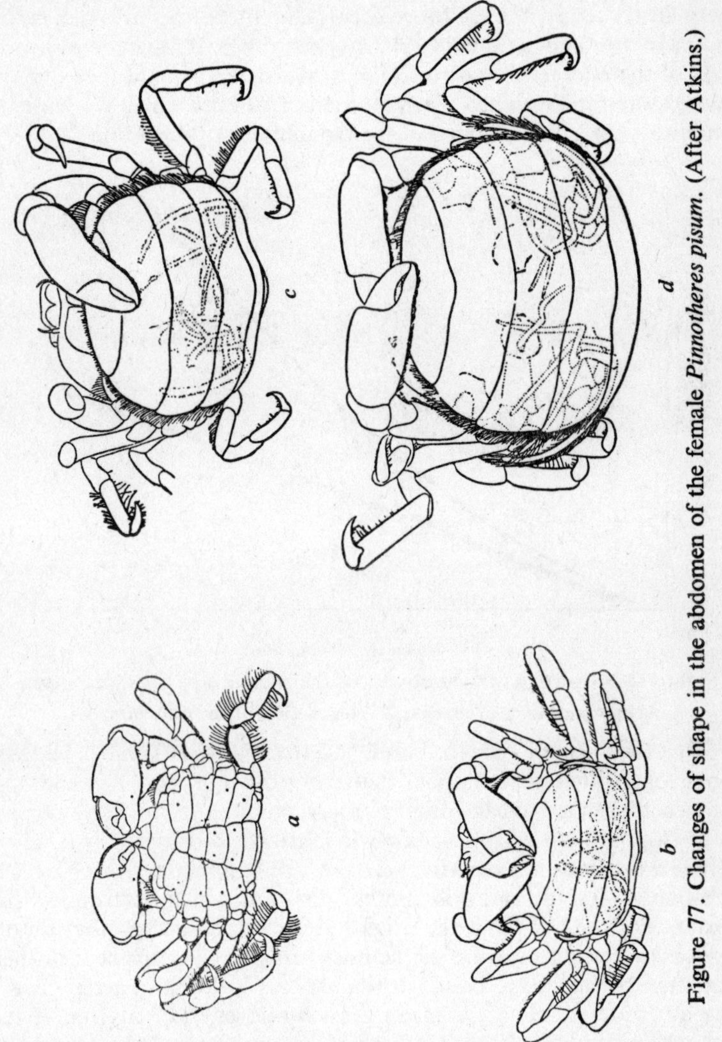

Figure 77. Changes of shape in the abdomen of the female *Pinnotheres pisum*. (After Atkins.)

grows much faster in the female than in the male. Also the form of the curve shows that the female abdomen is growing throughout the life-history faster than the body, *i.e.* its growth is positively allometric, whereas that of the male abdomen is about equal to that of the body, or isometric. Since it is so, the curve of its growth is almost straight.

If these same data are plotted on a logarithmic scale (Fig. 79), another characteristic of allometric growth becomes apparent. Plotted on this scale, the curves, for both the males and females, are very nearly straight lines. More accurately, these lines are each composed of two lines at small angles to each other. It is a general property of the allometric growth of an organ that it should give one or more straight lines when plotted on a logarithmic scale. We have to enquire what is the meaning of the straightness of these lines.

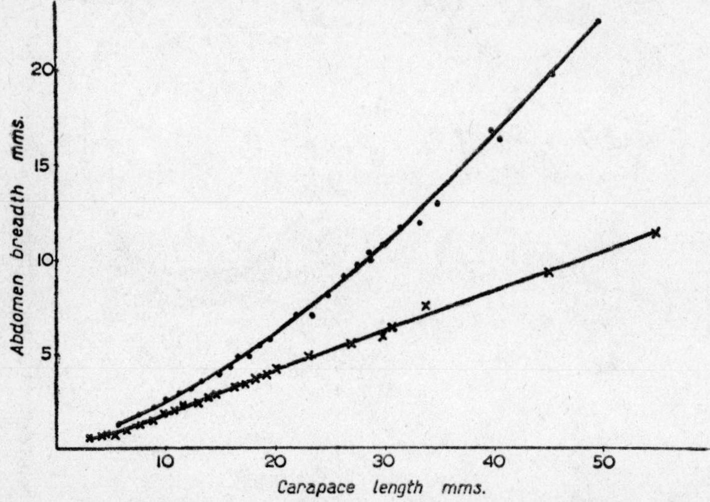

Figure 78. Growth in the abdomen of the shore-crab, *Carcinus mænas*. Arithmetic scale. • females; ×, males. (Redrawn from Huxley.)

That the curve of growth should be a straight line when it is plotted on a logarithmic scale implies that the growth of carapace and abdomen are related to each other by an equation of the following type:

$$\text{log. growth of abdomen} = \alpha \text{ log. growth of carapace} + b$$

where α is a constant over the period of the life-history during which the line is straight and b is another constant which determines the distance of the line from the origin. Since we have taken the size of the carapace as a measure of the body size, we can replace it in this equation by the body. This is justifiable only if the carapace is growing at a rate equal to the mean growth-rate of the body, *i.e.* if its growth is isometric, but we ought not to have chosen it as a suitable character to estimate the growth of the body unless this were so. Thus, the equation becomes:

$$\text{log. growth of abdomen} = \alpha \text{ log. growth of body} + b.$$

The constant coefficient α may be called the *growth-coefficient* of the organ. It represents the gradient of the line on the logarithmic scale, and is an expression for the relative growth-rate of the organ compared with the mean growth-rate of the body. If α is equal to unity, the organ is growing at the same rate as the body and the growth is isometric. If α is greater or less than unity, the growth is positive or negatively allometric. The values of α in Fig. 79 are 1·26 for the unsexable young and for the females up to 15 mm. carapace length; 1·42 for the older females; 1·07 for the males up to 15 mm.,

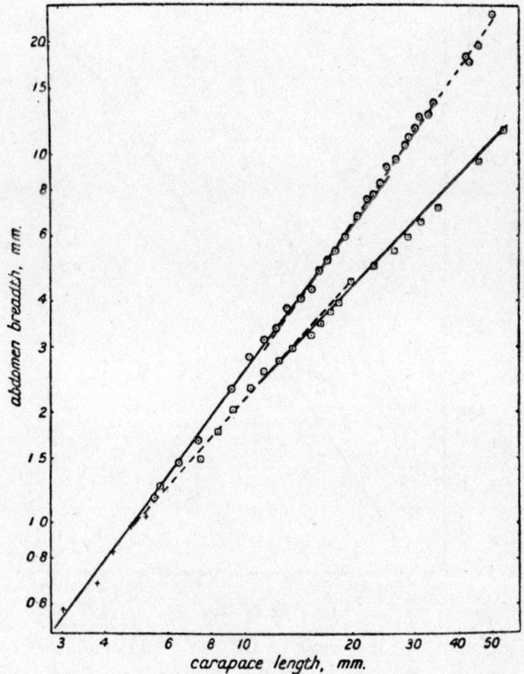

Figure 79. Growth in the abdomen of the shore-crab, *Carcinus mænas*.

Logarithmic scale. Upper lines, females; lower males; +unsexable young. (From Huxley.)

and 0·94 for the older males. The growth is therefore positively allometric for all the animals except the older males, but is nearly isometric in all the males.

In Fig. 80 another example of allometric growth, that of the chela of the male fiddler-crab, is given. It is plotted on a logarithmic scale against the weight of the body. Again, the growth, so plotted, is represented by two straight lines. The growth coefficient for the smaller crabs is 1·62, for the larger 1·255. It is strongly positively allometric throughout, but more so in the smaller crabs.

The growth of a large number of organs in many animals has been analysed on these lines. It has almost always been found that the growth-coefficients are constant, or very nearly constant, over large parts of the life-history. That changes in the growth-coefficients occur during the life-history is evident from the fact that change of form in the body is much more rapid at some parts of the life-history (and especially during early development) than at others. Indeed, it is

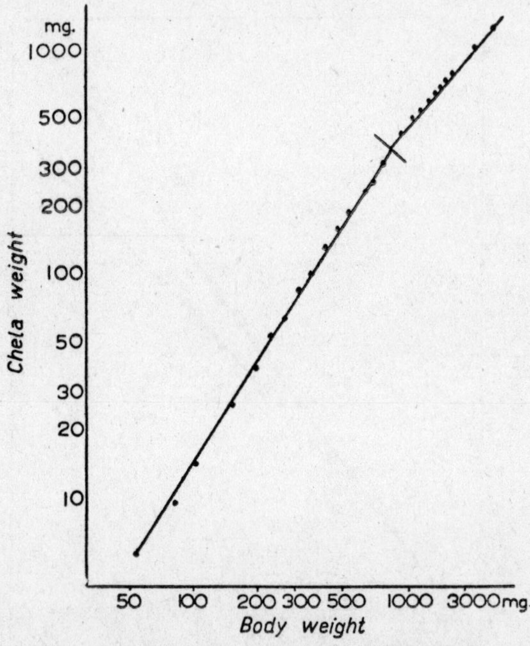

Figure 80. Growth of the chela of the male fiddler crab, *Uca pugnax*. Logarithmic scale. (After Huxley.)

doubtful whether the principle of the constancy of the coefficients holds over the early stages of development. In one animal, *Asellus aquaticus* (Isopoda) the growth of the segments of the body has been very accurately worked out, and it has been found that, although the growth-coefficients of the various segments are constant, or nearly so, for long periods in later development and adult life, this is not true in the earliest stages of the life-history. Either the coefficients change continuously at that time, or their periods of constancy are too short to be recognised.

These results are shown in Fig. 81, in which "growth-contours"

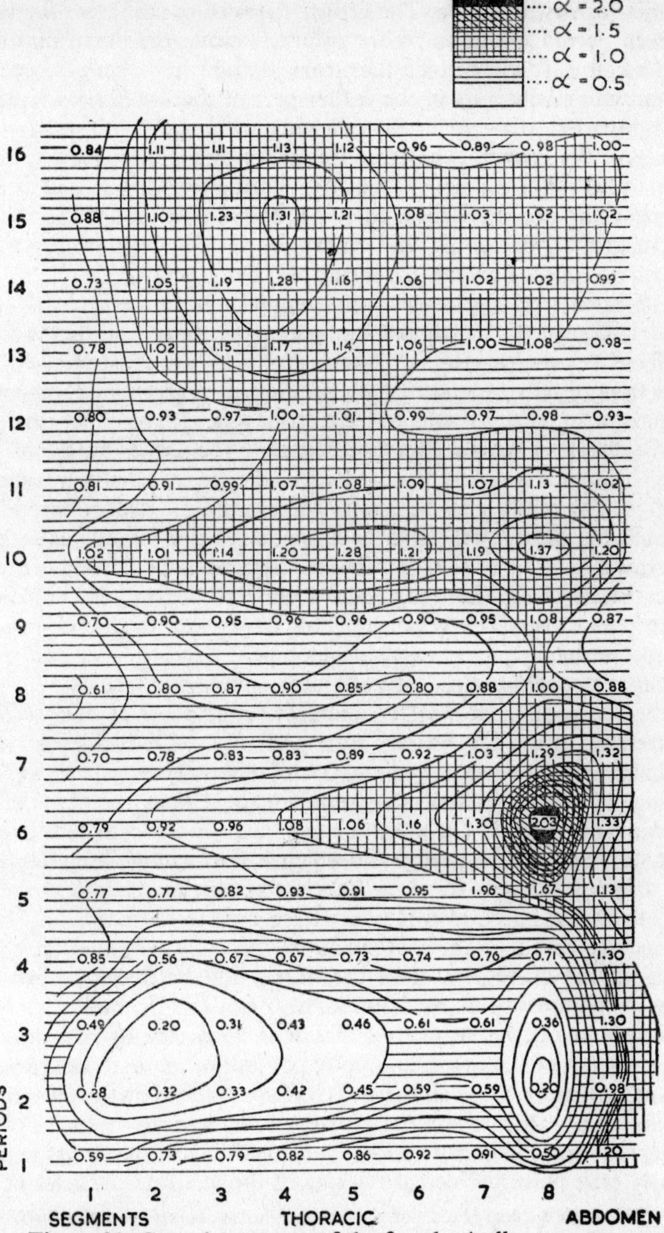

Figure 81. Growth contours of the female *Asellus aquaticus*.
Ordinates, periods of the life-history; figures on the graph, growth coefficients. (After Needham.)

for the growth of segments of female *Asellus aquaticus* throughout the life-history are given. The growth-rates of the different segments in each period are given by the numbers along the horizontal lines of the figure. It will be seen that marked and rapid changes occur in the growth-coefficients in the earlier part of the life-history (periods 1–7), but that after this the coefficients are much more nearly constant, *i.e.* the growth is much more nearly simple allometric growth. One other point is brought out by this figure. This is that in this animal there is a rhythmical change in the rate of growth, periods of active growth preceding and following periods of slower growth. We do not know how far this is true of other animals.

The results on the growth of *Asellus* show us very clearly that though complete, or almost complete, constancy of the growth-coefficients over long periods often appears to be characteristic of the growth of organs, change of these coefficients is an equally important feature in animal growth. Indeed, it may be doubtful whether the coefficients ever remain *exactly* constant in the tissues over considerable periods. The apparently exact constancy of the coefficients shown in Figs. 79 and 80 may be due to the roughness of our methods in considering the growth of large and complicated organs as wholes. But this does not reduce the value of the conclusions we have drawn from these figures. There can be no doubt that the growth-coefficients often remain very nearly constant for large parts of the life-history, except perhaps during early development; and this is for us as valuable a conclusion as if the constancy were complete.

This complete, or nearly complete, constancy of the growth-coefficients of the organs over large parts of the life-history is a very striking phenomenon, but here, as in other places where we find biological phenomena obeying mathematical laws (p. 51), the explanation is simple. The constancy of the growth-coefficient implies that, throughout the period for which it is constant, the growth of the organ *per unit of its mass* bears a constant relation to the mean growth of the body, also measured per unit of its mass. This is an immediate result of the mathematical form of the equation.* The value of the coefficient gives the proportion between the growth-rates of the units of living tissue in the organ and the body.

It should not be surprising that it is necessary to compare the growth-rates of the organ and body per unit of mass in order to find a simple relation between them. To compare the growth-rates in this way is simply to compare the growth of the separate particles of the living substance in organ and body. Growth in any living tissue must clearly take place by increase in size of the separate particles of the

* This whole subject is discussed more fully in *Problems of Relative Growth*, J. S. Huxley, ch. 1. *Cf.* also Hersh, *3rd Growth Symp.*, 113, 1941.

protoplasm. Our results imply that the particles of the substance of the organ are growing throughout the period for which the growth-coefficient is constant at a rate which bears a constant proportion to the mean growth-rate of the living particles of the body as a whole.

This is a simple interpretation, but the conclusions that the relations between the growth-rates of the body and its organs are constant, or nearly so, over large parts of the life-history, and that this is true although the growth of the organ is allometric, are important, and not conclusions that we could have deduced from our general knowledge without experiment. The growth-rate of the body as a whole varies greatly during the life-history. It sometimes, as we have seen, gives a parabolic growth-curve, and sometimes becomes zero in the adult. Our conclusions imply that the growth-rates of the organs follow these variations in the growth-rate of the body, maintaining a constant proportion to it. This is by no means a conclusion we could have reached from general knowledge.

Since changes of form occur throughout the life-history of an animal and in all parts of its body, we must conclude that exactly isometric growth is comparatively rare among the organs. We must think of the body as containing a distribution of relative growth-rates varying from one organ to another.

Not all the structural differentiation of the body can be produced by allometric growth. The protoplasm of the tissues is chemically different in the various parts of the body, and the cells themselves are different in structure. Epithelium, gland-cells, and nerve-cells are all different and some of the structural differentiation of the body is made up of these differences, and of differences which result directly from these varying characters of the cells. Nevertheless, there can be no doubt that a great deal of the structure of the body is produced by allometric growth. Not only change in the sizes of the organs but also new structure can be so produced. Differential growth-rates arise in a part of the body which was previously undifferentiated, and a new structure is formed by the alterations in form so produced. To take but a single instance, the various diverticula of the gut are so formed. Parts of the endodermal epithelium grow actively and bulge outwards as a result of this active growth, producing hollow diverticula. At the same time the cells forming the epithelia may be modified in structure.

Other changes of form besides those which occur normally during the life-history may be produced by allometric growth. Changes in specific form produced by changes in the external environment arise in this way. The relative growth-rates of the organs may be altered by changes in the external environment, even, as in *Artemia* (p. 119), by changes in the physical conditions of the environment.

Again, in regeneration we have seen that the return to the normal specific form is partly due to active growth of the remaining tissues near the place of the damage. One result of damage must therefore be a great increase in the relative growth-rates of tissues near the damage. In other parts of the regenerating body the organs decrease in size, so as to fit a body of the size to be formed by the regeneration. The growth-rates of tissues at a distance from the damage become negatively allometric as a result of the damage.

Some other facts of regeneration are also direct results of the changes in the growth-rates of parts of the body which result from damage. Occasionally, as we have seen, pp. 133–5, the form of the regenerated body is not the same as that of the undamaged animal. An example of this which we have not yet considered occurs in many decapod crustaceans, in which the large chelæ are asymmetrical on the two sides of the body, one being larger and stronger than the other. A chela regenerates at the next moult if it has been lost. In some species (*e.g.* a shrimp, *Alpheus*), if the larger chela is lost, it regenerates as the smaller, the originally smaller chela growing larger at the moult to become the larger of the two. In the lobster this reversal occurs only if the chela is lost while the animal is young; in other species it never occurs. Several theories have been put forward to account for this reversal in the asymmetry of the chela in some species. It has been suggested that the remaining chela grows larger because the removal of the opposite chela allows it a larger supply of some substance necessary for its growth. We need not discuss these theories; probably, none of them wholly fits the facts. But at least it is clear that the reversal of asymmetry is the result of changes in the relative growth-rates caused by loss of one of the chelæ.

Allometric growth therefore lies behind not only much of the development of new structure and much of the change of form which occurs in the normal life-history of the animal, but also many of the structural reactions of the animal to abnormal circumstances.

It is clear that the distribution of relative growth-rates is the expression of the action of the individuating and evocating fields in the body. These fields control the relative growth-rates of organs and so produce their effects. But we may ask whether the distribution of growth-rates shows in itself any orderliness, and, if so, whether this orderliness shows any correlation with the known properties of the individuating and evocating fields. Our present evidence on this subject is scanty, but it suggests that the distribution of growth-rates does show certain types of orderliness.

The distribution of relative growth-rates in the abdomen of male and female shore-crabs, *Carcinus mænas*, at four periods of the life-history, is shown in Fig. 82. The growth coefficients of the various segments of the abdomen are plotted as ordinates. The strongly positive allometric growth of the female abdomen in the period following

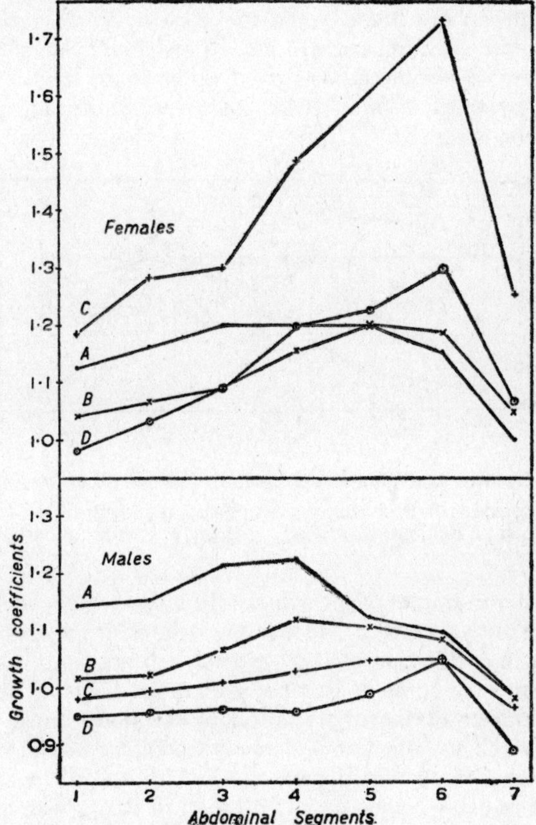

Figure 82. Growth gradients in the abdomen of male and female shore-crabs, *Carcinus mænas*.

Males: A, 3–6 mm.; B, 6–12 mm.; C, 12–21 mm.; D, 21–36 and 36–55 mm. Females: A, 3–6 mm.; B, 6–21 mm.; C, 21–36 mm.; D, 36–50 mm.; all carapace length. (After Day.)

the oncoming of maturity (C) is clear; the maximum growth-coefficient—in the sixth segment—is 1·75. In the male the growth-coefficients vary much less markedly from unity. The point that is of chief interest in the present connection is that there is an orderly and *quantitative* distribution of growth-rates extending over the whole abdomen.

The data of Fig. 81 show similar distributions of growth-rates over the body, and also show that the distribution may alter greatly during the life-history.

Similar gradients of growth-coefficients (or, as they may be called, *growth gradients*) are found when the growth of the various segments of a limb are compared. In Fig. 83 results for the large (right) chela of the male hermit-crab are given, in the young stage (A) before the chela becomes asymmetrical, and during the asymmetrical growth of the chela (B).

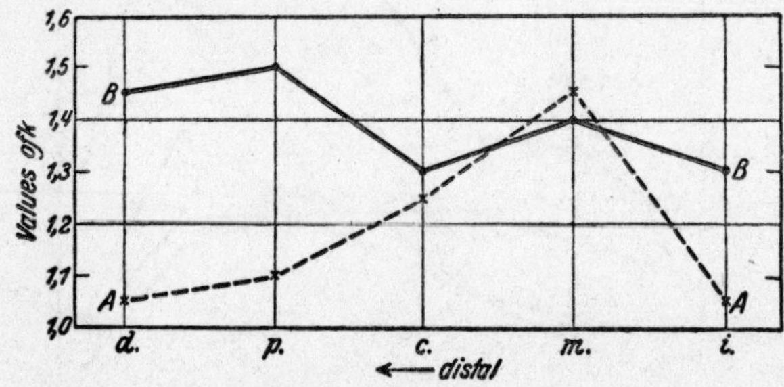

Figure 83. Growth gradients in the chela of the hermit crab, *Eupagurus*. A–A, young crabs; B–B, during the asymmetrical growth of the chela. Segments of chela; *i*, ischium; *m*, merus; *c*, carpus; *p*, propus; *d*, dactylus. (After Bush.)

A few other examples of growth gradients have been worked out, but we have not yet enough evidence to say how far the arrangement of the growth-coefficients of the body in such gradients is general. Specific form is so complex that the growth gradients, if they are a general character of the organisation of the body, must be very elaborate. Much investigation will be needed before we can form any general conclusion on this subject.

We have to ask whether the distribution of the growth gradients bears any relation to the distribution of the known types of organisation in the body, and especially to that of the axial organisation. We have seen that the axial gradient is possibly accompanied by a gradient in the activity of the tissues (p. 123), and it might at first sight appear that the growth gradients should follow this gradient of activity. The facts given in Fig. 82 are sufficient to show that this is not, at any rate always, so. The area of most rapid growth is not at the front end of the body—it is nearer the posterior end—and the gradient is not a simple one passing backwards over the body from the head. But there is no real reason to expect that the distribution of growth gradients should be identical with that of the axial organisation. If there is a gradient of activity parallel with the axial gradient, it is a gradient in the activity of *similar* tissues in different parts of the body. The growth gradients are usually gradients in the rate of growth of *different* organs, and therefore of the *different* tissues which form these organs. Even where this is not so, growth gradients do not

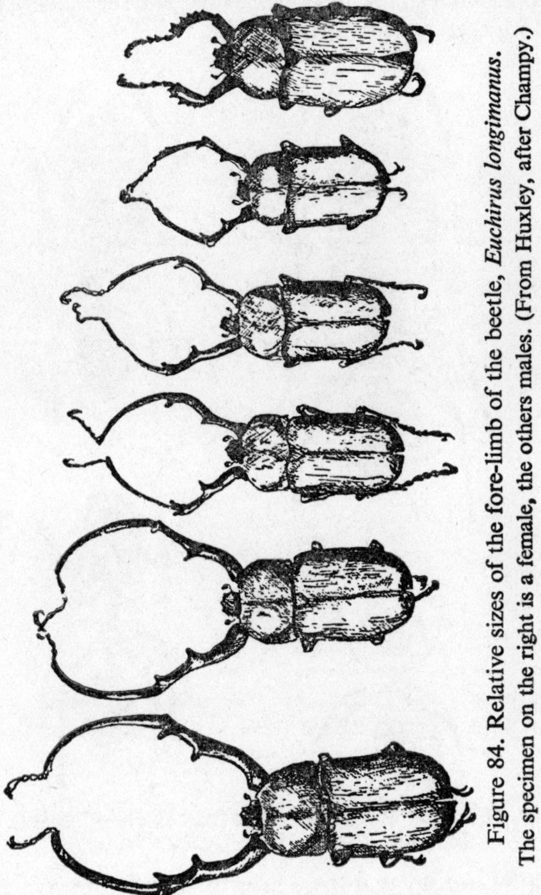

Figure 84. Relative sizes of the fore-limb of the beetle, *Euchirus longimanus*. The specimen on the right is a female, the others males. (From Huxley, after Champy.)

follow exactly the distribution of the axial organisation. In planarians there are indications of a growth gradient with a maximum at the posterior end.

Nevertheless, there is reason to think that the distribution of the growth gradients *is* sometimes correlated with that of the axial gradient. In very many embryos and larvæ, the parts at the front end of the body grow and differentiate more rapidly than those farther back. Here, there seems to be a growth gradient in the body as a whole, with a distribution identical in form with that of the axial gradient. But Fig. 82 shows that this is not true of all growth gradients in the body. Even in the embryo many smaller growth gradients, which have not this distribution, must be present. If there is any general correlation between these two types of organisation, it is by no means a simple or obvious one. The subject is very speculative, and we need not discuss it further.

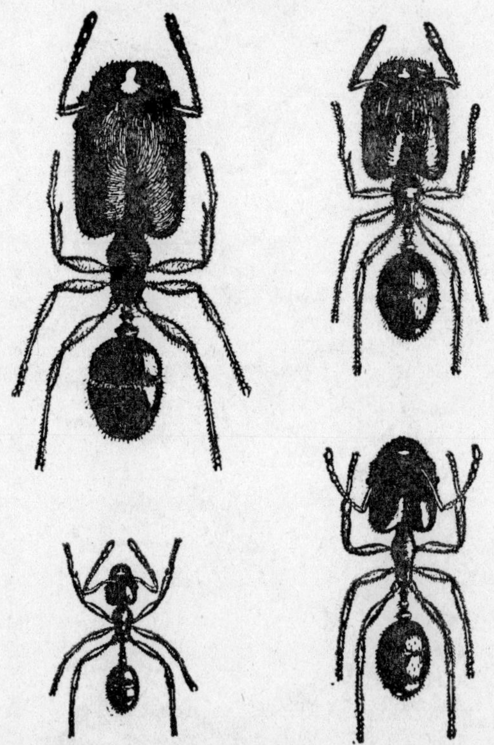

Figure 85. Head size and body size in the neuters of an ant, *Pheidole instabilis*. (From Huxley, after Champy.)

At least we can say that these growth gradients form a part of the *general* organisation of the body. In Fig. 82, p. 169, it is clear that change in the growth-rate of one part of the body is associated with similar changes in the neighbouring parts. The growth gradient changes as a whole; its change is not due to altered rate of growth in a single organ but to a change in the organisation of growth in a large part of the body, here the abdomen.

We find an exponential correlation between the size of an organ and that of the body in some phenomena in which the correlation is not obviously the result of allometric growth. Sometimes this correlation may result from allometric growth in earlier parts of the life-history. Thus, in some adult insects the sizes of certain organs have been found to be correlated exponentially with the size of the body, the organ usually being relatively larger in the larger animal. This is so, for instance, of the fore-limbs of the beetle *Euchirus* (Fig. 84) or of the heads of workers of the ant *Pheidole* (Fig. 85). No growth is possible in the adult insect, for the size of the body is determined by the hard cuticle. Probably these correlations result from allometric growth in the pupal period, when the sizes of the parts of the

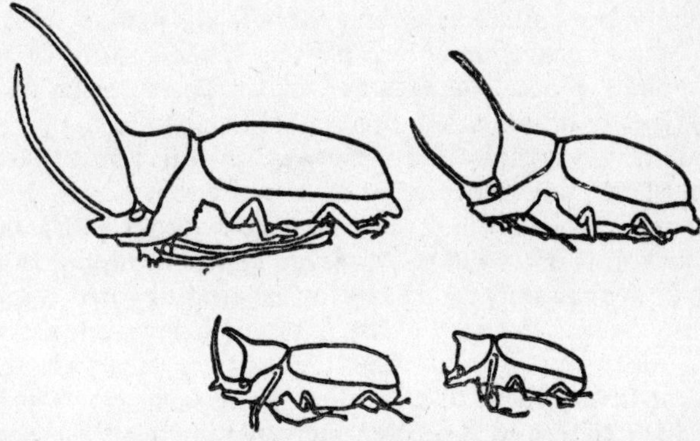

Figure 86. Relative sizes of the processes on the head and thorax of different species of a genus of beetles (*Golofa*). (From Huxley, after Champy.)

Below two specimens of *G. porteri*; above, right, *G. cæcum*, left, *G. imperialis*.

body are determined. If so, they are examples in which the results of previous growth are permanently fixed in the shape of the body.

If the specific forms of related species are compared, they sometimes show an exponential correlation between the size of the body and the size of some of its organs. It is, at least, often true that the larger species has the relatively larger organs, and sometimes the relation between size of body and organ seems to be exponential. An example is the size of the processes on the head and thorax of the beetles of the genus *Golofa* (Fig. 86). It seems that the growth of these organs must be positively allometric in all the species and that this results in relatively larger organs in the larger species.

CHAPTER XI

THE ORGANISATION OF THE MULTICELLULAR BODY: SUMMARY AND CONCLUSIONS

THE conclusions we have reached in the preceding chapters give us some general conception of the organisation which enables the animal body to maintain its specific form. In the present state of our knowledge any conception we can form of the control of specific form is bound to be incomplete and vague. There can be no doubt that the types of organisation we have been able to recognise are not the whole of the organisation which has this function in the body. There must be many other types of organisation, of which we are at present entirely ignorant. Even where we can recognise organisation which controls form in the body, we are almost always only able to describe it. We can only rarely explain the means by which it is produced. But the fact that our account is bound to be mainly descriptive does not mean that it is valueless. Description is always the first stage in the investigation of natural phenomena; it may later be followed by correlation with simpler phenomena.

In summary, the conclusions to which the discussions of the preceding chapters have led us may be stated as follows:

1. At least in some groups of the simpler multicellular animals, it is characteristic of every piece of animal tissue which has become separated from other tissue of the same species that it should develop, if the conditions allow, within itself a complete specific form. This development of the specific form consists, so far as we can see, in a direct remoulding of the tissues, mainly by differential growth. It is the fundamental process in regeneration and redifferentiation, and is certainly different in many important respects from the differentiation of the animal in its development from the egg to the adult. It may be that this tendency to return to the specific form is a general property of all animal tissue. We have not the knowledge to state this as a fact, and it is certainly true that the power of regaining the specific form is much greater in the simpler animals, in which even small masses of cells may regain the specific form completely. If all animal tissue has this tendency, it is far less effective in the more evolved animals.

2. Constancy of the specific form among the individuals of a

species is one of the most striking features of animals, but it is not complete. The specific form must be regarded as an expression of the condition of the tissues, and their condition, although mainly determined by the hereditary constitution of the species, may be modified by the conditions of the external environment. Thus, in some animals the specific form varies to some extent with environmental conditions.

For maintenance of specific form it is necessary that the tissues should be in a healthy state. In certain circumstances the tissues may continue to live although the specific form may be entirely lost. If the condition again becomes healthy, the specific form may sometimes be regained by redifferentiation.

3. At least in certain groups of animals (*e.g.* planarians, and cœlenterates), and possibly in all groups (though in the higher groups our evidence is restricted to early developmental stages), each individual animal contains within its body an axial organisation consisting of a centre of dominance in the head region and a field extending from this centre over the body. This axial organisation expresses itself in the susceptibility gradient, in physiological gradients, and in the dominance of anterior parts in the regeneration of, at least, some groups of animals—the cœlenterates and planarians. Posterior regions of the axial organisation may persist in a body in the absence of more anterior parts. We see this in the regeneration of posterior organs in separated pieces of a planarian in which no head is formed.

4. Where the axial organisation is single we find a single specific form. In colonies and monsters, where the form of the body is complex, the axial organisation is also complex. Where a new specific form is being developed, as in buds and regenerating pieces, we find a new axial organisation. The axial organisation has the same general arrangement in all examples of the specific form of animals, *i.e.* with a centre in the anterior part of the body and a field distributed over the body. These facts demonstrate that the axial organisation is in some way causally related to the assumption and maintenance of specific form.

5. Tissues may become isolated from the axial organisation, although still attached to the body. This happens in bud-formation.

6. There is a tendency for complex axial organisations in a mass of tissue to be replaced by a single axial organisation. The replacement does not always occur. It is absent in monsters and colonies. But the tendency is evident in the absorption of small grafts into the host body and in the restitution of specific form in a mass of tissue formed of several originally separate pieces.

7. The axial organisation in a normal animal body is a single three-dimensional field around a centre of dominance. It determines

the arrangement of organs in the body. Such a field may be called an *individuation field*. Another individuation field is associated with the amphibian organiser. Since these fields control the arrangement of structure, they are at least part of the control of specific form. We have no knowledge of the physico-chemical nature of these fields. The axial organisation also gives rise, in all probability, to the susceptibility gradient and to the gradients in physiological characters, quantitative fields extending over the body with maxima in the head region.

We have found evidence of other quantitative fields, those consisting of the distribution of chemical substances about a centre of origin. These are the *evocation fields*. By them the development of structure in tissues which have already gained the capacity for producing the structure is instigated. They do not, however, determine the development of the capacity for producing structure in a tissue. In this they differ fundamentally from the individuation fields.

8. Much of the structure in the organs of the body is formed by differential growth. This growth often conforms nearly, if not completely, to simple allometry, except perhaps in the earliest stages of development. The growth rates of parts of the body are arranged in growth gradients which extend over large parts of the body and are part of its general organisation. By these growth gradients the growth of organs over wide areas are correlated. We do not know much of the control of the arrangement of the growth gradients. They must certainly be, at least in part, under the control of the individuation fields—the axial organisation, and any other individuation field present in the body; they may also be controlled by some other unknown organisation. Differential growth is the means by which much, but not all, the structure is formed under the influence of the organising systems.

We are clearly very far at present from a complete understanding of the control of the development of structure and the maintenance of form in the animal body. We are able to recognise some systems of organisation, but this does not take us very far. Not only are there very probably other systems of which at present we know nothing, but we cannot define the physico-chemical nature of some of the systems we can recognise, such as the individuation fields. Even in the evocation fields, we can say nothing of the cause of the development of evocating power in a tissue, or of the reasons why other tissues react to the presence of the evocating chemical substances in the way they do. For the ultimate nature of the control of form in the animal body we are at present entirely at a loss. Almost all the matter discussed in these chapters is the product of recent investigation.

Some of our conclusions will probably have to be modified as a result of future work, and it is likely that others will be extended.

One point is clear. Analysis of specific form in animals, so far as it can be carried at present, emphasises the uniqueness of the animal organisation. Thus, it emphasises the character of the animal as an organism, and an indivisible organism (p. 3). We have found in the animal body—at least in the simpler animal bodies which, owing to the simplicity of their structure, allow us to study their organisation most easily—a single axial organisation corresponding to, and controlling, the development and maintenance of each single specific form. Even where other individuation fields are present in the body, this single organisation seems to be present. Both in its specific form and in this organisation, the animal is a unit, and a unit which loses its essential characters when it is divided, unless the separated parts remodel themselves by regeneration into units of the same kind as that from which they were separated.

PART III

COMPARATIVE PHYSIOLOGY

CHAPTER XII

INTRODUCTION

In this and the following chapters we shall discuss how the invertebrate Metazoa carry out the various functions which are necessary for the maintenance of their life—the capture and assimilation of food, the removal of excretory material, the correlation of the activities of the different parts of the body, and so on. This is the subject-matter of Comparative Physiology.

When we were considering the unicellular bodies of the Protista, we saw that parts of the protoplasm of their cells often become specialised to perform different functions, and we have spoken of these specialised parts of the cell as organs. Even in the simplest multicellular body, that of a sponge or cœlenterate for instance, differentiation of organs can be seen. These organs are themselves very often multicellular, but unicellular organs are present even in complex animals, *e.g.* unicellular glands. As the body becomes more complex, elaboration and specialisation of the organs proceeds continuously, until in the end many of the vital needs are each carried out for the whole body by a single organ, all the tissues of the body depending for the satisfaction of each need on the functioning of one of these organs. It is the manner in which these organs carry out their different functions that we have now to discuss.

Since each organ or system of organs is specialised to serve one of the vital needs of the body, it is convenient to discuss each system separately with reference to the function it serves. This will be done in the following chapters, but before we pass on to this there are some general points concerning the comparative physiology of the multicellular body to be considered.

1. The essential physiological functions of the body may be divided into those which make up the interactions of the animal with its environment and those which must go on within the body in order that its life may be maintained. Capture of food, absorption of oxygen from the environment, and the passing of excretory material out of the body, are examples of the first type of function. For these

functions almost all free-living Metazoa, except the simplest and smallest, depend upon special organs. Only in the simplest multicellular animals are many of these functions carried out without special organs. Thus, in some small Metazoa oxygen can reach the tissues in sufficient quantity for their life by direct diffusion from the environment, but in all other Metazoa it must be taken up by organs specialised for its absorption, the respiratory organs, and the life of the animal is dependent on the efficient functioning of these organs. So, also, the majority of Metazoa are dependent on specialised organs for the capture of food. Only some highly modified forms, such as parasites and free-living saprophytes, can absorb their food directly through their surface from the medium surrounding them.

It is equally true that many of the functions of the second type are carried out by specialised organs in the body. Food is digested by the organs of the alimentary canal, and in many animals it is transported about the body by the special organs of the circulatory system. But it must be emphasised that this is not true of all the essential physiological processes of the body. The most fundamental of these processes are intracellular, carried out in the cells themselves and not in special organs for the whole body. The functions of the organs are to prepare substances for the use of the tissues in these intracellular processes, to store them for future use, to transport them to and from the tissues, and to control the activities of the tissues. The essential processes of metabolism, such as those by which new tissue is built up and those by which food material is oxidised to provide energy, are carried out by each cell for itself.

It is becoming more and more clear as investigation proceeds that the metabolism of each tissue is a modified form of one metabolic process which is common to all tissues. Intracellular metabolism has been modified in various ways in the course of evolution, and thus varies in its details in different animals and in the different tissues of each animal, but in its essentials it is probably the same throughout animal evolution. The modifications that metabolism has undergone have been of several kinds. The commonest of them is that one of the vital functions is exaggerated beyond that normal to protoplasm. Though all protoplasm is to some extent contractile and can conduct stimuli, muscle is more highly contractile than other tissues and nerve more efficient in conduction; the sense cell is more than normally sensitive to external stimulation. In other features the metabolism of the tissues become simplified; part of their metabolism becomes unnecessary owing to the provisions made for them by the organs of the body, and is therefore reduced or lost.

Nevertheless, the behaviour of metazoan cells in tissue cultures shows clearly that the cells of the multicellular body are capable of independent life—and therefore of complete metabolism—when conditions demand it. Tissue cultures can be made from most tissues of the metazoan body, invertebrate as well as vertebrate.

2. Although in the following chapters we shall consider each system of organs separately, it must never be forgotten that they are parts of a single animal, which is an organism (p. 3). It is only for convenience that we deal with each organ separately in comparative physiology. In life all the organs function together in the one body. None is capable of life as an organism after it has been separated from the body, although some may continue to function for a time.

3. In the simplest multicellular animals, the sponges and cœlenterates, wherever spaces between the tissue cells are filled with a medium, the medium is usually gelatinous.* This is also true of a few tissues in more complicated animals, *e.g.* the cartilage of the vertebrates. But, except in these simple animals and in these few tissues, the intercellular spaces of the metazoan body are filled with liquids. These liquids may be of more than one kind in the different parts of the body—blood, for instance, differs from lymph—but together the whole of them may be spoken of as the internal medium of the body.

Realisation of the functions and importance of the internal medium is essential to an understanding of metazoan physiology. The liquids of the internal medium bathe the surfaces of all the cells of the body: these liquids are, in fact, the medium in which the cells are actually living. The internal medium will contain in one part or another all the substances which are transported about the body in solution, not only food materials, respiratory and excretory substances, but also any other substance secreted into its liquids by the cells—the substances used for the chemical correlation of the body, for instance (ch. XVI).

Since the cells are living in contact with the liquids of the internal medium, it is necessary for the life of the animal that the constitution of the medium should be controlled within the range of conditions in which the tissues can live. This range of conditions is often very different from the conditions in the external medium. In freshwater animals the osmotic pressure of the internal medium must be kept far above that of the external medium, and even in marine invertebrates, where the osmotic pressure of the internal medium is equal to that of the external medium, the two media differ in many of their constituents. For instance, the proportional concentrations of the

* We are here concerned with intercellular spaces within and between the tissues of the body, not with spaces enclosed in the body but outside its tissues, *e.g.* the spaces of the archenteron. These are always filled with liquids.

inorganic ions is never the same in the internal media of marine animals and sea-water. Some figures for the proportional concentrations of inorganic ions in the marine invertebrates are given in the following table.

	Proportional concentrations			
	Na	Ca	K	Mg
Sea-water	100	3·84	3·66	11·99
Fluid expressed from the body of Aurelia .	100	4·13	5·18	11·43
Fluid of the hæmocœle of the lobster . .	100	8·03	7·12	2·88

The body must be able to maintain these differences between its internal medium and the external medium. It must, in fact, be able to maintain the isolation of its internal medium from the external medium in all characters in which they differ. As a rule the differences between the internal and external media increase as the body becomes more complex. We have seen that this is true in general of the isolation of the organism from its environment (p. 49).

The constitution of the internal medium is, however, never entirely stable. Since it contains all the substances secreted into it by the cells, its constitution must alter with every change in the condition of the cells, not only with changes due to the normal variations of metabolism, such as the progress of digestion and assimilation of food or changes in the activities of the muscles, but also with other variations in the conditions of the tissues—their health, development or senility, and so on. If the animal is to survive, these variations in the constitution of the internal medium must be kept within the viable range.

Thus, we must regard the multicellular body as consisting of a mass of protoplasm containing within its interstices a medium, usually fluid but in some simple animals gelatinous, which is controlled in its constitution by the body, and which reflects every change in the condition of the body in changes in its constitution. The multicellular animal has often been compared to a pond filled with a fauna of organisms, the internal medium representing the water of the pond, and the cells animals living in the pond. But if this simile is adopted it must be remembered that the whole pond, the animal, acts and behaves as an organism, which no natural pond can do. The simile is dangerous because it tends to make us look upon the cells as separate living systems rather than as parts of a single body.

4. Invertebrate animals may be classified in many different ways. Morphological, physiological, ecological, and many other characters may be used as the basis of classification, and each classification is valuable in the circumstances for which it is suitable.* Here, we are

* Another type of classification is that of systematic zoology, a "natural" classification, *i.e.* one which expresses the evolutionary relationships of animals. We are not here concerned with this type of classification.

discussing the physiology of these animals and a physiological classification will be of most use to us. Perhaps, the most fundamental physiological classification is one based on the different ways in which substances are carried about the internal medium. We shall consider how this function is carried out in the bodies of invertebrate animals.

(*a*) The sponges and cœlenterates are not only the lowest invertebrates in the morphological scale, but they are also those in which the division of the body into organs is least advanced. In this important character they are physiologically the simplest multicellular animals. It is therefore not surprising that the organisation of their internal medium is simpler than in other invertebrates.

In the animal of these groups there can be no circulation of the internal medium, since this is almost always gelatinous. Unless they are carried by motile cells, substances can be transported about the body only by diffusion through the intercellular jelly.

Thus, it becomes necessary at the start of our discussion of transport in the invertebrate body, to consider the process of diffusion in liquid and gelatinous media.

The conditions under which diffusion occurs in the animal body are complex, and it is not possible to give accurate figures for the rate at which tissues will be supplied by the diffusion of a substance across different distances. Figures can, however, be given for diffusion in water, and there can be no doubt that diffusion in liquids and jellies within the body will be controlled by the same laws as in water. In most types of protoplasm and in its hard secretions it has been shown that diffusion is slower than in water—in muscle and connective tissue the rate is from one-half to one-third that in water, and in chitin one-thirtieth. But in protoplasm with a high fat content the rate may be higher than in water. This is said to occur in the respiratory epithelium of the vertebrate lung, where the rate is given as twice that in water. Diffusion in jellies is slower than in water,* but is governed by the same laws. These laws are the same whatever the diffusing substance.

Let us take the case of a substance which is a gas at normal temperatures, since transport of gases is an essential process in animal metabolism. Respiration entirely depends on exchange of gases between the tissues and the external medium.

The rate at which dissolved substances diffuse through a thin layer of water varies with the difference of concentration on the two sides of the layer, and with the thickness of the layer. It also differs for the diffusion of each dissolved substance. For a gas, the volume at

* Not much slower. In 15 per cent. gelatine it is 80 per cent. of the rate in water.

atmospheric pressure which will pass through a layer of water 1 sq. cm. in area and d mm. thick is given by the formula:

$$\text{Volume} = \frac{K \,.\, (p_1 - p_2) \,.\, C}{760 \,.\, d} \text{ c.cm. per min.,}$$

where K is a number which varies only with changes in the medium of diffusion, C varies with the substance diffusing and with the temperature, and $p_1 - p_2$ is the difference of pressure of the gas in mm. Hg on the two sides of the layer.

Let us apply this formula, as accurately as we can, to the cases of oxygen diffusing into the surface of an animal and carbon dioxide out of it. We will suppose that the thickness of the layer through which the gases have to diffuse is 10μ (0·01 mm.); that the temperature is 16° C.; that the oxygen pressure in the tissues at the inner end of the diffusion path is 50 mm. Hg (*i.e.* 100 mm. less than that in the saturated water which we may suppose to surround the animal); and that the carbon dioxide pressure is 40 mm. Hg in the tissues and zero in the medium. These are values which might obtain in the respiration of an animal.

	Oxygen	Carbon dioxide
Then: d	0·01	0·01
$p_1 - p_2$	100	40
C at 16° C.	0·0085	0·15

We will assume the value of K to be the same as in water, 0·065.

Introducing these values into the formula we find that the volume of oxygen which will diffuse into the tissue per min. is 0·0072 c.c., and the volume of carbon dioxide which will diffuse outwards is 0·052 c.c. Even with the lower carbon dioxide pressure-difference, carbon dioxide diffusion is much more rapid than that of oxygen.

Since the conditions of respiration are much more complicated than those of diffusion across a simpler layer of liquid, these results cannot be applied in detail to respiration in the animal body. There can, however, be no doubt that transport of carbon dioxide by diffusion in animal tissues will be more rapid than that of oxygen, and that the amounts of the gases reaching and leaving the tissues must decrease as the distance over which they have to be transported by diffusion increases, and approximately in proportion to the increase in this distance. Diffusion is a rapid means of transport over distances a few μ in length; it becomes a very slow process over distances which are much longer than this. This is true not only of transport of the respiratory gases but of transport of any dissolved substance by diffusion. Wherever in the animal body transport is carried out by diffusion alone, either the distance over which the dissolved substances are to be transported must not exceed a small fraction of a millimetre, or the tissue must be able to live at a very slow rate of supply.

In the sponges and the cœlenterates both these conditions are satisfied. The tissues are inactive and the diffusion distances are small. The oxygen consumption of the tissues of the sea-anemone *Anemonia* have been found to be not more than one-thirtieth of that of the tissues of an active invertebrate (cockchafer) at rest. Also everywhere in the bodies of the sponges and cœlenterates, except in the mesoglœa of some cœlenterates, which is either non-cellular or a very inactive tissue, the distance over which diffusion takes place is kept small. This is brought about by the arrangement of the tissues in thin layers, an arrangement which is especially well seen in the ectoderm and endoderm of cœlenterates, but is also present in sponge bodies.

In one group of the cœlenterates, the Scyphozoa, there is a peculiar circulatory system which we shall consider below (p. 203).

(*b*) The second type of invertebrate organisation is characteristic of the Platyhelminthes. In them the active tissues of the body are much more compact than in the animals of the first group. There are still no large spaces between the tissues filled with liquids of the internal medium: the latter are only present in small interstices between the cells. Transport from one tissue to another is still entirely by diffusion. Many of the parasitic forms are very inactive but some of the free-living planarians show considerable activity.

In these animals, as in those of the first group, the distance over which substances must diffuse is kept small by the arrangement of the tissues, but the arrangement is very different from that in the animals of the first group. In a typical platyhelminth body each system of organs is dispersed in small pieces through the body, so that no cell is far distant from tissue of every kind. Except in the respiration of the animal, diffusion need only take place over the short distances between these small pieces of tissue. For much of the respiration, oxygen and carbon dioxide must diffuse inwards or outwards from the surface of the body to the tissues, but in the platyhelminth the body is thin and the distance of any part from the surface is not great. Also, those tissues which make the greatest demand for oxygen, the effector organs—here the muscles and cilia—are mostly close to the surface. It is possible that the fluid in the gut supplies some of the respiratory needs of the internal organs.

We find the same type of organisation in the tracheal system of insects (ch. XIII, p. 201).

(*c*) We come now to the first animals which possess a body cavity which may be cœlome, blastocœle, or of some other morphological nature. In the animals of the present group there is no organ for circulating the liquids contained in the body cavity. The Echinodermata, Rotifera, Nematoda, Polyzoa, and many larvæ of annelids, molluscs, and other groups are of this type of organisation. Substances can be transported through the liquid of the body by diffusion, but it is probable that most of the transport is not by this means. One result of the possession of a body cavity is that the organs lying in this cavity can move relatively to each other much more readily than in an animal with no body cavity. The movements, for instance, of peristalsis in the alimentary canal become possible. Such movements must result in slow circulation of the liquid content of the body cavity. Alterations of the shape of the body in locomotion will also have this effect. The slow circulation so caused will make transport about the cavity much quicker than diffusion alone could effect. In some of these animals the wall of the body cavity is ciliated. The beat of these cilia will also help to circulate the liquids in the cavity.

We have little knowledge of the nature of the substances which are transported about the body cavity in these animals, but there can be no doubt that most of the exchanges between the tissues occur in this way. In most of these animals the only other way by which substances can be transported about the body is by diffusion through the tissues themselves, and this will be at least as slow as diffusion in the body cavity. At any rate, we can say that transport in the liquid of the body cavity certainly occurs in some invertebrates. In the earthworm, for instance, which has a circulatory system and therefore belongs to a later group, excretory material is said to be carried by the yellow cells (*cf.* p. 226): in some sipunculids (*Phascolosoma*), and echiuroids (*Thalassema*), which belong to the group under discussion, the body cavity contains corpuscles with a respiratory pigment (hæmerythrin, p. 194). These serve the function of transporting oxygen about the body.

(*d*) In the next group the internal medium is in the same condition as in the animals we have just discussed except that the body cavity contains a special organ, usually called a heart, by which the liquids are actively circulated. In these animals the body cavity is often a hæmocœle, expanded blood spaces derived from the blastocœle, and is not a cœlome. There is not yet any clear separation between the circulating and the non-circulating liquids of the internal medium. This type of organisation occurs in many of the smaller arthropods (*e.g. Daphnia*) and molluscs, probably in the brachiopods and perhaps in some echinoderm larvæ. In animals of this group the presence of a respiratory pigment first becomes common.

(*e*) Lastly, we have animals in which the circulating liquid is contained in vessels—arteries, veins, and capillaries—and the remaining liquids of the internal medium either do not circulate at all or do so much more slowly. The evolution from the type of organisation of the last group to this is a gradual one. In many invertebrates, *e.g.* many arthropods and molluscs, arteries carry the circulating liquid from the heart, but these open into the body cavity and the rest of the circulation is not enclosed in vessels. In others, *e.g.* many gastropods, veins are also present, but the circulation is open between the arteries and veins. Among the invertebrates, the closed system is most nearly complete in the annelids, especially in the oligochætes, where wide blood sinuses may occur round some of the organs, but the blood never mixes with the non-circulating fluid of the body cavity; and in the Cephalopods where the whole circulation is in blood vessels.

It is probable that a circulation enclosed in vessels is more efficient than an open circulation, in which dead spaces are more likely to occur. But an open circulation can be rapid in small organisms; this we can readily see in *Daphnia*.

In animals of both the last two groups the circulating blood is brought close to each cell, either in capillaries or in blood sinuses. Thus, the distances over which diffusion must occur in the tissues are reduced to very small lengths. By this means one of the most potent obstacles to increase in the size of the body is removed. We find that the largest animals have a well-organised blood system (cephalopods, vertebrates). Also, the evolution of an efficient circulation makes very much easier the development of single organs in separate parts of the body, each to serve one of the physiological needs for the whole body. By bringing the blood to these organs in turn, each function can be performed efficiently by a single organ for the whole body, even in the largest multicellular body. It is therefore not surprising that development of single, discrete and complicated organs is one of the most striking features of the evolution of those groups of the more complex invertebrates which possess an efficient circulation.

Both the evolution of better organisation of the internal medium and that of the division of the body into organs are examples of the general increase in the complexity and efficiency of the body which has gone on throughout evolution. We shall find the same process in the evolution of other systems in the body; in the nervous system, for example. With increasing complexity animals have not only become, in general, larger while still remaining active, but they have also attained greater isolation from the changes of their environment and have, in fact, in this and other ways, become more efficient living mechanisms (*cf.* pp. 46–9). It is true that the simplest animals are able to live and reproduce and are therefore effective organisms. They are adapted to their environments and must be supposed to have survived from very early periods of the world's history. But they survive either by remaining small or by living inactively; perhaps also in some cases by developing insensitivity to the changes of the environment. They have less control over their living conditions than larger and more complex animals.

CHAPTER XIII

RESPIRATION

PART of the metabolism of animal tissues is oxidative, requiring a supply of oxygen for its maintenance and producing carbon dioxide among its end-products. Respiration is the process by which this oxygen is brought to the tissues and the carbon dioxide removed. The process of respiration may be divided into three parts:

1. The exchange with the external medium at the surface of the body, either the surface of the respiratory organ or, in simple animals, the general body surface.
2. The passage of the respiratory gases through the internal medium of the body, carried by a circulating fluid or by diffusion.
3. The exchange between the internal medium and the tissues.

Where the interior of the animal body is filled with liquid, it is clear that the second and third of these are aquatic processes. Where parts of the body are filled with solid jellies, transport can, as we have seen, only be by diffusion, which is governed in jellies by the same laws as that in water. The process of transport in these parts of the body will therefore be similar to that in liquid media within the body. We need not consider respiration in animals with solid internal media separately.

In animals living in water the exchange at the respiratory surface is also an aquatic process. Even in terrestrial animals the exchange at the respiratory surfaces is in reality aquatic, for the surfaces of air-breathing organs are always moist in natural conditions, being covered with a thin, stagnant layer of liquid which has oozed out of the tissues. Across this liquid layer the gases have to pass by diffusion on their way into and out of the tissues.

In aquatic respiratory organs the surface is often washed by a current of the water of the external medium, and, if this is so, no stagnant layer thick enough to have an appreciable effect on the rate of the exchange can be formed on the surface. It is interesting that we find many adaptations to wash these surfaces and prevent the formation of stagnant layers upon them. Gills in many aquatic invertebrates take the form of branched and movable processes on the outer surface of the body. The chief function of their movements is presumably to renew the water on the respiratory surface. In the planarians the dorsal surface of the body is ciliated. Cilia in that position cannot assist in the locomotion of the animal as the similar cilia on the ventral surface do. If the beat of the dorsal cilia is watched, it will be seen that particles are thrown down on the surface of the ectodermal epithelium by the current produced by the beat of the cilia and are then thrown off again. The function of the cilia is probably to wash the surface of the epithelium. Many other adaptations for this purpose occur in invertebrate animals. If the animal possesses no effective adaptation of this type, stagnant layers may form on its respiratory epithelia, and diffusion will then control the passage of gases into the surface.

Within the surface of the respiratory organ the exchange is governed by diffusion in all animals. If the animal possesses a circulation the gases must reach the blood by diffusion, and in animals without a circulation they must pass into all the tissues by this process.

We have seen in the last chapter (p. 183) that diffusion in liquids is a slow process except over very short distances, and we saw that in active animals the diffusion distances are kept short. This is so in the respiratory organs. In many vertebrate lungs the diffusion distance between the alveolar air and the blood is certainly not more than 4μ. In the respiratory organs of those invertebrates which possess a circulation the distances may often be greater than this. But they probably do not exceed a few μ in any efficient respiratory organ.

The transport of the respiratory gases about the body has been discussed in the last chapter. And little need be said here of the exchange between the tissues and the internal medium. There also, the process is one of diffusion and, for efficiency, the distance between the cells and the medium must be kept small. This, as we have seen (p. 186), is one result of an efficient circulatory system. It is one reason why capillaries, when they are present, are small, the large surface area of small capillaries being another reason. In invertebrates which do not possess capillaries the tissues are generally loose, so that the fluid of the internal medium can bathe the surfaces of all the cells.

THE AMOUNT OF THE RESPIRATORY EXCHANGE

It is obvious that in any efficient animal each physiological system must be capable of meeting all demands made upon it in the normal life of the animal. The demands made upon the respiratory system will vary with the activity of the tissues. The oxygen need of the body may be divided into that required for the maintenance of the life of the body in a resting condition (that needed for the *basal metabolism* of the tissues) and that required for the production of energy for locomotion and other purposes. The basal metabolism of the tissues varies greatly in different animals, and in the different tissues of the same animal. It varies also with the conditions in which the animal is living, *e.g.* the temperature of its body. The oxygen needed for energy production varies, still more greatly, with the activity of the animal. The demands on the respiratory system will therefore be very variable both in different animals and from time to time in the life of any one animal. Some figures for the oxygen consumption of a few invertebrates in a condition of normal activity are given in the following table.

	Temp. °C.	c.c. O_2 consumed per kg. per hour
Protista: Amœba	15	150
Protista: Paramecium	19	2310
Cœlenterata: Anemonia	18	13·4
Mollusca: Pecten	—	9·7
Mollusca: Limax	19	319
Echinodermata: Asterias	19	32
Insecta: Cockchafer	20	930

It will be seen that the great variability of these figures bears no relation to the systematic position of the animals in morphological classification. It is related much more closely to their activity.

The oxygen consumption will be much greater than the figures given in this table when the animals are maximally active. Their respiratory systems must therefore be competent to provide oxygen much in excess of these figures.

Further, an animal may occasionally need to live in conditions where respiration is difficult: an aquatic animal, for instance, may sometimes find itself in stagnant water, where the oxygen pressure is low. It will be of advantage to the animal to extend its range of living conditions as far as possible, and we may therefore expect to find respiratory systems adapted to life in conditions of the external environment which are not the best possible for their functioning.

For these reasons large "safety factors" are to be expected in the respiratory (and other physiological) systems of animals. The systems will be much more efficient than is required at most times during the life of the animal.

The simplest way to test whether a physiological system has a safety factor of this kind is to make its functioning more than normally difficult and to observe whether the functioning is reduced. If the respiratory system is being investigated, the oxygen tension in the environment may be lowered and the consumption measured at various oxygen tensions. The safety factor will then be proportional to the extent to which the tension can be lowered below the atmospheric pressure without proportionate reduction in the consumption.

In the following table the results of some observations of this kind are given for a few invertebrates.

It will be seen that the respiratory safety factor is extremely variable in size. In the stick-insect it is large; there is practically no reduction of the oxygen consumption until the pressure of oxygen is reduced to 2·5 per cent. (about one-eighth of the atmospheric pressure, 21 per cent.). The slug shows a safety factor which is considerable, though much smaller than that of the stick-insect, and the lobster shows at most a very small one. The other animals have no safety factor. They can only live in regions of low oxygen pressure by reducing their consumption of oxygen and therefore their activity. In the sea-anemone the reduction in respiration is greater than that in oxygen pressure.

TABLE *

Actinia aquina (sea-anemone)		*Nereis virens* (ragworm)		*Sipunculus nudus*	
O_2 content of water. % satn.	Respiration	O_2 content of water. % satn.	Respiration	O_2 content of water. % satn.	Respiration
90	100	93	100	98	100
61	48	83	86	81	62
43	38	62	64	31	53
40	36	41	40	24	29
34	31	21	21		
		10	13		

Limax (slug)		*Homarus americanus* (lobster)		*Dixippus morosus* (stick-insect)	
O_2 content of air. %	Respiration	O_2 content of water. % satn.	Respiration	O_2 content of air. %	Respiration
96	100	98	100	100	100
50	95	83	90	50	100
16	71	62	75	21	100
10·5	60	41	65	10	98·5
5·2	38	21	35	5	98·5
		10	20	2·5	88
				1·5	62

The size of the safety factor bears little relation to the systematic position of the animal. It is true that *Actinia*, *Nereis*, and *Sipunculus* are all somewhat simple animals and are all low in the systematic table, but some much more complicated animals also have no respiratory safety factor. This is true of *Limulus* (Arachnida) and some crabs (*Callinectes*, the American blue crab). On the other hand, the shore-crab, *Carcinus*, shows no reduction of its oxygen consumption down to 50 per cent. saturation. In the cephalopod *Loligo* there

* In reading this table it must be remembered that the oxygen-pressure of 100 per cent. saturated water is equivalent to an oxygen content of 21 per cent. in the air.

is no reduction down to 30 per cent. saturation. The simplest animals are probably the least efficient, so that we should not expect to find that their respiratory systems have large safety factors. But the differences in the size of the respiratory safety factor between animals on more or less the same level of complexity, *e.g.* the crabs, are related to the habits of the animals and to the size of the exceptional demands made upon the respiratory system by occasional periods of activity and not to their systematic position.

We must never conclude that the efficiency of a physiological system is uselessly great until we know the largest demands that are made upon the system in the life of the animal. Nevertheless there is no reason to believe that excess safety factors never occur in physiological systems. There is no obvious disadvantage to the animal in possessing in some of its physiological systems safety factors larger than are ever likely to be used. It is probable, for instance, that the respiratory system of the stick-insect has an unnecessarily large safety factor. It is a terrestrial animal and therefore the oxygen tension in its environment is not likely to fall greatly. Also, it is inactive and not likely to require a high oxygen consumption for rapid locomotion. Yet its respiratory system has, as the table shows, a very large safety factor. The tracheal system of insects is known from other evidence to be very efficient (*cf.* p. 201), and great efficiency in this system is needed in many active insects. In the stick-insect it is probably much more efficient than the life of the animal requires.

AERIAL AND AQUATIC RESPIRATION

We have seen that the exchange at the surface of the respiratory organ always takes place in an aquatic medium, whether the animal is aquatic or terrestrial (p. 188). Nevertheless, there are some differences between air-breathing and water-breathing, and these need mention.

The most obvious of these differences is the much greater *quantity* of oxygen in air as compared with the same volume of water. Water saturated with oxygen at atmospheric pressure contains the gas at the same pressure as in air, but it contains only about one-thirtieth of the quantity in air. Water is saturated with about 10 c.c. of oxygen per litre at 0° C. and with about 5 c.c. at 30° C., between which figures the temperatures of natural environments lie. Air contains 21 per cent. of oxygen or 210 c.c. per litre. As a result of this, the water-breathing animal will need to absorb its oxygen from a much greater volume of water than the air-breathing animal needs of air. The water at the respiratory surface will need much more frequent renewal than the air in a similar air-breathing organ. This difference between the two media will be greatly magnified by the fact that diffusion of gases in water is slow, whereas in a gaseous medium diffusion is very rapid. Indeed, if the air-breathing organ is on the outer surface of the body, renewal of air at its surface is sufficiently provided for by the currents always present in air. But air-breathing organs are almost always in spaces within the body and renewal of the air in them is then necessary. As we have seen (p. 189), adaptations for renewal of the water on aquatic respiratory surfaces are very frequent.

For these reasons, and also because water is a much heavier medium than air, the aquatic animal must in general do much more work than the air-breathing animal to satisfy its respiratory needs.

Carbon dioxide is much more soluble in water than oxygen; in natural conditions water will contain 500–1000 c.c. of carbon dioxide per litre at atmospheric pressure. The diffusion of carbon dioxide is also much more rapid than that of oxygen (p. 183). And, again, in clean natural waters any free carbon dioxide is at once combined with the inorganic ions present to form carbonates and bicarbonates, and so removed. It may, in fact, be accepted that in almost all natural waters, except those of stagnant pools and swamps, the content of free carbon dioxide is negligible so far as the respiration of animals is concerned. Even in the waters of pools and swamps, it is rare that the carbon dioxide content is large enough to affect the diffusion of the gas greatly.

Thus, it is clear that diffusion of a given volume of carbon dioxide from the surface of a respiratory epithelium is likely to be a much easier process than absorption of an equal volume of oxygen. This will be true of both aquatic and aerial respiratory organs, though the difference may be greater in aquatic respiration. This does not necessarily imply that oxygen respiration as a whole is a slower process than carbon dioxide respiration, for within the tissues, other conditions control the rates.

The proportion between the volumes of carbon dioxide released and of oxygen absorbed in the respiration of an animal is called the *respiratory quotient*. Most of the carbon dioxide released in respiration is formed in the oxidation of food material, and the value of this quotient varies with the character of the foodstuff being consumed. For the main types of food approximate values are given in the following table:

	Respiratory quotient $\frac{\text{vols. } CO_2 \text{ released}}{\text{vols. } O_2 \text{ absorbed}}$
Carbohydrates . . .	1·0
Fats	0·7
Proteins .	0·8

Since in normal circumstances the food of animals contains all these substances, the respiratory quotient will lie between 0·7 and

1·0, *i.e.* the carbon dioxide set free will be a little, but not greatly, less than the oxygen absorbed. Variations in the quotient (with other data) can be used to indicate the proportions of these different food-substances used in the metabolism of the animal. But if the animal is starved of oxygen the quotient may rise to high values (10 or higher). The animal is then either making use of abnormal, non-oxidative types of metabolism, or is using oxygen reserves in its tissues (*cf.* p. 198, 204).

RESPIRATORY PIGMENTS

A respiratory pigment is a chemical substance present in the circulation of an animal which will combine with oxygen at high pressures of the gas and release it again when the pressure falls. Hæmoglobin is the best known of these pigments, owing to its occurrence in the vertebrates. Among the invertebrates,* it occurs in most of the annelids and in several other animals scattered through many groups. Invertebrates which possess it are, besides the annelids, some molluscs—*Planorbis* (Gastropoda), *Arca* and some species of *Solen* (Lamellibranchiata) and a few others—*Chironomus* larvæ (Insecta), *Lernanthropus* (a parasitic copepod), *Caudina* (a holothurian), *Daphnia*, some nemertines and a few other forms.

Other respiratory pigments found in invertebrates are:

1. Hæmocyanin, a substance containing copper in place of the iron which hæmoglobin contains. It occurs in many molluscs (some lamellibranchs, many gastropods and cephalopods), many crustacea and some arachnids (*Limulus* and *Scorpio*).

2. Chlorocruorin, a green, iron-containing pigment which occurs in some polychætes (*Spirographis*, *Sabella*, etc.).

3. Hæmerythrin, also an iron-containing pigment, occurring in sipunculids.

In contrast with the hæmoglobin of vertebrates, the respiratory pigments of invertebrates are almost always in solution in the plasma of the blood and not contained in corpuscles. Exceptions are the hæmoglobin of the nemertines and *Arca*, and the hæmerythrin of sipunculids, which are in corpuscles.

The respiratory pigments of animals have two main functions:

1. Blood containing a pigment will carry much more oxygen than the same blood could carry without the pigment. Vertebrate blood can carry up to 20 volumes of oxygen per cent. (*i.e.* 20 c.c. O_2 at

* The invertebrate "hæmoglobins" are often distinguished from vertebrate hæmoglobin and called *erythrocruorins*. *Cf.* Florkin, *Bio-chemical Evolution*, 1949. But Keilin and Hartree (*Nature*, **168**, 266, 1957) maintain that there is no essential difference between the vertebrate and invertebrate pigments. They should all be called "hæmoglobins."

atmospheric pressure can be carried by 100 c.c. of blood), and invertebrate bloods up to 10 volumes per cent. (*Spirographis* 10·2, *Arenicola* 5·7–8·7, cephalopods 4–5 volumes per cent.). The greater efficiency of vertebrate blood is largely due to the fact that the hæmoglobin in its corpuscles is at a higher concentration than is possible in solution. In the absence of the pigment the oxygen could be carried only in solution, and the amount carried could not exceed 0·5–1·0 volumes per cent., which is the amount of oxygen in saturated water.

2. All respiratory pigments become almost completely combined with oxygen at pressures of the gas far below that present in the atmosphere or in saturated water. Blood containing a pigment will therefore become almost fully saturated with oxygen when in contact with water that is far from saturation, or with air in which the oxygen is greatly reduced (though this is less likely to occur in nature). In contrast, a liquid taking up oxygen into simple solution will dissolve the gas in proportion to its pressure in the medium from which it is being taken up.

The oxygen pressures at which the respiratory pigments become saturated vary greatly. This is true not only of the different pigments but also of the forms of the same pigment occurring in different animals. Also, the pressures at which the pigments are saturated are modified by many conditions (temperature, *p*H, presence of carbon dioxide, etc.) in the medium containing the pigment, *i.e.* the blood. For these reasons, the curve giving the percentage saturation of the pigment at various pressures of oxygen, known as the "*dissociation curve*," must, if it is to show the behaviour of the pigment in the body of the animal, be drawn for the blood of each animal, and in the conditions which are likely to occur in the blood within the body.

Hæmoglobin. Dissociation curves for the blood of a vertebrate (man) and for three hæmoglobin-containing bloods of invertebrates in approximately natural conditions are given in Fig. 87, curves a, e, f, g. Curve b of this figure gives the dissociation curve for vertebrate hæmoglobin removed from the corpuscles and in solution in the plasma, other conditions being as nearly as possible those of the natural blood. Curves c, d are for blood from which carbon dioxide is absent.

It is evident in this figure that the invertebrate bloods combine with oxygen at much lower oxygen pressures than vertebrate blood. The figure also shows that part, but not all, of this difference is due to the fact that the invertebrate hæmoglobins are not in corpuscles, for curve b is closer to curves e, f, g than curve a is. These differences in the dissociation curves are of great importance to the physiology of the animals.

It may be assumed that in an actively functioning respiratory organ the blood reaches at least 95 per cent. saturation; and that, if the respiratory pigment is functioning effectively, the saturation falls to about 50 per cent. in the veins, after the blood has passed through the tissues. These are the figures which are accepted for vertebrate blood and it seems probable that they will be approximately true of invertebrate bloods. At any rate, it is clear that, if the pigment is to

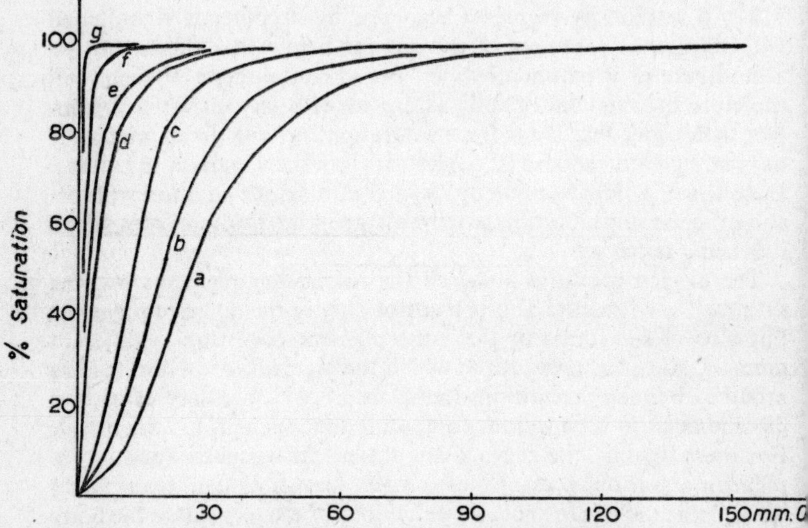

Figure 87. Dissociation curves of hæmoglobin.

a–d, human hæmoglobin; *a*, in the corpuscles of the blood, 40 mm. CO_2 pressure, 38° C., *p*H 7·4; *b*, in solution in the plasma under the same conditions; *c*, in corpuscles in the absence of CO_2; *d*, in solution in the absence of CO_2; *e*, *f*, *g*, invertebrate hæmoglobins in conditions similar to those in the blood of each animal; *e*, *Planorbis*; *f*, *Arenicola*; *g*, *Chironomus*.

function at all, the oxygen pressure in the tissues must be less than the pressure at which the pigment is almost completely saturated, for, if this were not so, no oxygen would be released. We will assume it to be the pressure at which the blood is 50 per cent. oxygenated.

The forms of the dissociation curves for invertebrate bloods therefore imply that the pressure of oxygen in the tissues of these animals must be very low. Curves e–g show that it will not exceed 3 mm. in any of them: in *Chironomus* larvæ it must be below 1 mm. Nevertheless, the amount of oxygen given off by the hæmoglobin will always be proportional to the difference between the saturation percentages in the respiratory organ and in the veins, and will not be affected by the pressure at which it is given off. If the saturation falls from 95 to 50 per cent., almost half the amount of oxygen needed to saturate the blood will be released. All this oxygen must be taken up by the tissues, which will therefore receive as much oxygen as if the saturation pressure was higher. But they will receive it at a much lower pressure and must be adapted to absorb it at this low pressure. Thus, the chief difference between vertebrate tissues and the tissues of these invertebrates is the low oxygen pressure at which the invertebrate tissues must be able to live. This does not mean that the tissues must be inactive. The activity of the tissues will be proportional to the amount of their oxidative metabolism and therefore to the amount of oxygen they receive. This may be less in invertebrate than in vertebrate tissues, but such a difference is not a result of the low oxygen pressure in invertebrate tissues.

The importance of the form of the dissociation curve in the physiology of the animal is due more to its effects on the exchange in the respiratory organ, than on that in the tissues. In general, the pressure of oxygen in the external medium may fall to the lowest value at which the blood is still almost completely (let us say 95 per cent.) oxygenated without appreciably affecting the physiology of the animal. At all higher pressures the blood will be saturated in the respiratory organ. Such animals can live safely until the oxygen tension in the medium falls to this value. It is true that this pressure will be greater than that corresponding to the point of 95 per cent. saturation on the dissociation curve, for the oxygen pressure in the blood as it passes through the respiratory organ will be below that in the external medium. Nevertheless, the lower the oxygen pressure at which the hæmoglobin becomes saturated the lower the pressure in the medium at which the animal can live safely. It has been found that the oxygen uptake of *Chironomus* larvæ does not become appreciably reduced until the oxygen pressure in the external medium falls to 7·7 mm. This is considerably above the pressure at which its blood is 95 per cent. saturated but it is still a very low pressure. For other invertebrates the limiting pressures will be higher than this, and in all cases they will vary with the efficiency of the respiratory organ, for if the organ is inefficient there may be large differences between the oxygen pressure in the medium and that in the arterial blood. This is often so. Thus in *Sipunculus* (with hæmerythrin, not hæmoglobin, as the respiratory pigment) the arterial pressure in saturated water (150 mm. O_2 pressure) is 32 mm., and in *Busycon*, a gastropod (hæmocyanin), it is 36 mm.* In these animals the blood is never fully

* M. Florkin, *Biochemical Evolution*, Acad. Press, N.Y., 1949.

aerated. The absence of any safety factor for *Sipunculus* blood (Table, p. 191) is therefore explicable.

Nevertheless, in view of the steep dissociation curves of invertebrate hæmoglobins, we might expect the presence of the pigment to be correlated with life in poorly oxygenated surroundings. Some other properties of the respiratory pigment increase its value in such conditions. Thus:

If oxygen is absent from the medium for short periods and not continuously, the pigment may be oxygenated when the medium contains oxygen and may release it when there is none. It may therefore serve as a store of oxygen to be called upon at need. It has been suggested that it serves this purpose in *Arenicola*, the lugworm, which burrows in sand in the intertidal zone, the combined oxygen being released when the tide is out and the worm is unable to obtain more oxygen by renewing the water in its burrow.

Secondly, a steep dissociation curve will mean that the tissues are living at a low oxygen pressure, for the pressure in the tissues cannot be greater than that at which the pigment releases the oxygen. The low pressure in the tissues will increase diffusion of oxygen from the medium into the body, and may make a supply of oxygen by diffusion possible even though the medium is poorly oxygenated.*

On these grounds correlation between the presence of hæmoglobin and life in poorly oxygenated surroundings is to be expected.

Observation shows that this correlation holds for many invertebrates which possess hæmoglobin. *Chironomus* larvæ live in mud at the bottom of freshwater pools, and mud is always highly deoxygenated owing to the large amount of bacterial decay which goes on in it.† *Arca* lives in marine muds, and *Solen* in tubes in sand, also a poorly oxygenated habitat. Many of the nemertines inhabit muddy marine habitats. In the annelids, as in the vertebrates, the occurrence of hæmoglobin is general, and its occurrence is therefore less likely to be correlated with the conditions in which the animal lives. Many annelids live in poorly oxygenated surroundings (*Arenicola* in tubes in sand, many earthworms in muddy soil), but others do not. We may conclude that the possession of hæmoglobin does not necessarily imply that an invertebrate lives in a deoxygenated environment, but that many of those which have it do live in such environments. To possess hæmoglobin is clearly a valuable character for an animal living in such an environment.

The occurrence of hæmoglobin in *Planorbis* is especially interest-

* H. M. Fox, *J. exp. Biol.*, **21**, 164, 1938.

† B. M. Walshe (*J. exp. Biol.*, **27**, 73, 1954) shows that the hæmoglobin is functional in these larvæ.

ing. This snail lives in freshwater pools and streams, not necessarily where the water is deoxygenated. In any event the oxygen content of the water is not of great importance to it, for it respires chiefly by breathing air in its mantle cavity, which has become a lung. It obtains the air by visiting the surface at intervals. When the presence of hæmoglobin in its blood was first noticed, it was found that the hæmoglobin was fully oxygenated in the veins as well as in the arteries. The conclusion was drawn that the hæmoglobin was functionless, and this seemed to be confirmed by the observation that the oxygen combined with the hæmoglobin was only enough to maintain the respiration for 2 or 3 minutes. The hæmoglobin could not act as an effective store of oxygen.

Later it was found that the hæmoglobin was oxygenated in the veins only when the air in the lung contained a high percentage of oxygen. When the oxygen pressure in the lung fell to 50 mm. (one-third of the atmospheric pressure of oxygen), the hæmoglobin was oxygenated in the arteries but not in the veins, and so became of use in the respiration of the animal. The hæmoglobin serves to enable the snail to stay below the surface until the oxygen pressure in its lung falls to 30–40 mm. of oxygen, which is the lowest pressure that allows the hæmoglobin in the blood to be oxygenated. Without the hæmoglobin it would have to visit the surface more frequently. This example may serve to emphasise again the danger of concluding too hastily that some feature of the organisation of an animal is useless. That conclusion should not be drawn until we know the whole of the biology of the animal. We have seen this danger in discussing safety factors in physiological systems (p. 190).

Hæmoglobin has been found to serve much the same function in an aquatic insect larva (*Tanytarsus*, Chironomidæ).*

Other Respiratory Pigments. The dissociation curves of all the respiratory pigments are of the same type as that of hæmoglobin. Examples of the curves given by bloods containing these pigments are compared with the curve of human blood in Fig. 88. It will be seen that all the invertebrate bloods except that of the cephalopod *Loligo* combine with oxygen at lower oxygen pressures than human blood, but at higher pressures than the hæmoglobin-containing invertebrate bloods. The exceptional form of the curve for Loligo blood is probably due to its acid *p*H (5·5). If true, this is an example of the large effects of the conditions of the medium on the dissociation curves of the respiratory pigments. Living in the open waters of the sea, which are normally well oxygenated, *Loligo* is unlikely to meet low oxygen pressures in its environment.

These other respiratory pigments share with hæmoglobin the

* B. M. Walshe, *J. exp. Biol.*, **24**, 343, 1947.

advantages which we have seen the latter to possess for life in deoxygenated environments.

CARBON DIOXIDE TRANSPORT

In spite of the high solubility of carbon dioxide in water, both vertebrate and invertebrate bloods carry more of this gas than can be accounted for by simple solution. Part of the carbon dioxide is carried in the blood in chemical combination mainly as bicarbonate, chiefly ionised as carbonic acid (HCO_3^-) ions.

In the respiratory organs carbon dioxide is excreted by diffusion as free carbon dioxide. As we have seen (p. 183), diffusion of free carbon dioxide both in the respiratory organ and in the neighbourhood of the tissues is governed by much the same conditions as the diffusion of oxygen, though its diffusion is more rapid than that of oxygen.

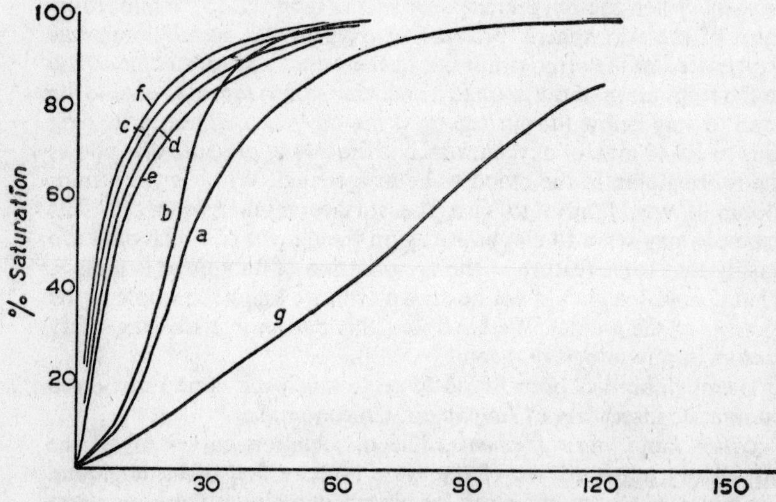

Figure 88. Dissociation curves of various respiratory pigments compared with that of hæmoglobin.

a, human hæmoglobin in the conditions of Fig. 87, *a*; *b*, chlorocruorin in the blood of *Spirographis* (after Fox); *c*, hæmerythrin in the blood of *Sipunculus* (after Florkin); *d, e, f, g*, hæmocyanin in the bloods of Helix (*d*), *Palinurus* (*e*), *Limulus* (*f*) and *Loligo* (*g*). (After Pantin and Hogben, and Redfield and Hurd.)

If, then, more carbon dioxide is to be excreted than is present in the blood as such, it is clear that HCO_3^- ions must be converted into free carbon dioxide in the respiratory organ. This conversion will occur when the carbon dioxide pressure is lowered by diffusion across the respiratory surface, but, unassisted, this is a slow process. Even in the mammalian lung, a highly efficient respiratory organ, almost all the HCO_3^- ions would still be unconverted when the blood left the lung if no other mechanism was involved. The carbonic acid remaining in the blood would then raise the pressure of free carbon dioxide after the blood had left the lung, by the slow conversion process. Thus, the carbon dioxide pressure in arterial blood would be very little less than that in venous blood.

In vertebrate blood there is an enzyme, carbonic anhydrase, which greatly increases the speed of the conversion of HCO_3^- into CO_2 by catalysis, so that much of the carbonic acid of the blood is converted into free carbon dioxide while the blood is in the lung. The carbon dioxide so formed is excreted by diffusion before the blood leaves the lung, and, the carbonic acid content of the blood being lowered, little carbon dioxide is set free in the blood after it leaves the lung.

It has been found that this enzyme occurs in some but not in all invertebrate bloods. Its distribution is sporadic and not correlated with the presence of hæmoglobin nor, so far as one can see, with any condition in the life of the animals. It occurs in some cœlenterates (*Alcyonium* and sea-anemones), in *Nereis* and *Arenicola* but not in *Lumbricus*, in nemertines and so on. We cannot at present find any reason for its occurrence in some animals but not in others.

THE TRACHEAL SYSTEM OF INSECTS

We cannot discuss the respiration of insects in detail here, but their respiratory system is so peculiar that some mention of it is necessary, and some comparison of its functioning with that of the respiratory systems of other invertebrates.

Air is carried into the insect body through the *spiracles*, openings, usually segmentally arranged, in the chitinous cuticle. Each spiracle is provided in the adult insect with an apparatus by which it can be closed. From the spiracles the air reaches the tissues through the *tracheæ*, branching and ramifying tubes, lined except in their finest branches with chitin. The chitinous lining is strengthened by a spiral thickening. This prevents collapse of the tracheæ when they are round in section, but in some insects the tracheæ are elliptic and can be collapsed by pressure from the surrounding organs. The tracheæ end in very fine *tracheoles* (Fig. 89), either within or among the cells of the tissues, every small group of cells being supplied with these tracheoles. In many of the more active insects there are, within the spiracles, large thin-walled air-sacs from which the tracheæ arise (plate IX, Fig. 90). These can be compressed and expanded by pressure of the neighbouring organs.

Oxygen diffuses inwards and carbon dioxide outwards through the tracheæ, but diffusion in air, in contrast with that in liquids, is a very rapid process. It has been shown that the partial pressure of oxygen in the smallest tracheoles of a typical insect is probably not more than 2–3 per cent. below that in the atmosphere. The respiratory exchange is, however, helped in many insects by ventilation produced either by the general movements of the body or by the special breathing movements that can be seen in many insects, such as the wasp. By these means the air-sacs (and the tracheæ, if they are elliptical) are rhythmically expanded and compressed. In some insects the spiracles are opened and closed in such a way as to produce, in conjunction with the breathing movements, a continuous current of air through the air-sacs or the larger tracheæ, which often extend up and down the body. Up to two-thirds of the air in the whole system may be exchanged by ventilation.

To a terrestrial animal such as an insect, loss of water is always a danger which must be avoided or reduced to a minimum. In the insect most of the loss of water takes place through the tracheal

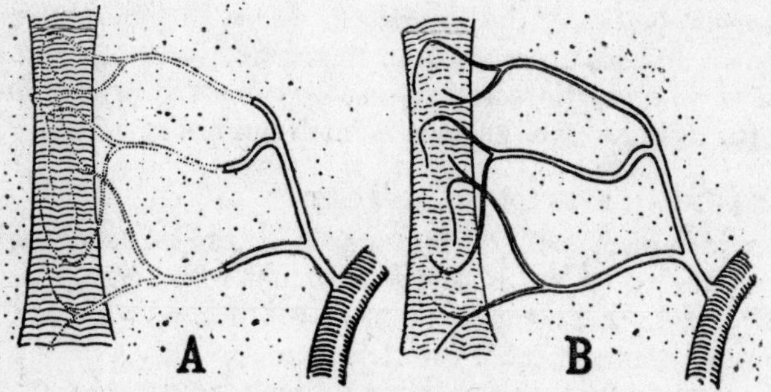

Figure 89. Tracheoles in insect muscle.
A, resting; B, fatigued. (After Wigglesworth.)

system, and we find that the system is controlled so as to reduce this loss to a minimum. The spiracles are opened just enough to allow sufficient respiration and the breathing movements are similarly controlled. The effective stimuli for this control are both the oxygen and the carbon dioxide tensions in the body, the nervous centres being stimulated by the acidity produced by excess carbon dioxide, as they are in the control of respiration in us. In the slug also, where the respiration is controlled by alterations in the size of the opening of the lung (mantle cavity), it has been shown that the control is by means of the carbon dioxide tension.

Another type of control of the respiration in insects lies in the movements of liquid into and out of the terminal parts of the tracheoles (Fig. 89). In a tissue with high respiratory needs, such as a fatigued muscle, air extends to the ends of the tracheoles, but where the respiratory needs are less (*e.g.* unfatigued muscle) the tracheoles are filled with liquid for some distance, and the respiratory exchange

PLATE IX

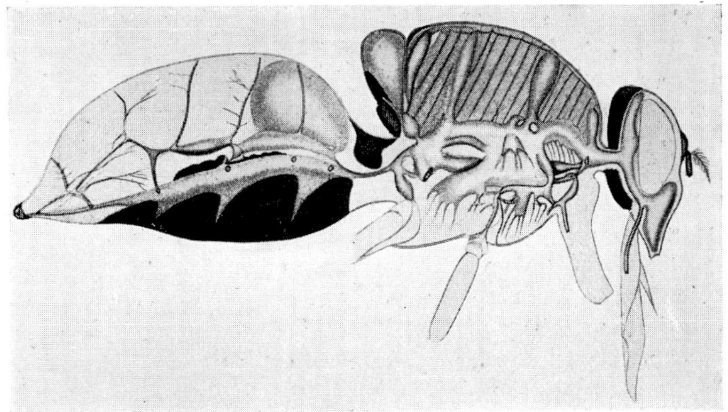

Figure 90.

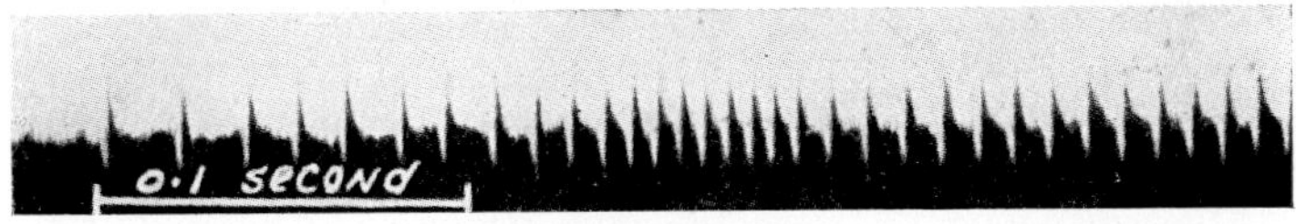

Figure 109 (*a*).

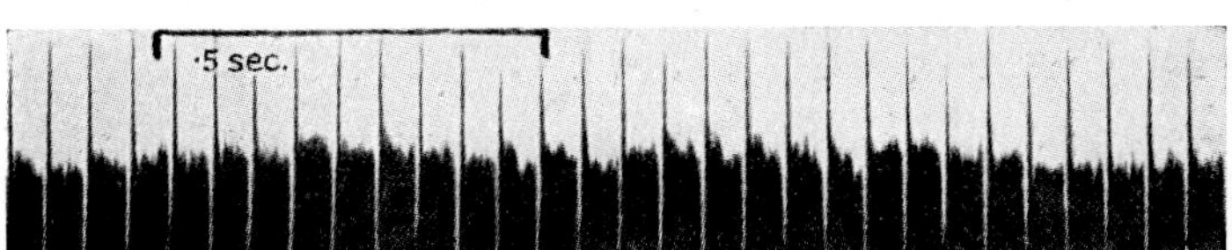

Figure 109 (*b*).

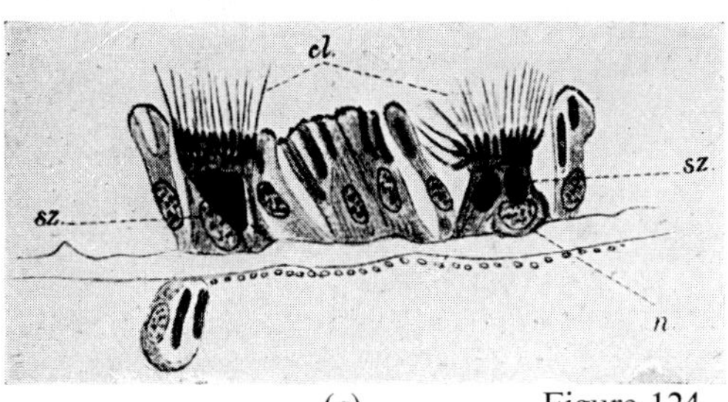

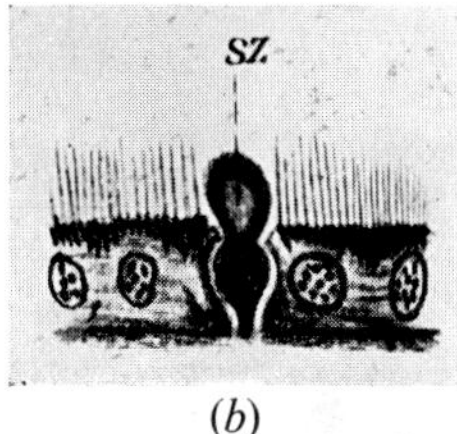

(*a*) Figure 124. (*b*)

Figure 90. Air-sacs in a fly (*Volucella*). (After D'Herculais.) The air-sacs are shown as solid, bladder-like structures within the body.

Figure 109. Discharges of trains of impulses from single neurones in (*a*) a sensory nerve bearing proprioceptive impulses from a muscle of the frog; (*b*) the nerve-cord of a caterpillar. (After Adrian.)

Figure 124. Ectodermal receptor cells of planarians: *cl*, receptive processes; *n*, nucleus; *sz*, receptor cells. (After Wilhelmi and Subarrow.)

[*To face p.* 202.

is presumably less. It is believed that this control is entirely automatic. The distance which the liquid extends up the tracheoles is probably determined by a balance between the capillary forces in the tracheole, which draw water into it, and the osmotic pressure of the internal medium. The latter will be greater in a fatigued tissue.

The tracheal system is thus a highly subdivided lung. It is also a circulatory system for the transport of oxygen and carbon dioxide. And since this system is distributed through the whole body, the blood has lost its respiratory function. The respiratory exchange in the tracheal system is partly by diffusion and partly by ventilation, as it is in other lungs. The vertebrate lung is never more than two-thirds emptied by compression, and, there also, the composition of the air in contact with the respiratory epithelium is partly determined by diffusion. It is interesting to find in the insects the whole respiratory system arranged on this diffuse plan; in most animals only the capillaries of the blood-circulation are so arranged. In insects the tracheal system has taken over the respiratory function of the blood and with it this type of organisation. We have seen that this diffuse arrangement is characteristic of all the organs in the body of a platyhelminth. In a large multicellular body, the only way in which this diffuse arrangement of all the organs can be avoided is by the evolution of a diffuse transporting system.

WATER-VASCULAR SYSTEMS

In a few animals we find circulatory systems in which the circulating liquid is not a part of the internal medium but consists of water from the external medium. This water is taken into the body, passed through vessels, and then passed out again. Such a system will help the respiration of the body, if the external medium is well oxygenated; it may serve to distribute food material if the current passes through the digestive organs; it may carry away excretory material and sometimes serve other purposes. The propulsion of the current is usually by the beat of cilia.

A system of this kind occurs in the following animals:

1. The large jelly-fishes such as *Aurelia*. Sea-water is carried through a complicated system of gastro-vascular vessels which extends throughout the disc. The current passes through the gastric pouches and carries food as well as being respiratory. This food is absorbed by the endoderm cells of the walls of the gastro-vascular vessels. The eggs are carried out of the gastric pouches by the current.

The currents which circulate the fluids in the enteron of other cœlenterates and other invertebrates may have a respiratory function as well as assisting in the digestion and assimilation of the food.

2. Echinoderms have the most highly developed water-vascular

system of any animals. A pressure is kept up in the cœlomic canals of the water-vascular system by the beat of the cilia of the stone-canal. The canals of this system end blindly in the cavities of the tube-feet but it is possible that water is driven outwards through the walls of the tube-feet by the pressure behind it, and that a slow current is thus kept up through the system. Possibly, contraction of the muscles in the walls of the ampullæ (by which means the tube-feet are expanded) may help to drive water outwards through the walls of the tube-feet. It may be that one of the functions of the system is to assist respiration, though there is no evidence for this. It is not likely that any significant part of the respiration of the body is so caused.

3. A few animals belonging to several groups have a siphon, or collateral intestine, along a part of their gut. This is a tube which opens into the gut near the mouth and again farther back. It is usually ciliated and does not contain solid food. It is possible that its function is to keep up a circulation of water of the external medium near the gut, and so assist in the respiration of the gut wall and neighbouring tissues. But, again, we have no direct evidence of the respiratory function. A siphon of this kind occurs in the Capitellidæ (Polychæta), echiuroids and in many echinoids.

ANÆROBIOSIS

In this section we have to discuss whether anærobic life, *i.e.* life in complete absence of oxygen, is possible in animals.

We have seen (p. 197) that the possession of a respiratory pigment enables some animals to live in media which contain very low pressures of oxygen. Even animals which have no respiratory pigment can live in environments in which the oxygen pressure is far below that in the atmosphere, if large safety factors are present in their respiratory systems. This has been shown for the stick-insect, *Dixippus* (p. 191). In this way, many aquatic invertebrates without respiratory pigments can live in water with an oxygen content of not more than 0·5 c.c. per litre (one-tenth to one-twentieth of the saturation value). These animals are carrying on the normal oxidative metabolism of the animal body in spite of the low oxygen pressure in their tissues.

Anærobic life is a very different thing from life at a low oxygen pressure. In true anærobiosis there is no supply of oxygen and metabolism must be entirely non-oxidative.

There is no doubt that many animals can survive *temporary* anærobiosis. We can ourselves live without oxygen for a few minutes, and many invertebrates can do so for a much longer time—an hour or more. The question whether permanently anærobic life is possible is much more difficult. The presence of parasitic worms in the alimentary canals of vertebrates, where oxygen, if not completely absent, is at least extremely scanty, and the occurrence of animals in the mud at the bottom of stagnant pools, also a highly deoxygenated environment, suggests that permanent anærobic life may occur. These facts do not prove its occurrence, for a low concentration of oxygen may perhaps reach even these environments, at least occasionally.

Investigation of the physiology of animals during temporary anærobiosis has been of use in defining the changes in the body produced by lack of oxygen. Knowledge of these changes will help us to estimate the possibility of permanently anærobic life. The cockroach has been the object of the most careful of these investigations; it can survive complete lack of oxygen for more than an hour.

It is chiefly the carbohydrate metabolism during anærobiosis that has been studied in the cockroach. In normal carbohydrate metabolism lactic acid is produced from the carbohydrate food-substances by chemical processes which are non-oxidative. Some of this lactic acid is then oxidised to carbon dioxide and water, the rest being treated in other ways. About half the energy set free in the metabolism is derived from the oxidation of this lactic acid, and half from the non-oxidative processes.

If a cockroach is made to live for an hour without oxygen and then returned to normal air, it is found that:

1. much lactic acid is produced during the time that the animal is deprived of oxygen;
2. much carbon dioxide is excreted during this time;
3. much more oxygen is absorbed immediately after the animal is returned to air than during normal life in air;
4. less than the normal amount of carbon dioxide is given out during this last period.

All these observations are in accord with the view that the animal during its period of anærobic life is carrying out the non-oxidative part of the carbohydrate metabolism in the normal manner and thereby producing lactic acid; but that, owing to the lack of oxygen, no lactic acid is being oxidised. This lactic acid remains in the body as such, and is oxidised when oxygen is again available. The animal is in fact storing up an oxygen debt during its period of anærobiosis, and this debt is paid when the oxygen is readmitted. The release of carbon dioxide during the anærobiosis is probably a reaction against the increased acidity of the tissues which must be produced by the presence of excess lactic acid. Release of carbon dioxide from the internal medium will reduce this acidity. When oxygen is readmitted, and the lactic acid oxidised, carbon dioxide is retained to replace the oxidised lactic acid.

If this interpretation is correct, it seems that the conditions in a cockroach during anærobiosis are very similar to those in muscle during fatigue, where, also, excess of lactic acid accumulates owing to shortage of oxygen.

Such a metabolism is not possible for permanent life if the lactic acid produced is allowed to accumulate in the body, for the tissues will be poisoned by its accumulation. But, if the lactic acid could be excreted and removed from the neighbourhood of the animal, it is possible that life might go on permanently on this basis, so far as carbohydrate metabolism is concerned. It may be that this happens in some intestinal parasites which are bathed in a continuous current of liquid. The metabolism would be an extravagant one, for only a part of the energy of carbohydrate metabolism is derived from the non-oxidative production of lactic acid, but this would be unimportant for a parasite with a plentiful food supply and small needs for energy.

Even if it were possible for animals in completely deoxygenated environments to make permanent use of this modified carbohydrate metabolism, we should not be able to say that they were capable of permanent anærobic life, for which the whole of the metabolism of the body, not merely its carbohydrate metabolism, would have to be non-oxidative. We cannot say at present whether anærobic life can be permanent.

CHAPTER XIV

NUTRITION

THE nutrition of most animals is holozoic, that is to say, the food consists of the bodies of other organisms, living or recently dead. Nutrition by photosynthesis occurs only secondarily among the Metazoa—where some animals take advantage of the presence of symbiotic algæ in their tissues to obtain from them a part of their food (Cœlenterata, Platyhelminths, etc.). Parasites and other Metazoa, *e.g.* free-living nematodes, are saprophytic (or, perhaps better, saprozoic), but there can be no doubt that this also is a secondary and not a primitive method of feeding. In this chapter only holozoic nutrition will be considered.

In the sac-like enteron of the cœlenterates and platyhelminths, food is taken in at the single opening, the mouth, and circulated through the cavity of the enteron, in the cœlenterates by the beat of cilia on the endodermal cells. The undigested remains are cast out through the mouth.

In the tubular alimentary canal of all Metazoa which possess an anus, several functionally different regions, which are more or less parallel to those of the vertebrate gut, can be recognised. Typically these regions are those mentioned below, but some of them may be undifferentiated in animals with simple alimentary canals, and in other animals more numerous regions can be distinguished. Histological differentiation of the tissues of the gut-wall is associated with the functional differentiations. It is worth noting that in the alimentary canal (as in other physiological systems) organs are usually named by their functions and not their morphological homologies, so that organs with the same name are often not morphologically homologous.

The regions of a typical alimentary canal are:

1. The mouth and the region just posterior to it, which is sometimes differentiated as a muscular pharynx. Here the food is taken into the body, often with the assistance of various organs outside the alimentary canal, such as tentacles or oral appendages. The pharynx, when it is present, may serve to suck more or less liquid food into the mouth, to break up solid food into smaller fragments, or to push the food onwards into the œsophagus. In the annelids the pharynx

has glands, the secretion of which starts the process of digestion, much as the salivary glands of the vertebrates do.

2. The œsophagus and crop. The œsophagus is typically a passage by which food is passed back to the digestive and absorptive regions of the gut. When a part of this region is differentiated as a crop, this serves as a store for the food, so that it may be passed back at suitable intervals and in suitable quantities. Crops occur in many animals but, as is to be expected from their function, they are especially well developed in animals which feed infrequently, *e.g.* the leeches or blood-sucking insects.

3. The stomach and gizzard. This is the region where the main part of digestion is commenced. The gizzard is a muscular part of the stomach in which the food is further broken up and mixed with the digestive enzymes.

4. The intestine. Here digestion is completed and absorption takes place. In many invertebrates this region is not well differentiated from the stomach region. Often absorption goes on mainly in diverticula, which are sometimes called the liver (annelids, such as *Aphrodite*, gastropods, the pyloric cœca of echinoderms, higher crustacea, etc.). Into these diverticula the food or its digested products are passed.

5. The rectum and proctodæum, the most posterior regions of the gut. Here the undigested remains of the food are formed into the fæces, which are frequently made much more solid than the contents of the intestine by absorption of water. Since economy of water, though of no importance to an aquatic animal, is an essential physiological function in terrestrial animals, it is not surprising that we find in such animals many specialisations of the rectum for the purpose of abstracting water from the fæces. Some also use this part of the gut for taking up water from the environment. This occurs in the woodlice (Isopoda), which possess a system of capillary tubes by which any water on the surface of the body is conducted either to the thin-walled respiratory appendages or to the rectum, in both of which places it is absorbed.

It is not only in terrestrial animals that the formation of more or less solid fæces occurs. The fæces of many aquatic animals are solid, so much so that the shapes impressed upon the fæcal pellets by the form of the rectum and anus are often characteristic of the species. In the annelids the pellets have been used for the purpose of distinguishing species not easily recognisable otherwise.

COLLECTION OF FOOD

The holozoic animal must collect its food from the surrounding environment. The ways in which this is done are very various but all belong to one of three types. (1) Most free-living animals go actively in search for their food, which is usually in pieces of considerable size when compared with the size of the animal. (2) A few animals, of which the earthworm is a familiar example, pass the external medium with which they are surrounded into their alimentary canal and extract their nutriment from it. (3) Many aquatic animals pass water from the external environment through a filter—of which several kinds are to be found in these animals—and filter off any solid particles present in the water. These particles are then eaten. This is known as filter-feeding.

1. *Search for Food*

This is the typical method of feeding of the free-living animal. It is probable that active movement in animals and the features of animal organisation which go with it—bilateral symmetry, development of the nervous system, sense organs, locomotory organs, etc. (*cf.* ch. XXII)—have been evolved largely as adaptations for more efficient capture of food. In fact, we may look upon the need for collection of food as having caused the evolution of much of the complexity of the animal body.

The adaptations of animals for the capture of food by this method are too various to be summarised here. We find special adaptations for this purpose in almost every species—teeth, jaws, an extrusible pharynx, and so on—the structures of each species being adapted to the food upon which it feeds. In the higher invertebrates, especially the arthropods, the complex behaviour makes possible the building of apparatus outside the body which is used for the collection of food, *e.g.* the traps of insects and spiders. We will not here discuss the feeding habits of these animals any further.*

2. *The External Medium used directly as Food*

This type of feeding is relatively rare, but it occurs in several groups of animals. Many annelids (*Nerine*, *Arenicola*, *Lumbricus*, etc.), some echinoderms (certain ophiuroids, holothurians, *e.g.* *Synapta*, echinoids, *e.g.* *Spatangus*, *Echinocardium*), *Balanoglossus*, and certain other animals feed in this way. The food is passed directly into the gut and there mixed with digestive enzymes by which any nutritive material in it is digested. The feeding of these animals is probably to some extent saprozoic; any suitable substance already in solution in the food will be absorbed without digestion. But the fact that digestive enzymes occur in the guts of these animals shows that they can feed holozoically on organisms present in the food. This method of

* A longer discussion of these subjects will be found in the review by C. M. Yonge—see Bibliography.

feeding is only possible for animals living in environments rich in nutriment; all the animals which make use of it live in soil, mud, or muddy sand.

A character which is common in these animals is that the wall of most of the digestive and absorptive parts of the gut is very thin. This is well seen in *Lumbricus*, *Arenicola*, and the spatangoid echinoderms. It results from reduction of the muscle layers of the wall, but the reason for this reduction is not well understood. In the earthworm at least, in spite of the thinness of the muscle layers, peristalsis occurs, though it is necessarily weak. Probably the movement of the food down the gut is mainly brought about by pressure exerted by parts of the gut wall nearer the mouth, and not by the peristalsis. Perhaps, the function of the weak peristalsis in these animals is rather to disturb the layers of the food near the absorptive surfaces (and so to assist absorption) than to move the food down the gut.

3. *Filter-feeding*

The means by which animals filter solid particles of food from the medium are almost as various as those by which they catch the food that they have sought. These methods of filter-feeding give a good example of variety of adaptational response to the same need in different animals. In most natural environments the concentration of food material is not great, and the filter-feeding animal has to filter a bulk of the external medium which is large compared with the size of its body. The animal must also be provided with some means by which the food can be transferred to the mouth after it has been collected. The filter-feeding apparatus must serve both these ends.

Since the animal which feeds in this manner does not need to move, it is not surprising to find that many sessile animals should have adopted this method of feeding. It is, in fact, the typical feeding method of such animals. But it is not restricted to sessile animals. Many small planktonic animals are filter-feeders (Cladocera, Copepoda, *Chirocephalus*, for at least a part of its food, *Mysis*, appendicularians, *e.g. Oikopleura*, etc.). These animals may use their power of locomotion to take them into areas where food is plentiful, but they do not search for and catch their food in separate masses.

The various types of filter-feeding apparatus fall into several groups, of which the following are the chief.

1. The method of ciliary currents. This method is characteristic of the ciliate Protista but it is also used, in almost exactly the same form, by the rotifers. It can be well seen in such a ciliate as *Stentor* (Fig. 91) or *Vorticella*. A current in the water is produced by the beat of the cilia surrounding the disc of the animal, and particles in the current which fall upon the disc pass into a groove near its edge

and are thence carried to the gullet. There they are passed inwards by the beat of other cilia and enclosed in food vacuoles at the base of the gullet. In free-moving ciliates such as *Paramecium* the mechanism appears somewhat different, for the animal is moving and not the water around it. In *Paramecium* the oral groove contains strong cilia and these set up a current towards the groove and the gullet. This current can be seen when the animal is approaching an area in which there are more particles than in the rest of the water (Fig. 92). In the

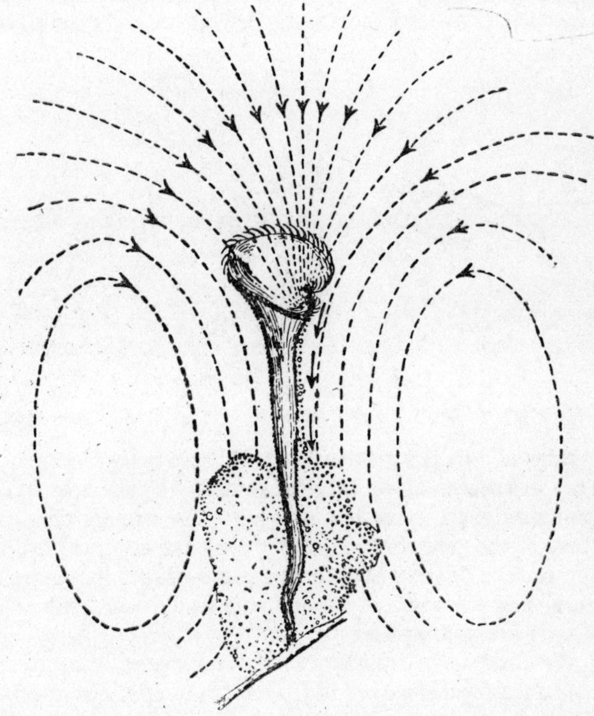

Figure 91. Feeding current of *Stentor rœselii.* (After Jennings.)

gullet the particles are passed inwards by the beat of the cilia on its walls. In both *Paramecium* and *Stentor* it is the movement of the water across the surface of the body that serves as the source of food. No difference of principle is involved in the fact that in one animal the body is at rest and in the other moving. It is possible that some mucus-like secretion assists in the passage of the particles after they reach the surface of the body, as it does in the third type of ciliary feeding mechanism. But this has not been proved.

In the rotifers the method of feeding varies in association with the form of the body. Both are greatly variable. Many rotifers are sessile, attached to the substratum by their posterior ends. We shall consider here only a simple form of the feeding mechanism in a sessile rotifer (Fig. 93). In free-swimming rotifers the feeding mechanism is more difficult to observe, though probably similar in principle to that of the sessile species.

The disc at the front end of the animal is surrounded by two, often incomplete, rings of cilia. The inner of these, the *trochus*, beats towards the animal's base and causes a current in this direction with two large vortices around the unattached end of the animal. Between

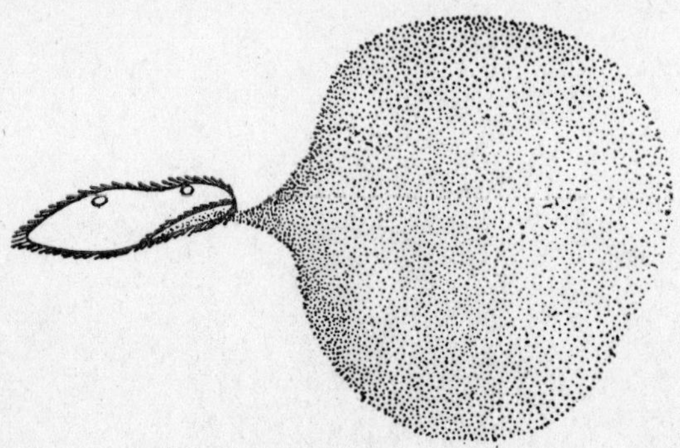

Figure 92. Feeding current of *Paramecium*. (After Jennings.)

the two rings of cilia is a groove into which particles from the current pass. They are driven along the groove partly by the beat of the cilia of the outer ring, the *cingulum*, and partly by smaller cilia covering the surface of the groove. From the groove the accepted food passes on to the surface of the disc, where the mouth lies in a cone-shaped depression, and the rejected food is cast away over a lip where the rings of cilia are incomplete.

As in the ciliates, the source of food is a current set up by the beat of cilia, and the food is passed to the mouth by the beat of other cilia. Many of the rotifers are among the smallest of the metazoa, and it is of interest that in them the same method of feeding has been evolved, by parallel evolution, as in some of the Protista.

2. A net of tentacles. This method of feeding is characteristic of the Cœlenterata. It is well seen in *Hydra*. In a well-expanded *Hydra* the tentacles are very long and hang down in the water, acting as a trap for the capture of any small animal which swims against them. The food is killed by the nematocysts, and the tentacles carry it to the mouth by contraction. The method differs from other filter-feeding methods in that it depends on the movements of the prey to bring it into contact with the catching apparatus; no current is set up in the

water by the animal. But, since the actively moving fauna of a natural environment will pass continually through the net formed by the tentacles, it is a true filtering method. Relatively large animals are caught in this way. Hydra will feed upon *Daphnia*, and many marine medusæ catch fish larvæ. The prey is often attached to the tentacles by a sticky secretion.

In some of the large Scyphozoa the food is digested externally by the lips of the manubrium and only the products of its direction passed into the body through the mouths, which are small and numerous.

Most cœlenterates (but not all—see next section) have this method of feeding. It is the usual method in the Hydrozoa—siphonophores

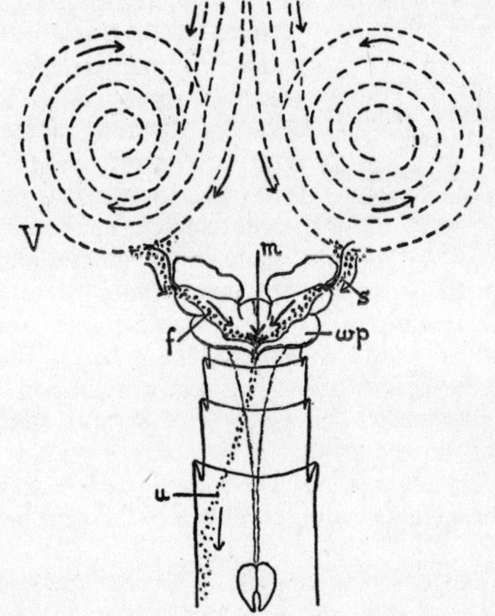

Figure 93. Feeding current of *Callidina symbiotica* (Rotifera).

The arrows show the directions of the currents. *f*, groove between the trochus and cingulum; *wp*, cingulum; *s*, current of food towards the mouth (*m*); *u*, rejected partcles; V vortical currents, round the animal's head. (After Zelinka.)

have it particularly well developed; and some deep-sea hydroids (*Branchiocerianthus*) have tentacles several yards long. Many medusæ, corals and sea-anemones make use of it, but in the last two groups the tentacles are much shorter than in the medusæ. In the ctenophores the tentacles, if they are present, are used in the same way as the tentacles of these cœlenterates, but the prey is caught by the sticky lasso-cells and not by nematocysts.

3. The ciliary field with mucus. The principle of this method is

that parts of the surface of the body are covered with cilia, which, during feeding, beat downwards on to the surface of the ectoderm and, also, towards the mouth. The ectoderm below the cilia secretes a thin layer of mucus (Fig. 94). Particles in the surrounding water are thrown down on to this layer of mucus by the beat of the cilia, and adhere to it. The beat of the cilia also causes a slow current in the mucus towards the mouth, so that the food is conveyed to the mouth and eaten. The mucus is presumably reabsorbed.*

The essential function of the mucus in this method can be well seen if a respiratory epithelium such as that on the dorsal side of the planarian is compared with a feeding apparatus of this type (*cf.* p. 189). No mucus is secreted on the dorsal ectoderm of the planarian, and particles in the water which are thrown down on to the ectoderm by the beat of the cilia are at once thrown off again. In the ciliary feeding apparatus it is the mucus that serves to catch the food.

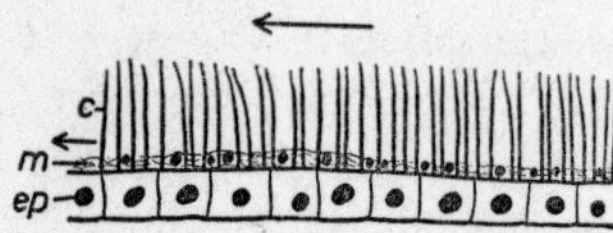

Figure 94. Mode of action of the cilia-and-mucus field in collection of food particles.

The arrows show the directions of the ciliary beat and the current of mucus. *c*, cilia; *m*, mucus stream; *ep*, epithelium.

This is the most widespread of all filter-feeding methods among the invertebrate Metazoa. It occurs in many cœlenterates, *e.g.* many sea-anemones, of which the common *Metridium* is an example, and many corals. Many annelids, especially the tube-living forms, polyzoa, brachiopods, the crinoids among the echinoderms, and animals of several other groups use this method. We have seen that it may play some part in filter feeding by means of ciliary currents. The complicated feeding mechanisms of the Lamellibranchiata are elaborations of this type of filter-feeding apparatus.

4. A mucus net covering gill-slits. This may be regarded as an elaboration of the method just described. Since the Chordata is the only group of animals which possesses gill-slits, the method is restricted to that group. It seems to have been the primitive chordate feeding method and occurs to-day in the Urochordata (Tunicata), *Amphioxus*, and, among the vertebrates, in the ammocœte larva of the lamprey. The Hemichordata have other methods of feeding.†

This method is well seen in *Amphioxus* (Fig. 95). Its principle consists in filtering a current of water, drawn in through the animal's

* MacGinitie (*Biol. Bull.*, **88**, 107, 1945) shows that particles of colloidal size may be collected from water by mucus. D. L. Fox *et al.* (*J. mar. Res.*, **12**, 233, 1953) find that colloidal hæmoglobin may be removed from water on mucus by *Mytilus* and a mysid Crustacean.

† Some Chironomid larvæ make a filtering net within their tubes (B. M. Walshe, *Proc. zool. Soc., London*, **121**, 63, 1957).

mouth and passed out through the gill-slits. The current is filtered by means of a layer of mucus which covers the inner wall of the pharynx. The mucus, with the food adhering to it, is then passed back to the intestine and absorbed.

In *Amphioxus*, the mucus is secreted in the endostyle on the ventral side of the pharynx and is passed forwards by the cilia of the endostyle. Part of it reaches the front end of the pharynx and passes dorsally along the peripharyngeal bands, but part is diverted on its way forwards and passed, by cilia on the inner wall of the pharnyx, obliquely over the gill-slits to the dorsal side of the pharynx, where

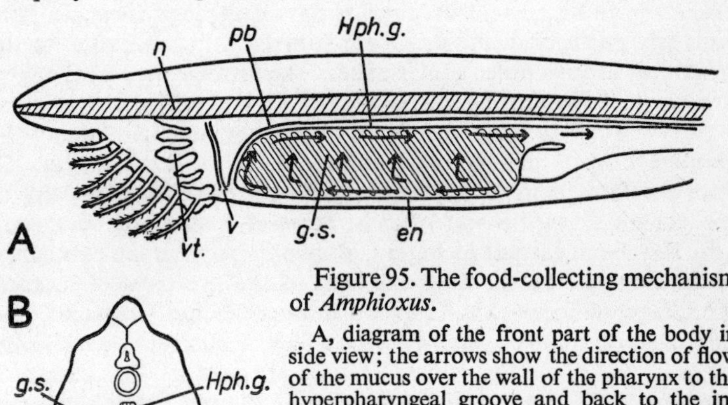

Figure 95. The food-collecting mechanism of *Amphioxus*.

A, diagram of the front part of the body in side view; the arrows show the direction of flow of the mucus over the wall of the pharynx to the hyperpharyngeal groove and back to the intestine. B, transverse section of the pharyngeal region; the arrows show (1) the direction of flow of the mucus over the wall of the pharynx, and (2) the direction of the feeding current through the gill-slits into the atrium. (After Orton.) *a*, atrium; *en*, endostyle; *n*, notochord; *g.s.*, gill-slits; *Hph.g.*, hyperpharyngeal groove; *pb*, peripharyngeal bands; *v*, velum; *vt.* velar tentacles.

there is a groove, the hyperpharyngeal groove, in which all the mucus passes back to the intestine. The current through the gill-slits is driven by the beat of cilia on the walls of the slits. Any food particles in the current adhere to the mucus net, through which the current passes, and are digested and absorbed with the mucus in the intestine.

That the mucus is here, as in the ciliary field, an essential part of the apparatus is well shown by the structure of the larva of *Amphioxus* soon after the animal begins to feed. At that time the gill-slits are round holes as large as the mouth and much larger than the opening of the intestine. If there were no mucus net, any particle small enough to pass into the intestine would have previously passed out through the gill-slits.

The methods of feeding of the tunicates (except *Oikopleura*, which has a peculiar method of filter-feeding, mentioned below) and the ammocœte larva are essentially the same as that of *Amphioxus*.

Two annelids (*Chætopterus*, Polychæta, and *Urechis*, Echiuroidea) use a mucus net for collecting food. These mucus nets have been found to be capable of filtering ultra-microscopic particles—down to the size of serum globulin molecules—from the water.*

5. A net of hairs or setæ. This is the typical filter-feeding method of the Crustacea. A net is formed of numerous fine hairs, mostly attached to the appendages. Either these hairs are passed through the water by the movements of the appendages, or the hairs remain stationary and a current of water is passed through them. In both cases any particles in the water are strained off, and passed to the mouth by various other contrivances. The arrangement of the filter hairs and of the appendages is usually very complex and it is extremely difficult to make out exactly how they function. One of the simplest forms of this type of apparatus is that of *Daphnia* (Fig. 96), since the filter hairs are in that animal restricted to two pairs of appendages. Even this apparatus is, however, sufficiently complex.

In *Daphnia* a current of water is drawn in between the two halves of the carapace by the rhythmic beat of the five pairs of thoracic appendages (Fig. 96 A). As in other filter-feeding Crustacea, this current is respiratory as well as being a feeding current; it passes over the gills, which are also situated on the appendages. The current is drawn in at the front, just behind the mouth and passes out again behind, in the region of the abdomen. The filtering hairs are on lobes of the inner parts of the third and fourth pairs of the appendages (morphologically the gnathobases of these limbs). These hairs lie across the current and filter any particles in it. The food is brushed into a groove in the ventral middle line of the body by setæ on the second and third pairs of appendages. It is carried forwards by a secondary current which is a backwash from the main current. On its way forwards (at the level of the second pair of appendages) it becomes mixed with the secretion from glands which are situated on the labrum, immediately behind the mouth. It is passed to the mouth-parts as a sticky mass, first to the maxillules and later, at intervals, to the mandibles, by which it is masticated. It is then eaten.

The principle on which apparatus of this type works is the same in all filter-feeding Crustacea. The difficulty in understanding the functioning of the apparatus is due to the complex form of the appendages and filters, and their exact correlation with the complicated currents they cause. Not all the Crustacea feed by these means: many, especially the larger Malacostraca, feed directly on large pieces of food which they masticate with their oral appendages, and some may

* G. E. MacGinetie, *Biol. Bull.*, **88**, 107, 1944.

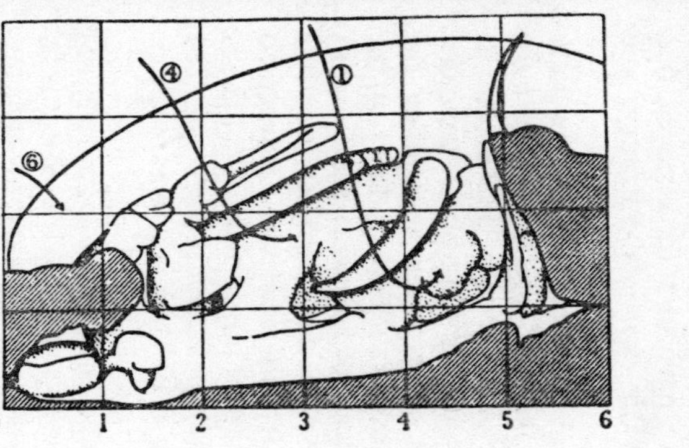

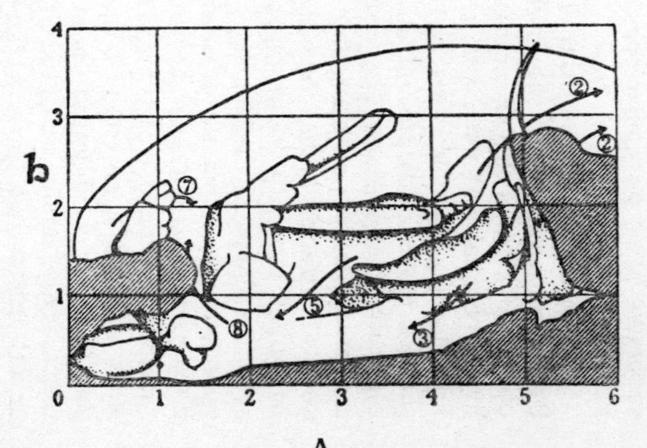

A

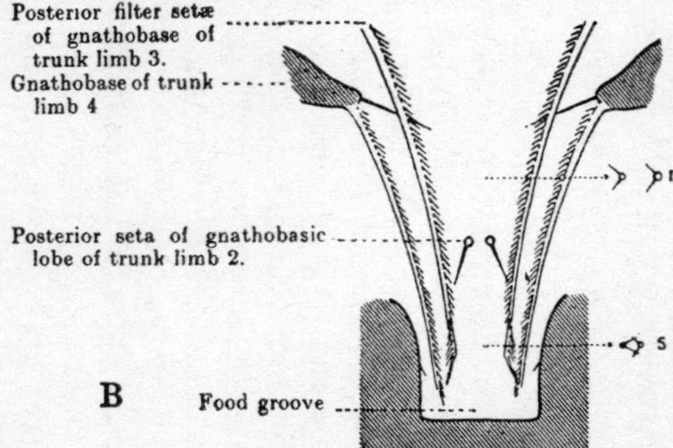

B

Figure 96. Food-collecting apparatus of *Daphnia magna*.

A, diagrams in which the positions of the limbs are shown (*a*) at the end of their forward stroke, and (*b*) at the end of their backward stroke. The animal is drawn as if cut in half longitudinally in the median plane and the right side removed. The head is therefore to the left. The arrows show the directions of the currents set up by the movements of the legs. 1, 2, 4, 6, the main backward currents across which the filter setæ lie—these are not shown. 3, 5, the forward (backwash) current into the food-groove in the middle line of the body between the legs. 8, the path by which the water of this current escapes. B, transverse section of the food groove showing the positions of the filter setæ on the gnathobases of the third and fourth legs. Particles on the setæ of the third leg are combed into the groove by the posterior setæ of the second leg, which move across them. Those on the fourth leg are combed by the thickened tips of the setæ on the third leg. (After Cannon.)

feed in both ways at different times. Filter-feeding is typical of the smaller Crustacea, but it is not the exclusive feeding method even among them. Some aquatic insect larvæ (*e.g.* *Simulium*, Diptera) have apparatus made of hairs that are waved through the water and serve for filter-feeding.

Not all types of filtering apparatus among the invertebrates can be classified into these five groups. There is, for example, the peculiar apparatus of *Oikopleura* (Tunicata). This animal forms a complicated "house" from a secretion of the surface of its body and uses this apparatus to catch minute planktonic food. This house is frequently deserted by the animal and a new one secreted. Again, some holothurians wave their tentacles, which are covered by a sticky secretion, through the water. Food particles in the water adhere to the secretion. The tentacles are then taken into the mouth and the secretion licked off them. The feeding of the sponges is also a type of filter-feeding. It will be described in ch. XIX. Still other filter-feeding methods occur, but the great majority of the methods used by invertebrates for filter-feeding belong to one or other of the types we have discussed. Besides showing variety of adaptation to the same need in different groups of animals, these methods of filter-feeding give many examples of convergent evolution. We have seen, for instance, that apparatus based on similar principles is used in the Rotifera and Protista.

There are some features in which all types of filter-feeding differ from feeding methods in which the food is sought for. The most obvious of these is that the selection of the food in filter-feeding is by its physical and not by its chemical or biological characters. Filter-feeding animals often possess sense-organs for testing the chemical nature of the medium upon which they are feeding (*e.g.* the osphradium of molluscs). They may cease to feed when these organs are unfavourably stimulated. But in the filtering apparatus itself it is physical characters of the food which determine whether it is accepted or rejected, especially the weight and size of the particles. That this is so is well shown by the fact that ciliates or lamellibranchs will feed upon unnutritious particles of carmine or Indian ink in their medium, if the particles are of the right size.

Selection of the food by its physical and not by its biological characters is true of all filter-feeding. It implies, what is perhaps self-evident, that there is very little truly poisonous matter in natural environments. It also implies that most filter-feeding animals must be more or less omnivorous, so far as the biological nature of their food is concerned. Those filter-feeders which eat the smallest planktonic organisms will feed upon plants, for these smallest forms, the nannoplankton, are almost exclusively plants. Other filter-feeders must feed upon plant or animal matter, and detritus, without selection.

Secondly, the filter-feeding animal is feeding on particles which are small compared with its own size. This does not imply that the animal cannot become large. Some of the largest animals are filter-feeders—the giant clam among the invertebrates and the basking shark and the whalebone whale among the vertebrates.* But it results in differences in the way the food is dealt with when it reaches the region of the mouth. Mandibles become grinding organs rather than cutting organs. The radula is absent in the filter-feeding lamellibranchs. These are merely examples of the adaptations to the nature of the food which are to be expected in all animals.

Finally, the association of filter-feeding with sessile habit has already been mentioned. For the sessile animal some form of filter-feeding or some form of trap is almost essential. We shall deal with other results of the habit of sessility in a later chapter (ch. XXII).

DIGESTION AND ASSIMILATION

The primitive method of digestion in the invertebrates was intracellular. Solid particles of food were taken into the cells of the endoderm, and digested and assimilated there. Digestion is still mainly intracellular in the Cœlenterata, Ctenophora, and most Turbellaria. It is still largely intracellular even in so complex an animal as *Limulus*. Some intracellular digestion persists in many groups—most Mollusca except Cephalopods, Brachiopoda, Rotifera, Arachnida, etc.—but in most of these animals the greater part of the digestion is extracellular. In most lamellibranchs and echinoderms it has been shown that amœbocytes from the body cavity pass through the endodermal epithelium into the gut and there take up particles of food which they carry back through the tissues and digest.

Thus, in most invertebrates the primitive method has been largely lost and the greater part of digestion has become extracellular, that is to say it is carried out by enzymes secreted into the lumen of the gut by the endodermal epithelium. These enzymes are secreted from glands in the epithelium of the gut or in the walls of diverticula of the gut, which are often present. The part these diverticula play in digestion and assimilation varies: they may be digestive—either producing enzymes or carrying out intracellular digestion, or both—and they may also be absorptive.

The liquid in the lumen of the gut is, in extracellular digestion, the

* These large filter-feeding animals may feed on organisms which are of considerable absolute size, though their size relative to the animal feeding on them is small. The whalebone whale feeds on Crustacea (Euphausiids) about two inches long.

medium in which the digestive enzymes act, and it is therefore necessary that the conditions in this medium should be suitable for the action of the enzymes. It is especially necessary that the *p*H should be suitable, for the enzymes are very sensitive to changes in the *p*H of the medium. The *p*H of the contents of the gut often varies in different parts of the gut, the anterior region where digestion is commenced being usually the most acid (*cf.* digestion in the Protista, p. 53). The *p*H may also vary with the condition of the animal, being less acid in the starving animal. In general, the *p*H of each region is controlled near the optima of the enzymes acting in that region. It is often between *p*H 6·5 and *p*H 7·0, but in some guts it may be as low as 5·5 or lower, *e.g.* in the gut of those molluscs which possess a special organ, the style, by the secretion of which the *p*H is controlled.

The enzymes possessed by the invertebrates are very numerous. In general, it may be said that they possess all the enzymes needed to deal with the substances likely to be present in their food. Numerous proteoclastic, lipoclastic, sucroclastic, amyloclastic, and other enzymes are found. The relative abundance of the different enzymes is correlated with the character of the food: carnivorous animals have especially strong proteoclastic enzymes, and in herbivorous animals all types of the enzymes which split carbohydrates are strong.

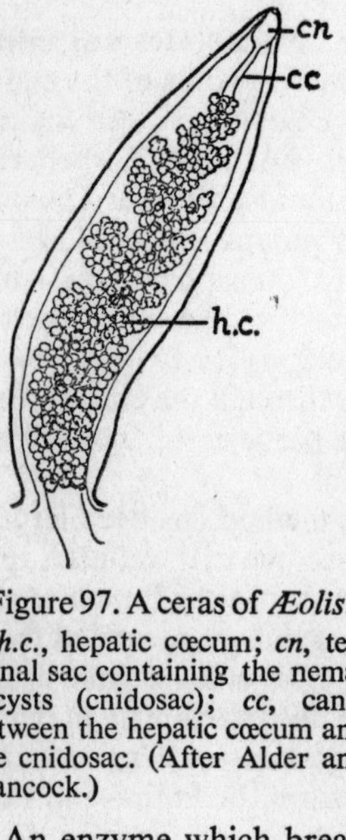

Some unusual enzymes occur in certain invertebrates. An enzyme which breaks down cellulose is not uncommon. It occurs in some herbivorous Gastropoda, *e.g. Helix* and the wood-eating ship-worm *Teredo*, where it is located in the diverticula of the gut which are called the liver. It also occurs in many insects which eat wood. In the termites, however, it is probable that the wood on which they feed is digested in the gut by symbiotic flagellates which are then themselves digested.

Figure 97. A ceras of *Æolis*.

h.c., hepatic cœcum; *cn*, terminal sac containing the nematocysts (cnidosac); *cc*, canal between the hepatic cœcum and the cnidosac. (After Alder and Hancock.)

An enzyme which breaks down chitin occurs in *Helix* and some insects, and one which breaks down keratin, the chief constituent of wool, occurs in the clothes moth.

NEMATOCYSTS IN PLATYHELMINTHS AND MOLLUSCS

It is a surprising fact that, although the nematocyst is an organ characteristic of the cœlenterates and of no other group of multicellular animals, nematocysts exactly similar in structure to those of the cœlenterates are found in two places in other multicellular animals.* They are found in the ectoderm of a few platyhelminths (the rhabdocœles *Microstomum* and *Stenostomum* and some genera of polyclads such as *Anonymus*) and in the endodermal epithelium of the terminal sacs of the cerata of some æolid molluscs. These cerata are processes on the dorsal side of the animal containing diverticula of the gut which open to the exterior at their tips (Fig. 97). It is in the walls of the terminal parts of these diverticula that the nematocysts are found. In both platyhelminths and molluscs the nematocysts are normally unexploded in these positions, but they can be exploded by the animal in whose body they are.

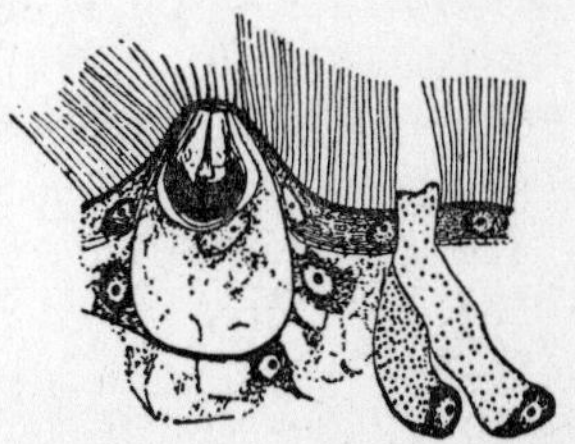

Figure 98. A nematocyst in the ectoderm of a platyhelminth.

The nematocyst is enclosed in a large cell and is directed outwards. (After Meixner.)

It has been clearly shown that the nematocysts of these animals are derived from cœlenterates upon which they feed. The clearest evidence for this is the fact that the detailed structure of the nematocysts agrees exactly with the structure of those of the species on which the animal feeds. Also, when the animal feeds on more than one species of cœlenterate, the structure of the nematocysts found in its body alters when the food is changed. If the animals are deprived of cœlenterate food, no nematocysts are found in their bodies.

The means by which the nematocysts reach their position in the bodies of the animals is different in the platyhelminths and molluscs. In both, the nematocysts remain unexploded when the food is eaten and digested. In the æolids the cœlenterate cell which forms and surrounds the nematocyst, the cnidoblast, is digested in the gut and the naked nematocysts are passed through the cavities of the gut to the terminal sac of the ceras (Fig. 97). Here they are taken up by the cells of the wall of the sac and arranged so that their threads can be exploded into the cavity of the sac. This sac opens to the exterior by a pore at the tip of the ceras and from their position in the wall of the sac the nematocysts can be shot out to the exterior when the animal is irritated. At that time the sac itself is opened out.

It has been disputed whether the cnidoblast is digested in the platyhelminths. The nematocyst is surrounded by a cell while it is

* Nematocysts have also been found in a ctenophore, *Hæckelia rubra* (Komai, *Proc. Imp. Acad., Tokyo*, **17**, 18, 1941). Hadzi (*Acad. Sci. Arts Slov.*, cl. 4, (6), 1957) gives reasons for believing them to be derived from cœlenterate food.

in the cavity of the gut of the platyhelminth, and this cell with its contained nematocyst passes through the tissues of the platyhelminth to the ectoderm, where the nematocysts are arranged so that they can be discharged outwards (Fig. 98). It is disputed whether the cell containing the nematocyst is the cœlenterate cnidoblast or an amœbocyte of the platyhelminth.

In both the platyhelminths and the molluscs we have the use of the defensive organs of one animal by a second animal which feeds on the first. This is an extraordinary adaptation: it occurs nowhere else in the animal kingdom. That the nematocysts should be arranged in the tissues of the platyhelminths and molluscs so as to be able to function for the advantage of these animals is no less extraordinary.

CHAPTER XV

EXCRETION AND OSMOTIC CONTROL

In the simplest Metazoa the removal of the nitrogenous excretory substances is carried out by direct diffusion from the tissues into the external medium. In the sponges and cœlenterates this is still the general method of excretion. One other group, the echinoderms, have no excretory organs; in almost all other invertebrates excretory organs of one kind or another have been evolved. Through these organs the end-products of nitrogenous metabolism pass out of the body either in solution or as solid precipitates. These end-products are various; the chief of them are ammonia, urea, and uric acid, in proportions which vary in different animals, but there are many other substances which are excreted in less quantities. Some of these other substances may form a large part of the excretion in certain animals; arachnids, for instance, are said to excrete mainly guanine.

It is probable that ammonia was the primitive excretory substance of invertebrate animals. It is highly poisonous but this is no disadvantage to an aquatic animal, since it can be excreted by such animals in low concentration. It is still excreted in large quantities by many invertebrates. Together with urea it forms the main bulk of the nitrogenous excretion of most aquatic invertebrates. Uric acid excretion is typical of terrestrial animals. We shall return to it later.

In some animals the excretory organs have a second function. The excreta they remove are, except uric acid and guanine, in solution, and they must excrete water in order to carry out the function of removing these excreta. It is hardly surprising, therefore, that these organs have, in some animals, taken over a part of the function of controlling the amount of water to be excreted from the body, and so of controlling the osmotic pressure of the internal medium. We know that they do so in mammals.

The amount of water which must be excreted is much greater in freshwater animals than in animals living in other environments. In freshwater animals the internal medium of the body must be maintained at a higher osmotic pressure than the external medium, and continuous excretion of water is necessary to remove that entering the body by osmosis. We have seen that the contractile vacuole probably performs this function in the Protista (p. 56). In marine and parasitic animals, the external medium is at the same osmotic pressure as the internal medium, and there is no similar need for the removal of water from the body. It is true that water is formed inside the bodies of all animals as one of the end-products of metabolism. In the oxidation of fats a weight of water rather greater than the original weight of the fat is formed (110 per cent.), and in the oxidation of carbohydrates and proteins 55 and 40 per cent. of the original weight respectively. But this metabolic water will not be of large bulk compared with that of the animal, and in marine and parasitic animals there will be loss of water by osmosis, if the osmotic pressure of the body is lowered by formation of metabolic water. In such animals there would seem to be little need for active excretion of water by the excretory organs.

So far as our knowledge goes, which is not far since little work has been done on the urine of invertebrate animals, these conclusions agree with the facts. Marine animals appear to secrete a urine at the same osmotic pressure as the body fluids. In the shore-crab (*Carcinus*), which is one of the few animals which have been investigated from this point of view, this is so as long as the animal is in normal sea-water. On the other hand, in the freshwater crayfish (*Astacus*) and in some freshwater molluscs (*Anodonta* and *Limnæa*) the osmotic pressure of the urine is constantly below that of the blood, so that active secretion of water from the excretory organs occurs. Nevertheless, even in these animals, the excretory organ cannot be the only means of osmotic control, for very little water is excreted in this way. Probably the epithelia in contact with the external medium, especially that of the gills, also do active work in maintaining the osmotic pressure of the blood.*

In terrestrial animals on the other hand, conservation of water is of importance to the animal, and we find adaptations of many kinds to this end in such animals. We have already noted that the respiratory system of the insects is adapted for this purpose (p. 202). Metabolic water may often be valuable to the terrestrial animal. Some terrestrial animals, such as the clothes moth, need no other supply of water; the water derived from their metabolism is sufficient for their needs. Loss of water is reduced to a minimum in terrestrial animals not only in their respiratory systems but also through their skins. As a result of various types of adaptation, we find that a cockroach and a caterpillar, both animals well adapted to terrestrial life, lose water in a steady current of air at a rate only one-eightieth of that at which the less-adapted *Peripatus* loses water under similar conditions.

* In palæmonid prawns the excretory organ is not effective in osmotic control; there is some evidence that certain cells in the gills have this function (Panikker, *J. mar. Biol. Assn.*, **25**, 317, 1941).

Terrestrial animals are adapted to conservation of water in their excretion. Insects, pulmonate snails and some other terrestrial forms excrete uric acid as the chief end-product of their nitrogenous metabolism. Some terrestrial vertebrates—birds and most reptiles—also do so. The advantage to a terrestrial animal of uric acid excretion lies in the fact that its solubility is low compared with that of ammonia and urea. It can be precipitated as crystals from a solution not more concentrated than the tissues can produce; this is not true of either ammonia or urea. After the uric acid has been precipitated, the remaining saturated solution can be reabsorbed and the water saved for further use in the body. Thus, in animals with uric acid excretion the urine may be almost completely solid, and far less water is lost in the excretory organs. Guanine in the excretion of arachnids has the same advantages as uric acid. It is only slightly soluble in water.

THE EXCRETORY ORGANS OF THE INVERTEBRATES

Except in those Metazoa in which the excretory substances diffuse directly from the tissues to the external medium (Cœlenterata, Porifera, and a few others), these substances must be carried through the internal medium to the excretory organ. This is one of the functions of the circulatory system, where it exists, and elsewhere it is carried out by diffusion or by slow currents in the liquids of the internal medium. The echinoderms are in the peculiar position of possessing no known excretory organs and yet a highly developed body cavity. It is probable that excretory substances are carried about in the liquids of the body cavity and excreted in places where the body cavity comes close to the external medium.

In the majority of invertebrate animals the excretory organ is either a nephridium (of the closed or open type), a cœlomoduct, *i.e.* a mesodermal excretory tube, or some derivative of these organs. The insects have their peculiar Malpighian tubes, and some other groups such as the nematodes have excretory organs which cannot easily be derived from nephridia or cœlomoducts.

It must be noted, however, that other parts of the body have an excretory function in many invertebrates. This is especially true of the epithelium of the gut. In many Annelida parts of the gut wall contain granules which are apparently excretory, and these are thrown out into the lumen of the gut. It has been shown that in the Turbellaria pigment injected into the body is taken up by certain endodermal cells and excreted into the lumen of the gut. The conclusion has been drawn that these cells are excretory. But this evidence, though suggestive of excretory function, is not conclusive. The fact that certain cells will take up and excrete pigment which has been introduced into the body does not prove that they excrete the end-products of the metabolism of the animal's normal life. The presence of granules of excretory matter is much better evidence, if it can be shown that these granules are in fact of excretory material and that they are excreted. This has been done for the gut wall in the annelids and some other invertebrates.

Not all excretory matter in the invertebrate body is excreted at once. Many invertebrates possess cells or tissues which are able to take up excretory substances and store them in a state in which they are apparently innocuous. In the fat body of insects there are "urate cells" which seem to perform this function. They certainly contain large quantities of urate. The "giant cells" of *Ascaris* and other nematodes contain material which is apparently excretory and which they take up from the body cavity. The chief function of these cells may, however, be to remove foreign bodies, such as bacteria, from the liquid of the body cavity, rather than dissolved excretory substances. In doing this, they would not be concerned with true excretion. The yellow cells of the cœlomic wall of *Lumbricus* have been said to have an excretory function. They are said to take up excretory material and pass it to the nephridium, collecting near the nephrostome when they are full, and liberating their contents there. It has, however, recently been disputed that these cells have any excretory function.* In general, it may be said that stores of excretory material, are frequent in the invertebrates.

Excretory material may also be put to useful purposes in the animal body. The material then becomes a secretion as well as an excretion. The secretion of the calcareous glands of the earthworm contains much calcium carbonate. This secretion is said to be useful in neutralising acidity in the contents of the gut, when the soil on which the worm feeds is acid. However this may be, this secretion appears to be one means by which carbon dioxide is excreted in these animals. Much of the pigment of insects consists of minute crystals of urates and related substances. Chitin itself is a protein substance in which nitrogen is bound up. This nitrogen will be lost when the animal moults. Secretion and excretion are therefore often by no means easily distinguishable.

TYPES OF EXCRETORY ORGANS IN THE INVERTEBRATES

1. *The Closed Nephridium* (*Protonephridium*)

There are two forms of this organ, the "flame-cell" nephridium of the Turbellaria, Rotifera, and many other animals, and the solenocyte nephridium of some annelids and of *Amphioxus*.

* E. Liebmann, *J. Morph.*, **73**, 583, 1943; *cf.* K. R. Bahl, *Quart. J. Microsc. Sci.*, **85**, 343, 1945.

(*a*) *The "Flame-cell" Nephridium.* In this type the excretory tubes end in intracellular tubules which are surrounded by protoplasm of the terminal cells (Fig. 99). In the lumen of the tubules are one or more "flames," bunches of cilia on the wall of the terminal cells. These beat with a spiral flame-like movement down the tubule. The terminal cells are therefore called "flame-cells." Granules which appear to be excretory are present in these cells.

The experimental difficulties of analysing the minute amount of liquid excreted by these organs has so far prevented our having any accurate knowledge of its chemical composition. The structure of the organ is clearly adapted for passing liquid out of the body, and it can hardly be doubted that they are true excretory organs. We may accept them as such. If they are excretory organs, it must be the protoplasm of the flame-cells which is responsible for the active excretion, for there can be no doubt that the liquid passes through this protoplasm into the tubule and there is no evidence that it is modified on its way down the excretory ducts.

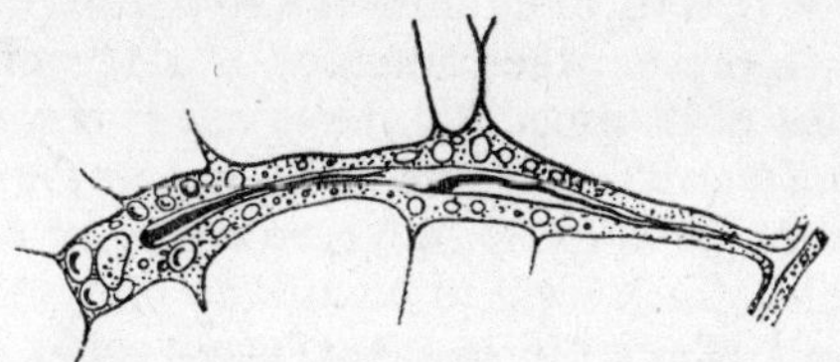

Figure 99. A flame-cell (*Thysanozoon*, Polyclada).

The cytoplasm of the cell can be seen to contain excretory granules and vacuoles. (From Willem after Lang.)

The question whether these organs play any part in controlling the osmotic pressure of the internal medium is equally undecided. We have no direct evidence on this point, for we do not know that the excreted liquid is at a lower osmotic pressure than the internal medium, even in freshwater species. On the whole such evidence as there is favours the view that in the Turbellaria the flame-cell nephridium is not an organ of osmotic control. Work on *Planaria* and *Dendrocœlum* has suggested that the skin rather than the nephridial system has this function.* In *Gunda*, a turbellarian which lives in places where freshwater streams pass through the tidal zone of the sea, and is therefore exposed to large changes of osmotic pressure at each tide, evidence has been brought forward that the epithelium of the gut is responsible for the osmotic control of the internal medium. When the osmotic pressure is lowered in the medium in which this animal is living, the cells of the gut epithelium form large vacuoles,

* But see G. A. Krumhout, *J. Morph.*, 72, 163, 1943, for evidence of osmoregulatory power in the flame-cell nephridia of a turbellarian, *Gyratrix*.

apparently containing the excess water which has entered the body by osmosis. Later the animal becomes acclimatised in some unknown manner to the lower osmotic pressure of the medium. It can live permanently in media as dilute as 5 per cent. sea-water. There is no evidence that the flame-cell plays any part in the osmotic control.

In any event, it is clear that the pressure produced by the beat of the flame, which cannot exceed at most a few millimetres of water (*cf.* ch. XIX, p. 314), is not capable of balancing any osmotic difference large enough to be of much value to the animal. Thus, the pressure set up by the flame cannot draw the excretory fluid out of the cell against an osmotic gradient of any significant size.* If an osmotic pressure-difference exists, it must be due to active excretion of water by the flame cells and not to any pressure set up by the flame. Nor can the flame push the liquid down the tubule, for the latter is blind and movement of the liquid down it can only be caused by excretion of more liquid at the top of the tubule. What function the flame serves has never been satisfactorily explained. The most obvious suggestion would seem to be that its true function is to disturb the liquid in the tubule, and so to prevent the formation of stagnant layers on the excretory surfaces of its walls. But the tubule is very small—its diameter is not more than a few μ—and diffusion over the short distances within it should be rapid (p. 183). Nevertheless, we find on respiratory epithelia cilia which seem to be used to prevent the formation of stagnant layers where the stagnant layers could never be more than a few μ thick (p. 189). It may be that this is the true function of the flame. Even though only very thin stagnant layers could form, the excretory function would be accelerated to some extent if their formation were prevented.

In nephridia of this type the intracellular tubules open into larger intercellular vessels, and these reach the exterior by the excretory pores.

(*b*) *The Solenocyte-nephridium*. These nephridia are built on the same plan as the flame-cell nephridia, but the terminal cells, called *solenocytes*, are different in structure from the flame-cells. The solenocyte (Fig. 100) consists of a cell body with an extremely thin-walled tubule. This tubule is continuous with the intercellular excretory duct, attached to it. The wall of the tubular part of the solenocyte is said to be not more than 0·2μ thick. In the tubule are one or more cilia, which beat in the same manner as the flame of the flame-cell.

* In land-nemerteans (*Geonemertes*) the cilia of the flame are fused into a single strap- or tongue-like structure, which might exert more pressure. It is possible that the pressure of the flame might be enough to overcome a small difference in osmotic pressure due to retention of colloidal substances in the internal medium, without being an organ of active osmotic control. (C. F. A. Pantin, *Quart. J. Microsc. Sci.*, **88**, 15, 1947.)

The solenocyte usually lies in the cavity of the cœlome, surrounded by the cœlomic fluid, and the excretory duct passes through the body wall to the exterior. Liquid passes from the body cavity into the excretory duct through the thin wall of the tubule. This has been proved by experiments in which pigment was injected into the cœlome. The pigment passed into the tubule and so into the excretory tube, but the body of the solenocyte was unstained. It could only have been carried into the tubule across the thin part of its wall. The wall of the duct below the solenocyte contains granules which are

Figure 100. Solenocytes from *Amphioxus* (*a*), and *Eone normanni*, a polychæte (*b*).

In *b* excretory materials is shown in the thick wall of the tubule below the solenocyte. (After Willem.)

apparently excretory, and it is probable that the selective excretion goes on there and that cœlomic fluid passes unchanged through the wall of the thin part of the tubule.

It is possible that the solenocyte was evolved from the flame-cell by thinning of the wall of the intracellular duct of the flame-cell.*

The function of the cilia of the solenocyte is as uncertain as that of the flame of the flame-cell. It is possible that the pressure they set up may be enough to draw liquid from the body cavity through the thin part of the wall of the tubule, since here there is no evidence of

* See the paper by E. S. Goodrich quoted in the bibliography, p. 121.

difference in chemical nature between the liquids on the two sides of the wall. If this is not so, and it may well be doubted, their function is unknown.

2. *Open Tubular Excretory Organs*

These organs are of several morphological types—open nephridia, cœlomoducts, and fused nephridia and cœlomoducts (*nephromixia*). All these types give rise to organs which are functionally similar, excretory tubes leading from the cœlome to the exterior. There is here much convergent evolution.

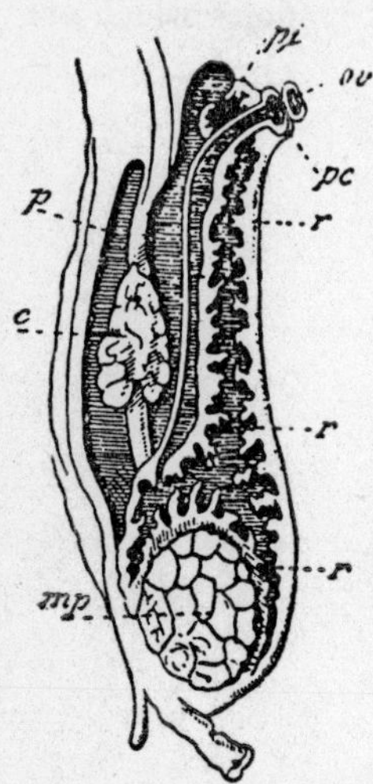

Figure 101. Pericardium and kidney tubule (cœlomoduct) of *Unio pictorum* (Lamellibranchiata).

mp, adductor muscle; *p*, pericardium; *c*, heart; *ov*, genital opening; *r*, renal sac; *pc*, external, *pi*, internal openings of the kidney tubule. (After Perrier.)

In simple form, this type of excretory organ is well exemplified by the nephridium of the earthworm. Similar nephridia occur in many polychætes. The nephridium consists of a narrow tube opening to the cœlome by a ciliated nephrostome, and parts at least of the tube are surrounded by a rich plexus of blood vessels. Water is driven outwards down the tube by the beat of the cilia on the nephrostome. It is probable that the fluid is altered during its course down the tube by selective excretion from the walls of the tube. The rich blood-supply of parts of the wall of the duct is evidence of this. In the earthworm it has been shown * that the urine is strongly hypotonic to the content of the cœlome except when the worm is placed in highly concentrated media. The selective excretion is probably from the wide part of the nephridium.

The nephromixium of many Polychæta (*e.g. Arenicola*) seems to act in the same way as the simple open nephridium, in spite of the fact that the tube is here much shorter and broader and there would therefore seem to be less opportunity for excretory exchange as the liquid passes down the tube. Large granules are often carried out of the cœlome through the opening of the nephridium. There is a rich blood-supply to the wall of the duct, as in the nephridium of the earthworm.

Modified cœlomoducts occur in certain groups of invertebrates and serve as excretory organs. In the Mollusca (Fig. 101) the renal tubes (a single pair except in the tetrabranchiate Cephalopoda, which have

* J. A. Ramsay, *J. exp. Biol.*, 26, 46, 57, 65, 1949.

two pairs) are cœlomoducts. They open into the pericardial cœlome. The heart wall contained in this space seems to act as a filter membrane and passes fluid from the blood into the cavity of the pericardium. This fluid is driven into the renal tube by the strong cilia of the wall of the part of the renal tube nearest the pericardium, the *renopericardial canal*. The wall of the next part of the tube (*renal sac*) is very thick and richly provided with blood. Sometimes, as in *Helix*, it is prolonged into the expanded cavity of the tube so as to form lamellæ.

The cells of this wall are actively excretory and are probably responsible for the selective excretion of the organ.

In those terrestrial Gastropoda that excrete uric acid, crystals of

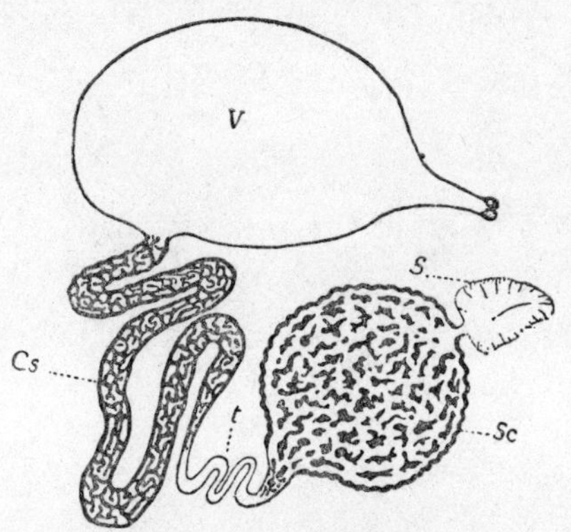

Figure 102. Excretory organ of *Astacus*.

S, cœlomic sac; *sc*, *t*, *Cs*, parts of the execretory tube (cœlomoduct); V, terminal bladder. (After Marchal.)

this substance occur in the renal sac, which sometimes becomes filled with them. This is especially noticeable during hibernation when the excreta are not passed out of the body.

The excretory organs of the Crustacea (*maxillary* and *antennal glands*) are complex, convoluted ducts ending in small sacs (Fig. 102), which appear always to be parts of the cœlome. Part at least of the tube is, in the Crustacea, ectodermal and may perhaps represent a true nephridium.* In the antennal, "green," glands of the Malacostraca the part of the excretory duct next to the sac forms a complicated labyrinth of tubules. Here most of the selective excretion occurs, but the wall of the end-sac is said to excrete ammonia. In the simpler maxillary gland of other Crustacea the excretory duct is a coiled tube and not a labyrinth, but the organ is believed to function in the same way as the antennal gland.

* *Cf.* Goodrich, *loc. cit.*, pp. 308 ff.

Similar excretory cœlomoducts occur in *Peripatus* and the Arachnida (coxal glands).

In the annelids, at any rate, the open nephridium is sometimes an organ of osmotic control. In the earthworm it is (p. 230), but this function may also be carried out by the skin and the epithelium of the gut. We have seen that in certain crustacea and molluscs the excretory organs may play some part in osmotic control (p. 224).

3. *The Malpighian Tubes of the Arthropods*

These differ from all types of excretory organ previously described in that they neither terminate in flame-cells or solenocytes nor open into the cœlome. They are tubular glands opening into the alimentary canal near the junction of the endoderm and the proctodæum.

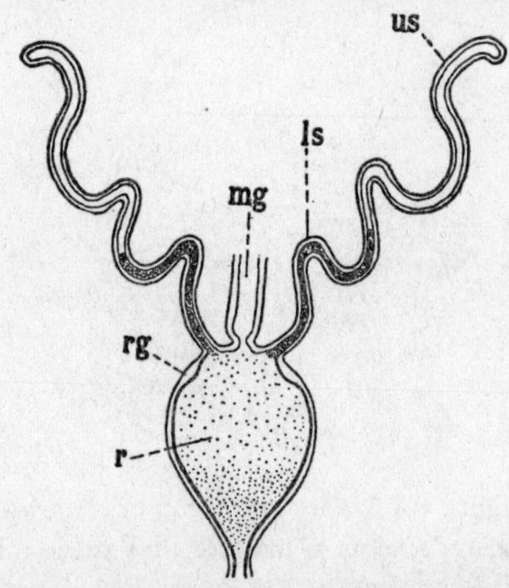

Figure 103. Malpighian tubes of *Rhodnius* (Hemiptera).

mg, midgut; *r*, rectum; *rg*, rectal gland; *us*, upper, *ls*, lower parts of the Malpighian tubes; only the lower part contains crystals in uric acid. (After Wigglesworth.)

They are endodermal in some groups, ectodermal in others. They occur in the Arachnida (except *Limulus*), Myriopoda and Insecta. They are endodermal in the arachnids, ectodermal in the other two groups. Probably they are not homologous in all these groups, the resemblances between them in the various groups being due to convergent evolution. Similar organs occur in some Amphipoda.

Their physiology has been best worked out in the insects, especially in *Rhodnius*, one of the Hemiptera. In *Rhodnius* the Malpighian tubes are in two segments (Fig. 103), which are both histologically and physiologically distinct. The histological differentiation need not concern us here. The physiological difference is shown by the content of the tubes. This is a clear liquid with a *p*H of 7·2 in the terminal part, *i.e.* that farthest from the rectum. The wall of this part of the tube is probably excretory; it certainly excretes pigment introduced into the hæmocœle. The lumen of the part of the tube nearer the rectum contains crystals of uric acid, which increase in size towards the rectum. The liquid in this proximal part of the tube is at *p*H 6·6. It is believed that soluble sodium and potassium urates are excreted into the lumen in the terminal part of the tube and that the Na^+ and K^+ ions are reabsorbed in the proximal part, leaving in the liquid the slightly soluble uric acid, which precipitates. The solution from which it has precipitated is then reabsorbed, so that the rectal end of the tube contains little but crystals of uric acid. We have here a good example of the use of uric acid to economise water in the excretion of a terrestrial animal (p. 225).

The Malpighian tubes of the insects vary in structure and probably also in their physiology. Crystals of uric acid are present throughout the whole length of the tube in the Diptera. In many exopterygote insects reabsorption of water takes place in the rectum. This is probably the function of the organs known (incorrectly, if this is so) as the rectal glands. The physiology of the similar tubes in other arthropods is largely unknown.*

4. *Other Types of Invertebrate Excretory Organ*

Not all the excretory organs of the invertebrates can be referred to the types we have discussed. It has been mentioned that the excretory tubes of the Nematoda are of a peculiar type. Their physiology is not understood. In some Rotifera a part of the duct of the excretory organ, which is a typical flame-cell nephridium, is enlarged to form a bladder, which is contractile. This bladder seems to act in precisely the same way as the contractile vacuole of the Protista. In *Asplanchna*, which is a freshwater form, it contracts once in every 15 secs. and evacuates water to the extent of 1/25th of the volume of the animal at each contraction. There can be little doubt that it serves to remove from the body water which has entered by osmosis from the exterior, and therefore that it is an organ of osmotic control.

It will be seen from this account that in all the chief types of invertebrate excretory organ, except the flame-cell nephridium, the physiological principle on which the organ works is the same. In all, including the flame-cell nephridium, water derived from the internal medium of the animal is driven into the excretory tube. This liquid may be the more or less unaltered liquid of the internal medium, as in the solenocyte- and open nephridia, or it may be altered by selective excretion as it passes into the tube, as in the Malpighian tubes.

* *Cf.* Ramsay, *Jour. exp. Biol.*, **35**, 871, 1958.

Except in the flame-cell nephridium, the excretory liquid is modified on its way down the tube by selective excretion (and often reabsorption) carried out by the cells of the wall, which are provided with a rich blood supply. The kidney tubule of the vertebrate also acts on this plan. There, the excretory liquid is filtered into the tubule at the glomerulus and the urine is modified on its way down the tubule. This may be regarded as the general physiological scheme of the excretory organs of the Metazoa.

CHAPTER XVI

CO-ORDINATION

CO-ORDINATION of the activities of the various parts of the body, so that they act together to serve the needs of the whole organism is as essential a function in multicellular animals as we have seen it to be in the Protista (p. 68).

This function is carried out in the multicellular body in three ways. These are:

(1) By impulses passed from one part to another through the protoplasm of specially adapted conducting cells, the nerve cells.

(2) By transference of dissolved chemical substances about the body, either through the protoplasm of the cells or in the liquids of the internal medium. Passage through the protoplasm is probably of more importance in the simpler multicellular animals.

(3) By direct, mechanical action of one part of the body on another, *e.g.* by the pull exerted by a contracting muscle (p. 255).

Co-ordination in the animal body is itself of two types, both of which are essential to the life of the animal. The first of these is the most obvious—the co-ordination of the activity of the individual organs, so that their activities together build up the behaviour of the animal. But it is also necessary that the condition of the body as a whole should be adapted to the conditions of the environment in which it is living; at one time the animal as a whole needs to be active, at another inactive. Co-ordination in physiological condition between all the parts of the body is necessary to achieve this. This is the second type of co-ordination which we have to discuss. To some extent, but not entirely, the function of chemical co-ordination is the control of the physiological condition of the body as a whole, and that of the nervous system co-ordination of the activities of the organs. We shall return later (p. 265) to discuss how far this statement is true. Direct action of one part on another never controls more than the activity of the part acted on.

The co-ordinating system of the animal becomes more and more complex as we pass up the evolutionary series, as do all the other physiological systems of the body. In the sponges (Porifera) there is no nervous system, and such co-ordination as there is must be chemical, or due to direct, mechanical action of one part of the body on another. We have very little knowledge of the means of co-ordination in this group. In the simplest Metazoa, the nervous system is in the form of a diffuse nerve-net, extending over the whole body. This system may be differentiated in its parts, but it is entirely uncentralised. Stimulation radiates outwards in all directions through the nerve-net from the organ which receives it, the receptor organ. It thus finally reaches the organs of response, the effector organs, without passing through any single co-ordinating centre in the body, such as is provided in the central nervous system of higher animals. As the body becomes more complex, a second type of nervous system is evolved from this primitive diffuse system. Conducting paths—nerves—and a central nervous system are developed, both lying in the interior tissues of the body (though they are almost always developed in the embryology of the animal from the ectoderm). Stimulation passes by defined paths along the nerves to the effector organs, and frequently through the central nervous system on the way. Thus, the stimulation reaches only certain of the effector organs of the body; it does not spread radially over large parts of the body, as it does in the nerve-net. Establishment of these "reflex" paths and their organisation to produce the co-ordinated behaviour of the animal are the primitive functions of the central nervous system. A further stage in the elaboration of co-ordination is the development of a controlling centre of co-ordination, generally called the "brain."

I. THE NERVOUS SYSTEM

1. THE NERVE CELL AND THE CONDUCTION OF THE NERVE IMPULSE

So far as our present knowledge goes conduction of stimulation through a nerve cell is essentially the same process in all animals that possess nerve cells, though there are many quantitative differences in the process in nerve cells of different types. We cannot here discuss nervous conduction in any detail, but there are some general results of investigation of this phenomenon which we must consider if we are to reach any understanding of nervous co-ordination in animals. Almost all these results have been obtained by investigation of the nervous systems of the higher animals, especially the vertebrates. But, since conduction is essentially the same process in all nerve cells, these results may in general be taken to be true of all nervous systems. Some exceptions to this statement will be mentioned.

(1) Stimuli (see p. 268) are almost always received by special cells adapted for this purpose, the receptive cells of the receptor organs. These stimuli may originate outside the body, when they are called *exteroceptive stimuli*, and the sense cells *exteroceptors*; or within the

body, either in the internal surfaces of the body, *e.g.* the surfaces of the alimentary canal (*interoceptive stimuli*), or in the tissues themselves (*proprioceptive*). The latter are due to changes in the tissues, very largely caused by the activities of the animal (*e.g.* changes in the muscles, tendons, etc., that take place during locomotion).

Unless the receptive cell is in direct contact with the effector organ (p. 269), the stimulation is passed from the receptive cell to a nerve cell, through which it travels as nerve impulses. The impulses pass through one, or more often several nerve cells, and finally reach the effector organ, the activity of which is modified by the arrival of the impulses. The effector organs include glands, electric organs, light-producing organs, etc., as well as muscles.

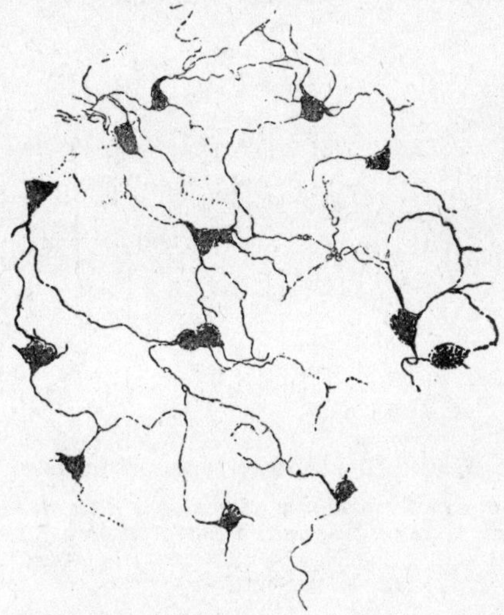

Figure 104. Nerve-net in a polyzoan. (After Gewertzhagen.)

(2) The undifferentiated nerve cell (*neurone*) consists of a cell-body with a single, large nucleus and with fine branches extending from the cell-body (Fig. 104). Fibrillæ running in the directions in which impulses cross the cell can be seen in the protoplasm of the neurone after coagulation, but it is doubtful whether true fibrillæ are present in the living protoplasm. Nevertheless, the appearance of fibrillæ in the coagulated protoplasm must represent arrangement of some kind in the elements of the living protoplasm (micellæ). Evidence of such arrangement has been obtained in the processes of large, living nerve cells (Cephalopoda); there it has been definitely shown that no solid fibrillæ are present. An impulse will pass along a process of a nerve cell after it has been separated from the body of the cell. The parts

within the cell-body are therefore not essential for passage of the impulse.

The arrangement of the processes of the cell varies greatly in different types of neurone. In the cells of the nerve-net, the branches are either equally developed on all sides of the cell, which is then called *multipolar*, or developed on two opposite sides of the cell only (*bipolar*). In many of the cells of the nervous systems of higher animals one of the processes becomes very long (Fig. 105). These cells are polarised, *i.e.* impulses only pass across them in one direction, inwards from the receptive cell in a sensory neurone, outwards to the effector organ in a motor neurone. The elongate process of the cell (axon) may be that by which the impulse reaches the cell-body or that by which it passes away from it. In sensory neurones the cell-

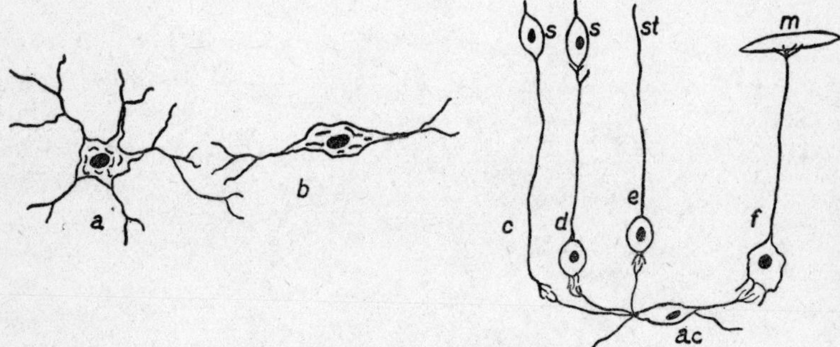

Figure 105. Various types of neurone.

a, multipolar, *b*, bipolar neurones of the nerve-net; *d*, *e*, polarised sensory neurones; *f*, polarised motor neurone; *ac*, association neurone; *st*, sensory termination of a neurone; *s*, receptive cells near the sensory terminations; *c*, termination of receptive cell; *m*, muscle fibre.

body may be placed near the central nervous system and the terminations of the receptive process at the surface of the body; or the body of the cell may be at the surface near the receptive terminations, and a long process conducts the impulse far within the body. The receptive cells may themselves possess long processes. In motor neurones the process which carries the impulse to the effector organ may be several metres long in the largest animals.

Besides the sensory and motor neurones, there are in all nervous systems many neurones which are in contact on both sides with other neurones, and not with receptor or effector cells. These are called "*association neurones*." They become more numerous as the nervous system increases in complexity.

In Fig. 106 a diagram of a simple "reflex" nervous path from sensory to effector organ is given. This diagram shows the path in the earthworm from sense organs in the skin through the nerve cord to the longitudinal ventral muscles. It is much simplified. The stimulation is received by cells in the epidermis and is passed to the nerve cord along the processes of these cells. There it is transferred to motor neurones. In the cord there will also be many association neurones by which the stimulation is passed to other motor neurones. Only one of these is shown.

Where the branches of a neurone reach another neurone or the surface of a receptor or effector organ, there is close contact but probably not in general protoplasmic continuity. The giant nerve fibres of *Loligo* (Cephalopoda) provide an exception to this statement. In them there has been shown to be direct protoplasmic continuity.* The point of contact is called a *synapse*.

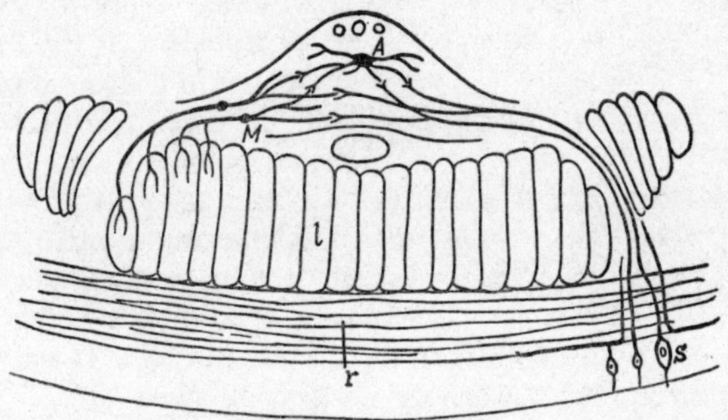

Figure 106. Simplified diagram of the reflex paths in an earthworm.

s, sense cells; M, motor neurones; A, association neurone; *l*, longitudinal, *r*, circular muscles. (From Bayliss.)

(3) The stimulation from a sense cell is conducted through the protoplasm of the neurones as one or more impulses, which are accompanied by electrical disturbances (Fig. 107). The electrical disturbance is the only feature by which we can conveniently measure the passage of the impulse. As an impulse passes a region of the protoplasm, this region becomes electrically negative as compared with other parts of the protoplasm. There is also some evidence that at least in large nerve fibres the negative phase is followed by a positive phase, in which the region through which the impulse is passing is electrically positive compared with other parts.† The electrical change is diphasic.

It is found almost everywhere in the nervous system that, if a nerve cell is stimulated, a propagated impulse is set up either completely or not at all: a partial impulse is impossible, and the impulses conducted by a nerve cell are identical so long as its condition is

* J. Z. Young, *Phil. Trans. R.S. London*, **B229**, 465, 1939.

† Curtis and Cole, *J. cell. comp. Physiol.*, **19**, 135, 1942.

9*

unaltered. This is known as the "*all or nothing*" law. It is, so far as we know, true of all types of nervous conduction except perhaps of the conduction of certain impulses within the central nervous systems of the higher animals.

The size of the impulse* in a nerve cell is not determined by the distance it has travelled—there is no fading out of the impulse as it travels farther. This may be expressed by saying that conduction occurs in a nerve cell "*without decrement.*" It is true whatever the length the impulse has travelled, and however many cells it has crossed. The size of the impulse is, however, determined by the structural characters of the nerve cell as well as by the activity of its protoplasm. If the impulse is travelling in a process of a nerve cell, its size varies with the diameter of the process, being smaller in the finer processes. The size of the impulse also varies with the condition of the nerve cell. It is less when the activity of the cell is reduced by a narcotic or by other treatment. It may thus be reduced to zero, when the cell ceases to conduct.

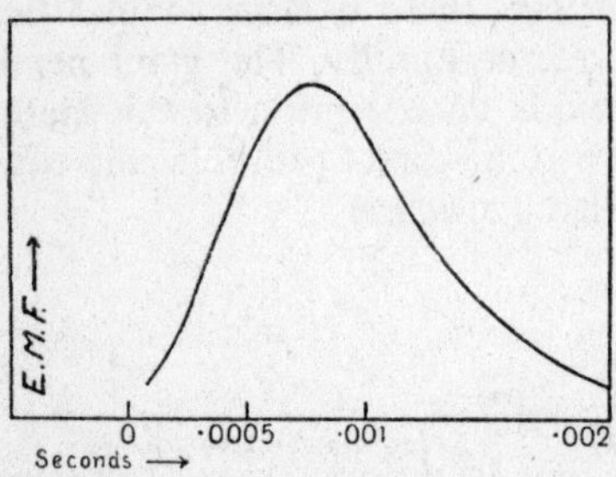

Figure 107. Rise and fall of E.M.F. during the passage of a nerve-impulse across a point in the frog's sciatic nerve. (From Adrian.)

The rate of conduction of an impulse within a nerve cell is very different in different types of nerve. It may be as high as 100 m. per sec. in the axons of mammalian nerve, and as low as 50 cm. per sec. in those of the nerves of molluscs. In axons of the same type, the rate increases with the diameter of the axon.

In the cœlenterate nerve-net the rate of conduction varies (*cf.* p. 247) from 4 to about 120 cm. per sec. These rates, however, include the time spent in traversing many synapses between the cells of the net. If the conditions at the synapses in the net are similar to those at synapses in the nervous systems of higher animals, a considerable delay may be expected at each synapse. The rates of conduction in the net are therefore not comparable to the rates of conduction along axons, *i.e.* within a nerve cell.

After an impulse has passed through a nerve cell, the protoplasm is for a short time insensitive to further stimulation. The insensitivity is at first absolute, the cell being unable to respond to any stimulation however great. It then becomes relative; as time goes on, the cell responds to smaller and smaller stimuli until the original sensitivity is regained. These are called the *absolute* and *relative refractory*

* As measured by the size of the electrical disturbance.

periods of the cell. The lengths of these periods vary in different types of nerve cell. Some comparative values are:

	Refractory period	
	Absolute	Relative
	sec.	sec.
Cœlenterate nerve-net . .	0·04–0·06	0·5
Crustacean nerve . . .	0·0008–0·001	0·004
Mammalian nerve . . .	0·0025	0·012

The refractory period in the nerve-net of a cœlenterate is shown in Fig. 108.

The ease with which a nerve cell is stimulated is also variable, but measure of the sensitivity is not an easy subject, and it is difficult to

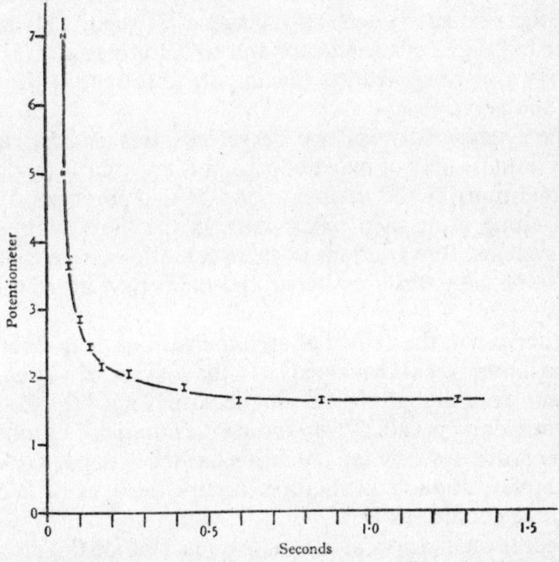

Figure 108. Refractory period in the nerve-net of *Calliactis*.

Ordinates, intensity of potentiometer discharge required to stimulate; abscissæ, times after last stimulation. (After Pantin.)

reach accurately comparable values for different types of nerve. It is stated that the cœlenterate nerve-net is of about the same sensitivity as the least sensitive vertebrate nerves, and that crustacean nerve is about five times as sensitive as these vertebrate nerves.

When the refractory period which follows an impulse is over, the nerve cell is, so far as conduction is concerned, in precisely the same condition as before the impulse. Its sensitivity is the same, and a second impulse passes in precisely the same way as the first. This implies that the nerve cell has not been fatigued by the first impulse, and this is certainly very largely, and perhaps completely, true of all nerve cells in active and healthy conditions. Nerve, like other tissues, has a metabolism, but its metabolism is small compared with that of many tissues. The fact that the cell is not fatigued by the conduction of an impulse implies that recovery of the cell from the expenditure of energy in the passage of the impulse is complete before the refractory period is over.

Fatigue in nervous conduction probably occurs in abnormal circumstances. There is evidence that nerve cells may become fatigued when their metabolism is reduced, *e.g.* by deprivation of oxygen or by narcotics. Fatigue also occurs in other functions of the nervous system, and in the receptor and effector organs. It is, again, unquestionably true that conduction of stimulation along a reflex path through the nervous system may become fatigued. This is not entirely due to fatigue of the effector and receptor organs. It is believed that it may also be sometimes due in part to fatigue at the synapses between the nerve cells.

(4) The synapse between two nerve cells acts as a barrier across which an impulse may or may not pass. It is apparently by differences in the conditions at the various synapses that impulses are forced to travel along prescribed reflex paths in the more highly evolved nervous systems. By variations of these conditions from time to time the course of the paths are altered and the behaviour of the animal modified.

In the nerve-net, the arrival of an impulse at a synapse reduces for a time the hindrance at that synapse to the passage of a later impulse. This occurs even though the first impulse does not pass the synapse. This phenomenon is called "*interneural facilitation.*" In more highly evolved nervous systems the conditions at the synapse are certainly more complex, though facilitation occurs there also. We cannot discuss these conditions here.

Interneural facilitation at a synapse must be distinguished from "*neuro-muscular facilitation.*" In muscle a stimulus which is too small to produce contraction in the muscle may increase the excitability of the muscle. For this reason, a muscle may respond to a succession of similar impulses, although the first few of the succession are ineffective. This is neuro-muscular facilitation.

(5) When a nerve cell is stimulated with an electric shock, a single impulse is set up in it, but this is probably hardly ever so when sense organs are stimulated naturally. Almost all forms of natural stimulation last considerably longer than the refractory periods of nerve cells. The sense organ continues to stimulate the nerve so long as it is itself stimulated, and so long as it does not become fatigued, as it does sooner or later. The result of this continued stimulation of a nerve is the initiation in it of a *series* or train of impulses (plate IX,

Fig. 109). The separate impulses of the train succeed one another at intervals which may be nearly as small as the refractory period of the nerve, but may be much longer. The interval is determined in the sense-organ or the nerve termination in contact with it, except in so far as its minimum is determined by the refractory period. So long as the interval is not so far reduced as to approach the refractory period, the impulses are, in many types of nerve, closer together the more intense the stimulation.

We must think of all natural stimulation as consisting of these trains of impulses. In this important respect natural stimulation differs from artificial stimulation of a nerve cell by an electric shock.

(6) In most effector organs, stimulation when it reaches the organ may either increase or decrease the activity of the organ—nervous stimulation may be either excitatory or inhibitory. In the nerve-net and in some effector organs of more complex animals, *e.g.* vertebrate voluntary muscle, inhibitory stimuli do not occur. The effector organ returns of itself to an inactive state when the excitatory stimulation ceases. In other systems inhibition is very marked. This is so in the muscular systems of the Crustacea, and in some vertebrate organs, such as the heart (*cf.* ch. XVIII, pp. 298–301).

(7) A nerve impulse may be initiated within the nervous system itself without any stimulation of a sense organ.* A clear example of this occurs in some types of rhythmical movement. Rhythmical movements may be controlled in either of two ways. First, the control may be due to automatic rhythm in the nervous system, the type of control which is of interest to us at this point. This type of control is found in the beat of a scyphozoan medusa such as *Aurelia*. The medusa will continue to beat when it receives no stimulation. It is true that in these medusæ the rate of the beat may be modified by stimulation arising in sense-organs at the edge of the disc, the tentaculocysts, but nevertheless the primary control is automatic. Automatic control of rhythm in the nervous system occurs in other animals. The control of the rate of the heart-beat in some molluscs (*Mya*) and in *Limulus* has been shown to be of this nature. In vertebrates the respiratory movements are so controlled. This type of control is called *neurogenic*. Spontaneous activity of this kind occurs also in sea-anemones.

Secondly, the control of the rhythm may arise in the contractile tissue itself. This is *myogenic* control. The rhythms of the heart-beat in vertebrates and of the contractions of the uterus in mammals are under myogenic control.

* Pantin, *Proc. R.S.*, **B140**, 159, 1952.

2. EVOLUTION OF THE NERVOUS SYSTEM

(A) *The Nerve-Net*

This, an uncentralised plexus or network of nerve cells extending all over the body, is the only nervous system of the cœlenterates. The nerve-net lies not only below the ectoderm on the outer surface of the body, but also between the endodermal cells where these are arranged as two layers on both sides of the mesoglæa, *e.g.* in the mesenteries (Fig. 110). A similar nerve-net occurs at the base of the ectoderm in the Platyhelminthes and the Echinodermata, but it is there in association with nervous systems of other types. In many other animals nerve-nets occur over parts of the body.

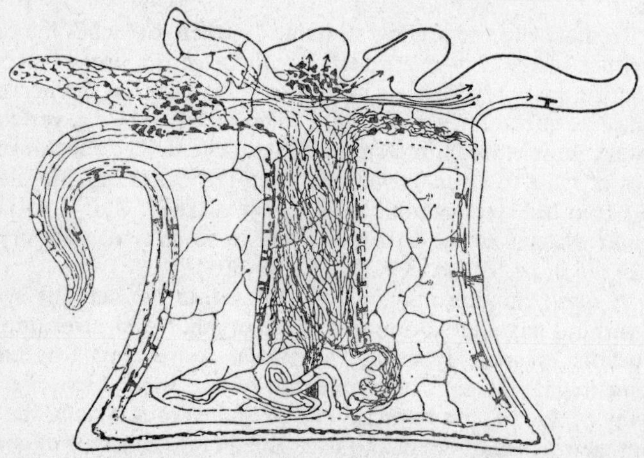

Figure 110. Distribution of the nerve-net in a sea-anemone. (From Jordan after Wolff.)

The nerve-net consists of multipolar and bipolar nerve cells, all the processes being more or less similar in form in the typical nerve-net (Fig. 104, p. 237). Many of the processes form synapses with the neighbouring nerve cells; others terminate on the receptor and effector cells. The net may be differentiated in parts of the body. In some parts the nerve cells may be closer together, and in some nerve-nets the branches of cells may be more developed in one direction than in others. Physiological differentiation, *i.e.* differentiation in the characters of the conduction of an impulse in different directions, also occurs, as we shall see later.

(1) In most nerve-nets, an impulse can pass in all directions from the source of stimulation. This can be seen if the central part of the body of an *Aurelia* is cut out (Fig. 111), so that a ring of tissue is left, and all but one of the tentaculocysts are removed. Stimulation of the tentaculocyst then results in a wave of contraction passing in both

directions round the ring, *i.e.* it passes in all the directions which are possible for it.

In the sea-urchin bending of the spines on the surface of the body is controlled by the nerve-net underlying the ectoderm. That impulses can pass in all directions across this nerve-net can be shown by experiments in which the ectoderm and the underlying net are cut. If the ectoderm is undamaged, neighbouring spines bend towards a stimulated point, for it is from that direction that the stimulation reaches the muscles that cause the bending of the spine. But, if a cut is made through the ectoderm between the stimulated point and a spine, the spine bends towards the end of the cut which is nearest to the direct line between the point of stimulation and the spine (Fig. 112). Clearly, this is because the stimulation first reaches the spine by the shortest undamaged path across the net. If so, stimulation must be able to pass through the net in other directions besides that which it follows in the undamaged net.

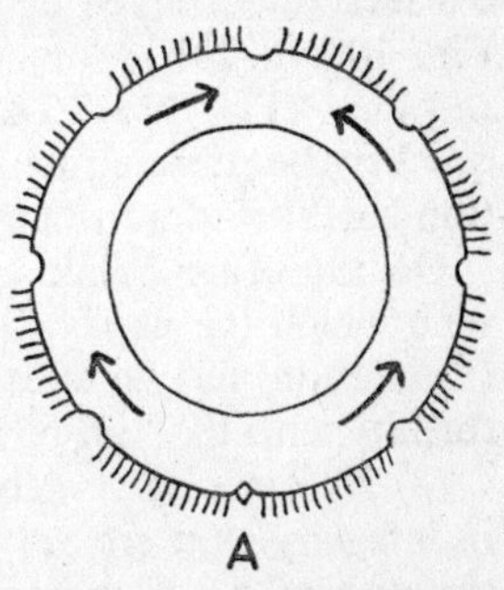

Figure 111. Passage of a stimulus around a ring of tissue cut from an *Aurelia* from which all the tentaculocysts except one have been removed. (After Romanes.)

The individual cells of the typical nerve-net are not obviously polarised, their branches being of the same type on all sides on which they occur. Since this is so and since, also, nerve impulses can be conducted in all directions across the net, we have no reason to doubt that an impulse can cross a single cell in any direction (*cf.* p. 249).

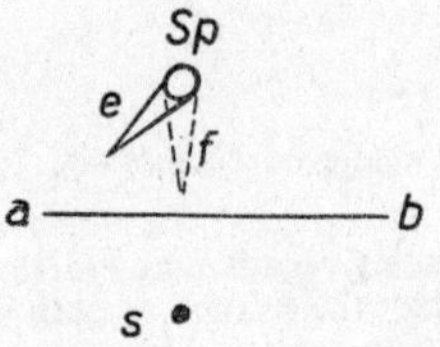

Figure 112. Bending of a spine of a sea-urchin.

When the nerve-net is cut along the line *a–b* between the point of stimulation (*s*) and the spine (*sp*), the spine bends towards the direction of the shortest undamaged path across the net (*e*). *f*, the direction of bending when the net is undamaged. (After Uexküll.)

(2) The cells of the nerve-net are never *greatly* elongated in any direction. Thus, an impulse in passing across a length of the net has to pass through many cells and across many synapses.

As we have seen, it is probably for this reason the rate of conduction across the net is slow (4–120 cm. per sec., p. 240).

(3) If a point on the column of a sea-anemone is stimulated electrically and the contraction of the sphincter which lies round the edge of the disc is recorded, it is found that the response to a single shock is slight or non-existent. But if a series of shocks are given at intervals of 0·5–1·5 secs., the response to each

shock increases gradually (Fig. 113). This "staircase effect" can only mean that each stimulation makes the muscle more sensitive to stimulation, *i.e.* "neuro-muscular facilitation" occurs (p. 242). The shorter the intervals between the shocks, until a minimum interval of about 0·5 secs. (determined by the refractory period of the nerve cells—see Fig. 108, p. 241) is reached, the more rapid the increase in the response (Fig. 113). The fact that the "staircase" is steeper, the quicker the stimulations follow each other, implies that the facilitation quickly fades from the muscle after the stimulation has reached it.

On the other hand, increase in the energy of the electric shock with which the net is stimulated (above the minimum required for stimulation) has no effect on the response (Fig. 114). This is in conformity with the "all or nothing" law of conduction (p. 240).

(4) In some nerve-nets it is found that stimulation may decrease in intensity as it crosses the net and finally die out. If, for instance, the disc of a sea-anemone (*Calliactis*) is stimulated by touch, the

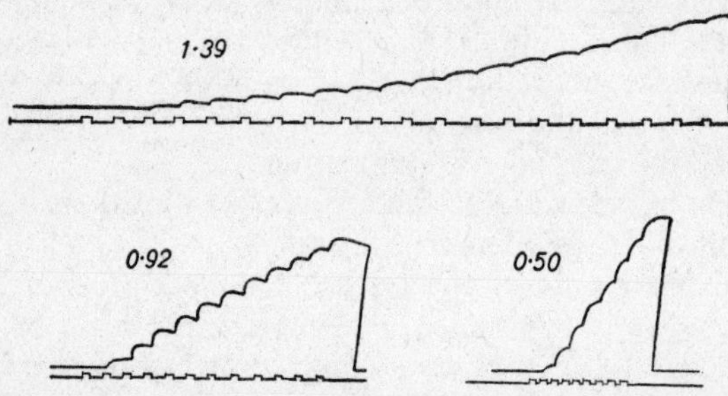

Figure 113. "Staircase effect" in the sphincter muscle of *Calliactis*.

Increase in the strength of contraction during a train of impulses; the increase is steeper the shorter the intervals between the impulses (recorded above the figures in secs.), so long as the intervals are not shorter than the refractory period (about 0·5 sec.). (After Pantin.)

animal reacts by bending the edge of the disc inwards (Fig. 115). This reaction *gradually* fades out as we pass round the disc; it extends farther round the disc the stronger the stimulation. This can only be interpreted by supposing that the stimulation becomes weaker as it passes over the net, and that a stronger stimulation extends farther than a weaker one.

Such a "decrement" in nervous conduction seems at first sight to be contrary to the "all or nothing" law of the conduction of a nerve impulse (p. 240). But the decrement is only observed after some types of stimulation, and not after other types. It is observed after stimulation by touch or by an irritating chemical. On the other hand, a momentary electric shock sets up a disturbance which passes for some distance across the net and then disappears suddenly, and without decrement. But, again, a series of electric shocks at appropriate intervals (about 1 sec. between each) gives a response with a typical decrement, a gradual fading of the response. We have seen (p. 243) that non-momentary stimulation, such as that caused by touch or a chemical substance, sets up a similar train of impulses and not one impulse as a single electric shock does.

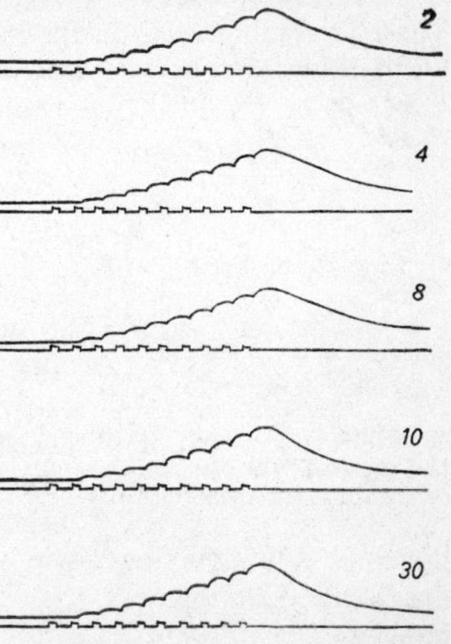

Figure 114. Identical responses in the sphincter muscle of *Calliactis* to stimuli at the same intervals but of different intensities.

The intensities are recorded to the right of the figures. (After Pantin.)

There is therefore no doubt that the "decrement" we observe is due to the stimulation in the form of repeated impulses, the later impulses passing farther across the disc than the earlier. This can only mean that we have here a case of *interneural* facilitation, *i.e.* the passage of each impulse from one nerve cell to another makes easier the passage of succeeding impulses. In non-momentary stimulation the stronger the stimulation the longer is the train of impulses originated and therefore the farther the later impulses will travel. Since the response of a muscle fibre becomes greater the longer the series of impulses which reach it, we shall observe an apparent "decrement" in the response, as in fact we do. The more distant muscles will receive fewer impulses and contract more weakly.

This "decrement" is therefore due to interneural facilitation and is not contrary to the view that the all-or-nothing law of the conduction of a single impulse applies to the nerve-net as to most other types of nervous conduction.

In some types of nerve-net no decrement can be observed in the disturbance produced by stimulation of any type. This is so in the nerve-net of the column of a sea-anemone. Here there is apparently little or no interneural facilitation.

(5) A nerve-net may be physiologically differentiated in its various parts in other characters besides these differences in the facilitation which occur in different areas of the net.

(*a*) The rate of conduction of an impulse across the net may vary. This is so in the net of an anemone. The rates of conduction in the parts of the net of *Calliactis* are shown in Fig. 116. It will be seen that the rates vary from 10 cm. per sec. in a longitudinal direction along the column and 4 cm. per sec. through the thickness of the wall of the column, to 120 cm. per sec. in the nerve-net of the mesenteries. These large differences in the rate of conduction result in impulses reaching distant parts of the body along routes which are not the shortest routes between the parts. Stimulation on the column near its base passes most rapidly to the sphincter of the disc by travelling inwards to the mesentery and then up the mesentery, rather than by passing up the wall of the column. It can be shown that the impulses follow the quickest routes by recording the latent times between stimulation on various parts of the body and the contractions of the sphincter so produced. These times are only in agreement with the rates of conduction in the various parts if the quickest routes are followed. In this way, the net of the mesenteries acts in the anemone as a very primitive "through-conducting" system of the same type as the nerves of more complicated animals. Similar specialised nervous paths occur on the bells of medusæ (*Aurelia*). The system of giant fibres in annelids (p. 253) is another "through-conducting" system.

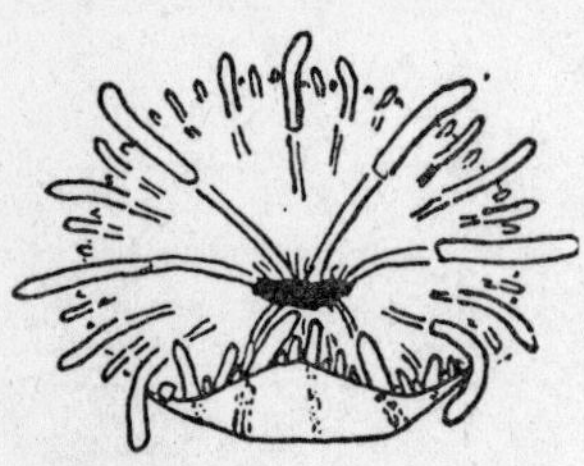

Figure 115. The "edge-raising reaction" of the disc of *Calliactis*. (After Pantin.)

(*b*) Although the *typical* nerve-net is unpolarised and impulses can pass across it equally easily in all directions, some nerve-nets are to some extent polarised—impulses can pass more easily across them in one direction than in others. This polarisation can be shown very clearly in the tentacles of a sea-anemone. If the end of a tentacle is cut off, its circular muscles contract only on the inner side of the cut (Fig. 117); the open end of the cut-off piece of the tentacle remains uncontracted. Here there is apparently hardly any conduction of the impulses in the outward direction.

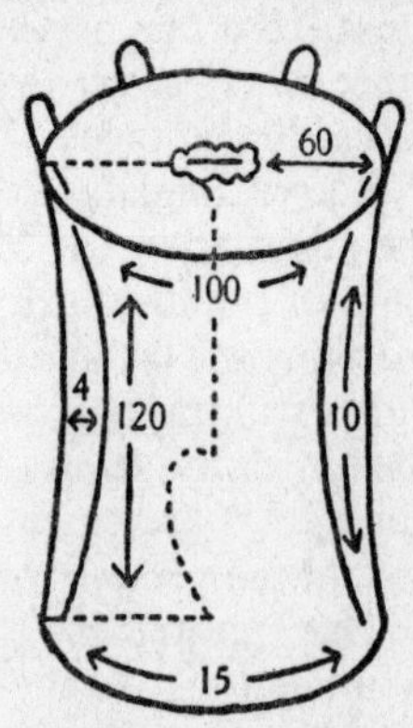

Figure 116. Rates of conduction (in cm. per sec.) in the various parts of the nerve-net of *Calliactis*. (After Pantin.)

Polarisation in the nerve-net is of two kinds, structural and physiological. Structural polarisation results from some structural character of the nerve cells, whereby impulses pass across the net more easily in one direction—the cells themselves are polarised. It is therefore of the same kind as the polarisation of the nerve cells in the higher animals (p. 238). The centripetal polarity shown in the contraction of a cut end of a tentacle is of this type. No contraction occurs beyond the cut because the nerve cells do not conduct the impulses in the outward direction.

Physiological polarity is the result of greater interneural facilitation in the one direction. It therefore only appears when the stimulation consists of a train of impulses. The tentacles of a sea-anemone possess physiological as well as structural polarity, but their physiological polarity is in the opposite direction to their structural polarity—stimulation is more easily facilitated if passing *outwards* from the disc. Long-continued mechanical stimulation of a tentacle results in contraction of the circular muscles outwards from the stimulation, rather than on the side towards the disc. The long train of impulses results in great facilitation of conduction outwards so that conduction becomes easier in this direction, although the earliest impulses of the train are conducted outwards hardly at all. The short stimulation of a cut does not produce this effect, because the train of impulses it sets up is too short.

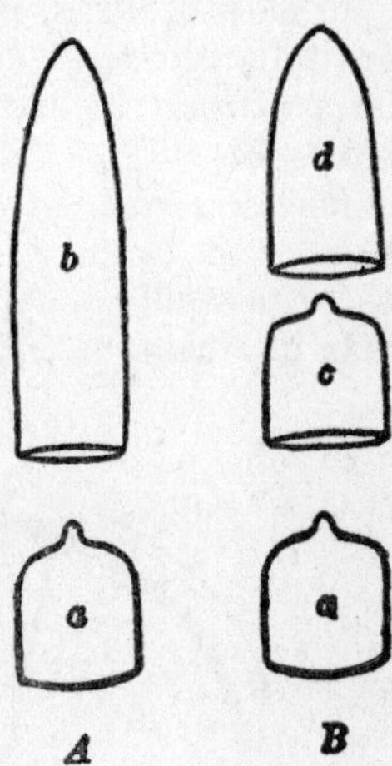

Figure 117. Reactions of the tentacle of a sea-anemone from which the tip is cut off.

Contraction of the circular muscles in the stump but not in the cut-off part. (After Parker.)

This account of the cœlenterate nerve-net has shown that conduction in the net differs in no essential features from that in other types of nervous system. The net is peculiar in that an impulse in passing from one part of the body to another has to pass a much larger number of synapses than in other nervous systems. Conduction is for this reason very slow in the net. Also, facilitation is greater than in other nervous systems, both at the synapses and in the effector organs. And the refractory period of the cells of the net is much longer than that of the cells of more highly evolved nervous systems. But these differences between the various types of nervous system are all quantitative. The process of conduction is essentially the same in all.

So far as we know, conduction in the nerve-nets of animals of other groups is essentially similar to that in the nerve-net of the cœlenterates.

(B) *Turbellaria*

In the planarians we find a nerve-net below the ectoderm, which is essentially the same in arrangement as the cœlenterate nerve-net. It is, however, associated with deeper-lying nervous structures, some of them arranged in a manner which foreshadows the internal nervous systems of higher animals. We may therefore regard the animals of this group as intermediate, so far as the nervous system is concerned, between the cœlenterates and the more complex animals.

In all planarians, in addition to the nerve-net lying immediately below the ectoderm (*outer nerve-net*), there is a second nerve-net lying farther within the body, though still in most parts outside the muscle layers (Fig. 118). This may be called the *inner nerve-net*. It is in communication with the outer net all over the body by fibres running between the two nets. In a few forms this inner net is undifferentiated over the whole body, except that it may be thicker in some parts than in others. But in almost all planarians it is concentrated along

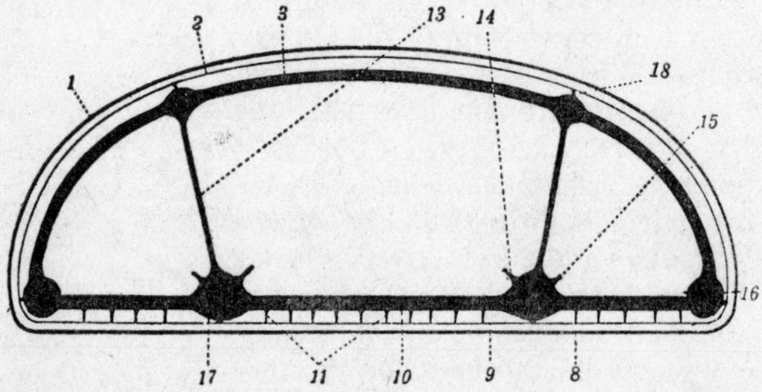

Figure 118. Arrangement of the nervous system in a planarian.

1, dorsal, 8, ventral ectoderm; 2, dorsal, 9, ventral outer nerve-net; 3, 10, inner nerve-net; 11, nerve fibres connecting the two nerve-nets; 13, 14, 15, transverse nerve cords; 16, 17, 18, longitudinal nerve cords. (From Kukenthal.)

certain lines to form what are usually known as the nerve cords. These nerve cords contain the bodies of nerve cells as well as nerve fibres (*i.e.* the processes of nerve cells). In this they differ from the nerves of many more complex animals, in which there are only nerve fibres, the bodies of the nerve cells being collected in ganglia, either within the central nervous system or outside it.

The nerve cords of a planarian differ from the unconcentrated parts of the nerve-net in other ways besides the concentration of nervous tissue in them. The nerve cells in the nerve cords are much more differentiated than those of the net. Many, at least, of them are polarised, so that an impulse can only pass in one direction. Also, many of their processes are prolonged into long fibres. The nerve cords themselves are arranged in different ways in the various planarians. Usually several longitudinal nerve cords, which come together in a central ganglion or "brain" near the front end of the body, can be recognised. These longitudinal nerve cords are connected by transverse cords so as to form a coarse network (Fig. 119). In some planarians, especially many with oval outlines, the longitudinal nerve cords can hardly be distinguished from the rest of the network. Nerve cords passing across the thickness of the body and so connecting the inner nerve-net on the two sides of the body are often present.

The "brain" is a mass of nervous tissue, containing, as the nerve cords themselves do, both the bodies of nerve cells and tracts of fibres. It may be regarded as little different in structure from the nerve cords, as little more than a thickened part of them. It receives mainly sensory fibres from the eyes and from the many other sense-organs of the front end of the body; the motor fibres pass out from the brain along the nerve cords. But sense cells occur over the whole of the body and many of them are connected directly with the nerve cords.

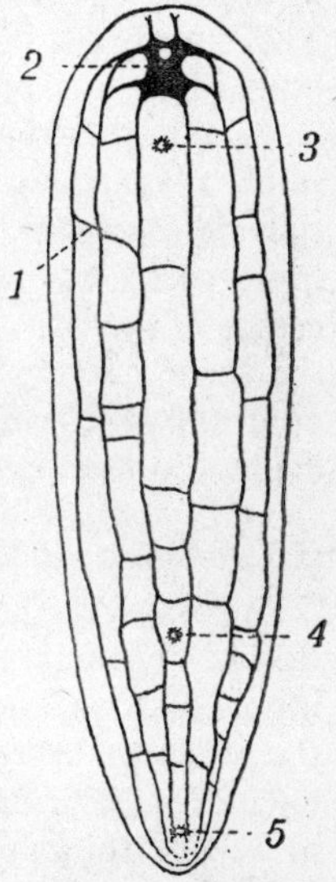

Figure 119. Inner nervous system of *Convoluta* (Turbellaria, Alloiocœla.)

1, nerve cords of inner nerve-net; 2, "brain"; 3, mouth; 4, bursa seminalis; 5, male opening. (From Kukenthal.)

We do not know how much co-ordination can take place in the superficial nerve-net alone, but, in general, the brain and the nerve cords may be regarded as controlling mainly the more complicated reactions of the animal to exteroceptive stimuli. By no means every type of reaction is controlled by the brain. Planarians from which the brain has been removed can still react to light and to tactile stimuli. Such stimuli are received by sense-organs in any part of the body. They must be distributed through parts of the nervous system other than the brain, but we do not know whether this is done in the superficial nerve-net or along the nerve cords.

The functions of the various parts of the inner nervous system can best be demonstrated by study of the movements of the animals. Some planarians (certain polyclads) have at least four distinct types of movement. These are:

(*a*) When in contact with a solid substratum—

(1) By the beat of the cilia of the ventral surface. This produces a steady, gliding movement.

(2) By small, rippling waves of contraction passed backwards over the ventral muscles.

(3) By a looping movement, rather like that of a leech. The front end of the body is stretched and attached, and the rest of the body is drawn up to it.

(*b*) When swimming freely—

(4) By waves of contraction down the lateral edges of the body after the manner of a skate.

The first of these types of movement is not under the control of the brain. Nor, in some forms at least, is type 2. Both can occur normally in brainless planarians. Type 4 does not normally occur after the brain has been removed, but it has been found possible to produce it in brainless planarians which have been made abnormally sensitive. Thus the brain is not necessary for its occurrence. Movements of type 3 have not been observed in the absence of the brain.

Thus it appears that most of the types of movement which occur in the planarian can be co-ordinated in parts of the nervous system outside the brain. But for the most complex type of movement the brain seems to be necessary. The brain is also the chief receptive centre of the body, but, otherwise, it differs little from other parts of the inner nervous system. There is no evidence of the dominating control by the brain over the whole behaviour of the animal that is so evident in the higher animals.

(C) *Annelids*

In passing to the annelids we come to animals in which co-ordination has become, almost or more probably entirely, restricted to the inner nervous system. Indeed the existence of a nerve-net below the ectoderm in the annelids has been disputed. In the earthworm the balance of evidence favours the view that there is no superficial nerve-net, though a plexus of nerve *fibres*, which arise as branches from the deeper-lying nerve cells, is present below the ectoderm. The nerve-net is probably absent in the annelids in general.

We will take the earthworm as an example of the group since its nervous system has been better investigated than that of other annelids.

The nervous system of the earthworm—and other annelids—is characterised by the presence of separate and more or less equal, paired ganglia arranged segmentally and united by paired longitudinal cords. Each pair of these ganglia controls the movements of the muscles of the segment in which it lies and receives sense impulses from that segment. This control is through paired nerves which arise from the ganglia in each segment. There is, however, overlap between the segments lying next to each other. The segmental nerves extend into the next segment in front of and the next segment behind that in which they arise. This is true of both motor and sensory nerves. There is also a double nervous supply of the wall of the gut.* The parts of this supply are antagonistic, the one activating and the

* N. Millott, *Proc. R.S.* **B131**, 271, 362, 1943; **132**, 200, 1944.

other inhibiting. In this they resemble the double autonomic supply of the organs of the vertebrate body cavity.

Only the supra- and subœsophageal ganglia are clearly differentiated (in size and other characters, see below, p. 254) from the rest of the ganglia of the body.

In the nervous system co-ordination between the segments is brought about in two ways:

1. There is connection between neighbouring segments in the longitudinal cords, as well as in the nerves outside the cords. Nerve cells in the cords extend from one segment to the next both up and down the cord. Most, at any rate, of these cells do not extend over more than three segments, and any impulse passed down the cord through them must be relayed across synapses between each pair of cells. Probably for this reason, conduction through this system in the cord is slow—about 25 mm. a sec.

2. There are present in the cord on the dorsal side a median and two lateral "giant" fibres.* These are nerve fibres of very large diameter running from one end of the body to the other. Their structure, however, is segmental. Each consists of a large number of axons within the single sheath of the fibre, and these axons arise in each segment from cells in the ganglia. In each ganglion there are two of these cells for the median fibre and one for each of the lateral fibres. The lateral fibres are also transversely connected in each segment. All the fibres are able to stimulate the organs of the segment through the branches of the ganglion cells.

Between the segments the lateral fibres are crossed by oblique septa, and here the axons within the fibres come into connection with those of the neighbouring segment, the septum acting as a very large synapse. There is therefore nervous connection throughout the length of the giant fibre though probably not continuity of the protoplasm within the fibre. The medium fibres are continuous.

The function of the giant fibres is conduction of impulses along the length of the cord at a much more rapid rate than through the segmentally relayed system. The rate of conduction in the giant fibres is 5-45 metres a sec. The median fibre is activated by stimulation in front of the clitellum, the lateral fibres by stimulation behind this organ. The giant fibres are responsible for the rapid contractions of the worm in response to strong stimulation.

In the ventral part of the cord of the annelid are two other large fibres, but the structure and function of these is less well known.

In the squid (*Loligo*, Cephalopoda) there are giant nerve fibres that control the movements of the mantle. Large nerve fibres have also

* H. B. Stough, *J. comp. Neur*, **40**, 409, 1926. *Cf.* also Nicol, *Quart. Rev. Biol.*, **23**, 219, 1948; J. E. Smith, *Phil. Trans. R.S.*, **B240**, 193, 1957.

been found in *Amphioxus*, nematodes, insects, and some fishes. These are probably not of the same kind as those of the annelid.

At the front end of the body of the annelid the supra- and subœsophageal ganglia lie in front of and behind the mouth. The supraœsophageal ganglia receive impulses from the sense-organs of the front end of the body and may be regarded as mainly receptive centres. The subœsophageal ganglia are the segmental ganglia of the peristomal segment. Both supra- and subœsophageal ganglia probably also have some other functions. They appear to control the "tone" (*i.e.* the state of contraction, *cf.* ch. XVIII) of the muscles in other parts of the body. An earthworm from which the supraœsophageal ganglia have been removed holds its head bent upwards, and one with the subœsophageal ganglia removed has the head bent ventrally. These effects are due to increase of the tone of the dorsal muscles after removal of the supraœsophageal ganglia, and increase of that of the ventral muscles after removal of the subœsophageal ganglia. The supraœsophageal ganglia appear also to have some control over the responsiveness of other parts of the system. Worms with these ganglia removed are more sensitive than normal worms, and therefore restless in natural conditions.

We shall find that these functions are much better developed in the brain of the arthropod. They are the first beginnings of the central control which the brain exerts over the rest of the nervous system in higher animals. Apart from these effects, the nervous system of the earthworm may be regarded as hardly at all centralised. Each pair of ganglia is concerned with the control of its own segment.

The normal forward movement of the earthworm will give us an example of the manner in which the behaviour of the annelids is co-ordinated. The worm moves forward (Fig. 120) by alternate waves of contraction in the circular and longitudinal muscles of the segments.

As the wave passes down the body, the muscles of each segment are contracted and expanded in turn. The wave of contraction passes down the body at a rate of about 20 mm. a second. The movement starts by contraction of the circular muscles at the front, so that the head is pushed forward. The initiation of the wave may be due to stimulation or, so far as can be seen, automatic. Next, the longitudinal muscles in the first few segments contract and, during this contraction, the anterior segments are held in place by their bristles, which are extruded and penetrate the substratum on which the worm is crawling. Thus, contraction of the longitudinal muscles draws the more posterior segments up on to the anterior segments. The wave of contraction then passes to more posterior segments, first in the circular, then in the longitudinal muscles.

We have now to ask what is the mechanism by which the wave of contraction is passed down the body. It may first be said that a background of stimulation of the sense-organs of each segment is necessary. This stimulation may arise from contact of the sense-organs of the ventral side of the body with the substratum, or from proprioceptive stimuli caused by stretching of the muscles. The wave will pass down the body in a worm lying on the ground owing to stimulation of the sense-organs on its ventral surface. A worm slung horizontally in the air only shows the rhythm of contraction if it is stretched; one hung vertically in the air shows it, for its weight provides the stretching stimulus, but the rhythm disappears if the worm is hung in water.

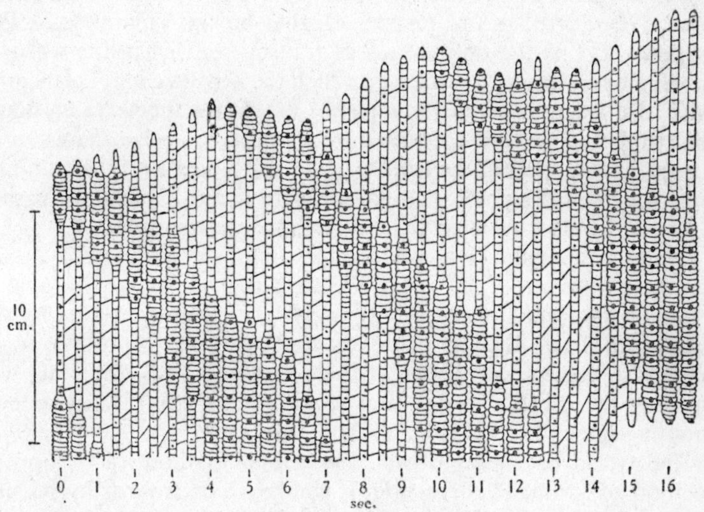

Figure 120. The locomotion of the earthworm. (After Gray and Lissmann.)

If this background of stimulation is present, the contraction is conducted from one segment to the next in two ways:

1. When the longitudinal muscles of a segment contract, those of the next segment are stretched. This active stretching sets up stronger proprioceptive stimulation, and, in response to this, the longitudinal muscles contract, if they are extended—as they will be in the normal movement of the animal. That this is an effective means of passing the contraction from segment to segment can be shown by experiments in which a worm is completely divided into two halves and the halves connected by some inorganic means such as a bandage. The pull is transmitted by the bandage and the wave of contraction passes the

point of division. In such experiments no nervous impulses can pass along the nerve cord, since this is divided. Contraction of the circular muscles follows that of the longitudinal muscles owing to stimulation by proprioceptive stimuli in a simple reflex within the segment.

In this type of conduction we have an example of the third type of co-ordination mentioned at the beginning of this chapter, co-ordination by direct action of one part on another.

2. Secondly, the contraction may be passed by bisegmental reflexes relayed through the nerve cord. The stimulation arises as proprioceptive impulses caused by contraction of the muscles of the anterior segment and is passed to those of the next segment through the two ganglia and the nerve cord between them, *i.e.* through nerve cells in the cord which extend over the two segments. That the contraction can be conducted in this manner can be shown in many ways. For instance, this is the only means of transmission when the worm is moving over a smooth surface on which the bristles cannot get a grip. Also, if a worm is divided completely except for the nerve cord and the two halves are not connected by a bandage, so that there can be no mechanical pull of the front part on the hinder part, the stimulation will pass the point of division. Here it must clearly be passed through the cord, which is the only remaining connection.

These two methods of conduction reinforce each other in the natural movement of the worm. We have here, in fact, an example of "double assurance"—the occurrence of the effect is ensured by the provision of two distinct processes each working to produce it. In natural circumstances, if one of these processes fails, the other will produce the effect. This double causation of an effect is not uncommon in animal organisation.

The worm has many other reflexes besides those of its normal method of forward progression. It can move backwards by passing waves of contraction from tail to head. Both backward and forward movement can be inhibited in response to strong stimulation at the end of the body which is in front in the movement; or accelerated by stimulation at the end which is behind. Also, the worm responds to very strong and noxious stimuli by sudden contraction of the longitudinal muscles throughout the length of the body—this is produced by impulses conducted by the giant fibres. There are also the feeding reflexes, and many others.

The reflexes of other annelids may be more complicated than those of the earthworm, but co-ordination in all the members of this group seems to be of the same type as that of the earthworm. As in the earthworm, co-ordination is produced partly by sensory stimulation resulting from the earlier parts of the behaviour, and partly by segmentally relayed impulses. The looping movements of the leech are an example of complicated behaviour of the first type. Fixation of the suckers at the front and hind end of the body produce alternate contraction and relaxation of the muscles of the body wall, and so elongation and shortening of the body. The stimulation arises from sensory organs in the suckers. These are stimulated when the suckers are fixed.

The swimming movements of such polychætes as *Nereis* appear to differ from the ambulatory movements of the earthworm chiefly in that the waves of contraction are passed down the sides of the body alternately. These movements may originate automatically in the nervous system, *i.e.* their origin is neurogenic (p. 243).

In summary, we may say that we have in the annelids a nervous system which is entirely internal but very little centralised. The only evidence of centralisation is the control of tone and of general sensibility by the supra- and subœsophageal ganglia.

(D) *Arthropoda*

The behaviour of the arthropods, and especially that of the insects, is far more complicated than that of the annelids. We shall discuss this behaviour, with that of other invertebrates, in a later chapter. Here we are concerned only with the co-ordination in the nervous system which is necessary to control this behaviour. We must consider whether co-ordination in the arthropods differs in any essential features from that in the annelids.

1. It is clear that the complex behaviour of the arthropod demands a much higher level of organisation in the nervous system than does the relatively simple behaviour of the annelid. Much arthropod behaviour consists of elaborate chains of reflexes and acts, the sequence of which is determined in the nervous system. In annelids, chains of reflexes, though they occur, are always much simpler and less numerous. Also, the muscular system and sense-organs of the arthropod are more complicated than those of annelids. For the co-ordination of these organs a more highly differentiated nervous system is necessary.

2. In its general arrangement the arthropod nervous system is similar to that of the annelid. Each segment has a pair of ganglia and the nervous control of the organs is still segmental; nerves pass from the segmental ganglia to the organs of the segment in which the ganglion lies, and not, in general, to the organs of other segments. But conduction up and down the cord is far better developed in the arthropod nervous system than in that of the annelid. Reflexes are more often plurisegmental than bi- or unisegmental: they extend over several segments or even over the whole body. The cells in the nerve cord that control these reflexes also extend over many

segments, and are not restricted to two or three segments as most of them are in the annelids.

If, for instance, an insect such as a dragon-fly is held stationary and the end of the abdomen is stimulated by compression, the reaction occurs in all parts of the body, so far as we can see, simultaneously. The abdomen is bent ventrally as a whole, the legs begin to move and the wings vibrate, so that the animal would fly if it were allowed to do so. There is here much more rapid co-ordination between the various parts of the body than in the annelid, and this is due to the greater extension of the nerve cells in the cord and the smaller number of synapses which the impulses have to pass. The co-ordination is more parallel to that produced by the giant fibres of the annelid nervous system than to the passage of a wave of contraction down the body. Giant fibres are present in the insect.

However, not all reflexes in the arthropod extend over the whole body. The use of the legs in the insect in walking illustrates this. Reflexes are passed between the segments of the thorax that bear the legs, and from side to side of the body within a segment. In the cockroach* (Fig. 121, *a*) the legs in normal walking are moved in the order R_3 L_1 R_2 L_3 R_1 L_2 R_3 L_1 - - -. The speed of the walking is varied by alterations in the time relations of the cycle of movement in each leg. In very slow walking changes of these kinds may result in the succession L_3 L_2 L_1 R_3 R_2 R_1. At the fastest speeds the three legs in each of the triangles L_1 R_2 L_3 and R_1 L_2 R_3 may move almost simultaneously.

The whole behaviour follows the following two rules: (1) the two legs of a segment alternate in their movement; and (2) the three legs of one side move in the order hind, middle, front.

Here we have co-ordination between the legs of the three segments, and this is dependent on co-ordination within the segmental ganglia. That the ganglia of the brain are not concerned in the primary control of the co-ordination is shown by the fact that many insects are able to run after the head has been lost. This, however, does not exclude an overriding influence of the brain on the whole behaviour (*cf.* p. 349).

If one or more of the legs are removed, an immediate result is that the general posture of the legs is altered so that the body is efficiently supported by the remaining legs. Alterations of the rhythm of movement and of the extent of movement of each leg (Fig. 121, *b–e*) occur, and these alterations vary with the legs removed. But the second of the two rules given above is always obeyed, though, again, in some circumstances two or more legs may move almost simultane-

* G. M. Hughes, *J. exp. Biol.*, **29**, 267, 1952; **34**, 306, 1957.

ously. Equilibrium is always maintained so long as the mechanical conditions make this possible.

These experiments in which legs are amputated make it clear that the nervous control of the movements is by no means absolutely fixed.

3. Central control of the nervous system in the ganglia in the head is much better developed in the arthropod than in the annelid. The

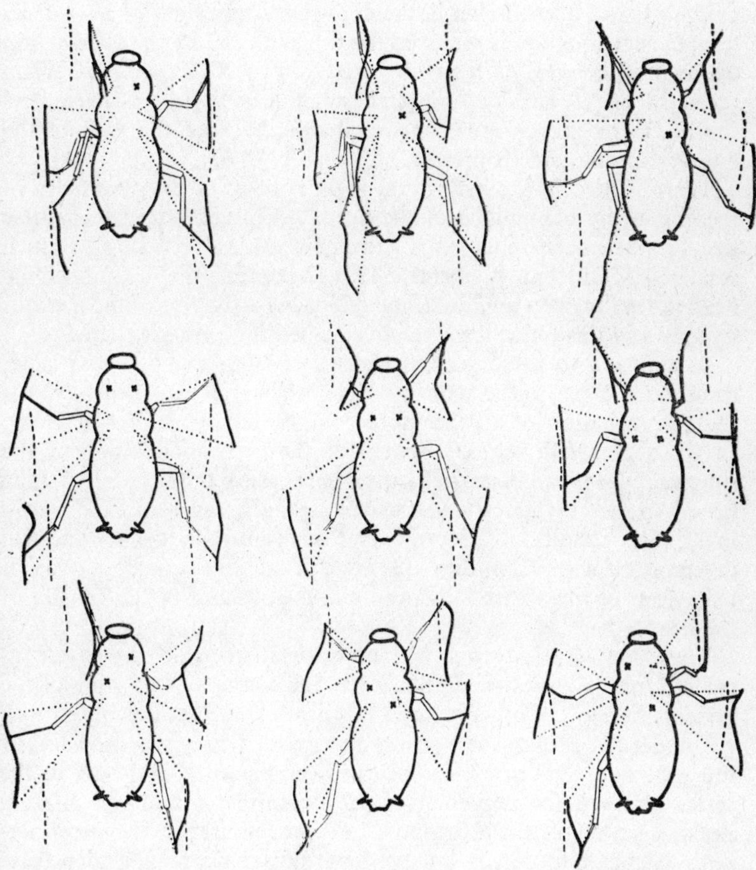

Figure 121. Movements of legs in the cockroach after amputation of some of the legs. X—amputated legs; dotted lines, movements of the tips of the legs in the intact insect; firm lines, their movements after amputations. (After Hughes.)

supraœsophageal ganglia are still the chief receptive centres for impulses from the sense organs of the head, and the subœsophageal ganglia are still the motor centres for the control of the organs of the segments to which they belong, especially the mouth parts.

In the annelid we saw that these ganglia already had other functions, and it is these other functions which are greatly developed in the arthropod. As in the annelid, the supraœsophageal ganglion controls the tone of the muscles of the whole body, each half of this ganglion controlling especially the muscles on the same side of the animal. It has been shown in the crab that if the right or left supraœsophageal ganglion is removed the force exerted by the contraction of the limb muscles on that side is reduced by 20–40 per cent. When the right or left supraœsophageal ganglion of an insect is removed the body is bent towards the sound side, because the tone of the muscles on that side is greater.

There is also in the arthropod great control of the sensitivity of the animal by the ganglia of the head. An insect from which these ganglia have been removed is extremely restless, reacting to much smaller stimuli than is normal. This is because the ganglia of the head normally exert an inhibiting influence on the rest of the nervous system, and this influence is removed when they are extirpated.

In addition to these general actions of the ganglia of the head, these ganglia are, in the arthropod as in the vertebrate, necessary for the co-ordination of all the more complicated types of behaviour. In the segmented nervous system of the arthropod many of the simpler reflexes can be carried out in the absence of the ganglia of the head. An insect which has lost its head ganglia can walk, and a crab in a similar condition will turn over if it is placed on its back and will defend itself with its pincers. But none of the more complex types of behaviour of the arthropods occurs in the absence of the ganglia of the head.

The examples of invertebrate nervous systems which we have considered form a series which illustrates the course of evolution of the system. Animals of other invertebrate groups, such as the molluscs or echinoderms, possess nervous systems which may, so far as their more obvious features are concerned, be placed somewhere in the series between the nerve-net of the cœlenterates and the internal nervous system of the arthropod. In some features each type of nervous system is peculiar, but we have not space to consider these peculiarities here.

II. CHEMICAL CO-ORDINATION

The system of chemical co-ordination is much better understood in the vertebrate than in other animals. For this reason we shall summarise the general features of the vertebrate system before passing on to discuss what evidence there is that chemical co-ordination occurs in the invertebrates.

1. THE VERTEBRATE ENDOCRINE SYSTEM

Chemical co-ordination consists of control of the activities of the parts of the body by means of variations in the concentrations of certain substances in the protoplasm of the tissues. In the vertebrate the system of chemical co-ordination takes part in both the two types of co-ordination mentioned at the start of this chapter (p. 235). Reactions of individual organs are directly stimulated by changes in the concentrations of the co-ordinating substances in the protoplasm—as, for instance, when the pigment cells of the amphibian skin are stimulated to expand under the influence of a secretion of the pituitary; and the level of general metabolism in the organs, and so in the whole body, is often modified. The changes in the level of basal metabolism which accompany changes in the concentration of the thyroid secretion in the organism exemplify this second type of control.

In the vertebrate a number of organs, the endocrine organs, have the function of controlling the concentration in the circulation, and so in the organs, of many, but not all, of the substances which produce these effects. As an example of chemical co-ordination not under the control of endocrine organs we may take the release of chemical substances at motor nerve endings. When a nerve impulse reaches a motor nerve ending, one or other of two chemical substances is released in the ending, and the reaction of the effector organ is due to the diffusion of these substances into it. The substances are acetylcholine and sympathin, the latter a substance similar in its effects to adrenaline and perhaps chemically related to it. Acetylcholine is released at some types of motor nerve endings, sympathin at others. It is probable that acetylcholine is also released at the synapse between nerve cells when an impulse reaches the synapse; and that its release is necessary for the passage of the impulse across the synapse. These are examples of co-ordination of the activity of parts of the body by chemical substances. They are therefore examples of chemical co-ordination, though the co-ordination is not controlled by the endocrine organs.

In these last examples the transport of the co-ordinating substances is by diffusion and not in the circulating fluids of the body. Acetylcholine is, in fact, very rapidly destroyed in the blood by an enzyme by which it is broken down: its destruction is necessary for its effective function—so that distant tissues may not be affected. Other examples of chemical co-ordination by diffusing substances are known. If a small area of the skin of a vertebrate is stimulated by direct stimulation from the outside of the body, it is sometimes found that the effect of the stimulation slowly spreads to parts of the skin not originally stimulated. It has been shown that some of these effects are due to diffusion of chemical substances outwards through the skin from the stimulated area. The co-ordination of growth and differentiation in development by the organising substances (p. 155) is another example of chemical co-ordination by a diffusing substance, though it is co-ordination of a type different from the types we have so far considered.

We may thus distinguish the substances of which the only known function is chemical co-ordination (often called *distance activators*) into two categories:

(1) the *circulatory activators* which are carried in the circulating fluids;

(2) the *diffusion activators*, which are transported by diffusion.

In addition some products of metabolism may control the activities of certain tissues in the vertebrate (*e.g.* the control of breathing movements by carbon dioxide). These may be called *para-activators*. The term "hormone" may be used in place of "activator" but it has been used in so many senses that it is better to discard it. The subject is discussed in the review by Huxley (see Bibliography).

Wherever chemical co-ordination forms a part of the general co-ordinating system of the body, it must be linked to other parts of that system, *i.e.* to the nervous system. In the vertebrates we find that the secretory activity of the endocrine organs is under the control of the central nervous system. The nervous control of some of these organs is direct, of others indirect—through other endocrine organs. The activity of the thyroid, for example, is governed by a secretion of the pituitary, which is itself under direct nervous control.

It is, however, not necessary that all chemical co-ordination in the body should be under nervous control. The skin reactions to external stimulation, which have just been mentioned, are not controlled by the nervous system. They are local responses of small areas of the body and are outside the general co-ordinating system of the body. It is only where chemical co-ordination is a part of this general system that it must be under nervous control.

Diffusion activators will act only upon tissues close to their point of origin, since their effects will be reduced as they diffuse farther, either by destruction or dilution. But substances which are carried in the circulation without destruction (circulatory activators) must reach all the parts of the body and all the organs. Yet we know that many of the endocrine substances of the vertebrate have special effects on certain tissues and no apparent effects on other tissues. This is due to the special sensitivities of the tissues to these substances. In the

Amphibia the pigment cells of the skin are sensitive to the pigment-controlling secretion of the pituitary. This secretion has some other effects in the body, but it appears to have little effect on many tissues.

Lastly, the responses effected by the system of chemical co-ordination may be either sudden and of short period, or long-lasting. The response of a muscle to acetylcholine set free by a nerve impulse is over in less than a second, and the expansion of the pigment cells in the Amphibia may be complete in an hour. Adrenaline also controls responses of relatively short period. It is secreted in greater quantities in circumstances which require increased activity, for instance, in association with the emotions of fear or anger, and the response may be over in a few minutes. But other endocrine changes are much longer lasting. For instance, many of the seasonal changes in the physiology of vertebrates are almost certainly due to complex endocrine changes in which many endocrine organs probably take part. These changes may be very great, as in the winter sleep of mammals, and they may last for several months. Seasonal changes of certain types (*e.g.* changes in secondary sexual characters) are unquestionably controlled by the endocrine system.

In changes of the general metabolic level in the vertebrate body, whether they last for a short or a long time, it is probable that the direct control is always very largely through the endocrine system, though the ultimate control is nervous. Control of changes of this kind is one of the chief functions of the endocrine system. On the other hand, by far the greater part of the control of the activities of the separate organs is directly through the nerves. But we have seen that the endocrine system plays some part in this type of co-ordination also, *e.g.* in the control of pigment expansion in the Amphibia.

In summary, we may say that the general features of the system of chemical co-ordination in the vertebrate are these. Many of the chemical substances concerned in co-ordination are controlled in concentration by the endocrine organs; these substances act on tissue either by stimulating direct responses or by altering the general level of metabolism in tissues; the substances are either circulatory, diffusion or para-activators; and, when chemical co-ordination plays a part in the general co-ordinating system of the body, it is ultimately under the control of the nervous system—by far the greater part of the system is so controlled. The system is very complex, and by no means all its complexity has been mentioned. There is intricate interaction between the endocrine organs. Change in the secretory activity of one organ often alters the activity of many other organs, and thus produces results which are much more complicated than those directly due to its own change of activity. There are, also, numerous examples of antagonism between endocrine substances;

two substances act on the same physiological process but have opposite effects. Probably even so we have not fully described the complexity of the system.

2. THE OCCURRENCE OF VERTEBRATE ENDOCRINE SUBSTANCES IN OTHER ANIMALS

It is probable that many of the endocrine substances of the vertebrates produce their effects on the cells of the tissues by altering the rates of essential processes of the metabolism by some type of catalysis. We have seen (p. 179) that the essential metabolism of the animal cell is probably similar throughout the animal kingdom, and we might therefore expect that these substances would have effects in the bodies of the invertebrates similar to those which we know them to have in the vertebrates. There is evidence that this is true of some at least of them. Adrenaline, for instance, stimulates the heart of the crab *Maia squinado* in a way very like its effect on the vertebrate heart. Acetylcholine produces contraction in the muscle of the leech and other invertebrates.

Further, since physiological evolution in the Metazoa has been rather a process of specialisation and elaboration than of the development of new systems (p. 179), we might expect the vertebrate endocrine substance not only to act on invertebrate tissues but also to occur in the bodies of the invertebrates, if not in the identical forms in which they occur in the vertebrates, at least in related forms. The evidence of their action on invertebrate tissues which has just been mentioned is not enough to prove this. We need evidence that these substances can actually be extracted from invertebrate tissues.

Evidence on this subject is at present scanty. A substance which produced the same effects on the frog's heart and intestine as adrenaline has been found in extracts of *Paramecium*. This substance also gave the same reactions as adrenaline to some forms of chemical treatment. Adrenaline has also been found in a gastropod (*Purpura*). A substance which was identified as acetylcholine was also found in the extracts of *Paramecium*. Extracts of echinoderm eggs and sperm have been found to contain a substance which had a metamorphic effect on tadpoles similar to but not identical with that of the thyroid secretion of the vertebrate. This substance was also similar in chemical properties to thyroxine, the essential component of the thyroid secretion. Substances similar to some pituitary secretions of the vertebrate have been found in the subneural gland of tunicates. Œstrogenic substances with action on the external genital organs of mammalia have been found in the ovaries of Lepidoptera, and in some other invertebrates.

So far as this evidence goes it seems to support the belief that the tissues of invertebrates contain substances which are at least related to the endocrine substances of the vertebrate. But, since the evidence on this subject is so slight, we must wait for further results before we can say how generally this belief is true. If it were true, it would imply that the vertebrate differs from other animals not in possessing these substances, but in possessing a system of organs, the endocrine organs, specialised for the control of the amounts of them in the circulation and so in the tissues.

3. CHEMICAL CO-ORDINATION IN THE INVERTEBRATES

The occurrence of substances related to the vertebrate endocrine substances in the tissues of other animals, even if it were proved beyond doubt, would not establish that these substances are used for the purposes of chemical co-ordination in invertebrate animals. We must now discuss whether there is any evidence that chemical co-ordination does occur in the invertebrates.

It may be said at once that there is hardly any evidence that the substances related to the vertebrate endocrine substances are used in chemical co-ordination in the invertebrates. There is, however, considerable evidence that chemical co-ordination of one kind or another occurs in some invertebrates.

In some invertebrates the presence of one organ is necessary for the development of another. In the female *Gammarus* the eggs are held in the brood-sac, after they are laid, by long bristles on the oostegites. These bristles do not develop if the ovary fails to develop. And, in *Asellus* the brood-sac develops at the moults before the eggs are laid; it does not develop if the ovary has been destroyed. These facts strongly suggest that the development of the brood-sac in these animals is controlled by the gonad, and, if so, the control may be by an internal secretion of the gonad, much as the secondary sexual characters of the vertebrate are controlled, but it is also possible that the controlling change is a modification of conditions of some other kind within the body caused by the development of the gonad. No endocrine secretion need be involved. Knowles and Catlan came to the conclusion that patches of white pigment cells in the prawn, *Leander serratus*, which only occur in ripening females, are due to a non-endocrine change of this kind.* A few other examples of the dependence of one organ on the presence of another are known in invertebrates.

The evidence in these examples is not complete, for up to the present it has not been definitely shown that the effects are due to internal secretions produced by the controlling organs. However, in a few invertebrates certain organs have been definitely shown to

* *J. exp. Biol.*, **17**, 262, 1940.

produce internal secretions, and this is the only known function of these organs. Such organs are typical endocrine organs of the vertebrate type. The majority of the invertebrates which possess these organs belong to the Arthropoda (Insecta and Crustacea), but a few are of other groups (Annelida—*Physcosoma*—and Cephalopoda). We will here consider only a single example of these organs, those which control the expansion of pigment in certain shrimps (*Crangon* and *Palæmonetes*).

In these shrimps the expansion of the pigment cells, and therefore the colour of the body, varies with the environment. The shrimp goes dark on a dark background in 30–60 minutes, and light on a white background in the same time. The reaction is through the eyes; blind animals do not react. Experiment shows that two internal secretions are concerned in these reactions. These are:

(1) A darkening substance which is secreted by an endocrine organ in the rostral region (Fig. 122).

(2) A lightening substance secreted by an endocrine organ in the eye-stalk.

The secretory activity of these organs is controlled through the nervous system in response to visual stimuli received in the eyes.

Examples of the experimental results on which these conclusions are founded are given in the following table. Extracts of various parts of the body were made and injected into both light and dark animals. The results were as follows:

TABLE

Source of extract	Extract of	Injected into: Light animal	Injected into: Dark animal
Light animal . .	Blood	No effect	No effect
	Rostrum	Darkening	,,
	Eye-stalk	No effect	Lightening
	Abdomen *	,,	No effect
Dark animal . .	Blood	Darkening	,,
	Rostrum	,,	,,
	Eye-stalk	No effect	Lightening
	Abdomen *	,,	No effect

* As a control.

It will be seen that these results are in agreement with the conclusions which have been stated. The concentration of the lightening substance in the blood of the light animal was apparently not sufficiently great to cause obvious lightening of the dark animal when it was injected into it.*

* The crustacean endocrine system is much more complex than here described. *Cf.* Carlisle and Knowles, *Endocrine Control in Crustaceans*, C.U. Press, 1959.

We have here clear evidence of the occurrence of endocrine control of exactly the type that occurs in the vertebrate. Equally clear evidence of endocrine control of pigment has been obtained in the stick-insect *Dixippus*. And the evidence is also clear for the control of moulting and metamorphosis in insects by secretions of certain endocrine organs.*

None of the few invertebrates which possess endocrine organs of this type has, so far as we know, an endocrine system in any way comparable in complexity with that of the vertebrate. This does not prove that chemical co-ordination is poorly developed in invertebrates. It may well be widespread, especially if the substances concerned in the chemical co-ordination are secreted by tissues which have other functions also, and not by special endocrine organs. Our

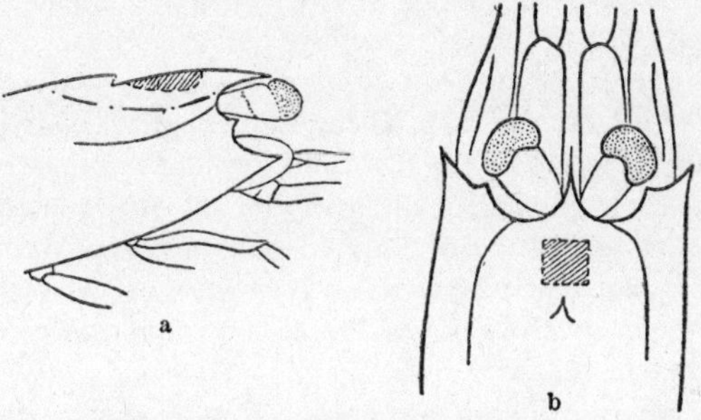

Figure 122. Position of the endocrine organ which controls the darkening substance in *Crangon*.

a, side view; b, dorsal view. The position of the organ is cross-hatched. (After Koller.)

present methods could be expected to demonstrate such functions only in a few cases. It may, in fact, be said that the changes in metabolic level of the body as a whole (*e.g.* seasonal changes), which invertebrates show as clearly as the vertebrates, can hardly be produced by any other means than co-ordinated chemical changes in the tissues. But, in the invertebrates, we have no knowledge of the co-ordination by which these changes are controlled.

* *Cf.* books by Wigglesworth mentioned in the bibliography.

CHAPTER XVII

RECEPTOR ORGANS

ALL multicellular animals are sensitive, that is to say they may be stimulated to alterations of their activities by changes in the environment outside their bodies. By stimulation of an animal, or a cell of a multicellular body, we mean the production in it of these changes in its activities. The change in the environment which causes the change in the activity of the animal or cell we call the *stimulus*.*

We have seen that in the Protista the whole body is sensitive and that parts of the cell specialised for the reception of stimuli are rare (p. 59). The Protista rely for this function on the universal sensitivity of protoplasm. In the multicellular body, also, the general bulk of the protoplasm is sensitive. In the sponges (Porifera) the reception of stimuli is organised hardly any further than this. Almost all stimulation is received by the cells of the tissues, and these cells react independently (ch. XIX).

In the Metazoa, though the protoplasm in general remains sensitive, the receptor cells—the cells adapted to receive stimuli—are more sensitive than the other cells of the body and will respond to smaller stimuli. This characteristic of the receptor cells is, however, no more than a development of the general sensitivity of protoplasm.

Wherever the receptor cell forms a part of the general co-ordinating system of the body, it must be able to pass its stimulation to one of the nerve cells of which this system consists. For this purpose it must be in contact with a nerve cell at a synapse. The great majority of the receptor cells in the multicellular body are thus in communication with the nervous system, but localised responses in a small part of the body occur in many multicellular animals and may be entirely independent of the general co-ordinating system of the body. We have seen (p. 262) that similar local responses under chemical control occur in the multicellular body. For control of these local responses it is not necessary for the receptor cell to have any communication with the nervous system—it may pass on its stimulation directly to the effector organ. In a cœlenterate, for instance, a receptor cell may

* In a multicellular body, cells may be stimulated by changes within the body; a proprioceptive cell (p. 237) may be stimulated by pressure or chemical stimuli; and a muscle cell by the changes which result from arrival of a nerve impulse.

have direct contact with a muscle fibre (Fig. 123)*. An even simpler reaction is that of a pigment cell in the skin of an animal when it responds to light falling directly upon it—as pigment cells do in many animals. The same cell is here acting both as receptor and effector organ. The cœlenterate cnidoblast may itself be stimulated at the cnidocil and react by explosion of the nematocyst—another example of this simple type of response.

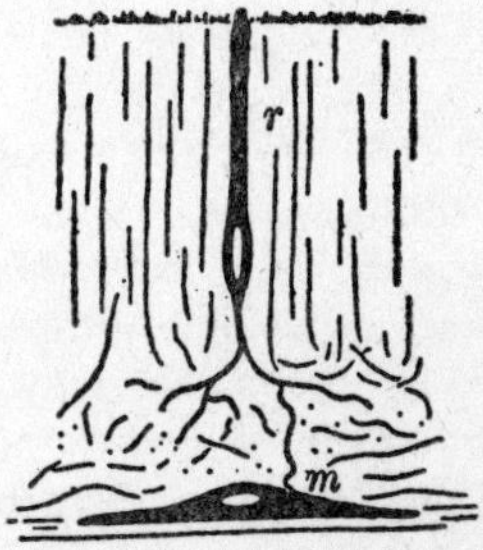

Where the receptor cell is in communication with the nervous system and passes its stimulation to that system, stimulation of the receptor cell results in the initiation of impulses in the nerve cell. Many receptor cells have branches through which the stimulation is conducted. These branches are very similar in appearance to the conducting branches of nerve cells, and it is probable that the stimulation is passed through these branches as impulses.

Figure 123. Direct connection between a receptor cell (*r*) and an effector cell (*m*) in a sea-anemone. (After Parker.)

Stimulation of a receptor cell consists of changes of some kind in the protoplasm of the cell; we do not know their nature. The stimulus which causes stimulation is always the impact of some form of energy on the receptor cell, but energy reaching the receptor cell does not necessarily cause stimulation. If it is to cause stimulation, it must, first, be sufficient in amount, that is to say it must exceed a minimum or "threshold" value. Secondly, stimulation of a receptor cell can be initiated only by some *change* in the amount of energy reaching the cell. If energy continues to reach the cell in an unvarying stream after its first impact upon it, the cell may continue to react for some time, but sooner or later the reaction ceases however large the amount of energy reaching the cell.† The cell is then said to have become *adapted* to the condition of receiving this stream of energy. All receptor cells adapt to a stream of energy in time, but the speed with which they do so varies greatly in the different types of receptor cell.

Thus, stimulation may be maintained for a time by an unvarying stream of energy, but it can only be initiated by a change in the

* Pantin (*Pubbl. Staz. Zool. Napoli*, **28**, 171, 1956) doubts the occurrence of such contact in cœlenterates.

† This at first sight does not seem to be true of all receptor organs. The eye, for instance, does not become insensitive in continuous light. This apparent contradiction is due to the fact that a complex receptor organ such as the eye contains a large number of receptor cells. In the eye the stimuli reaching each receptor cell are continually altered as the eye moves. No single receptor cell is equally stimulated for any considerable time: they therefore do not become insensitive.

amount of energy reaching the cell. A stimulus, if we define it as that which *initiates* stimulation, is always a *change* in the amount of energy reaching the cell.

Continuous stimulation of a receptor cell, *i.e.* stimulation by a stream of energy, results in a train of impulses in the nerve cell in contact with the receptor cell. We have seen that natural stimulation is almost always such a train of impulses and not a single impulse (p. 243). The frequency of the impulses in the train varies with the amount of energy reaching the cell. It varies also with the state of adaptation of the cell—the impulses become less frequent as the cell adapts until they finally cease—and possibly in some receptor cells with other conditions—see immediately below.

Receptor cells may be stimulated by very many kinds of energy. Changes in the direction of gravity, in temperature, in the amount of light falling on the cell, and in the mechanical forces acting upon it, all produce stimulation in receptor cells. Mechanical stimulation may be of several different kinds. It may be produced by pressure or by various types of vibratory forces, both vibrations of long period in solid bodies or water, and the more rapid vibrations of sound either in water or air. Again, stimulation may be caused by changes in the chemical energy in the cell. On such stimuli animals depend for estimation of the chemical characters of their environments and their food; in ourselves they are the stimuli for our senses of taste and smell. Lastly, a receptor cell may be stimulated by electrical energy, but this type of stimulation rarely occurs in nature.

Stimuli may be received from regions either within the body (but outside the receptor organ), or outside the body. On this basis we have the classification of receptor cells into extero-, intero-, and proprioceptors of which mention has already been made (p. 237). Intero- and proprioceptive stimuli are either chemical or are produced by mechanical forces, pressure and tension. Very little more is known of their nature in the bodies of invertebrates.

Although receptor cells, like any other cells, are sensitive to all forms of stimulation—they will respond to stimulation of any kind so long as it is strong enough—most receptor cells in the multicellular body are specialised, *i.e.* they are especially sensitive to one type of stimulation, the type which it is their normal function to receive. Specialised receptor cells are present in animals for most of those types of energy which occur in nature. There are no specialised receptors for X-rays, wireless waves or high-power electric currents, though the last may stimulate cells not specialised for their reception. X-rays and wireless waves do not give the cell sufficient energy for stimulation.

A single receptor cell is hardly ever in contact with more than one nerve cell, and as we have seen (p. 240), a nerve cell can transmit only a single type of impulse. Thus, the only differences in the stimulation passed by the receptor cell to the nervous system must consist of differences in the frequency of the impulses. These frequency differences are, almost if not quite, always appreciated as differences in the *strength* of the stimulation, not as differences in its nature. They are thus appreciated whether they are due to variations in the size of the stimulus or in the state of adaptation of the cell. In such circumstances, the receptor cell can record only one type of stimulation, though it can record differences in its strength. We have an example of this in the flash of light which we see when one of our eyes is struck by a blow. The retinal cells are stimulated, and the impulses initiated by them are perceived as if the cells had been stimulated by their normal stimulus.

Though it is certain that most receptor cells can record only one type of stimulation, we cannot say that this is necessarily true of every receptor cell. It may be that differences in the frequency of the impulses from a receptor cell are in some cases appreciated as differences in the nature of the stimulus. Some receptor cells of chemical stimuli respond to stimulation by more than one chemical substance and appear to give more than one sensation. Also, it is said that in certain invertebrates (Cephalopods) light of different colours gives impulses of different frequencies in the nerve from the eye. If the same receptor cells are stimulated by light of all colours (which we do not know), we have here an example in which differences in the nature of the stimulus are passed on by the receptor cells as differences in the frequency of the nerve impulses. If so, it is probable that the differences in frequency are appreciated in the nervous system as arising from differences in the nature of the stimulation, *i.e.* in the colour of the light.

In the remainder of this chapter we shall consider first the simple, frequently unicellular, receptor organs of the invertebrates. We shall then pass on to consider some of the more complex receptor organs of these animals. We shall not have space to consider by any means all these organs.

1. SIMPLE RECEPTOR ORGANS

Receptor cells occur in the ectoderm of almost all the invertebrates. In the planarians there are ectodermal receptor cells of more than one type. Two examples of these cells are shown in Fig. 124 (Plate IX). These cells bear processes which project beyond the surface of the ectoderm. These are sensory terminations where the stimulation is taken up and passed on to the body of the cell. The processes of some of the cells are stiff hairs projecting between the cilia of the ectoderm (a); these are believed to be receptors for mechanical stimuli such as those produced by currents in the water. Others bear thin-walled processes (b) and are believed to receive chemical stimuli. Similar receptor cells occur in the ectoderm of most invertebrates in which the body is not covered with a thick cuticle. It is a usual, and natural, differentiation that receptor cells of tactile and mechanical senses should bear stiff processes, and that those which receive chemical stimuli should have thin-walled processes, into which substances can diffuse readily.

The bodies of many receptor cells (*e.g.* those of Plate IX, Fig. 124) lie close to their sensory terminations. The synapses between these cells and the nerve cells are either close to the receptor cells, or much farther within the body of the animal at the end of long processes of the receptor cells. In some invertebrates (*e.g.* molluscs) the body of the receptor cell is itself at a distance from the sensory termination

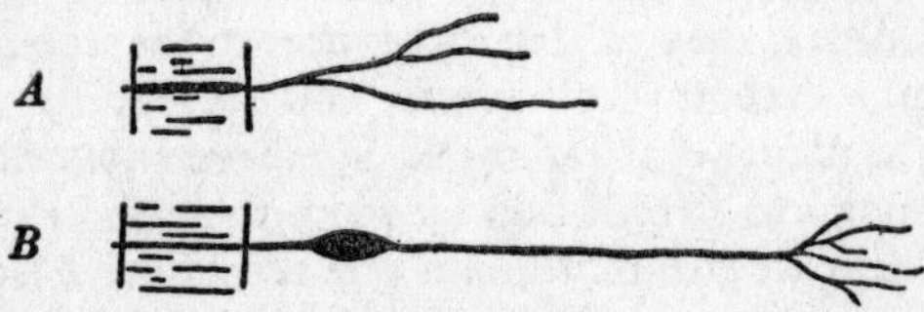

Figure 125. Invertebrate receptor cells with long conducting processes.
A, the cell-body is close to the receptive terminations; *B*, the cell-body is distant from these terminations. (After Parker.)

which is at the end of a long process of the cell (Fig. 125). No clear line can be drawn between receptor cells of this type and nerve cells which end in free receptive terminations in an ectodermal or other tissue (Plate X, Fig. 126). Such nerve cells are otherwise indistinguishable from the typical cells of the nervous system. These free sensory terminations of nerve cells occur commonly in all the Metazoa.

Little more need be said of the various types of unicellular receptor organs. We have no direct knowledge of the sense served by many of them. We can only judge their function by considering their structure. This is especially true of the receptor cells of the simpler invertebrates. Nor need we say much of the intero- and proprioceptors of the invertebrates, except that receptor cells or, more frequently, free nerve terminations, are present in very many of the tissues.

In the arthropods the receptor organs of the tactile and chemical senses are more highly differentiated. Both in insects and crustaceans many of the tactile sense-organs are modified hairs. These are so arranged as to be highly movable. They have at their bases one or more receptor cells (Fig. 127*a*), and these are stimulated by the move-

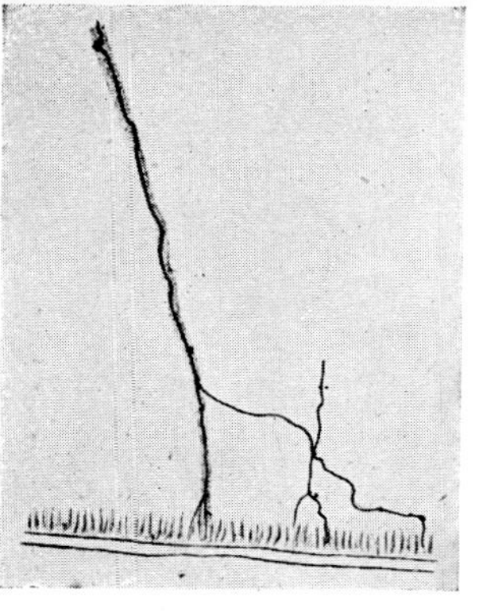

Figure 126 (*a*).

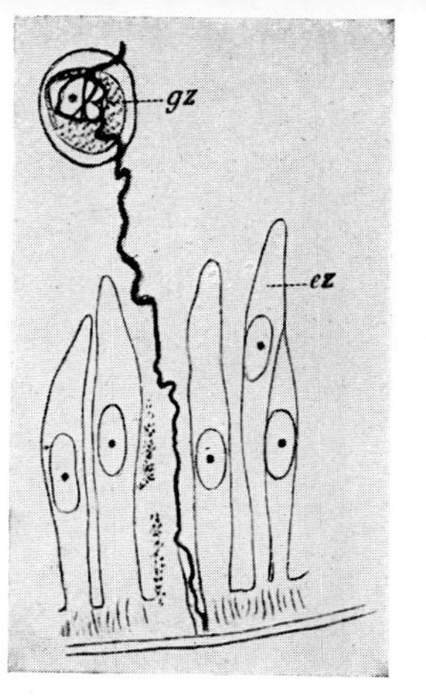

Figure 126 (*b*).

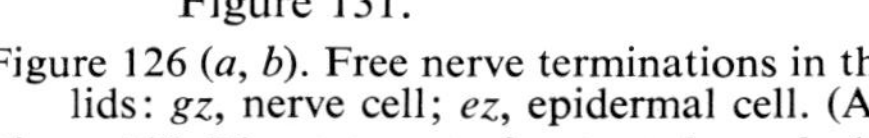

Figure 131.

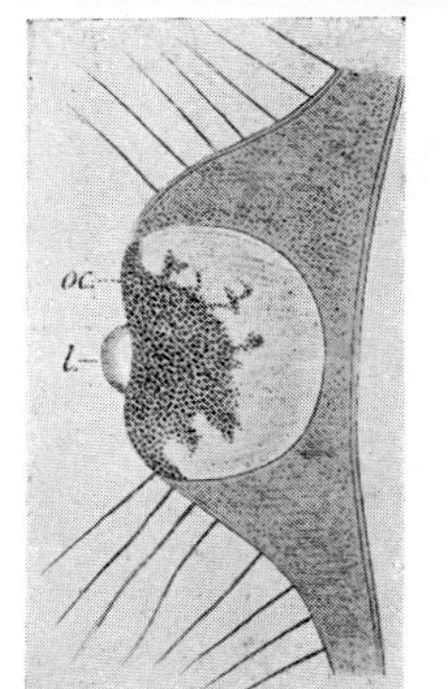
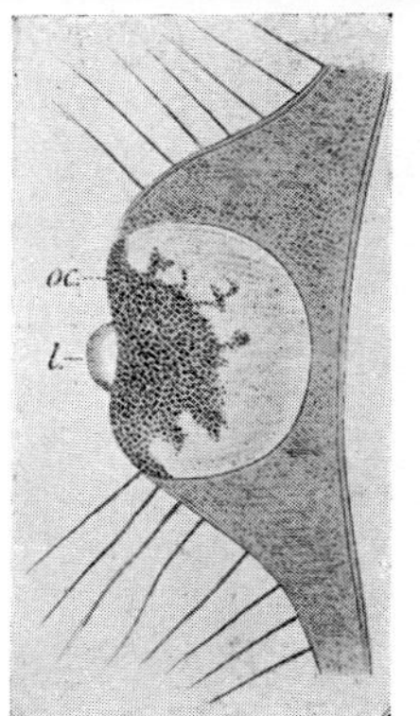
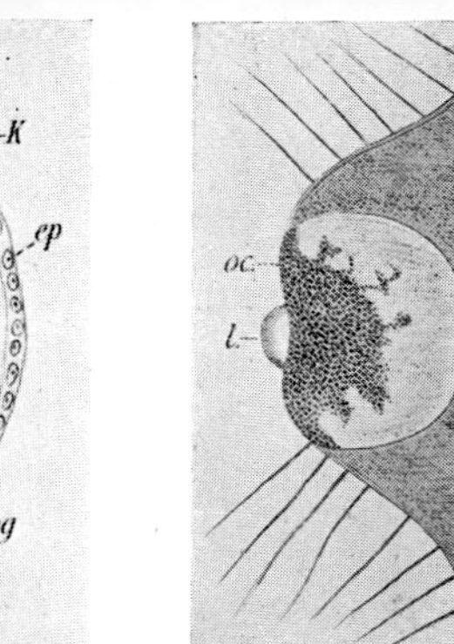

Figure 134.

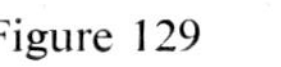

Figure 129

PLATE X

Figure 126 (*a*, *b*). Free nerve terminations in the ectoderm of annelids: *gz*, nerve cell; *ez*, epidermal cell. (After Apathy.)

Figure 129. The statocyst of a ctenophore. *b*, dome-shaped cover of the organ; *c.p.*, basal plate bearing the supports of fused cilia (*sp*) on which the statolith (*l*) rests; *cgr*, ciliated grooves connecting the organ with the ciliary combs. (From Parker and Haswell.)

Figure 131. Structure of the sphæridium of a sea-urchin. *ep*, epithelium; *K*, ossicle; *p*, pigment; *M*, muscle layer; *RN*, nerve ring; *nf*, ectodermal nerve plexus; *bg*, connective tissue. (After Ludwig.)

Figure 134. Eye-spot of an anthomedusan (*Rathkea*). *oc*, receptor cells; *l*, lens. (After Chun.)

[*To face p.* 272

ments of the hairs. Cells of other types occur round the receptor cells. Receptors of the chemical sense in the insects are also often hairs, but these hairs are thin-walled and the receptor cell extends into them and often to their tips (Fig. 127*b*). Campaniform sensillæ (Fig. 127*c*) are sense organs covered by thin, dome or plate-shaped areas of the cuticle. They are proprioceptive, responding to strains in the cuticle produced by movement of the parts.

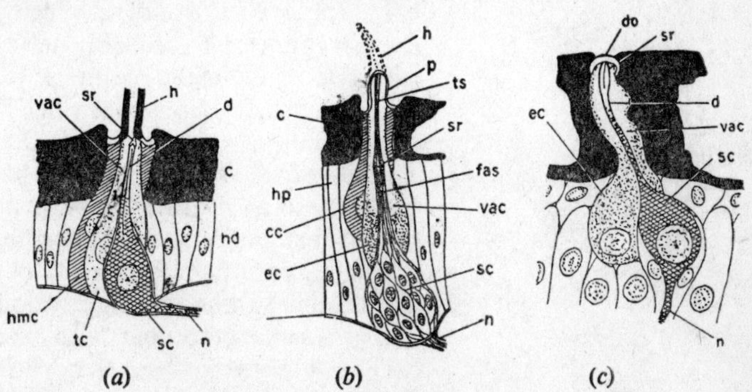

Figure 127. Receptor organs of insects.

a, hair-like receptor organ of the tactile sense; *b*, receptor organ of the chemical sense; *c*, dome-shaped sense organ. (From Eltringham after Snodgrass.) *h*, hair; *sc*, receptor cell or cells; *ec*, enveloping cell; *tc*, cell which secretes the hair; *hmc*, cell which secretes the membrane round the base of the hair; *cc*, cell surrounding the apices of the receptor cells; *sr*, *d*, sensory processes of the receptor cells; *ts*, terminal strands of the sensory processes; *fas*, bundle of fibrillæ in the sensory process; *c*, cuticle; *vac*, vacuole; *hd*, ectoderm; *p*, peg-like process which may replace the hair in chemical sense organs; *n*, nerve; *do*, dome.

2. ORGANS FOR THE PERCEPTION OF THE FORCES OF GRAVITY

Almost all the organs which have this function depend for the source of their stimulation on the weight of a heavy body, the *statolith*, in a medium of lower specific gravity. This is the principle of the *statocyst*. Statocysts occur in cœlenterates, turbellarians, molluscs, annelids, crustaceans, echinoderms, and animals of other groups. The statocyst is therefore a widespread organ in invertebrate animals.

In the commonest type of statocyst (Fig. 128*A*) the sensory epithelium forms a hollow sphere within which one or more heavy bodies, the *statoliths*, lie free. The statoliths are often formed of calcium carbonate, which is secreted during the development of the organ. According to the direction of the force of gravity the statoliths stimulate different receptor cells of the epithelium.

Various other types of statocyst occur. In some Decapoda no

statoliths are secreted, but after each moult sand grains are placed in the statocyst, which opens to the exterior. In the Ctenophora (Plate X, Fig. 129), Trachomedusæ and some Crustacea (*Mysis*, Fig. 128*B*), the statolith is not free. It is permanently attached to a number of sense hairs which form supports for it at one side of the statocyst. With changes in the direction of gravity it will bear more or less heavily on some of these hairs. In the ctenophores these sense hairs are in four bundles, which are each in connection (probably nervous) with two of the eight combs of fused cilia with which the animal swims. This connection is along eight ciliated grooves which radiate from the statocyst. The beat of the combs is controlled in strength by impulses coming from the sense hairs of the statocyst. The manner in which a single statocyst may govern the behaviour of an animal can be observed in these ctenophores. The resting ctenophore (*Beroe*) lies vertically with the mouth upwards; when it is swimming actively it is still vertical but the mouth is downwards (Fig. 130). In either of these positions the statocyst stimulates all its supports equally. When the animal is placed on its side or at some angle to the vertical, the supports are unequally stimulated, and the combs beat unequally. If the animal is in the resting condition at the time that its position is disturbed, the upper combs beat more actively than the lower; if swimming actively, the reverse occurs. In both cases the result is that the animal is turned again into its original position, always vertical, but with the mouth below in one condition and above in the other.

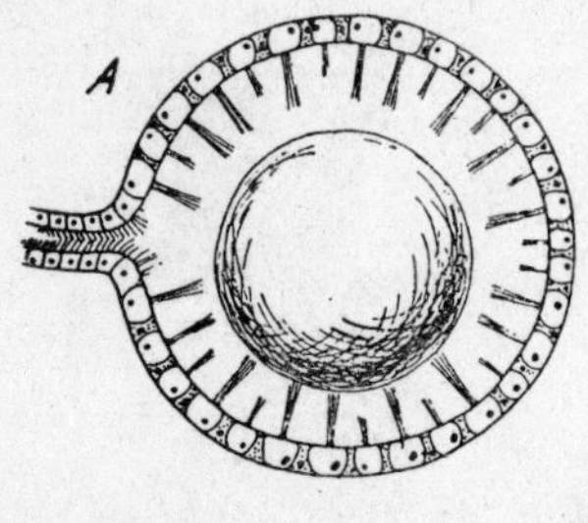

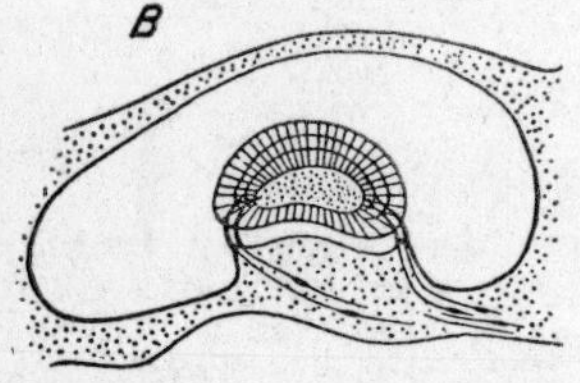

Figure 128. Diagrams of statocysts.

A, in *Pecten* (Lamellibranchiata); *B*, in *Mysis*. (After von Buddenbrock.)

Many invertebrates possess symmetrically paired statocysts. The chief function of these paired statocysts is to enable the animal to maintain the normal position with the right-left axis horizontal. This result is reached in two ways. In some Crustacea (mysids and the shrimps and prawns), the two statocysts act independently. Each is able to provide the necessary impulses for the maintenance of position if the other is removed, and both give the same stimulation. In other invertebrates (lobsters, Macrura reptantia, and molluscs) the two statocysts are balanced against each other. When the body is horizontal, the impulses from the statocysts are in equilibrium. If the body is rotated about its longitudinal axis, this balance is destroyed, and the animal returns to the horizontal. That there is a true balance in these animals between the stimulation from the two statocysts can be seen from the results of removal of one of them. When this is done, the animal does not continue to act normally, as an animal with independent statocysts does. The balance of the stimulation is upset, and the animal takes up an abnormal position. This position is almost always with the undamaged side higher, a fact which can only be interpreted on the assumption that the stimulation of a statocyst is decreased when it is on the upper side of the animal, and increased when it is on the lower side. After removal of

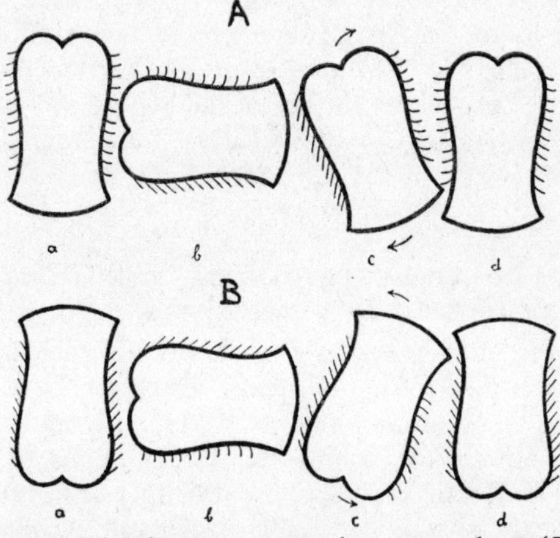

Figure 130. Righting movements in a ctenophore (*Beroe*).

A, active condition; the upper cilia are inhibited, and the lower activated, after the animal is placed on its side, so that the animal is turned in a clockwise direction. B, resting condition; reverse reactions of the cilia and the opposite direction of turning. Both reactions result in the animal regaining the original position. (After Bauer.)

a statocyst, there will be no stimulation on the operated side, and the animal will react so as to decrease the lack of equilibrium in the balance of stimulation. It moves the undamaged statocyst upwards, and we must suppose that this decreases the stimulation coming from it.

Other gravity-perceptive sense-organs which depend, like the statocyst, on the weight of a heavy body for their stimulation are the *tentaculocysts* of the Scyphozoa (*e.g. Aurelia*); and the *sphæridia* of the sea-urchins, if the latter are really organs with this function. These sphæridia (Plate X, Fig. 131) are small bodies which project from the ectoderm of the sea-urchin on its oral side. The greater part of the sphæridium consists of an ovoid calcareous ossicle, which is covered with ectoderm. The ossicle is borne on a short stalk, round which is a ring of nervous tissue. In the normal position of the animal—with the mouth below—the ossicle hangs vertically downwards. When the animal's oral-aboral axis is at an angle to the vertical, the ossicle will hang to one side of the stalk. The structure suggests that when the ossicle is not hanging vertically the nerve ring is unequally stimulated in its different parts, and this enables the animal to appreciate the direction of gravity. We have no direct proof that the sphæridia act in this way.

The only organs that may serve the purpose of appreciating the direction of gravity but are not stimulated by the weight of a heavy body occur in certain aquatic insects (Nepidæ). These animals carry bubbles of air in hollows in the cuticle on their ventral side, and it is said that sense hairs round the openings of these cavities are stimulated by the pressure of the surface of the bubble. If so, the stimulation will alter with changes in the position of the animal. It has been suggested that a sense of the direction of gravity is obtained in this way.

3. ORGANS FOR APPRECIATION OF VIBRATORY STIMULI; AUDITORY ORGANS IN THE INSECTS

We have seen that many of the ectodermal receptor cells of a planarian are adapted to appreciate movement of the water over the surface. These sense-organs will probably be stimulated by some types of vibration in the water, and the reactions of many other invertebrates to vibration in water are probably due to stimulation of simple sense-organs such as these (cœlenterates, platyhelminths, annelids, molluscs, etc.). In most aquatic arthropods vibratory stimuli are received by hairs very similar to those which serve the tactile sense. Probably, the same sense-organ often serves both senses. But in the insects there is developed a special type of sense-organ, the *scolophore*, which is adapted to appreciate changes of tension in a fibre which runs along its length. In many insects some of the scolophores are stimulated by sound waves in the surrounding air, which cause the changes of tension to which the organs are sensitive. In a few insects large numbers of scolophores are arranged as complicated sense organs which have the special function of receiving sound stimuli. These are the *auditory organs*.

The structure of the scolophore varies considerably in details, but its essential features are similar in all insects. A diagram of a well-developed form is given in Fig. 132. The organ is always attached to the cuticle at one end and frequently at both ends, so that it lies across a part of the body. When it is not attached at both ends to the cuticle, it projects freely, and more or less stiffly, into the body from the cuticle. At one end is a receptor cell (sc) to which a nerve (n) is attached. Traversing the receptor cell is an axial fibre (af), which passes through a vacuole (v) and ends among complicated and minute structures at the apex of the receptor cell. The apical part of the receptor cell is surrounded by an envelope cell (ec) and, beyond this, by a cap cell (cc) which projects beyond the receptor cell and ends on the inside of the cuticle. Through the cap cell runs a terminal fibre (t) which is attached to the cuticle and to the apex of the receptor cell. It is not possible to interpret accurately how these complicated structures work, but the arrangement of the organ suggests very strongly that its function is to appreciate changes of tension in the terminal fibre.

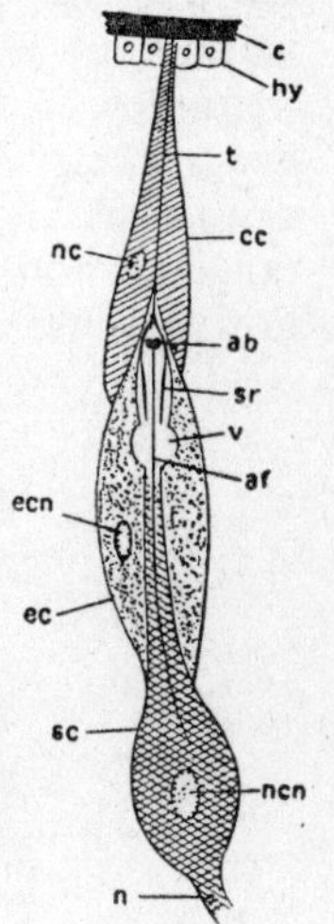

Figure 132. Diagram of a scolophore.

c, cuticle; hy, ectoderm; cc, cap cell surrounding the terminal fibre (t); nc, nucleus of the cap cell; ec, enveloping cell; ecn, nucleus of the enveloping cell; af axial fibre; v, vacuole; sr, supporting rods; ab, apical body; sc, receptor cell; ncn, nucleus of the receptor cell; n, nerve. (From Eltringham after Snodgrass.)

Let us suppose that this is so. Any change in the shape of the cuticle will cause changes in the tension of the fibre and so stimulate them. Sound in the air outside the body will stimulate them, if the cuticle to which they are attached is sufficiently sensitive to react to the vibrations of sound waves. Apparently, it is so in many insects. A large number of insects are sensitive to sound but have no special auditory organs. The bee is an example, and it seems that the only organs it possesses which can be responsible for this sensitivity are the scolophores. Presumably the cuticle in certain parts of the body vibrates in response to the sound waves and stimulates the scolophores.

The true auditory organs of the insects may be regarded as a further development from the scolophore. In these auditory organs the structure is elaborated for the purpose of magnifying the stimulatory effects of sound waves, and so increasing the sensitivity. A diagram of one type of auditory organ (in the cicada) is given in Fig. 133. Sound waves set in vibration a thin tympanum (T) which is surrounded on both sides by spaces filled with air, on one side the outside air (AL) and on the other air in a tracheal space (Tr). By the vibrations of this tympanum groups of scolophores (S) are stimulated. Some other auditory organs are more complicated than this, but they are all built on similar plans. In all of them scolophores are stimulated by the vibration of a tympanum.

It is not clear how far these organs can enable the animal to distinguish sounds of different frequency. Even a simple tympanum may vibrate differently in response to different frequencies, if its structure is adapted to this purpose. In some auditory organs there are muscles which alter the tension of the tympanum, and changes of its tension would alter its sensitivity to different frequencies. It is also possible that differentiation is present among the scolophores, of which there are 1500 in some auditory organs. Discrimination of the frequency of sound in these organs is therefore possible, but how much discrimination the insect in fact has is more doubtful. The cicada has been found to be sensitive only to a somewhat narrow range of notes around the note given out by the sound-emitting organs of the same species. Other insects may be sensitive to a wider

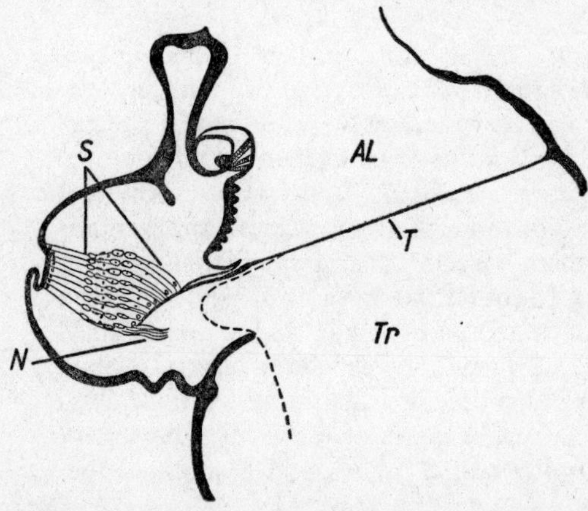

Figure 133. The auditory organ of a *Cicada*.

AL, external air-space; Tr, tracheal space; T, tympanum; N, nerve; S, scolophores. (After Vogel.)

range of notes. There is evidence of discrimination of sounds in the long-horned grasshoppers (Locustidæ), but the discrimination differs in type from our own.*

4. LIGHT-PERCEPTIVE ORGANS

When we were discussing the eyespots of the Protista (p. 60), we saw that even so simple a light-perceptive organ as an eyespot might

* In a locust (Acridiidæ) it has recently been shown that it is probably not the pure tone of a sound that the insect appreciates, but rather modulations of the intensity of the sound waves. The auditory organ responds to a pure note but the impulses in its nerve set up by a pure note probably serve only to carry modulations present in the sound, just as wireless waves carry the sounds we receive in wireless reception (Pumphrey and Rawdon Smith—see Bibliography).

appreciate not only the intensity of light but also its direction. In the simplest Metazoa we find light-perceptive organs which have no functions other than these. On the other hand, the elaborate light-perceptive organs of the more complicated Metazoa give the animals several other types of information about the world outside the body. These organs may be so arranged that they inform the animal (1) of movement in a light source or illuminated object; (2) of the shape of objects, by forming an image of them; (3) of the colour of the light with which they are stimulated, and (4), in certain insects and vertebrates, of the distance of objects. As we pass up the evolutionary table, we find continually more elaborate light-perceptive organs which serve more and more of these functions, the earlier functions being always retained. In considering the light-perceptive organs of the invertebrates, we must enquire how many of these functions each type of organ serves.

(a) *Unicellular light-receptors, and eyespots*

Many sea-anemones respond by contraction to a strong light thrown upon them. Here the response is due either to the general sensitivity of the tissue cells or, perhaps, to stimulation of light-sensitive receptor cells in the ectoderm. Receptor cells for this stimulus occur in the ectoderm of most of the simpler invertebrates (platyhelminthes, molluscs, annelids, etc.), some of which have also more complicated light-perceptive organs. These unicellular organs give appreciation of the presence and probably of the intensity of the light. In some animals they may be able, like the protistan eye-spots (p. 59), to record the direction of the light relatively to the body, for they are often unsymmetrically placed and will be shaded from light coming from certain directions. In this way animals which have no other light-perceptive organs may be able to orientate themselves to light. Simple light-perceptive organs such as these cannot serve any other functions.

The ectodermal receptor cells are often arranged in patches so as to form what are called in the multicellular body "eyespots" (cœlenterates, echinoderms, etc.). Simple eyespots can have no more elaborate functions than unicellular light-receptors, but some of them are further differentiated. In the Anthomedusæ, for instance, the eyespots are provided with a transparent spherical body on the outer surface (Plate X, Fig. 134). These bodies have the form of lenses, and will clearly concentrate the light on the receptor cells which lie inside them. They will also help to discriminate light from different directions, for light striking the lens at right-angles to the ectoderm will be more effective than light at an angle to the surface. The arrangement recalls that of the eyespot of *Proterythropsis* (p. 60).

(b) *Simple invertebrate "eyes"*

In many of the Turbellaria the light-perceptive organs are little more complex than eyespots. They consist of spherical masses of receptor cells, the whole mass being surrounded by a layer of opaque pigment except for a small part of its surface. This pigment layer is clearly an adaptation to perception of the direction of the light. In the light-perceptive organs of *Planaria* (Fig. 135) there is further adaptation for this purpose. The "eye" of this animal consists of several receptor cells (*retinulæ*), each provided with a separate nerve fibre. About two-thirds of the surface of the whole organ is surrounded by pigment. Not only will light coming from any direction in which the organ is covered by pigment fail to stimulate, but it has been shown that the individual retinulæ are sensitive only to light which strikes them at right-angles to their breadth, *i.e.* only to light reaching them along the line a, Fig. 135*b*.

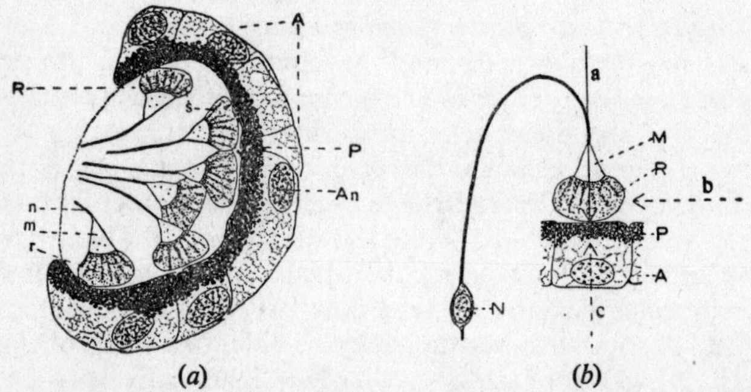

Figure 135. Structure of the eye of *Planaria*.

a, optical section of the whole eye; *b*, a single retinula. A, pigment cells, An, their nuclei; R, retinula; P, pigment; *n*, thin process of the retinula cell in which its nucleus (N) lies; *s*, *m*, M, parts of the retinula cell. Light from the direction *a* is effective in stimulation, that from the directions *b* and *c* is ineffective. (After Taliaferro.)

By far the majority of the more complex light-perceptive organs in all invertebrate groups except the arthropods are built on a plan which is shown in a simple form in Fig. 136. The receptor cells form a retina surrounding a more or less spherical space. Nerves reach the outside of this retina from farther within the body. The spherical space within the eye is sometimes filled with a hard lens (as in *Nereis*, Fig. 136), or a lens may be developed in the ectoderm over the eye. Other eyes of this type have no lens and light reaches the interior of the eye through a small opening where the organ is in contact with the ectoderm. Such eyes function in the same way as a pin-hole camera. Organs of these types occur in annelids, molluscs, and many other invertebrate groups. The ocelli of the arthropods may be regarded as modifications of this type of eye.

Eyes such as these will be stimulated whenever the illumination of any of the retinal cells is altered. They will record a change in the general illumination. The contraction of some tube-living annelids (Sabellids) into their tubes when a shadow passes over them is a reaction of this type; it results from stimulation of eyes situated on the tentacles. Such eyes may also give appreciation of the direction of light, for different retinal cells will be stimulated by light from different directions. They may thus enable the animal to orientate itself to the light. The very large eyes of some planktonic polychætes (*Alciope*, *Asterope*) probably enable the animal to orientate.

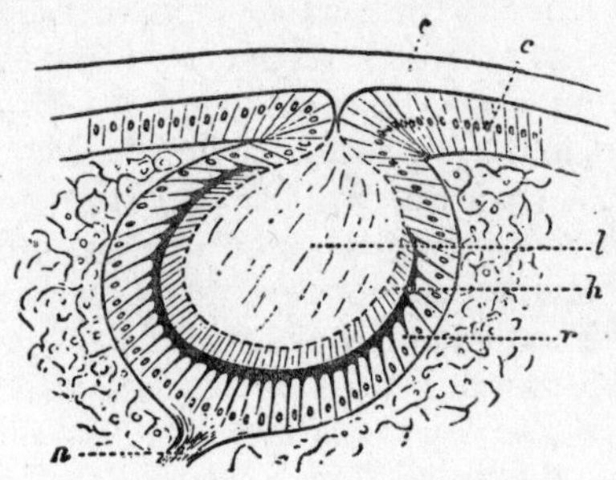

Figure 136. The eye of *Nereis*.

l, lens; *r*, retinal cells; *h*, receptive terminations of the retinal cells; *n*, nerve. (After Andrews.)

With the exception of the eyes of the cephalopods and of some spiders (see below), it is very improbable that any of these eyes can provide an image of an object outside the body. The image of any image-forming eye consists of a mosaic of the sensations given by a large number of retinal elements, much as in some forms of printing a picture consists of a large number of dots. This is illustrated in Plate XI, Fig. 137*b*, p. 282, where the image of a spider which might be expected to be given by the eye of another spider at a distance of 8 cm. is shown. It is also illustrated in Plate XII, Fig. 140. The images are made up of dots, each produced by stimulation of a single retinal element. The dots in these images are large, and the images poor*—the perfection of the image, as of the printed picture, increases as the size of the dots diminishes. Thus, if a good image is to be given by an eye, a part of the outside field must be focused on a large number of retinal elements; and the larger the number of elements to any given part of the field the better the image may be.

* Eyes too simple to form a worth-while image may be of use in other ways, *e.g.* in orientation (*Daphnia*, Harris, *Quar. J. micr. Sci.*, **94**, 537, 1953).

The unit of the field is best measured as that subtending a unit angle at the eye, and we may say that in general the value of the eye as an image-forming apparatus varies directly with the number of retinal elements on which a unit angle of the field is focused. For accuracy this statement needs qualification, since the performance of an eye clearly depends on the efficiency of all its parts, and not only on the structure of the retina. If full advantage is to be taken of the retinal elements as a means of forming an image, the other parts of the eye—its focusing apparatus, its means of collecting light and so on—must be efficient enough to allow the retinal elements to play their part. But, supposing that is so, the statement is true.

In invertebrate eyes of the type we are considering, except those of cephalopods and spiders, the number of retinal elements is almost always far too small to give a recognisable image of an external object. This does not imply that invertebrates with eyes of this type are unable to react to the presence of objects in their neighbourhood. They do so react. A snail will avoid an object in its path, and it can be shown that this is due to visual stimulation. A scallop (*Pecten*) has on the edge of its mantle numerous eyes of a type which appears to be functionally similar to that of the eyes we are considering. The scallop reacts to an object moved near it by extending the tentacles on the mantle edge. This is also due to visual stimulation. But these reactions do not imply that the animals are able to "see" the form of the objects.* An object placed in the field of one of the simple eyes we are considering will alter the illumination of some of the retinal cells by reflecting a greater or less amount of light than was reflected in the field before the object was placed there. These changes may stimulate the cells and cause a reaction. There is no need to assume any image-formation to account for the reaction.

The eyes of cephalopods can probably form good images of objects outside the body. In many cephalopods the eye itself is large, and the size of the retinal elements is no larger than in some vertebrate eyes, *e.g.* that of the frog. The angle subtended by a retinal element in the outside field is in some cephalopod eyes probably about 5–10 mins. This is as small as or smaller than the corresponding angle in any compound eye (p. 286) and compares with an angle of 1 min. in our own eyes. The other parts of the cephalopod eye seem to be efficient enough for use to be made of the complex retina. Also the cephalopod eye has an elaborate apparatus for adjusting the focus of the lens to the distance of the object in view, and this is only to be expected if accurate appreciation of the form of the object is to be obtained. The behaviour of cephalopods supports the belief that they can see objects. If an octopus is watched when it is feeding, it

* Still less to realise them as objects in the world outside its body—see p. 362.

PLATE XI

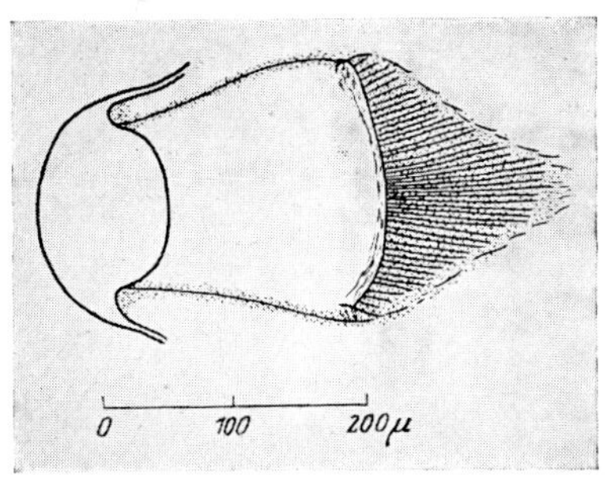

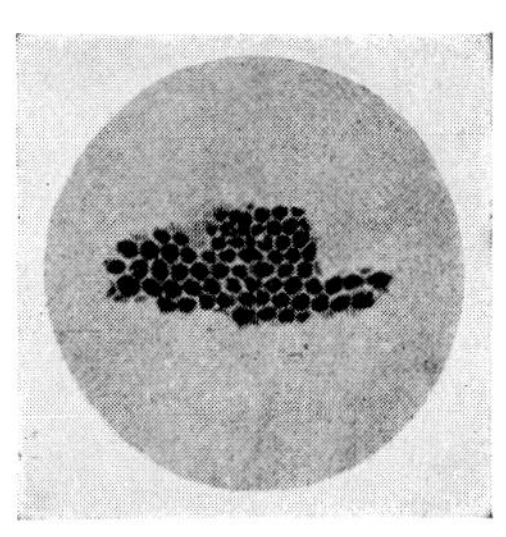

(*a*) (*b*)

Figure 137.

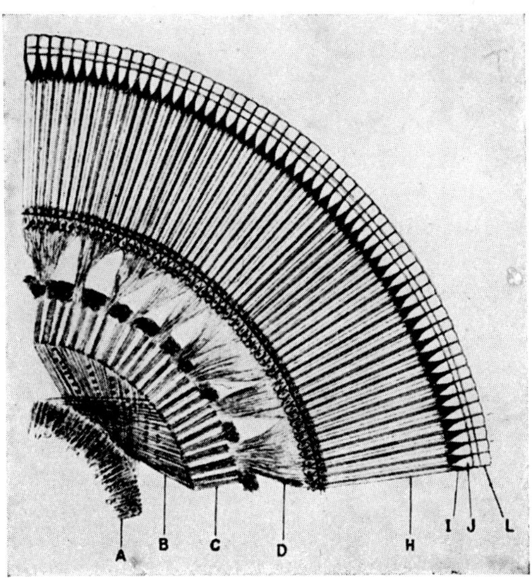

Figure 138.

Figure 137. (*a*) Section of the eye of a salticid spider (*Evarcha*). (*b*) Image of another spider given by an efficient type of spider's eye at 8 cm. (After Homann.)

Figure 138. Section of the eye of a butterfly. A–D, nerve fibres; H, retinulæ; I, pigment cells; J, cones; L, lenses. (After Eltringham.)

[*To face p.* 282.

will be seen to seize prey such as an active crab always from behind. This is difficult to understand if it cannot see the form of the crab. Still, it is chiefly from consideration of the structure of the eye that we are led to conclude that these animals can probably see objects, and that they can see them almost, if not quite, as clearly as some vertebrates do. Such a conclusion assumes that the brain of the cephalopod has the power of correlating the impulses received from the eye so as to form a single image.

Some jumping spiders have eyes (Plate XI, Fig. 137), of the type we are discussing in this section, which are probably capable of forming images. They owe their power of doing so, if it exists, to the arrangement of the structure of the whole eye. The eye is cylindrical and the retina placed at a considerable distance from the lens, and at a large radius of curvature. The result of this arrangement is that the angle of the field subtended by a retinal element is small, and image-formation is possible, though the field of view is small. In the best spider's eye the unit of the image subtends an angle of 12 mins. in the field of view. The type of image which might be given by such an eye is shown in Fig. 137*b* (Plate XI). This type of eye also occurs in some fishes. It has been called a "telescopic eye."

(c) *Compound Eyes*

The general plan of the eyes of cephalopods and spiders is identical with that of the vertebrate eye. Light is passed through a single lens and focused on a retina, which is arranged as a larger or smaller part of a sphere. This type of eye has reached the elaboration necessary for image-formation three times in the evolution of animals—in the cephalopods, spiders, and vertebrates. This parallel evolution has extended in the cephalopods and the vertebrates to the various accessory parts of the organs, which are extraordinarily similar in arrangement in the two groups. We may call these eyes "camera-eyes."

In other arthopods a second, quite different, type of image-forming eye has been evolved. This is the *compound eye*.

A diagram of the arrangement of the parts in a section of a well-developed compound eye, that of a butterfly, is given in Plate XI, Fig. 138. Many less elaborate types of compound eye occur. We will here consider this type of eye only in its better developed forms.

The compound eye consists of numerous *ommatidia*, each lying at small angles to its neighbours and abutting on a facet of the cuticle. The structure of the ommatidium varies considerably in different types of compound eye (Figs. 138, 139). In the butterfly's eye (Plate XI, Fig. 138) at the outer end of the ommatidium there is a *lens* (L) formed from the cuticle, and, inside this, a hard, transparent body, the *cone* (J)—this is not present in all compound eyes. Within the cone are the *retina cells*, *retinulæ* (H); of these there are up to eight in each ommatidium. They surround a central rod, the *rhabdome*, which lies in the axis of the ommatidium. The retinulæ are the light-sensitive receptor cells. At their base are complex arrangements of nerve fibres (A–D). Each retinula has a separate nerve fibre, and possibly two different types of nerve supply. They have also a tracheal supply. Finally, opaque pigment cells (I) lie on the outer surface of the ommatidium. When the eye is adapted to use in strong light, these pigment cells extend over the surfaces of the retinulæ and the cone, so as almost completely to isolate the ommatidium from its neighbours. When the light is weak, they contract towards the lens and the bases of the retinulæ.

In Fig. 139 the structure of two ommatidia of the eye of the crayfish, *Astacus*, is shown. It will be seen that the various parts of the ommatidium which have been mentioned as being present in the eye of the butterfly are also present in that of *Astacus*, but that they are different in form in the two eyes.

In each ommatidium in all compound eyes light is concentrated on the retinulæ by the lens, and by the cone, if this is present. It is possible that the light is distributed along the length of the retinulæ by passing through the rhabdome. In the light-adapted eye, the light is prevented from reaching other ommatidia by the pigment around the cone and the retinulæ.

The ommatidium is clearly arranged so as to receive light from only a small part of the field outside the eye. In the light-adapted eye, only light coming from the cone which the surface of the ommatidium forms when extended beyond the cuticle will reach the retinulæ. The question whether the ommatidium acts in all compound eyes as a single light-perceptive unit, or whether, in some, each retinula cell may send a separate sensation to the brain is still undecided. It has been shown that in each ommatidium of the eyes of butterflies and some other insects the lens and cones form at their inner side a small image of an object in line with the axis of the ommatidium. This makes it possible that the individual retinulæ are each differently stimulated in these eyes, and that they pass on these differences to the brain. But in many compound eyes no such image is formed. When that is so, there can be no differences in the stimulation of the retinulæ. The ommatidium can only act as a single unit. In the eye of Limulus there is only one nerve fibre to each ommatidium.* Here also the ommatidia can only act as units.

The acuity of the vision of a compound eye varies with the angle between neighbouring ommatidia. In many compound eyes this angle is large (10° or more), and any image formed by the eye

* Hartline and Graham, *Proc. Soc. exp. Biol. Med.*, **29**, 613, 1932.

must be extremely poor, for the units of which the image is formed will be very large. Indeed, very many compound eyes are not good enough to form any recognisable image. But this is not true of all. In the butterfly's eye the angle between the ommatidia is about 1·5° (Fig. 138), and in the best insect eyes (*e.g.* dragonfly) it may be

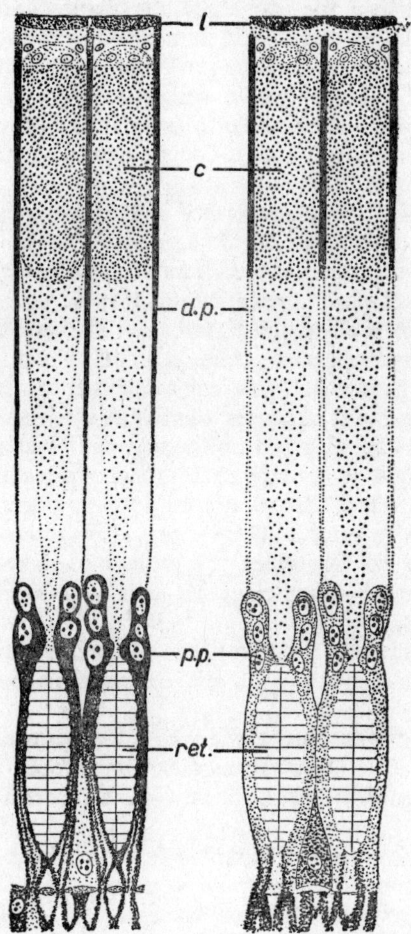

Figure 139. Ommatidia of the eye of *Astacus* in light-adapted (left) and dark-adapted (right) conditions.

l, lens; *c*, cones; *d.p.*, distal pigment cells; *p.p.*, proximal pigment cells; *ret.*, retinulæ. (After Bernhards.)

as small as 0·5°. If the ommatidium is acting as a single unit—as it certainly is in the eye of the dragonfly, in which no image is formed in each ommatidium—the unit of the image will be an area of the field subtending this angle at the eye. Even if we accept that the retinulæ may act separately in some eyes, this unit will only be reduced to one-third of its value on the assumption that the whole ommatidium acts as a unit, for the diameter of each retinula will be about one-third of that of the ommatidium. Accepting 0·5° as the smallest angle between the ommatidia, the smallest unit of the mosaic image will subtend an angle of 30 mins. if the ommatidium acts as a single unit, and of 10 mins. if the retinulæ act separately. In the one case the unit will be about the size which the sun or moon appears to us to be, in the other one-third of this diameter. The compound eye can therefore never give as good discrimination as many vertebrate eyes do.*

The coarseness of the image formed by the compound eye does not imply that it is of little use to the animal. As an object is brought closer to an eye, the angles subtended at the eye by its parts increase. Thus, an eye with poor discrimination may be able to show considerable detail in a close object, although at a greater distance no recognisable image is formed. It has been calculated that a butterfly would be clearly recognisable as such to another butterfly at 2 inches and just recognisable at 12 inches, but not at much greater distances, these conclusions being based on the assumption that the retinulæ act independently. It is not easy to test these conclusions by observation of the behaviour of the animals. Butterflies will certainly fly from greater distances to other butterflies and also to objects, *e.g.* pieces of paper, shaped like butterflies. It is difficult to be sure that it is the form and not some other character that is appreciated at these greater distances.

In Fig. 140 (Plate XII) an attempt has been made to show the image that a butterfly's eye might give of another butterfly at 12 inches.

The compound eye is thus a true image-forming eye, and its image is undoubtedly of value to the animal, but its poor discrimination makes it useful only at short distances—the arthropod is always very short-sighted.

The compound eye is well adapted to serve all the functions performed by simpler light-perceptive organs. It will distinguish the presence and absence of light, and the direction of a light source. It will also be very sensitive to movement of the light source, for as the

* It is true that in the mammalian eye acuity of vision may be in some forms of discrimination greater than the structure of the retina can account for. This is so in what is known as "vernier discrimination," and is due to chromatic aberration and differential stimulation of neighbouring retinal cells (H. Hartridge, *J. Physiol.*, **57**). Similar effects are possible in other eyes, but we have no knowledge of them. Scanning movements over the field of vision may also improve discrimination (Dethier, *J. cell. comp. Physiol.*, **22**, 115, 1943).

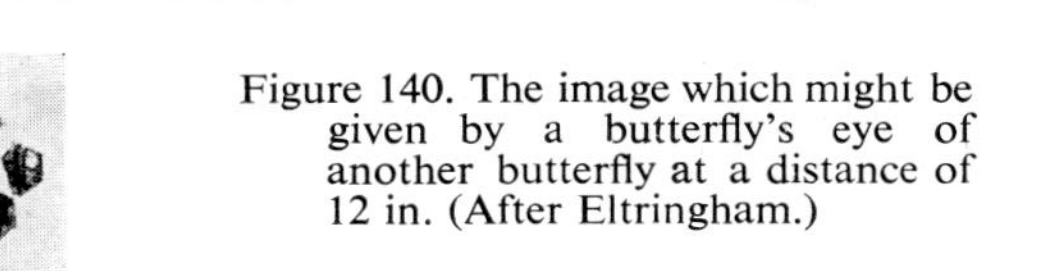

Figure 140.

Figure 140. The image which might be given by a butterfly's eye of another butterfly at a distance of 12 in. (After Eltringham.)

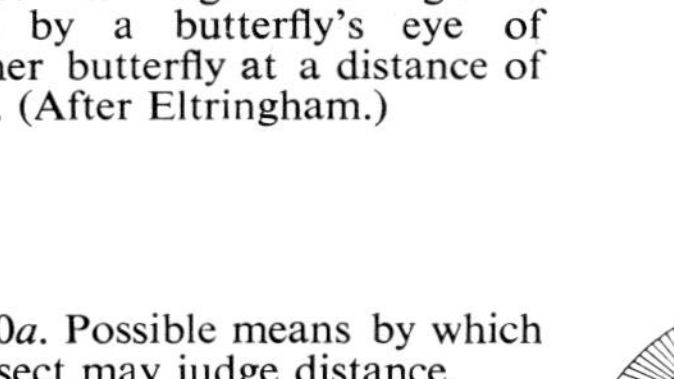

Figure 140 (*a*).

Figure 140*a*. Possible means by which an insect may judge distance.

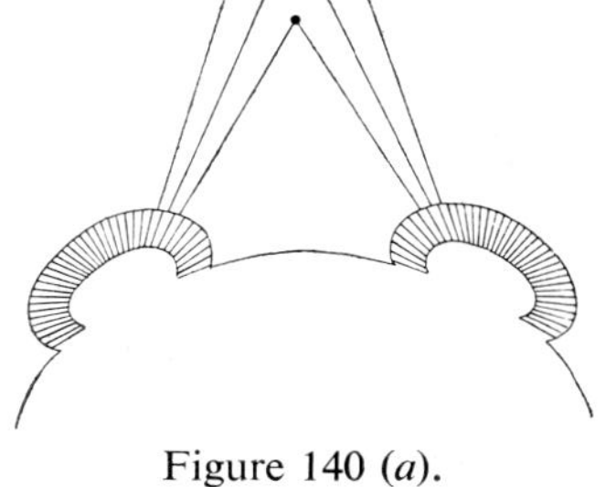

Figure 144.

Figure 144. Formation of a secretion in cells of the mid-gut of *Astacus*. *a*, *b*, *d*, *e*, *f*, *g*, successive stages in the formation of the secretion in vacuoles (*Vac*). *c*, another modification of the cells from stage *b*, with the formation of fat vacuoles. The Apparatus externum and apparatus internum are parts of the Golgi apparatus. (After Hirsch and Jordan.)

source moves different ommatidia will be stimulated. There is also no doubt that some insects can judge distance—in catching their prey, for instance.* They certainly cannot have stereoscopic vision of the same kind as that of the vertebrates, for they have no means of moving their eyes so as to adjust the angle between them to the distance of the object. They may be able to judge distance, as the many vertebrates without stereoscopic vision do—by experience and memory. The appearance of an object at different distances is recorded in the memory, and the distance recognised when the object is again seen. It is probable that judgment of distance in the insects is more often by another means. If the compound eyes have fields of vision that overlap in front of the animal, near and distant objects will be seen by different ommatidia when the animal is facing towards them (Plate XII, Fig. 140*a*). It is probable that the distance of an object is appreciated on the basis of these differences.

The movements of the pigment in the arthropod eye have already been mentioned. These movements are adaptations for correlating the functioning of the eye with the strength of the light reaching it. As we have seen, the pigment in the light-adapted eye almost completely surrounds each ommatidium and isolates it from its neighbours. In weak light this pigment sheath is removed by retraction of the pigment (Fig. 139, B). The result of this is that light that has passed through the lenses of other ommatidia can reach the retinulæ of the dark-adapted eye through the walls between the ommatidia; in the light-adapted eye this is impossible. Thus, the receptor cells will receive considerably more light in the dark-adapted eye than they would have received without this adaptation. They will therefore be more sensitive to weak intensities of light, but this increase in the light received will be at considerable loss of discrimination, for the cells will be stimulated by light coming from regions outside the field of view of their ommatidium. The dark-adapted eye will be sensitive to light but poor as an image-forming mechanism.

(d) *The visible spectrum*

The range of the visible spectrum is not identical for all animals. Unfortunately, our knowledge of the visible range of wave-lengths is confined to a few animals. For the large majority of invertebrate animals, and for some which almost certainly have colour vision, we have no exact knowledge of the visible range. Without this knowledge we cannot determine exactly the colours which they can distinguish, although we may be able to show that they are able to discriminate light of certain wave-lengths.

The visible spectral range is known for some vertebrates and a few

* V. B. Wigglesworth, *The Principles of Insect Physiology*, 1939, pp. 124–5.

arthropods. In Fig. 141, curves of the "stimulative efficiency" of light of different wave-lengths are given for the bee, a fly (*Drosophila*) and man. The ordinates of this figure may be regarded as the reciprocals of the energy in the light which is required to stimulate. It will be seen that the insects' visible spectra extend much farther into the shorter wave-lengths (ultra-violet) and less far into the longer wave-lengths (red) than man's. Some insects can see farther into the red than the bee and *Drosophila*. Certain butterflies have almost the

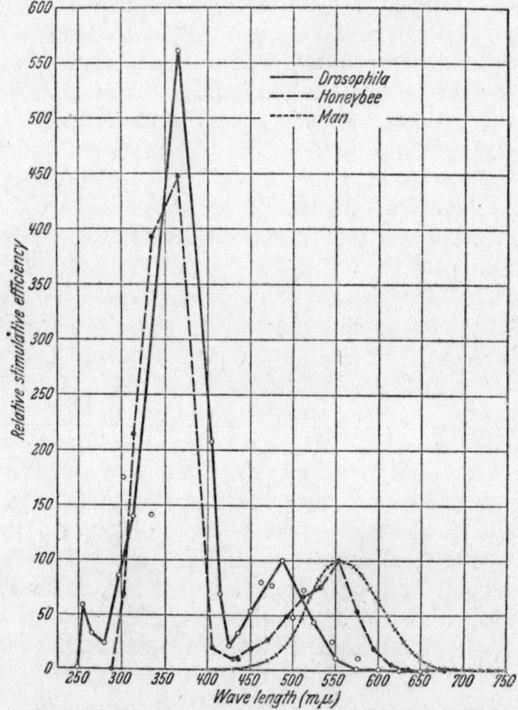

Figure 141. Relative stimulative efficiencies of light of different wave-lengths for man, the bee, and *Drosophila*. (After Bertholf.)

same visible range at the red end of the spectrum as we have. No insects see farther into the red than we do.

The visible range for all the other animals which have been investigated differs from our own in much the same way as those of the bee and *Drosophila* do. Many invertebrates are sensitive to ultra-violet light which is outside our visible range, and insensitive to red. But the animal's visible range always includes part of our own visible range. No animal can see a range of wave-lengths which, as a whole, is far removed from our own visible range.

(e) *Colour Vision**

To have colour vision implies the power of discriminating light of different wave-lengths. Since the visible spectrum is often different from ours and light of any wave-lengths which are visible to the animal may be discriminated, it is clear that some animals may see "colours" which are invisible to us and may be unable to see some of the colours we see. Insects, for instance, may see "colours" in the ultra-violet, but the bee and *Drosophila* can certainly not see colours in the red.

There is no evidence of discrimination of wave-length in the great majority of the simpler invertebrate animals (cœlenterates, platyhelminthes, worms, molluscs except cephalopods, most crustaceans, etc.).

That some invertebrates, especially arthropods, can appreciate differences in colour is clear from their behaviour. The prawn *Hippolyte* takes on colours similar to those of the weed among which it is living. This is due to the presence of variously coloured pigment cells in its skin. The reaction is through the eyes, and these must be able to discriminate colours. Similarly, the spider-crab *Maia*, which covers itself with weed, chooses pieces similar to the general colour of its surroundings.

In some arthropods the nature of the colour vision has been investigated by experiment. *Daphnia* possesses a very simple type of colour vision. In its normal light-adapted state *Daphnia* always swims away from white light immediately after the light has been increased, and towards the light after it has been decreased. But if the light is yellow it always swims towards the light—the behaviour is not altered by increasing or decreasing the light. Similarly, it always swims away from blue light. It behaves to red, orange and green light as to yellow; and to blue-green, violet and ultra-violet as to blue. This behaviour shows that the animal can distinguish between the red and blue-violet parts of the spectrum, but it seems to have no other colour sense. It may be called bichromatic.

By far the majority of experiments on invertebrate colour vision have been carried out on insects. Bees, for instance, can be conditioned (ch. XXI) to look for honey on a receptacle of some defined colour placed among similar receptacles of other colours. If the colour of the receptacle is slightly altered, it can be observed whether the bees still go to it. If they do not, the change of colour is presumably perceptible to them. In all such experiments great care is needed to avoid possible sources of error. It is necessary, for instance, to be sure that there are not differences in luminosity between the

* *Cf.* Wolff (*Physiol. Rev.*, **36**, 145, 1956) for recent work on colour vision in compound eyes.

receptacles (*i.e.* differences in the *amount* of light which they reflect), for, if there were such differences, the bees might be reacting to them and not to the colours. When precautions are taken to avoid this, and many other sources of error, it is found that the bees can distinguish light of four bands of wave-length—yellow, blue-green, blue, and ultra-violet. They do not distinguish orange and yellow-green from yellow, or violet and purple from blue. Also, they do not distinguish scarlet from black, red being outside their visible range. Pure scarlet flowers are never bee-pollinated though they may be pollinated by birds.

It is probable that colour vision occurs in a large number of insects. Evidence has been produced for its occurrence in some flies, butterflies, moths, and beetles.

CHAPTER XVIII

EFFECTOR ORGANS

THESE are the executive organs of the body. With them the animal carries out all the actions by which it reacts to changes in the environment and, also, many activities within its own body, such as the secretion of glands, peristalsis in the gut, the beat of the heart and so on. The effector organs are therefore various; besides muscles, they include glands, ciliated cells, amœboid cells, pigment cells, sound- and light-producing organs and, in the vertebrates, electric organs. The activities of most of these organs are controlled by the nervous and chemical co-ordinating systems of the body; but some may be continuously active throughout the life of the animal. Effector organs must be distinguished not only from the organs of the receptive and co-ordinating systems, but also from the many other organs which are not concerned in carrying out the actions of the animal—skeleton, absorptive, excretory, respiratory organs, etc. Some of these, *e.g.* the skeleton, may play a passive part in the animal's actions, but they are not the active effector organs of the body. In the activities of others, effector organs may play some part—cilia, for instance, and muscles are present in many of these organs—but the functions of respiration, excretion, etc., are not themselves the concern of the effector organs.

1. CILIARY MOVEMENT

Cilia occur in all the larger groups of the invertebrates with the exceptions of the arthropods and the nematodes.* We have already discussed ciliary movement in the Protista (p. 60). We need not again discuss the general characters of this type of activity, but there are some special features of metazoan cilia which need mention.

The beat of cilia in multicellular animals is much more often pendular (as in Fig. 26A, p. 62) than spiral and undulating like that of a protistan flagellum (Fig. 26B); but undulating beat occurs in the collar cells of the sponges, in spermatozoa and in some other types of ciliary movement in the Metazoa.

The essential structure of a cilium in the Metazoa is identical with

* Motile organs resembling cilia have been described in certain nematodes.

that of a protistan cilium (p. 60); it consists of a vibratile thread outside the cell, a basal granule within the surface, and, probably, a region of modified protoplasm near the basal granule. As in the Protista, cilia in the Metazoa are often combined together to form more complex organs. These are usually called "cilia," since their appearance is often that of large and solid cilia (Fig. 142), but the fact that they possess more than one basal granule shows that they are complex. Numerous simple cilia may be so combined into a single structure. These complex cilia occur commonly in very many groups of the invertebrates. The combs of the ctenophores are especially complex ciliary organs.

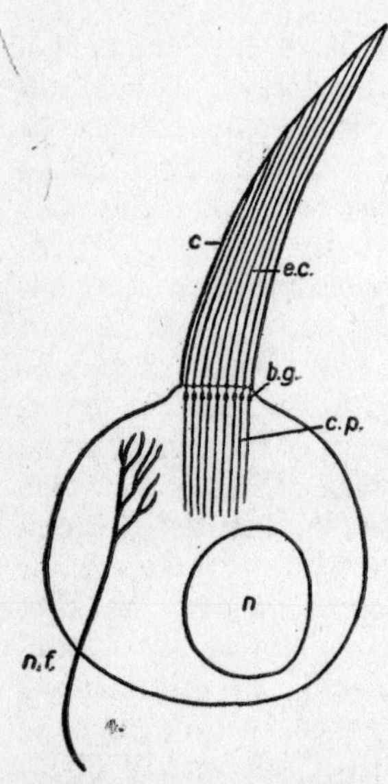

Figure 142. Complex cilium from the velum of an æolid veliger.

c, cilium; *ec*, ciliary elements; *b.g.*, basal granules; *c.p.*, ciliary protoplasm; *n*, nucleus; *n.f.*, nerve fibrils.

The cilia of the multicellular body are only rarely controlled by the co-ordinating system of the body. Their beat is very often continuous throughout the life of the animal. But there is no doubt that control of the beat of cilia does sometimes occur. We have seen, for instance, that the beat of the ciliary combs of the ctenophores is controlled by the statocyst. In a few other animals there is evidence that ciliated cells may be supplied by nerves and that the beat of the cilia is directly controlled through these nerves. In a snail (*Physa*) it has been shown that cilia on the lips, which are usually at rest, can be caused to beat if certain nerves which supply the ciliated cells are stimulated. The beat stops after a few minutes unless the stimulation of the nerves is maintained. Again, in æolid veligers the cilia of the velum are under nervous control. These cilia beat intermittently; they beat for a few seconds, stop suddenly and then recommence their beat after another few seconds. There is evidence that the stopping of the beat is due to impulses reaching the cells by nerves which end between or within them. Apart from these and a few other examples, the cilia in the multicellular body are uncontrolled.

In spite of this freedom from control by the co-ordinating system of the body, the beat of cilia is very often co-ordinated in phase with that of neighbouring cilia. This co-ordination takes the form of a *metachronal rhythm* (Fig. 143). Each cilium of a line or field beats at a short interval of time after the cilium next to it, the interval being never more than a small part of the whole period of the beat. This results in a rhythm of beat passing over the line or field of cilia. According to the position of the cilia, and the direction of their beat, the wave may pass towards the effector or recovery side of the beat (Fig. 26, p. 62) or at right-angles to the beat. Metachronal rhythm is not confined to metazoan cilia; it can be well seen in such ciliate protistans as *Opalina*.

The means by which metachronal rhythm is brought about is not well understood. It is certainly not due to nervous control, for it is shown by a line of ciliated cells which have been separated from the body. It is probable that each cilium is stimulated to beat by some stimulus provided by the beat of the cilium next to it, but the nature of the stimulus is uncertain. A short time-lag in such stimulation would give a regular metachronal rhythm.

In ch. XIX (p. 311) the activity of the flagella which drive the feeding current in sponges is discussed.

Figure 143. Metachronal beat in a line of cilia. (After Verworn.)

2. AMŒBOID MOVEMENT

This type of movement occurs commonly in certain cells of the multicellular body (amœbocytes, absorptive cells of the gut in many of the simpler invertebrates, p. 219). The pseudopodia of invertebrate amœbocytes are often of forms very different from those of protistan pseudopodia. Thus, polychæte amœbocytes often have broad, thin, sheet-like pseudopodia.

Much less is known of amœboid movement in the cells of the multicellular body than in the Protista (p. 63). It is probably in essentials similar in all organisms. We need not discuss it further here.

3. GLANDS

The function of a gland is to form some substance in its protoplasm and to secrete this substance either to the outside of the body or into a space within the body, such as the lumen of the gut or the tubes of the genital system. The glands of the invertebrates are various in form and structure. They may be uni- or multicellular; many are complex, being provided with accessory structures such as reservoirs for the accumulation of the secretion. The uses to which the secretions are put are still more various. Secretions are used in lubrication and digestion of the food, to assist in the locomotion of the animal (*e.g.*

the mucous secretion of the foot of the snail), in the collection of food (*e.g.* in the "cilia and mucus" feeding mechanisms, p. 213), as external skeleton (cuticle, which is frequently secreted by ectodermal glands) and for many other purposes.

Many glands are controlled by nerves. In some the nerves appear to control the secretory activity of the gland directly; in others they control muscles which are so arranged that they can compress either a reservoir in which the secretion is collected or the secretory cells themselves. Contraction of the muscles causes expulsion of the secretion. Other glands have no known nerve supply. Their activity is often controlled in other ways, sometimes perhaps by changes in the condition of the fluids circulating in the internal spaces of the body, the glands of the gut by the condition of the food as it is undergoing digestion, and so on.

We do not know much of the physiology of the formation of a secretion in the cells of a gland. Observation of the structure of the cells during the formation of the secretion shows that the process is a complicated one, taking place in more than one step (Plate XII, Fig. 144). The secretion is formed in modified protoplasm, known as *ergastoplasm*. Each cell passes through a series of changes from the first appearance of the granules which will later form the secretion to the final extrusion of the fully formed secretion. The process is cyclical; a cell is not occupied with different stages of the process at the same time. In most gland cells this cycle can be gone through many times. In some (*e.g.* those shown in Fig. 144) the gland cells are themselves thrown out with the secretion and die.

Formation of the secretion in a gland cell takes place in close association with the mitochondria and Golgi apparatus. Since, as we have seen (p. 34), there is other evidence that these structures are especially concerned with the chemical metabolism of the cell, it is not surprising that they play an important part in the formation of the secretion, which is necessarily a chemical process and part of the metabolism of the cell.

4. MUSCLE

(a) *Structure*

In the invertebrates, as in the vertebrates, there are two types of muscle fibre which differ both morphologically and physiologically. These are the striped and plain muscle fibres (Plate XIII, Fig. 145). These types of muscle are normally distinct but intermediate types occur. In the invertebrates plain fibres with striations in only their central parts are frequent. The heart muscle of the vertebrates, though morphologically striped, is in its physiological characters intermediate between striped and plain muscle. The involuntary muscle of

PLATE XIII

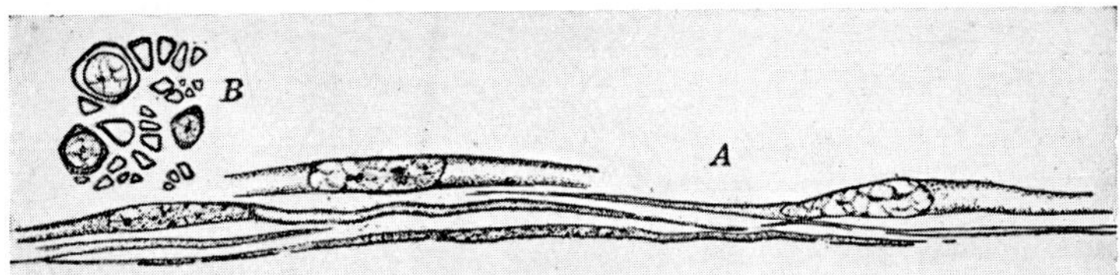

Figure 145 (*b*).

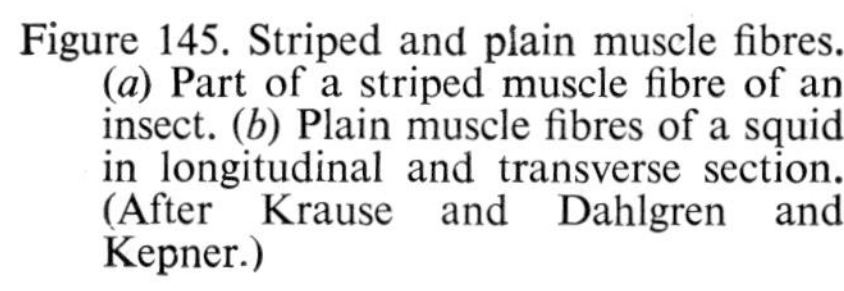

Figure 145. Striped and plain muscle fibres. (*a*) Part of a striped muscle fibre of an insect. (*b*) Plain muscle fibres of a squid in longitudinal and transverse section. (After Krause and Dahlgren and Kepner.)

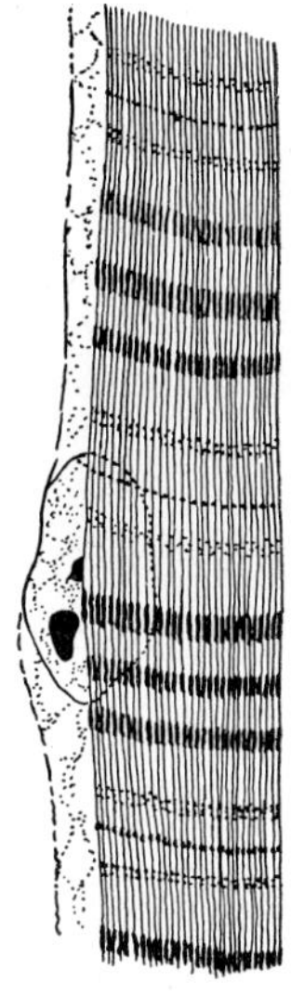

Figure 145 (*a*).

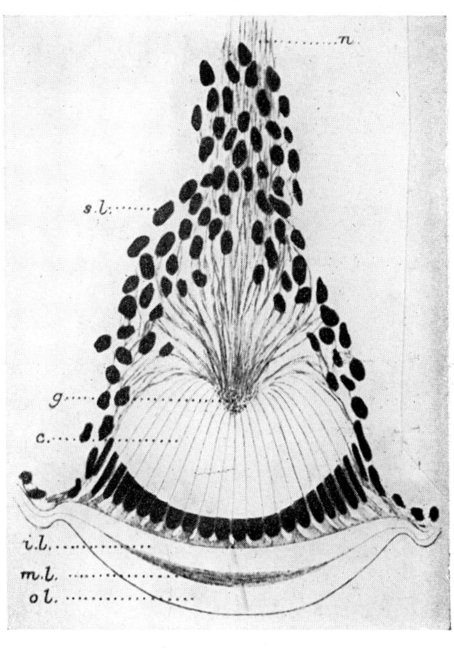

Figure 152.

Figure 152. Section of a luminous organ in *Systellaspis* (decapod Crustacean). *i.l.*, *m.l.*, *o.l.*, parts of the lens; *c*, light-producing cells; *g*, granules around the ends of the nerve fibrils (*n*); *s.l.*, sheath of cells around the organ. (After Kemp.)

Figure 151.

'igure 151. Molluscan pigment cells (*Loligo*). (After Hofmann.)

the insects is an example of a similar type of muscle in the invertebrates.

Striped muscle occurs in some of the simplest Metazoa—in many cœlenterates but not in the Hydrida or in the sponges. In the cœlenterates the muscles by which hydrozoan and scyphozoan medusæ contract in swimming are striped. Striped muscle also occurs in the annelids. But in all groups of the simpler invertebrates by far the greater part of the musculature of the body is plain. On the other hand, in the molluscs many of the muscles are striped; in cephalopods almost all the muscles are striped. By far the greater part of arthropod muscle is striped, and in the insects it is doubtful whether plain muscle occurs. Thus, as we pass up the series from the simpler to the more complex invertebrates the proportion of striped to plain muscle increases. This increase in the proportion of striped muscle goes parallel with increase in the activity of the animal. It should be noted, however, that the striations of much invertebrate striped muscle are spiral and not transverse as are those of vertebrate striped muscle. On the other hand, in insect muscle (Plate XIII, Fig. 145) the striations are transverse. It has been questioned whether the spiral striations are similar in function to the striations of vertebrate muscle.

(b) *Nerve Supply*

Control of the activities of effector organs by the co-ordinating system of the body takes the form of both activation and inhibition, *i.e.* the activity of the organ is either increased or decreased by the control (p. 243), and may be either nervous or chemical. In muscle chemical control is commonest in co-ordination of the tonic contraction of plain muscle and of rhythmical contraction (*e.g.* in heart muscle); the active contractions of both striped and plain muscle are usually controlled by nerves.

Many muscles have both excitatory (activating) and inhibitory nerves, but this is not true of all muscles. In vertebrate striped muscle, for instance, only excitatory nerves occur, and the muscle returns to rest when the activating impulses in these nerves cease. Inhibitory, as well as excitatory, nerves supply heart muscle and much plain muscle in the vertebrates and also many invertebrate muscles, both striped and plain.

The nerve fibrils which innervate muscle fibres end on or near the surface of the fibre, but their arrangement before they reach these terminations differs in the nerves of different types of muscle. In most vertebrate striped muscle the axons in the nerve branch two or three times and each of the branches so formed passes to a muscle fibre, ending in a special organ, the end-plate, on the surface of the fibre. Each fibre contracts when an impulse reaches its end-plate, and the contraction does not pass to other fibres. The result of this arrangement is that an impulse passing down one of these axons reaches only a few fibres, so that in a large muscle the fibres can be excited in many small groups. In molluscs and many other invertebrate groups it is probable that the excitatory innervation of striped muscle is functionally similar to that of vertebrate striped muscle, though the axons may branch more frequently before reaching the muscle. But in the arthropods, the innervation of striped muscle is very different. Each muscle, even though it is large, is supplied by only a few excitatory axons. Even the large closing muscle of a crab's claw is supplied by only three or four excitatory axons, and many arthropod muscles have only one such axon. These axons branch many times and their branches reach all the fibres of the muscle. It results from this arrangement that a single impulse in an excitatory axon will reach either all or a large proportion of the fibres of the muscle, and the fibres cannot be excited in small groups as are the fibres of a vertebrate muscle.

The nerve-endings in invertebrates may also be very different from those of vertebrate muscle. In many types of invertebrate muscle, end-plates occur, but in other types the nerve-fibres end in fine fibrils without any clearly distinguishable end-plates.

Arthropod striped muscle differs from vertebrate striped muscle in another character. It is always supplied with inhibitory as well as excitatory nerves. But in this it is not peculiar; striped muscles of many invertebrates have both types of nerve.

In plain muscle the nerves usually end in fine fibrils among or on the surface of the muscle fibres. The axons often branch frequently before reaching the muscle. Also, a contraction in plain muscle, may pass from one muscle fibre to another that has not been stimulated by a nerve impulse. By this means contraction of a single muscle fibre may set up contraction in a whole sheet of plain muscle.

(c) *The Contraction of Muscle*

Muscles, both striped and plain, may respond to a single impulse in the excitatory nerve by a contraction, which is at once followed by extension. This is the muscle *twitch* (Fig. 146). The period of the twitch is very different in the different types of muscle. It is shortest in striped muscle—in vertebrate striped muscle the whole twitch may be over in about 0·1 sec. In plain muscle the twitch may last from 0·5 sec. to more than 1 minute. When a contraction of a muscle of any type is recorded on a drum or other apparatus, a latent interval after the nerve impulse reaches the muscle is observed before the contraction starts (Fig. 146). When striped muscle is used, most of this apparent latent interval is due to sluggishness of the apparatus in recording the contraction and is therefore not a true latent period of the muscle. But a true latent period occurs in all muscle. This period is very short in striped muscle (0·0005–0·002 sec. in vertebrate striped muscle). It is much longer (0·2–2 sec.) in plain muscle.

If a muscle is stimulated by a train of impulses succeeding each other at short intervals, the contractions produced by the impulses fuse, and the muscle remains contracted throughout the period of stimulation. It extends very shortly after the stimulation ceases. Such a contraction is known as a *tetanus* (Fig. 147). The contraction during a tetanus is stronger than the maximum contraction of a twitch. We have already met, in the sphincter of a sea-anemone (Fig. 113, p. 246), an example of this fusion of the contractions in a muscle stimulated by a train of impulses. Since the natural stimulation of a muscle in the body is almost always by a train of impulses, and not by a single impulse (p. 242), the natural response of a muscle is a tetanus.

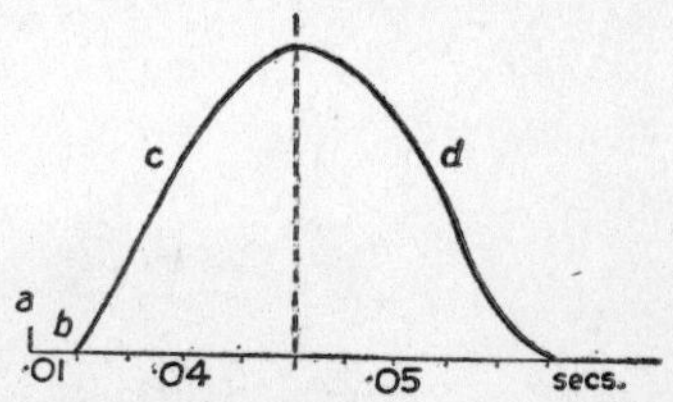

Figure 146. Diagram of a muscle twitch in vertebrate striped muscle. *a*, arrival of the stimulus; *b*, apparent latent period; *c*, contraction; *d*, relaxation.

The maximum interval between the impulses of a train which will produce a tetanus varies with the period of the twitch. The impulses must succeed one another at intervals which are considerably less than the period of the twitch, and the fusion of the contractions is more perfect the shorter the intervals between the impulses, until a minimum interval is reached. This minimum interval is determined by the *refractory period* of the muscle. This is a short period after the arrival of an impulse during which the muscle is insensitive to stimulation. Its length is about 0·005 sec. for vertebrate striped muscle and longer for other types of muscle.

In natural stimulation of a muscle within the body, the impulses pass down the excitatory nerves at intervals which vary greatly with the animal and the nature of the muscle. In the excitatory nerves of vertebrate muscle the impulses pass at 50–100 per second; in those of insects the rate is more variable but is frequently about 50 a second. The impulses which stimulate plain muscle are at longer intervals, and the intervals are often irregular.

(d) *Neuro-muscular Facilitation*

We saw (Fig. 113 and p. 246) in the sphincter of a sea-anemone that a muscle, which would respond to a single impulse with at most a very small contraction, might give strong contractions in response to each of the later impulses of a train, although these were identical with the earlier impulses. It appeared that the arrival of each impulse at the muscle increased the sensitivity of the muscle to another, subsequent impulse. This phenomenon we called *neuro-muscular facilitation.* It is very well developed in plain muscle and in arthropod, striped muscle, and it can be observed in all types of muscle, even in vertebrate striped muscle. It must be distinguished from the fusion of the total contraction of the muscle during a train of impulses which gives a tetanus.

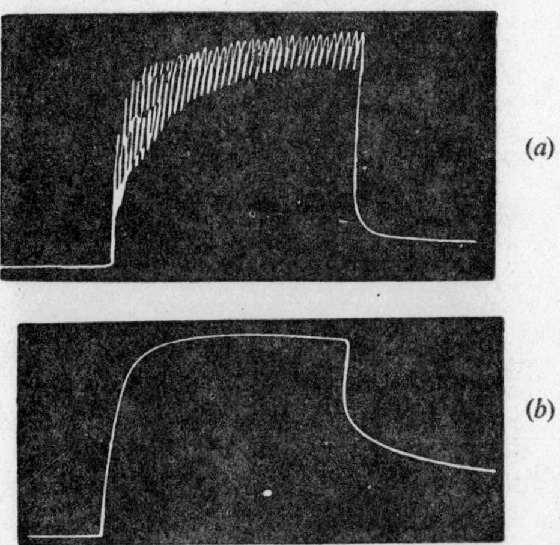

Figure 147. Fusion of muscle twitches to give a tetanus. *a*, incomplete, *b*, complete tetanus. (From Stempel and Koch.)

(e) *Excitation and Inhibition*

Excitatory nerve impulses increase the activity of muscle in either one or other of two ways. They may initiate contraction, which may be of any of the types we have discussed, or, in rhythmically contracting muscles (*e.g.* heart muscle), they increase the rate of the rhythm and the force of the contraction. Under inhibitory stimulation, a heart beats more slowly and weakly, muscles in tonic contraction (p. 301) relax, and muscles contract less strongly in response to stimulation of the excitatory nerves. The manner in which these various inhibitory effects are brought about is in general not well understood. It is believed that most of them are due to changes in the contractile tissue itself but these changes are certainly not of the same kind in all types of inhibition. In the striated muscles of the arthropods, which all possess inhibitory as well as excitatory nerves, inhibition plays a large part in the control of the contraction. It is probably by interplay between inhibitory and excitatory stimulation that arthropod muscles are able to give contractions finely graded in strength in spite of the fact that the whole of the fibres of a muscle may be supplied by a single excitatory and a single inhibitory axon (p. 296). We shall discuss how these effects are brought about, for they give us a good example of the interaction of inhibitory and excitatory stimulation in muscle. But it should be realised that the special type of inhibition shown by arthropod muscle is probably peculiar to that type of muscle.

The following results were obtained with the flexor and extensor muscles of the terminal segment of a crab's leg (*Carcinus*). These are typical arthropod striated muscles with both excitatory and inhibitory nerve fibres. Both types of fibre lie in the same nerve supplying the muscle. We will first consider the behaviour of muscle when separated from the body and set up with its nerve in a recording apparatus.

(1) These muscles show very strongly developed facilitation (p. 242). The muscle contracts hardly at all to a single impulse (caused by stimulation of the nerve by an electric shock), but contracts more and more strongly to each successive impulse of a train. As is usual in facilitation (*cf.* Fig. 113, p. 246), the increase in the contraction becomes more rapid as the interval between the impulses is reduced, until the refractory period of the muscle is reached. In this muscle the facilitation increases until the frequency reaches 150–300 a second.

(2) If the nerve is stimulated with shocks in short trains of the same length and frequency (*e.g.* 50 shocks per second for 4 seconds), and the strength of the shocks in each train is gradually increased, the contraction at first increases rapidly to a maximum, when all the muscle fibres are presumably contracting (Fig. 149). As the strength of the shocks is further increased, the contraction is unaltered for a time. This is to be expected if the all-or-none character of nervous conduction holds—a stronger shock cannot initiate a stronger impulse in a nerve. But with further increase in the strength of the shock, the contraction *decreases* in size and may disappear completely. Finally, with very strong shocks, the contraction reappears and is then more rapid than it was before.

These various effects have been explained on the ground that the nerve contains both excitatory and inhibitory fibres. The contractions caused by the weaker shocks (Fig. 149, left) are due to stimulation of the excitatory fibres. The inhibitory fibres have a higher threshold for stimulation and are only stimulated by stronger shocks. When these inhibitory fibres are stimulated, the muscle fails to respond to the impulses still reaching it through the excitatory fibres. The contraction therefore ceases (Fig. 149, centre). The strong and rapid contraction after very strong shocks (Fig. 149, right) are probably the results of experimental deficiencies. These strong shocks are very far above the threshold strength for the excitatory fibres and each shock probably initiates more than one impulse in the fibres, so that the muscle is in fact being stimulated with excitatory impulses at a more rapid rate. This high frequency produces a very strong contraction which the inhibitory impulses are unable to inhibit.

(3) It is believed that the inhibitory impulses act by decreasing the rate of facilitation in the muscle, so that the increase in the size of the

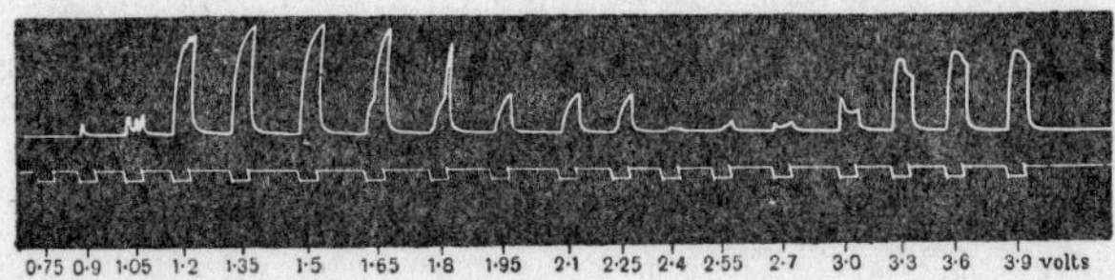

Figure 148. Responses of a crab's muscle to short trains of electrical stimuli of increasing voltage.

The lower marker gives the periods of stimulation (each 4 secs.). The drum was stopped after each stimulation. (After Pantin.)

contraction during a train of shocks is less during inhibitory stimulation. If this is so, a short train of impulses will produce a large contraction when the inhibitory nerve is not stimulated, and a smaller contraction or none at all when the nerve is stimulated. This is what is shown in Fig. 149. When the frequency is increased, there is much more rapid facilitation, which cannot be inhibited. This has been shown to be so in other experiments, and explains the strong and rapid contractions of the right-hand side of Fig. 149.

(4) Thus, under the experimental conditions, the speed and strength of the contractions of the muscle are controlled by these varying combinations of excitatory and inhibitory stimulation. But conditions in the body differ from those of the experiments. One such difference is of importance to us when we try to understand the control of the muscle in the body. An excised muscle receives no impulses from its nerves until the nerve is stimulated, but it has been shown to be probable that in the body all the muscles are continuously being stimulated by low-frequency excitatory impulses, so that they are always in slight tonic contraction. It can be shown that during low-frequency stimulation of this kind a few impulses at a higher frequency added to the continuous stimulation produce at once a strong contraction, and this is maintained by the low-frequency stimulation after the impulses at the higher frequency have ceased. This contraction can be abolished by (and only by) stimulation of the

inhibitory nerve. This is probably the manner in which the complex nerve supply of these muscles acts in the life of the animal. Contraction is produced by a few high-frequency impulses superimposed on the continuous low-frequency stimulation, and this contraction is abolished by inhibitory impulses. The strength of the contraction will vary with the number and frequency of excitatory impulses which stimulate the contraction.

Whether these views of the control of the contraction in arthropod muscle are correct in detail or not, it is clear that the control is very different from that of vertebrate striped muscle, where the strength of the contraction is controlled by the proportion of the fibres excited, and the fibres return to inactivity when the excitatory stimuli cease. Also, it must not be assumed that the contraction of other invertebrate striped muscle is controlled in the same way as these crab muscles. We know very little of the control of contraction in most invertebrate muscle. Indeed, we do not know that these views, even if they are true of the crustacean muscles used in these experiments, are true of all arthropod muscles. In some arthropod muscles the control is perhaps even more complex than that we have discussed. Thus, some crustacean muscles are said to have more than one type of excitatory nerve fibres, each of which produces a different type of contraction.*

(f) *Tonic Contraction*

Both striped and plain muscle may remain for long periods in a state of partial contraction. This is called *tonic contraction*, and the extent of the contraction is called the *tone* of the muscle.

Tonic contraction occurs in many types of muscle. Examples are: (1) the muscles that hold the spines of sea-urchins in fixed positions for long periods (p. 245); (2) muscles which control the pressure in spaces filled with liquid in a body, such as the bladder of the higher vertebrates or the body-cavity of the annelids; within limits the pressure is kept constant whatever the volume of liquid in the space, the muscles varying in length and therefore in tone; (3) the plain muscle which holds the shell of a lamellibranch (*e.g. Pecten or Mytilus*) closed; in *Pecten* there are two closing muscles, one striped which closes the shell by a sudden and rapid contraction, and the other plain which holds it shut; an enormous tension is needed to open the shell against the tonic contraction of this muscle.

Tonic contraction has been interpreted in two very different ways. Some have believed that they are tetani (p. 297), initiated and maintained by nervous stimulation. Others have thought that they are of

* *Cf.* Wiersma, *Ann. Rev. Physiol.*, **14**, 159, 1952; Pantin, *Brit. Med. Bull.* **12**, 199, 1956.

a fundamentally different nature from the normal contraction of muscle.

The first view has been held for many years of the tonic contractions of vertebrate muscle, but until recently the second view was generally held of invertebrate muscle, and it was adopted in the earlier editions of this book. It was thought that in tonic contraction the muscle passes into a highly viscous, more or less solid, state so that it is able to withstand a very large pull tending to lengthen it. This was thought to be supported by the fact that no release of energy in the form of heat could be observed during tonic contraction. Muscles in tonic contraction were also found to differ from other muscles in that after stretching they did not regain their original length elastically as other muscles do.

It is now thought that the difference in elasticity is due to changes in the connective-tissue sheath (*sarcolemma*) round the muscle fibres and not to the contractile mechanism itself; the sheath is believed to be more or less permanently deformed when stretched during tonic contraction, and is unable to regain its original form. Further, it has now been shown* that the adductor muscle of *Mytilus* receives continuous nervous stimulation during tonic contraction, and that there is some, small, release of heat.

Thus, it seems that these and probably all tonic contractions should be regarded as tetani. In some ways they differ from the tetani of striped muscle. The tetani of tonic contractions, being usually in slowly contracting smooth muscle, are maintained by far less frequent nervous impulses than are needed for the tetani of striped muscle—*Mytilus* adductor muscle goes into tetanus with impulses at a rate of 2 per sec.; and inhibitory nervous stimulation occurs at the end of the tonic contraction in *Mytilus* and probably other invertebrates. Also, much less heat is produced during the tonic contraction than in a tetanus of striped muscle. In addition, there are some phenomena in tonic contraction that have not yet found any interpretation on the tetanus theory, but at present there seems no reason to assume that the contractile mechanism of tonic contraction is fundamentally different from that of a twitch.

(g) *Myogenic Rhythms*

In some muscles repeated rhythmical contractions occur that are not controlled by the arrival of nerve impulses but by conditions within the muscle itself or near it. These are called *myogenic rhythms* (p. 243). The muscle of the vertebrate heart gives an example of this; the beat may continue in ventricular muscle separated from its nerve

* J. Lowy, *J. Physiol.*, **120**, 129, 1953; B. C. Abbott and J. Lowy, *idem*, **130** 25P, 1955.

supply. At least two examples occur in insects, the rhythms of the indirect wing muscles of some Diptera and other groups, and of the tymbal muscles of the sound-producing organs of the cicadas (Hemiptera). These control the vibration of the tymbal and so produce sound.

The indirect wing muscles cause the movements of the wings by deforming the shape of the cuticle of the thorax to which the wings are attached. They contract for each up and down movement of the wings. The tymbal muscle is attached to the tymbal and contracts for each in and out movement in its vibration. But both types of muscle, when removed from their attachments, go into tetanus when they receive impulses at much slower rates (10–20 per sec. for the flight muscle and about 30 per sec. for the tymbal muscle) than the rhythms of their normal contractions (up to 1000 per sec. for the flight muscle and 200–400 per sec. for the tymbal muscle).

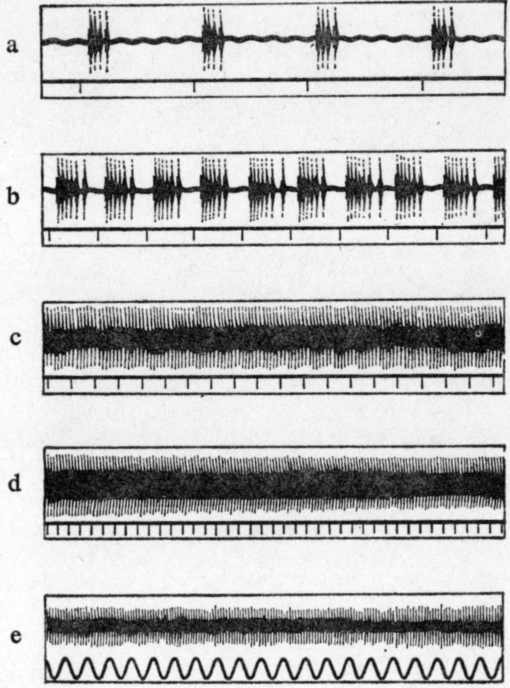

Figure 149. Response of the tymbal muscle of a cicada, *Platypleura capitata*, to stimulation at various frequencies

a, 9·5/sec; b, 22·5/sec; c, 47/sec; d, 97/sec; e, free song of this species from a tape-recording. Time-marker, 50/sec. below e. (After Pringle.)

In the tymbal muscle it has been shown* that the explanation is as follows. Each nerve impulse that reaches the muscle in its normal position in the body is followed by not one but a short series of contractions (Fig. 148 *a, b*; 4–6 contractions in this species), and that when the impulses are frequent enough (about 100 per sec.) these bursts fuse to give an even rhythm at the more rapid rate, which is also the normal rate of contraction in the production of sound (Fig. 148, *c–e*). It is believed that the repeated contractions in each burst are stimulated by the movements of the tymbal. When a nerve impulse reaches the muscle, it contracts and draws the tymbal inwards. When the tension on the tymbal becomes great enough, it clicks inwards as the lid of a tin may do when pressed and then proceeds to vibrate in and out at its natural frequency. Each time it moves inwards the muscle is deactivated by the release of the tension; it is stimulated to contract again when it is stretched by the next outward movement. Thus the nerve impulses initiate the rhythm by causing the initial contraction, and maintain it as long as they continue by initiating new bursts; the frequency of contraction is controlled by the vibration of the tymbal. The note of the sound is 4–5000 per sec., still more rapid than the main vibration of the tymbal. It is due to small secondary vibrations.

The contraction of the flight muscles of Diptera are probably controlled in a similar way by vibrations of the cuticle of the thorax.

5. PIGMENTARY EFFECTOR ORGANS

Most animals are pigmented over at least a part of their bodies. The greater part of this pigmentation is permanent and unchangeable during the animal's life; the animal has no power of modifying its colour. This permanent coloration is brought about in several different ways. Much of it is due to coloured substances deposited in various parts of the body, often in solid secretions such as the cuticle; or these solid secretions may possess minute structure which gives colour to reflected light by diffraction, interference or other physical means. Most of the pigmentation of insects is produced in these ways. Other pigmentation may be due to coloured substances of physiological importance present in the tissues, *e.g.* the green pigment of chlorophyll in many Protista, the red pigment of eye-spots and the various colours of the respiratory pigments. Or, again, coloration may be due to pigments derived from the food. Some insect larvæ are green or brown from this cause.

In this section we are concerned not with the permanent pigmentation of animals but with those cases in which animals are able to alter

* J. W. S. Pringle, *J. exp. Biol.*, **31**, 525, 1954.

the pigmentation of their bodies by control exerted through their co-ordinating systems. Organs which so control the colour of the body are known as *pigmentary effector organs*. Such organs occur in the Crustacea, insects and molluscs among the invertebrates, and in the vertebrates. They are of two distinct types.

(1) *Pigment cells*, typically branched cells which contain pigment granules and lie among the tissues. In these cells the granules can either be collected in the central body of the cell or spread throughout the branches (Fig. 150). When the pigment is collected in the central part of the cell, it covers a small area and is much less effective in producing colour in the body than when it is spread diffusely in the

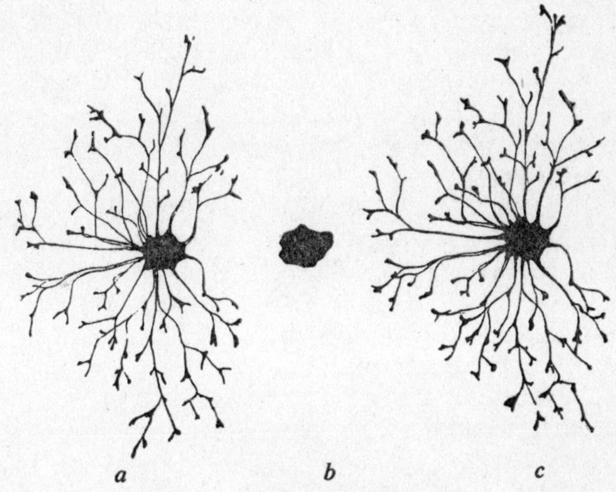

Figure 150. Expanded and contracted conditions of a pigment cell of *Macromysis*.

a, *b*, *c*, are three successive conditions of the cell; they show the similarity in the shape of the processes in two expansions. (After Degner.)

branches of the cell. The animal appears pale when the pigment is collected and coloured when it is diffuse. It has been disputed whether the pigment spreads in preformed branches of the cell, or whether the cell itself expands by putting out pseudopodia. The former alternative is more probably correct. Pigment cells have been observed in successive expansions of the pigment and it has been found that even when the branches are very complex the pigment cell in the expanded condition has exactly the same form in successive expansions (Fig. 150). Though this does not disprove the theory that the branches of the cell are active pseudopodia, it makes it unlikely.

In the vertebrates the pigmentary effector cells are usually arranged as separate branched cells scattered through the tissues. The arrangement of the pigment cells in the invertebrates varies. In *Dixippus*, the stick-insect, which has typical power of controlling the colour of its body, the pigment is carried by the ectodermal cells. The pigment cells are exceptional in not being branched; the pigment either collects in clumps in their protoplasm or is spread diffusely through the cell. In the Crustacea the pigment cells are branched cells much like those of the vertebrates, but they are often collected into multicellular pigmentary effector organs. These may be as much as 2 mm. across when expanded. They occur not only in the skin but also around internal organs such as the alimentary canal. Several groups of the Malacostraca possess them.

(2) To the second type of the pigmentary effector organs of the invertebrates the muscular organs of the Mollusca (Gastropoda and Cephalopoda) belong. In these organs the pigment is contained in a round cell which is surrounded by radial fibres of smooth muscle (Plate XIII, Fig. 151). By the contraction of these fibres the pigment cell is drawn out from a spherical shape to a thin disc, and the pigment is thus spread.

The pigment granules in the pigmentary effector cells may be of various colours. Often pigment cells of two or three different colours occur in the same animal but the one cell does not contain pigment granules of more than one colour. In the octopus, for instance, the pigment is red-brown and yellow, and in the squid, *Loligo*, there are pigment cells of three colours, red-brown, violet, and yellow. In the Crustacea the colours are equally various. In the shrimps *Crangon* and *Hippolyte* there are three pigment colours, in *Crangon* dark brown, reddish yellow, and white and in *Hippolyte* red, yellow, and blue. By different expansions of the cells of these three colours many different shades of coloration are produced. The white colour is obtained by reflection from the surfaces of numerous minute crystals within the cell.

Pigment cells are sometimes sensitive to some extent to direct stimulation by incident light. In such responses they are outside the co-ordinating system of the body, but in all other responses they are controlled by that system. This control may be directly through nerves, or through the internal medium by chemical co-ordination. Nervous control can usually be recognised by the rapidity with which the response follows stimulation—a response will follow in a very few seconds—whereas if the co-ordination is chemical the response may not be complete in an hour, though it often takes less. The only invertebrate pigmentary effector organs controlled directly by nerves are the muscular organs of the Mollusca. These are always under nervous control, but there is evidence of chemical control in addition in the cephalopods. In insects and Crustacea the control is chemical.

We have already discussed the manner in which it is brought about (ch. XVI, p. 266). It must be remembered, however, that even though the immediate control of the pigmentary effector organ is chemical, the ultimate control is nervous, for the endocrine organ responsible for the chemical co-ordination is itself controlled by the nervous system. In all pigmentary effector systems, except when the cell responds directly to incident light, the stimulus is received by the eye and thence passed to the pigment organs through nerves alone or through both the nervous and endocrine systems.

The stimuli which cause colour-change in animals are various. It is natural that the most usual stimulus is the amount and colour of the light reaching the body (*cf.* pp. 266, 289). Many Crustacea go dark on a black background and light on a white background (*Crangon*, *Hippolyte*, *Mysis*, etc.). *Crangon* also reacts to colours in the background. There is frequently also a reaction to the total amount of light in the environment. Many animals are dark at night and pale during the day, but *Crangon* is an exception, being pale at night. This day and night rhythm is sometimes fixed in the animal and will continue although the animal is kept permanently in the dark. The amphipod *Idothea* has been found to go light and dark rhythmically for 60 days when kept in the dark. Many other stimuli may produce colour change. *Dixippus* reacts to light, temperature and humidity. Tactile stimuli may also control colour-change. The octopus becomes dark grey on a stony surface and light on a smooth surface. Almost any stimulation, such as disturbance, the presence of food and so on, will produce a sudden colour change in this animal. Some of these responses, such as those to the colour of the background, are clearly adaptive and of value to the animal; it is difficult to see the value of many others.

6. ORGANS FOR THE PRODUCTION OF LIGHT

The power of producing light is widespread among animals. It occurs in many Protista (Sarcodina and Dinoflagellata) and in members of most of the larger groups of the invertebrate Metazoa. Among the Metazoa the larger number of luminous forms belong to the Cœlenterata, Annelida, Crustacea, Insecta, Mollusca (especially Cephalopoda), and Tunicata (*Pyrosoma*), but occasional luminous forms are scattered through other groups. Many fishes, some bacteria and some fungi are luminous. The power of producing light is therefore an adaptation which has very frequently been evolved in animals.

The light is given out from granules or globules which are formed in the protoplasm. In some animals these particles give out light while they are still contained in the cells within the body; in others they become luminous only after they have been thrown out of the cells in a secretion. Bacteria, fungi, and some fishes luminesce continuously; in all other organisms the luminescence is intermittent and occurs either when the animal is stimulated in some way, or rhythmically, without stimulation. In those Metazoa which possess a central nervous system, intermittent luminescence is under the control of that system. Environmental conditions may modify the animal's capacity to luminesce. Daylight, for instance, often has an inhibiting effect, so that the animals luminesce much more readily at night.

The structure of the luminous organs is various. In Protista, such as *Noctiluca* (Dinoflagellata), the luminous granules are scattered through the protoplasm of the cells and there are no luminous organs of larger size than these granules. In the Metazoa the simplest luminous organs are ectodermal glands which secrete a luminous secretion over the surface of the body—*Cavernularia* (a pennatulid), *Chætopterus* (Polychæta), *Cypridina* (Ostracoda), *Pholas* (Lamellibranchiata). But in many Cephalopoda, Crustacea, and Insecta the luminous organs are complex structures, provided with accessory organs such as lenses and reflecting layers (Plate XIII, Fig. 152). In these organs the light is produced in cells within the organ and not in a secretion.

The light produced by animals is accompanied by hardly any energy of other types. There is, so far as we can measure, no heat associated with the light, and by far the greater part, if not all, of the light is within the visible spectrum. In these respects the luminous organs differ greatly from such artificial sources of light as the arc lamp and the electric filament lamp, in which not more than a small proportion of the energy given out is in the form of visible light (1·5 per cent. for the filament lamp and about 4 per cent. for the arc lamp). In its physical characters animal light resembles chemical phosphorescence such as that of phosphorus much more closely than it does the incandescence of hot bodies.

Although it lies almost entirely within the visible range, the spectrum of animal light is variable. It may cover a wide or narrow band within that range and the wave-length of the maximum illumination may be at almost any point in the range. As a result of this, the colour of the light is variable. Yellow or white lights are the commonest, but red, green, and blue lights occur. In some animals light of more than one colour is given out by different luminous organs.

Investigation of the chemical nature of animal light has been largely restricted to the light of the lamellibranch *Pholas* and that of the ostracod *Cypridina*, and it is to these two animals that the following results particularly refer. It is probable, however, that the means by which light is produced is similar in all organisms.

The production of light in the luminous organs of animals requires (1) water—dried tissues do not luminesce—and (2) oxygen. Light-production is therefore due to an oxidative process. But a low pressure of oxygen is often sufficient for production of the light—7 per cent. of oxygen in the air has been found sufficient for the light-production of *Cypridina*.

Since the production is due to a chemical reaction, it is not surprising that the physical nature of the light resembles that of light produced by other chemical reactions.

It has been shown that in both *Pholas* and *Cypridina* the light is produced during the oxidation of a substance *luciferin* in the presence of an enzyme *luciferase*. Neither of these is identical in different animals, though they are probably similar in chemical nature in all animals. Luciferin can be extracted with hot water (60–70° C.), which destroys the luciferase. Such an extract does not luminesce. Luciferase is present in a cold-water extract. If the latter extract is kept until all its luciferin—which is also present in it—is oxidised, and its luminescence ceases, and if some of the former extract is now added to it, the luminescence reappears, for more luciferin has been added.

Oxidised luciferin (*oxyluciferin*) can be again reduced to luciferin by various chemical means (H_2S, nascent hydrogen, etc.) or by the reducing enzymes which are present in tissue extracts. If the luciferin so formed is added to luciferase, luminescence is again obtained. *Pholas* luciferin but not *Cypridina* luciferin can be oxidised by other means besides luciferase. $KMnO_4$, H_2O_2 and other oxidising agents produce the oxidation and with it the production of luminescence.

Luciferase, being an enzyme, is a protein. Luciferin is probably also a protein, but it dialyses slowly and its molecular size is therefore not large for a protein.

Thus, animal luminescence is produced by a biochemical reaction which is catalysed by an enzyme. The luminescence is almost always under the control of the nervous system but we do not know the means by which a nervous impulse produces the oxidation of the luciferin and so the production of light. It might do so by bringing together the luciferin and luciferase, if these were previously separated in the cell, or by allowing oxygen to reach the luciferin. Perhaps the means by which the nervous control is exerted is not the same in all organisms.

The biological value of luminescence to the luminous animal is very often obscure. We cannot see how luminescence can be of any value to a large number of the animals which luminesce (Protista, many planktonic animals). This is also true of the luminous bacteria and fungi. Yet it is hard to believe that the power of luminescence could have been evolved in so many organisms if it was of no value. The problem is unsolved. On the other hand, there is no doubt that some animals use the power of producing light for purposes which are clearly of advantage in their life. In some it is used as a sex-signal, to attract members of the opposite sex (fireflies, glow-worms, probably some deep-sea forms, etc.); bright luminescence probably has protective value for some animals, serving to disturb and frighten a predacious enemy; and some of the more complex and efficient luminous organs may perhaps have value as lanterns, enabling an animal in a dark environment to recognise objects in its neighbourhood, *e.g.* the organs of deep-sea Cephalopoda and Crustacea.

CHAPTER XIX

THE PHYSIOLOGY OF THE SPONGES

THE sponges (Parazoa) are multicellular animals, but the whole organisation of their bodies is so different from that of the bodies of other multicellular animals (Metazoa) that it is convenient to consider their physiology separately. Sponges differ radically from the Metazoa in the much smaller number of types into which the cells are differentiated, in the absence of protoplasmic bridges between the cells, in the presence of collar-cells or *choanocytes* (which occur in all sponges but in no metazoans) and in the absence of a nervous system. Their embryology is also very different from that of any of the Metazoa.

Nevertheless, the sponge is as definitely an organism (p. 3) as the metazoan is. During its life the sponge behaves as an efficient member of the animal kingdom; it has a physiology which maintains its life, a simple, but none the less definite, type of behaviour, and it has the power of reproduction. The sponge also has a definite specific form, though the form may not be as strictly controlled as those of many animals, and this form is regained by regeneration when it has been damaged. In all these characters the sponge shows itself to be an organism. It is, however, an organism with a much simpler organisation than most of the metazoans.

The characteristic feature of the activity of the sponge is the feeding current on which its life depends. This current is driven by the beat of the flagella of the collar-cells. In a typical but simple sponge the current has the following course (Figs. 153, 154). It enters the body by very numerous small openings (*ostia*) scattered over the surface. From these openings it passes through *inhalant canals* to cavities lined by the collar-cells (*flagellate chambers*), entering these cavities through minute pores in their walls, and thence to a large central cavity (*paragaster*). The paragaster opens to the exterior by a large opening (*osculum*), by which the current leaves the body. The arrangement of the parts through which the current flows differs greatly in the various types of sponge. In the simplest forms there are no ostia or inhalant canals and the current enters directly into the flagellate chambers through the pores. In more complicated sponges the current passes out of as well as into the flagellate chambers through a system of canals. These are called the *exhalant canals*. Also, the parts are very often multiplied; large sponges may have numerous paragasters and oscula.

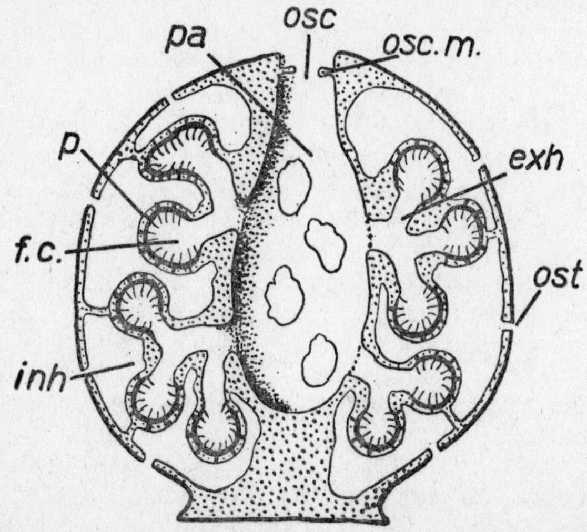

Figure 153. General diagram of the structure of a sponge.

ost, ostium; *fc*, flagellate chambers; *pa*, paragaster; *osc*, osculum; *osc. m.*, oscular membrane; *inh*, inhalant canals; *exh*, exhalant canals; *p*. porc.

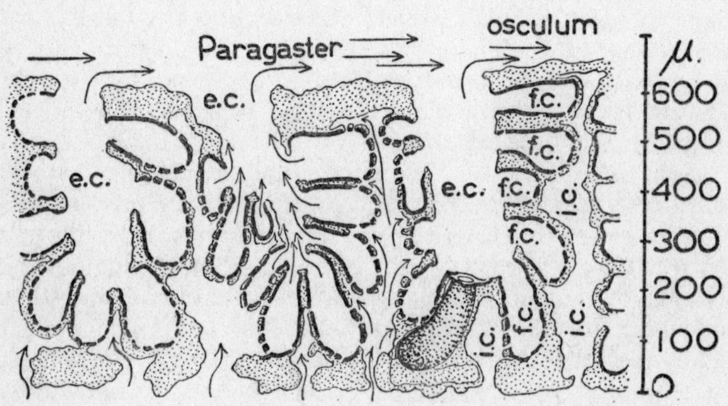

Figure 154. Diagram of part of the wall of a sponge.

The arrows show the direction of the feeding current. *i.c.*, inhalant canals; *e.c.*, exhalant canals; *f.c.*, flagellate chambers. (After Bidder.)

The physiology of the feeding current is similar in all sponges. The current is always driven by the beat of the flagella of the collar-cells. It always enters the flagellate chambers through the pores in their walls, whether these are on the surface or enclosed in inhalant canals. These pores pass through the substance of cells which surround them—the *porocytes*. They are thus intracellular and can be closed by the contraction of the porocytes. The flagella beat continuously during the life of the sponge, and the speed of the current is not normally controlled during the healthy life of the sponge by variations in their activity. However, the activity of the beat may vary with the health and other physiological conditions of the collar-cells. During normal life the current is controlled in two ways, by contraction and expansion of the porocytes or of a membrane just within the osculum. This membrane lies across the osculum in many, but not all, sponges, and has a central opening which can be closed. Both these reactions are slow: they may be complete in 7–10 minutes.

A diagram of a small part of the wall of a flagellate chamber is shown in Fig. 155. The water is drawn through the pores and along the length of the collar-cells by the pressure set up by the beat of their flagella. As the water passes through the chamber, food particles in it are thrown, by vortical currents set up by the beat of the flagella, within the collars of the collar-cells, and adhere to them. They are then ingested by the collar-cells, which are therefore the feeding organs of the sponge as well as the means by which the current is driven. The digested food is probably distributed through the tissues by wandering cells, *amœbocytes*, which take it up from the collar-cells. Excretory material is passed into the current by the collar-cells.

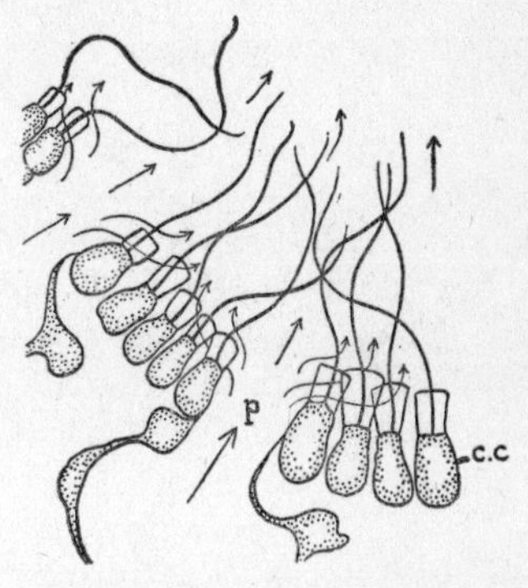

Figure 155. Part of the wall of a flagellate chamber.

One pore (*P*) and part of another is shown. *c.c*, collar-cells. (After Bidder.)

The feeding current of a sponge gives us a good opportunity for investigating the results produced by flagellar beat. If we are to form a sound conception of the physical results of this type of activity, the small scale of the effective organs, the flagella, must be realised. The flagellum of a collar-cell is about 60μ long and its diameter is about 0·3μ. Its beat is rapid—about 20 beats to a second. Under the microscope the parts of a flagellum appear to be moving rapidly through the water. This is, however, not so in fact. The tip of a flagellum may move, perhaps, 30μ from one side to the other in each beat, or 60μ in a complete beat. The tip is therefore moving at about 1·2 mm. a second, a very slow rate. Other parts of the flagellum are moving still more slowly. The appearance of rapid movement under the microscope is due to the fact that the microscope magnifies the linear dimensions of an object in the field of view, but does not magnify the time taken by any change. It therefore magnifies the rate of movement. This will apply equally to all types of movement seen under the microscope. It is not probable that any flagella or cilia move at rates much greater than those of the flagella of collar-cells.

A second result of the small scale of the flagella is that the water behaves to them—and to any objects on the same scale of size—as if it were a much more viscous fluid than water is in our normal experience. We see this if we watch a particle struck by a flagellum as it is stopped by the frictional resistance of the water; it appears to be moving through a very viscous fluid. This is because the frictional resistance varies with the area of the surface of a moving body, and the proportion of the surface to the mass increases as the size is reduced (p. 48). Frictional forces have much greater effect on the movement of microscopic particles than on that of larger bodies.

We must think, then, of the propulsive force of the flagellum as exerted by very slow movement of the lash through what is effectively a viscous fluid. The slowness of the beat will mean that the force exerted by each flagellum will be small, but the high viscosity will result in this force being transferred to the water with little loss.

The feeding current of a sponge is driven by an enormous number of flagella, and these together develop considerable energy. By this energy a considerable mass of water is passed through the body of the sponge. It has been found that a volume of water equal to the volume of the sponge may be ejected from an osculum every minute. But the pressure exerted by the flagella is not summated as the energy they produce is. The pressure at which the current is driven is equal to that produced in each flagellate chamber and is therefore small. This pressure has been measured by tying a glass tube into the osculum of a sponge and raising the tube above the surface of the water in which the sponge is living. The pressure produced by the flagella can then be observed by noting how far the water is driven up the tube above the general surface of the surrounding water. The pressure is found to vary between 1 and 4 mm. of water. This is of general interest since it gives us a direct measure of the pressure likely to be set up by flagella—or cilia—in an efficient system. It is not likely that any ciliated organ will produce a much greater pressure than this.

The speed of the feeding current through the sponge varies inversely with the sectional area of the space through which it is passing; it is greatest where the section is smallest, in narrow spaces, and least where the space is wide. The area of the osculum, through which all the water has to pass, is much less than the sum of the areas of the flagellate chambers or of any other part of the system. The speed is therefore greatest at the osculum. A speed of 2·5 cm. a second at the osculum has been observed in one sponge (*Leucandra*). In this sponge it has been calculated that the total sectional area of the flagellate chambers is 1,700 times that of the osculum, and that the speed of the current past the collar-cells is not more than 50μ a second. This speed is slow enough to allow even the very slow movement of the flagella in their beat to exert its full pressure on the water.

Thus, we may regard the sponge as an organism of which the chief activity is to act as a pump, passing through its body a current of water, of considerable volume but at low pressure. By means of this current all the exchanges between the sponge and the external medium are maintained. Food and oxygen are brought into the body and excreta carried out.

The absence of a nervous system in the sponges prevents any co-ordinated actions of the whole sponge body. The sponge does not move; it does not even react to stimulation by alterations of shape, such as those of bending. Nevertheless, responses to stimulation occur in the sponges—the feeding current may be stopped as we have seen, and the tissues may contract, *e.g.* when they are taken out of water. Since the sponge has no nervous system, we have to ask whether these responses are co-ordinated in any other way, and how such co-ordination, if it exists, is brought about.

Most of the responses of the parts of a sponge body are not co-ordinated by any co-ordinating system within the tissues. The parts respond independently, and their independent responses together build up the behaviour of the sponge. Each organ is both a receptor organ and an effector organ (*cf.* p. 269). This behaviour is usually adapted to the needs of the sponge, but it is so not because it is co-ordinated into a single whole, as the behaviour of the more complex Metazoa is by the control of the central nervous system, but because the behaviour of each part of the body is itself separately so adapted. For instance, the closing of each pore when the sponge is unfavourably stimulated, *e.g.* by the presence of some harmful chemical in the water, is due to direct stimulation of the porocyte which surrounds the pore. Closing of all the pores in the body of the sponge at the same time results in cessation of the feeding current, a result which will usually be of advantage to the sponge in these circumstances. In the simpler Metazoa that have no central nervous system (cœlenterates, echinoderms) there is much independent behaviour of the parts similar to that which occurs in the sponge body. We shall discuss this subject again in ch. XXI.

Similarly, the closing of the oscular membrane is probably due to local stimulation of the cells which form the membrane and close it by contraction.

This has been shown by experiment. The experiments were carried out on a sponge with finger-shaped branches, each with an osculum at the tip (*Stylotella*). The osculum remains open when the water around the sponge is moving and closes when the water is still. If a sponge was placed in an open tube so arranged that all the body except a small region in the neighbourhood of the osculum was exposed to stimulation by currents in the surrounding water (Fig. 156), the osculum was found to close. When, on the other hand, the oscular region alone was exposed and all the rest of the body was protected, the osculum remained open. Since there is no evidence of any cells specially sensitive to stimulation in the oscular region or indeed in any other part of the body, we can only conclude that the contractile cells of the membrane are themselves stimulated by movement of water over them and contract when this stimulation is absent. In any event, the closing of the osculum is clearly due solely to stimulation of this part of the body of the sponge.

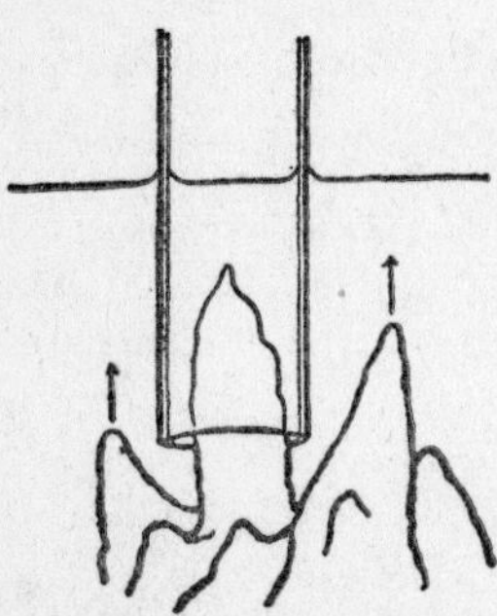

Figure 156. (After Parker.) Reactions of the osculum in *Stylotella*.

Conduction of stimulation does, however, occur in the sponge body under certain circumstances. The osculum at the end of a finger-shaped sponge closes when a small part containing it is cut off from the end of the body of the sponge. The same reaction occurs if the sponge is damaged by a prick a short distance (1–1$\frac{3}{4}$ cm.) from the osculum. These reactions are not due to stimulation of the osculum by substances escaping from the damaged tissues and carried to the osculum in the feeding current or diffusing to it through the surrounding water. This is proved by the observation that the juice of crushed sponge tissue introduced into the feeding current of a normal sponge does not cause the osculum to close. The reaction must be due to conduction of some kind through the tissues of the sponge between the site of the damage and the osculum. We do not know the nature of the stimulus which is conducted in this way. Such conduction through tissues can be shown to occur in the bodies of more complex animals (p. 261), but in them it plays only a subordinate part in conduction.

The sponge body shows adaptations to the conditions of its life in many features besides its responses to stimulation. Very perfect adaptation is shown in the correlation between the form of the body and the characters of the feeding current. If this current is to be effective as a source of food and oxygen and as a means of removing excreta, it is necessary that water which has been ejected at an osculum should not again enter the body through the ostia. For a round-bodied sponge such as a bath-sponge, this will be best provided for if the water ejected from the osculum is thrown as far as possible from the osculum (Fig. 157). The distance to which the jet of water from the osculum will travel varies with its velocity and its diameter. If the osculum is small, the jet will have large velocity, but its surface will be large compared with the volume of water in it and the frictional resistance of the surrounding water will be great. The jet will therefore be stopped more rapidly than a larger jet would be. If the osculum is large, the frictional resistance will be small, but the jet will be slow. Neither a very small osculum with a rapid but small

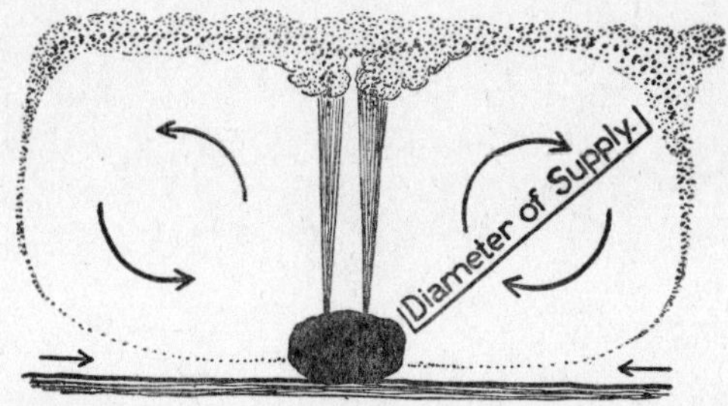

Figure 157. The currents set up by a bath sponge in the water surrounding it. (After Bidder.)

jet, nor a very large osculum with a slow and large jet will give the best results. There will be some intermediate size of the osculum which will throw the water to the greatest distance. The optimum size of the osculum will vary with the size and form of the sponge and with the volume of water ejected. For certain sponges the optimum size of the osculum can be roughly calculated from the known speed and volume of the current, and it is found that the observed sizes of the oscula agree closely with the calculated values of the optimum size. Further, the optimum oscular size will vary with changes in the volume of the current caused by variations in the activity of the sponge. It is probable that the size of the osculum is automatically adjusted to the optimum for each volume of the current by changes in the contractile tone of the cells which form the oscular membrane. When the volume is great and the current over these cells is rapid, they expand and so widen the effective diameter of the osculum. Conversely, when the volume is small, they contract. In all these characters there is accurate correlation in the sponge body between its form and its physiological efficiency.

This correlation can also be seen in the forms of the whole bodies of sponges. Many sponges are finger-shaped or more or less spherical,

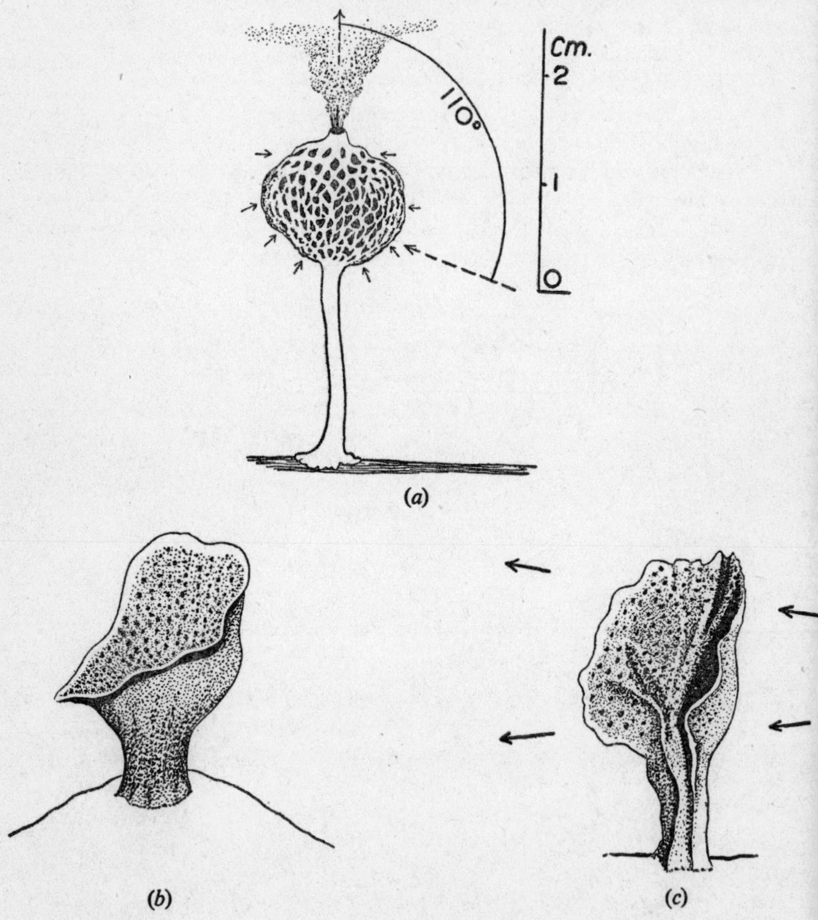

Figure 158. Three forms of the sponge body.

a, stalked form often found in still water; b, c, two sponges with wide and lateral exhalant openings, forms frequent in environments with constant currents. (After Bidder.)

but these are not necessarily the most efficient forms for the body of a sponge. Some sponges are stalked (Fig. 158*a*). One result of the presence of a stalk will be to increase the angle between the jet of water thrown out of the osculum and the average direction from which water is drawn into the surface of the body. In Fig. 158*a*, this angle is 110°, whereas in a sessile spherical sponge it is 90°. In a sponge living in quiet surroundings the possession of a stalk will therefore be an advantage in that it will reduce the likelihood of exhaled water being drawn back into the feeding current. Again, in some sponges, the osculum is placed on the side of the sponge and the water drawn in from the opposite side. The angle between the inhalant and exhalant currents will then be 180° and there will be no danger of the exhaled water being drawn into the ostia however slow the exhalant jet may be. In such sponges a narrow osculum is unnecessary and we often find it widened to a broad opening. The sponge becomes cup- or leaf-shaped (Fig. 158*b*, *c*). On the floor of the deep sea there is often a slow current which is constant in direction. Forms such as those of Fig. 158*b*, *c* are especially suitable for sponges living in these conditions, for, if the sponge is so placed that the feeding current is in the same direction as the current in the surrounding water, the exhaled water will be carried away. These forms occur commonly in deep-sea sponges.

PART IV

SOME GENERAL PROBLEMS OF INVERTEBRATE ZOOLOGY

CHAPTER XX

THE LIFE-HISTORIES OF THE INVERTEBRATES

DURING its life-history every multicellular animal goes through a series of changes from the beginning of development in the activated egg to death, which, unless caused by some accident or disease, results from senility. This series of changes includes development to the adult condition and the less rapid, but still recognisable, changes of form in the adult body. The course of these changes is determined very strictly for each animal species.

In all animal life-histories the adult form is reached as the end-result of development, but the changes of form which constitute development are not merely a direct modelling of the tissues into the adult form. Often the developing animal leads a life of a kind different from that of the adult, and is closely adapted in structure to its life. The larval organs developed in this adaptation are often far from being stages in the direct elaboration of the adult organs. Also, we find that the course of development is determined to some extent by the evolutionary history of the species, and not by the developmental needs alone. Organs are formed during development which were functional in the animals from which our modern animals were evolved, but which are no longer functional in the modern animals. Gill-slits, for instance, are functional in fish and are still formed in mammalian embryology. Such organs often disappear in later development. Their temporary formation shows very clearly that the course of development is not a direct elaboration into the adult form.

In the occurrence of these larval and vestigial organs and in many other ways, development from the egg differs from the other process by which animal tissues attain the specific form, that which occurs in bud-formation and regeneration. This last process is, as we have seen (p. 129), a direct modelling of the tissues into the specific form by differential growth. Whatever are the causes which determine that animals shall pass through the changes of their life-histories, and we know very little of them, we have no reason to think that they are identical with those which result in a bud or a separated piece taking on the specific form.

We shall return to some of these questions in ch. XXIII (p. 384). For the present we may look upon the normal life-history as a determined succession of forms in which the animal lives, each form being adapted to the animal's life at that stage.

1. THE COURSE OF A SIMPLE LIFE-HISTORY

In this chapter we shall discuss only some general problems concerned with the life-histories of invertebrate animals. We shall make no attempt to summarise the facts of invertebrate embryology. We shall try rather to see how far on the basis of our present knowledge we can classify the *types* of change which occur during the life-histories of invertebrates.

The simplest life-history which it is possible to imagine for an animal would be one in which development proceeded directly and continuously from the egg to the adult without the formation of any larval organs and with no other modifications of the course of development. No metazoan has so ideally simple a life-history as this. Some modifications of this direct course occur in all life-histories. But for the present we will not consider these modifications. From such a simple life-history as this the more elaborate life-histories may be supposed to have been derived.

Change of form is continuous throughout the whole of the life-history of every metazoan. It is rapid during development and slow during adult life, but it again becomes more rapid as senility comes on. However, the changes of form during the life-history are not all of one kind. We can conveniently divide the life-history into broad periods in each of which one kind of change is dominant. These periods are by no means sharply defined; all of them fade gradually into the periods which precede and follow them. This division of the life-history is, in fact, justified only for convenience. The following periods can be recognised:

1. The period of *Activation, i.e.* of the changes which follow either fertilisation or parthenogenesis, and result in initiation of the life-history. This period is always very short.

2. *Development*, the period in which the complexity of the body increases until it reaches the condition of the adult body. The period of development may be sub-divided into:

(*a*) The period of *Segmentation*, during which the egg is broken up into a number of smaller blastomeres.

(*b*) *Early Development*, the period up to the formation of a mouth and the beginning of feeding. During this period the arrangement and the outline of the structure of most of the organs is laid down (*i.e.* the body becomes *differentiated*). Growth of the body as a whole during this period is at the expense of yolk, and is slow.

(*c*) *Later Development*, the remainder of the period of development. During this period there is further differentiation, and growth is rapid.

3. *The Adult Period.* This is best defined as the part of the life-history after development is complete, *i.e.* after the body has reached its full complexity and all the adult organs are functional. Very often maturation of the gonad is one of the last changes in development, and the adult period can then be said to commence when the animal becomes reproductive. But in some animals this is not so; reproduction may occur during larval life (p. 334). Absence of growth is not characteristic of adult life. Growth goes on during adult life in all animals with a parabolic growth curve (p. 159), and in some animals in which growth ceases after a time it may continue beyond the beginning of the adult period.

Towards the end of the life-history *senile changes* become obvious. The oncoming of senility in invertebrates is gradual and, as we shall see (p. 331), probably not restricted to the final stages of the life-history. We cannot speak of any distinct senile period.

From this summary it will be seen that the main types of change that occur in the life-history of animals are the changes of differentiation, growth and senility. At the beginning of the life-history we have also activation and segmentation. We will now consider these various processes in more detail.

2. ACTIVATION

Activation is most frequently produced by fertilisation by a sperm, but natural parthenogenesis—*i.e.* activation without fertilisation—occurs in the life-histories of a large number of animals. Artificial parthenogenesis is also possible; the egg may be activated by various forms of experimental treatment.

Activation is, so far as we know, identical in its effects however it is caused. The result of activation is always that the changes which lead to the beginning of development are produced. The changes that take place in the egg about the time of activation are numerous. Polar bodies are formed in some eggs before, and in some after, activation. If the egg has been fertilised by the sperm, the pronucleus of the sperm enters the egg and fuses with the egg pronucleus to form the zygote. After activation either this nucleus or, in parthenogenetic eggs, the pronucleus of the egg proceeds to divide to form the nuclei of the first blastomeres. This is followed by division of the cytoplasm of the egg. Divisions proceed without break throughout segmentation.

Much work has been given to investigation of the physiological changes in the egg which occur at activation, but our knowledge of these changes is still indefinite. It is certain that the character of the surface layer of the egg changes at this time, but the nature of the surface changes is still not fully understood. It is also certain that after activation the metabolism of the egg (as measured by its consumption of oxygen * and output of carbon dioxide) is active. In many eggs there is a large rise of the oxygen consumption at activation, but this is not always so; animal eggs are known in which the oxygen consumption after activation is identical with that of the unactivated egg. It is probable that these differences result from differences in the condition of the egg before rather than after activation. Those eggs which show a rise of oxygen consumption at activation probably do so because the unactivated egg is in a very inactive state in which its oxygen consumption is low. We must wait for further knowledge before we can say more of the changes of activation.

3. SEGMENTATION

In this, the earliest part of development, the protoplasm of the egg becomes divided into a large number of blastomeres. Since the only substances which the egg can receive from the external medium during segmentation—and also later development up to the formation of the mouth—are water and those present in solution (mainly inorganic salts), growth must be at the expense of yolk already in the egg, and any large increase of size is impossible. The total volume of the blastomeres is therefore never much greater than that of the undivided egg. During the later parts of the segmentation period, spaces are often formed between the blastomeres, and the volume of the developing animal may increase, but this is not due to increase in the mass of the living protoplasm.

During segmentation the proportion of the nuclear to the cytoplasmic material increases. The effects of this change are not known; it is certainly not true that the metabolic rate of the developing animal increases during segmentation.

We have already seen (p. 107) that some differentiation may occur without segmentation, which is therefore not essential to all development.

The arrangement of the segmentation divisions, and consequently of the blastomeres, varies greatly in the life-histories of different animals. There are two chief types of arrangement—radial and spiral segmentation—and these types are each characteristic of one of the

* The consumption of oxygen and output of carbon dioxide are measures of the oxidative metabolism only, but we have no reason to believe this metabolism is a different fraction of the whole before and after activation (*cf.* p. 332).

two main groups into which invertebrate animals may be divided. We shall return to this subject in ch. XXIII. But various other arrangements occur. Thus, the speed of division in segmentation varies inversely with the amount of yolk in the protoplasm. Blastomeres are small in parts of an egg where there is little yolk and large where the protoplasm is yolky. When the egg contains a large amount of yolk, segmentation tends to become meroblastic—a small part of the protoplasm of the egg contains relatively little yolk and this part alone divides, forming a *blastoderm* from which the animal is developed. Meroblastic development occurs in many invertebrates, *e.g.* in many arthropods, in cephalopods and in some protochordates (*Pyrosoma*). In many other invertebrates, although the whole egg divides, the divisions are not arranged in the ways typical of either radial or spiral segmentation. This is so, for instance, in the Nematoda.

Segmentation is usually regarded as ending with the formation of the blastula. At this time the animal may consist of 500 to 1000 cells, which will be produced by 9 or 10 divisions. The earlier divisions succeed each other regularly and are often simultaneous throughout the egg; in later divisions the cells become differentiated in size and sometimes in other characters, and the divisions cease to be simultaneous. The speed of development, here as in all other parts of the life-history, varies with the temperature. The time taken by any developmental process is usually reduced by slightly more than 50 per cent. for each rise of 10° C., so long as the temperature remains within the viable range. During segmentation at 15–20° C., divisions in some eggs may follow each other at intervals of an hour, so that an egg may reach the blastula stage in 10 hours.

4. DIFFERENTIATION

During development the arrangement of the organs is laid down, and their structure is formed. This process, the differentiation of the body, is continuous throughout development. It starts during segmentation or even before the egg divides, but it is never so obvious during these early periods as during the later parts of development.

Evidence for the presence of differentiation in the undivided eggs of certain animals is of more than one kind. In *Dentalium* (Mollusca) a part of the cytoplasm of the egg behaves differently from the rest during the first two segmentation divisions, and passes entirely first into one of the first two and then into one of the first four blastomeres (Fig. 159). Its course during these divisions can be recognised since it forms lobes at one pole of the egg, and these do not divide when the egg segments. Certain of the organs do not form if the fourth blastomere or the modified part of the cytoplasm which passes into it is removed. We must conclude that this cytoplasm is in some way necessary for the development of these organs. If so, there is differentiation in the cytoplasm of the egg before segmentation, and this differentiation is associated with the later formation of the organs.

Again, coloured pigments are present in some eggs, and these pigments become rearranged after activation, so that they pass into some but not all the blastomeres, which are thus differentiated from the rest. This occurs in the egg of Styela (*Cynthia*), a urochordate (Fig. 160). The organs which the blastomeres containing this pigment form in normal development do not develop if these blastomeres are removed, and it thus seems that the presence of these pigments is at least associated with the formation of the organs. If so,

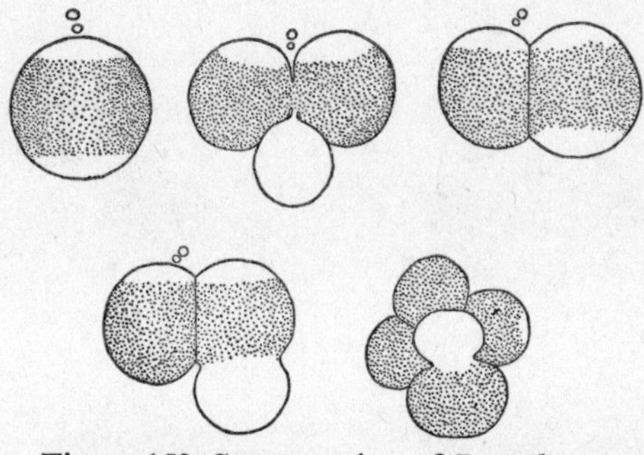

Figure 159. Segmentation of *Dentalium*.

A differentiated area of protoplasm (uncoloured, and at the pole opposite to that of the polar bodies) passes into one of the first two, and then into one of the first four blastomeres. (After Wilson.)

differentiations which are already visible in the undivided egg forecast the later differentiation between the organs.

On these facts the theory of *organ-forming substances* has been founded. These are defined to be substances which are present in the egg before the differentiation of the organs and which determine the course of the later differentiations of the parts of the body into which they pass. The facts which have been mentioned seem definitely to prove that differentiations of some kind are present in the undivided egg and that these differentiations are necessary for the later formation of the organs. But, in the egg of *Styela*, it is certainly not the pigment which is the *direct cause* of the formation of the organs. This pigment can be moved about the egg by means of the centrifuge, and it may then pass during segmentation into blastomeres into which it normally does not pass. But in these centrifuged eggs each blastomere may still form the organs which it normally forms,

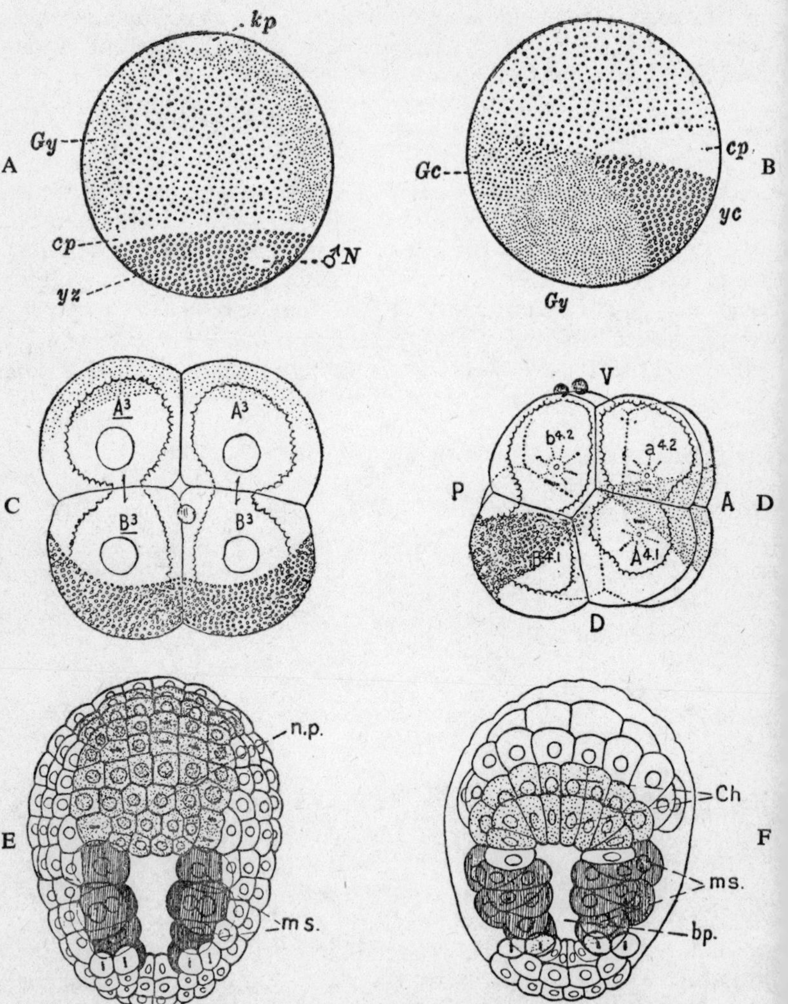

Figure 160. Development of the eggs of *Styela* (Urochordata).

A, shortly after the entrance of the sperm; the protoplasm is distributed in differently coloured layers at right-angles to the polarity axis—*kp*, clear protoplasm of animal pole; *Gy*, grey yolk; *cp*, layer of clear protoplasm; *yz*, yellow protoplasm. B, just before the first cleavage, from the left side: the layers are re-arranged and crescents of yellow protoplasm (*yc*) and grey protoplasm (*Gc*) have appeared. C, four-cell stage, and D, eight-cell stage: the crescents of yellow protoplasm (dark stipple) and grey protoplasm (light stipple) can be seen distributed among the blastomeres. E, F, dorsal views of gastrulæ: the coloured protoplasm of the crescents has become distributed to groups of cells which will give rise to certain organs—grey protoplasm to the neural plate (*np*) and chorda (*Ch*), and yellow protoplasm to the muscles (*ms*); *bp*, blastopore. (After Conklin.)

in spite of the abnormal arrangement of the pigment. The pigment itself is therefore not an "organ-forming substance." We can only conclude that the association of the pigment with definite organs must be due to some underlying organisation of the protoplasm by which the pigment is produced, and that this organisation is responsible for the formation of the organs. This is confirmed by the fact that if the whole protoplasm is moved about the cell by centrifugation, the resulting embryos are abnormal. We do not know the nature of the determining organisation. The presence of chemical organ-forming substances in the developing egg must be regarded as not yet proved.

During segmentation, differentiation is often obvious in differences in the sizes of the blastomeres. Thus, at the 8-cell stage of the echinoid egg four larger blastomeres are separated which later form the endoderm, and at the 16-cell stage four very small blastomeres are formed from the large blastomeres and give rise to the mesenchyme. In this egg the ectoderm, endoderm, and mesenchyme are thus separated from each other during the earliest segmentation divisions. Similar differentiations occur in many other eggs.

Even where there is no obvious differentiation between the early blastomeres, it can often be shown that the fate of the blastomeres in the differentiation of the animal is determined as soon as they are formed by division of the egg. The blastomeres are then clearly differentiated at this stage. This early determination of the fate of the blastomeres occurs in most spirally segmenting eggs. If a blastomere is removed from one of these eggs, the resulting animal is incomplete by the absence of the organs into which this blastomere would have developed. This is called "*mosaic development*," for the segmented egg is a mosaic of blastomeres determined in their fate. In contrast, if one or two of the first four blastomeres of a radially segmenting egg are separated, the egg usually develops into a normal, but small, animal. Here, the fate of the blastomeres is not determined as soon as they are formed, though differentiation between them occurs very shortly afterwards (in the echinoderm egg at the 8-cell stage). Such development is called *equipotential*, for the potentialities of all the blastomeres are equal before differentiation takes place in them.

A very early step in the differentiation of the developing animal body is the determination of the axes of symmetry of the body. These axes of symmetry are:

(1) The *axis of polarity* (p. 122), the anterior-posterior axis. This is differentiated in the bodies of all multicellular animals.

(2) In a bilaterally symmetrical body, the *dorso-ventral axis*.

(3) Also in bilaterally symmetrical bodies, the *right-left axis*. If the body is perfectly bilateral, the determination of the first two axes

determines also this axis, but animals are not often perfectly symmetrical on the two sides of the body. In such imperfectly symmetrical animals the direction of the right-left axis, *i.e.* on which side of the body the organs are to be formed which are normally on the right, has to be determined in development.

The axis of polarity is usually determined before fertilisation. It is believed that this axis is often determined by the position of the egg as it is attached to the wall of the ovary. The pole of the egg which lies free in the cavity of the ovary is believed to become the anterior end of the animal that develops from the egg. Whether this is so or not, there is no doubt that this axis is determined in all eggs before the first segmentation division and often before fertilisation. The pole of the egg which corresponds to the anterior end of the embryo is often called the *animal pole*, and the opposite pole the *vegetative pole*.

The dorso-ventral axis may also be determined before segmentation. In the eggs of insects the egg-shell is often bilaterally symmetrical, and the symmetry of the embryo follows that of the shell. It is therefore determined by the shape of the shell. In some other eggs this axis is determined by the shape of the egg, although there is no egg-shell. Thus, in some echinoderm eggs (*Asterina*) the undivided egg is elongated in the plane which will later occupy this axis. In other echinoderm eggs granules (*Echinus miliaris*) or yolk particles (*Arbacia*) can be shown to determine this axis by their arrangement. These granules or particles are normally ventral, and if they are collected in an unusual part of the egg by the centrifuge, this part becomes the ventral side of the animal. In many eggs we do not know how this axis is determined.

Asymmetry between the two sides of the body is characteristic of many invertebrates as well as of the vertebrates. We have already discussed an example of this in the chelæ of some Crustacea (p. 168). In that example the asymmetry may be reversed during the later parts of the life-history. This is not often so; the asymmetry is usually determined early in development and is retained throughout life.

In the vertebrates it has been shown that the right-left asymmetry is determined by the external conditions during early development. Temperature gradients between the two sides of the body may reverse the normal asymmetry, and in the united bodies of monstrous twins the asymmetry of one member of the pair is usually reversed—presumably owing to the presence of the other twin, which alters in some way the conditions in which development occurs. In some molluscs, *e.g.* the snail (*Limnœa*), the conditions under which this axis is determined have been worked out. In the snails and the great majority of gastropods the spiral of the shell is asymmetrical. In

Limnæa it is normally dextral, *i.e.* the opening is to the right if the shell is held with the spiral above and the opening in front, but occasional specimens with the opposite, sinistral, symmetry occur. It has been shown that the direction of the asymmetry of the shell depends on the direction of the spiral cleavage in the segmentation of the egg (Fig. 161). Here the asymmetry of the shell is one manifestation of the right-left asymmetry of the body, and this is determined by the

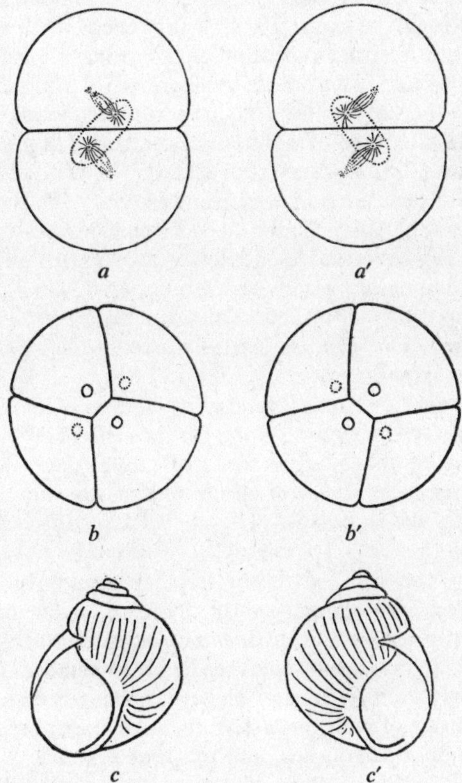

Figure 161. Spiral division and symmetry in *Limnæa*.

a, b and *a′, b′* the two types of division; *c, c′* the resulting left- and right-handed shells. (After Morgan.)

direction of the cleavage furrows. In certain snails (*Limnæa*) the direction of the cleavage furrows has been shown to be determined by genetic factors.

Thus we see that differentiations of more than one kind occur during segmentation, and some even before segmentation. After the period of segmentation, differentiation of the organs proceeds rapidly. We have discussed this later differentiation to some extent in Part II, especially in ch. X. We saw that the arrangement of the organs and their parts was laid down under the influence of the axial organisation, and that the organs were differentiated largely by unequal growth of the parts of the body. In this they differ from the differentiations which occur before and during segmentation. These are due to the arrangement of the substances in the egg and of the segmentation divisions. We also saw that the differentiation of certain organs might be controlled by influences arising from neighbouring organs, in either evocating or individuating fields. Very little more than this can be said of the control of differentiation. Our knowledge of the subject is, in fact, still rudimentary.

In the general course of differentiation, formation of structure in the organs proceeds always from coarser to finer detail. The first organ to be differentiated in something like its definitive shape is the alimentary canal. An archenteron is almost always formed immediately after segmentation by some form of gastrulation. Later the parts of the alimentary canal are differentiated. Similarly, the other organs are first formed in coarse detail, and later their finer detail is differentiated. This process extends through the whole of the later parts of development.

External conditions may modify the course of development just as they modify in some animals the form of the adult body (ch. VII). Indeed, many of the modifications of adult form which are produced by changes in the external conditions are due to effects produced during development. The structural differences between sexual and worker bees are examples of this. They are produced by differences in the food given to the developing young. Another example is the development of the larval *Bonellia* into a male or female according as it does or does not receive a chemical secretion from a female (p. 118). On the other hand, in some animals external conditions may modify form after development is complete. This is true of the forms of cœlenterate colonies, of the ephippial and non-ephippial forms of Cladocera, and of other examples.

5. GROWTH

We have already discussed growth and its part in determining the form of the body in ch. X. It is not necessary for much to be said of it here. Growth in total size must be distinguished from the differential growth of the parts to which the differentiation of the body is very largely due. The latter occurs, as we have seen, in all parts of the life-history after the early stages of development. It is present during adult life and is responsible for the changes of form which occur then. Growth in total size is most rapid soon after the animal begins to feed. Thereafter the proportionate growth of body, *i.e.* its growth measured as a fraction of the total size, slows: the growth follows a parabolic curve or ceases in the adult (p. 159). These curves disregard the initial period of development in which there is little growth.

Among the invertebrates it is probably only in insects that growth ceases in the adult; in them this is a necessary consequence of the single adult instar. So far as we know all other invertebrates have parabolic growth-curves, and their growth is continuous throughout the life-history.

6. SENILITY

That the body of an animal becomes inefficient as it grows old is as obvious in many of the more complex invertebrates as it is in the vertebrates. A large and old crab or lobster is inactive and slow in its responses; it shows these and many others of the changes which we are accustomed to recognise in the old vertebrate. It seems probable that senile changes of this kind occur in most, and perhaps in all, multicellular animals. They may be rare in nature since most animals die before they become senile.

In the mammals we know that many senile changes are caused by decrease in the endocrine secretions of the gonads. The changes can sometimes be reversed by replacing these secretions by injection or grafts of active gonad tissue. But this type of senility is so far as we know peculiar to the higher vertebrates. Though in some invertebrates the gonads seem to produce endocrine secretions (*cf.* p. 265), there is no evidence that in them senility is the result of reduction in these secretions.

The phenomena of senility have been investigated in very few invertebrates. Senility is certainly not a necessary result of long-continued life in all metazoan cells. It has been found possible to grow tissue-cultures for periods many times as long as the life-history of the species. So long as the cultures are kept healthy by renewal of the medium and maintenance of the food-supply, no signs of senile changes occur in the cells. They continue to live and divide in apparently the same condition as during the early stages of the culture. The absence of senile changes in these tissue cultures must be in some way the result of the abnormal conditions in the culture.

Even in the body senile changes do not inevitably appear after long-continued life. Planarians have been kept at the same size for long periods by giving them just enough food for their life and no more. In such conditions they have been found to live at a small size for periods during which other, well-fed, planarians have passed through as many as twelve generations, and they showed no senile changes at the end of this time. They were, both in form and so far as we know in physiology, identical with normal planarians of the same size. The oncoming of senile changes, which, as we shall see, normally occur in planarians, was presumably prevented by the semi-starvation. It is characteristic of the normal life-history, but not a necessary accompaniment of life.

The speed with which senile changes appear in the body of an animal is controlled by the temperature at which the animal is living. In this the senile changes agree with other features of the life-history. At a low temperature the life-history is longer and the animal lives longer before it begins to show senile changes. These facts suggest that the senile changes are closely associated with the metabolism of the animal.

In planarians it has been shown that the oxygen consumption per unit of tissue decreases regularly throughout the life-history. It is probably a reasonable assumption to take the oxygen consumption as a measure of the total metabolism of the body, for there is no reason to assume that the oxidative metabolism is a variable proportion of the total metabolism. If we make this assumption, the decrease of oxygen consumption implies that the tissues are living less actively as they become older. Some other invertebrates have given similar results, and it seems probable that this decrease of metabolic rate with age is a general character of the metazoan body. If so, we may regard it as probably the immediate cause of the changes in invertebrates which we describe as senile, for many of these changes are those which we should expect to result from a slowed rate of metabolism.

But we have to ask what is the cause of this reduction of metabolic rate with age. Since most invertebrates grow continuously larger throughout their life-history, and we have already seen that increase in size is likely to lead to reduction in the efficiency of metabolism (pp. 47–9), it is reasonable to ask whether there is any correlation between the size of the body and the metabolic rate.

In planarians correlation between these two characters of the body is very close. In fact, it is true to say that the metabolic rate in planarians is governed entirely by the size of the body. We have already seen that the physiology of planarians kept small by semi-starvation is identical with that of much younger animals of the same size. Among other physiological characters the oxygen consumption per unit of tissue is the same in the two groups. Also, if large planarians are completely starved so that they are forced to live upon their own tissues and decrease in size, they are found to regain the oxygen consumption normal to animals of the size to which they have become reduced. The reduction in size may be great—to a tenth or less of the original size—but the return of the metabolic rate to that normal to the smaller size still holds.

These facts seem to show that in planarians the reduction of metabolic rate with age is simply a result of the larger size of the older animal. How far this is true of other invertebrate animals we do not know. But, however this may be, we may conclude that a reduction of metabolic rate with age is probably characteristic of all metazoan animals, and that the inactivity which we observe in senility is probably, at least in part, a result of the reduction of metabolic rate. This may be so, but it must be emphasised that in many animals the senile changes are certainly complex. They include many changes besides the reduction of metabolic rate. The cells of many tissues become altered. Some cells degenerate, *e.g.* the cells of nervous tissue in both vertebrates and bees, and many other changes occur in the tissues. Some of these changes may be secondary results of the decreased metabolic rate, but we do not know that this is true of all of them.

Finally, in so far as senility is due to the lowered metabolic rate in the ageing animal, it is clearly not a condition restricted to the last stages of the life-history. The senile changes appear to be characteristic of the old animal only because in old age they are greatest and therefore most obvious. In the invertebrates this is borne out by observation of the behaviour of the animals. In their behaviour the oncoming of the senile changes is very gradual.*

7. MODIFICATIONS OF THE LIFE-HISTORY

1. *Parthenogenesis*

Parthenogenetic activation, *i.e.* activation without fertilisation, occurs in the life-histories of many invertebrates (Rotifera, Gastrotricha, Crustacea—Branchiopoda and Ostracoda—many insects). It may be:

(*a*) Occasional, as in some Lepidoptera, where eggs may sometimes develop parthenogenetically, although males commonly occur.

(*b*) Cyclical, *i.e.* phases of sexual and parthenogenetic reproduction alternate (Cladocera, Rotifera, aphids, etc.).

(*c*) Associated with the sex of the young, as in many Hymenoptera, where the fertilised eggs produce females, and parthenogenetic eggs produce males.

(*d*) The normal method of reproduction, and in some species perhaps the only method. In species with this type of reproduction males are infrequent or even absent. In some Ostracoda males are unknown and parthenogenesis is the only known means of reproduction.

* For further discussion see Comfort, *Biol. Rev.*, **29**, 284, 1954.

Activation is, so far as we know, physiologically identical whether produced by fertilisation or parthenogenesis. It is in their genetic effects that fertilisation and parthenogenesis differ. Natural parthenogenesis may be of two kinds, diploid and haploid. In the first (in some Crustacea and insects) there is no reduction of the chromosome number in the egg at meiosis, and the genetic constitution of the offspring is therefore identical with that of the parent. In haploid parthenogenesis meiotic reduction occurs and the activated egg therefore has the reduced number of chromosomes. In some forms the number is again doubled during development after activation. It follows that animals which have developed from eggs activated by haploid parthenogenesis must be homozygous in all characters. When parthenogenesis is occasional in a species, it is usually haploid.

2. *Multiplication during the Life-history*

Division of a developing animal so that it develops into more than one adult occurs commonly in parasitic life-histories and occasionally in the life-histories of other animals. In the life-history of the liver-fluke multiplication occurs at least twice and often more frequently. In the Cestoda the cysticerci of some species produce numerous scolices (*Tænia echinococcus*) and the formation of the proglottides by budding from the scolex may probably be regarded as asexual multiplication. When the multiplication takes place during an embryonic stage of the life-history, the process is often known as *polyembryony*. This occurs in some insects, *e.g. Encyrtus fuscicollis*, hymenopterous parasite of a moth, *Hyponomeuta*. The egg of the parasite develops within the egg of the moth into an embryonic mass of cells which buds off numerous smaller masses. Each of these develops into a larva of the parasite. Polyembryony is essentially the same process as the division of the gastrula by which identical twins are produced in vertebrates.

Reproduction at a later larval stage is known as *pædogenesis*. It also occurs in certain insects; it is always asexual. For instance, the larva of a gall-midge *Miastor* (Diptera) is known to produce parthenogenetic and viviparous eggs which develop into larvæ like their parents. In another midge, *Tanytarsus*, multiplication occurs at the pupal stage. *Neoteny*, *i.e.* retention of larval characters after maturity of the gonad, occurs in the axolotl among vertebrates and in certain beetles.

3. *Alternation of Generations*

It may perhaps be doubtful whether we should regard the various forms of a complicated life-history such as that of the liverfluke or a cestode as highly modified larvæ or as successive generations. More usually they are regarded as larvæ, for there is continuous increase of complexity of structure throughout the life-history from the egg to the sexually reproductive adult; but, if we take the other view, we have in these life-histories examples of alternation of sexual and asexual generations. Such an alternation of generations occurs in many other animals where it may appear probable that the alternating phases are generations and not parts of a single life-history. This is so, for instance, in the cœlenterates. The medusa and polyp, though they differ greatly in shape, are both modifications of the same specific form. They differ in the relative sizes of the parts but hardly at all in their arrangement. Medusa and polyp would thus seem both fully developed specific forms, *i.e.* adults.* It is still more obviously true of many other animals in which the differences between sexual and asexual generations are less than in the cœlenterates. Some polychætes, *e.g.* species of *Syllis* and other genera, have this alternation, reproducing by budding in one generation and sexually in the next. The sexual generation (*heterosyllis*) differs from the asexual generation only in details of structure, in the parapodia and other parts of the body. Indeed, in some species of *Nereis* there is no alternation of generations; the same individual may first reproduce asexually and then reproduce sexually. Neither in *Syllis* nor in *Nereis* can there be any doubt that the sexual and asexual forms are both adults. Whether we call them "generations" or not depends on our definition of the term generation. If it is the interval between two fertilisations the forms of *Nereis* and *Syllis* are not generations; if each assumption of the full specific form represents a generation, they are.†

Wherever both sexual and asexual reproduction occur in the same species we find a tendency for the two types of reproduction to alternate. This wide-spread phenomenon of "alternation of generations" occurs in many invertebrates besides the cœlenterates and the polychætes. It is well known, for instance, in the Rotifera, Cladocera, Urochordata, and in the insects (aphids). The alternation may be regular, a sexual generation regularly following and preceding an asexual, or it may be irregular. Regular alternation occurs in cœlenterates, some polychætes and urochordates. It also occurs among the Protista in the Polythalamia (*Polystomella*). When the alternation is irregular, it is frequent for several asexual generations to come between each sexual generation. This is so in the Cladocera, Rotifera, and aphids. In these groups also the alternation is often controlled by the environmental conditions. In the Cladocera, for example, sexual reproduction occurs when the temperature falls or the

* The polyp is sometimes regarded as a larva.

† *Cf.* Carter, *School. Sci. Rev.*, **33**, 228, 1952.

animals are crowded. Reproduction is asexual at high temperatures and in uncrowded conditions. Environmental conditions also play a large part in controlling the type of reproduction in rotifers and aphids.

4. *Larval and Embryonic Adaptation*

The greater part of the variations in animal life-histories from the direct and simple course which we have so far discussed are due to adaptation of the young animal to some mode of life different from that which the adult leads. The young animal is then known as a *larva*. Adaptation is often almost as perfect in the larva as in the adult, and this implies, if the mode of life changes in the course of development, specialisation in structure during development along lines which do not lead directly to the adult structure. Thus, development becomes indirect, and there is great change of structure when the animal passes to the adult mode of life. We shall consider only a few of the very numerous differences between the larval and adult modes of life which occur among invertebrates.

(a) *Protected Stages in Development*

One very frequent difference between the life of the developing young and the adult is that the former should be protected by some provision made for it by the parent. Clearly the life of a developing animal in such conditions is very different from that of the free-living adult. Such a protected developmental stage is called an *embryo*.

There is a short embryonic period in most animal life-histories. Up to the end of segmentation the egg is usually protected by some cover even when the later stages are free-living. But at early stages there is little opportunity for adaptation and the protection of the egg does not noticeably divert the course of development from the direct path. It is when the embryonic period is prolonged, as it is in many life-histories, that we find marked adaptation in the embryo to the conditions of embryonic life.

(i) *Embryos in Shelled Eggs*

The provision of a hard and impermeable egg-shell is very common. It occurs in some members of almost all the larger invertebrate groups. When the presence of such a shell is combined with a long embryonic period, the development becomes very greatly modified, perhaps more modified than in any other type of life-history. The embryo must satisfy all its needs within the shell for as long as the development is embryonic. Since the only substances which pass through the shell are those which can diffuse through it in solution, if the medium is aquatic, and only gases if the medium is aerial, the developing animal must have great adaptation to be able to live in such conditions. This adaptation must be both morphological and physiological.

The chief adaptations we find in animals with long embryonic development are the following:

(1) Some provision must be made for the sperm to reach the egg. Either the egg must be fertilised before the shell is laid down round it, or a path for the sperm through the shell must be provided. The first of these alternatives implies fertilisation of the egg within the body of the parent, for the shell is formed before the egg is laid. This again implies great modification of the genital system of the parent; cross-fertilisation must occur, provision must be made for the storage of the foreign sperm (*bursa copulatrix*, *spermatheca*, etc.), and so on. This need is probably the cause of much of the complication of the genital system in such animals as the Platyhelminthes, but we find provision for these needs where the genital system is not complex, *e.g.* in the Nematoda. The second alternative is the method adopted in some insects. The shell is laid down before the egg is fertilised and the sperm enters the egg through a small hole in the shell, the *micropyle*.

(2) The developing embryo must be provided with sufficient food for its embryonic life. This is provided in the form of yolk within the egg, and thus, if the embryonic period is long, the egg must be yolky. This, again, results in great modifications of the development, of which the most usual and obvious is the substitution of meroblastic for holoblastic segmentation (p. 324).

(3) We know very little of the physiological adaptations of invertebrate embryos. Their respiratory needs seem to be provided for by diffusion through the shell. The same is true of the excretory needs of aquatic embryos, and also of terrestrial embryos in the early stages of development in which the excretory material is probably mainly ammonia. In later stages of terrestrial embryonic development it is possible that the excretion of uric acid (p. 225) may be of value in allowing the excretory material to be stored in a harmless form, as it is in some vertebrate embryos.

(4) Embryos show many other adaptations to the conditions of their life. Pigment is generally absent during embryonic life. The cuticle is usually thin and soft, and the locomotory organs are frequently developed at a later stage than in corresponding free-living larvæ. These are, however, rather modifications of the time during development at which structures are formed than new adaptations.

(ii) *Cocoons*

Protection of the embryo may be provided by a cover within

which several eggs are enclosed. This is generally known as a cocoon. Such cocoons are formed by many Oligochæta, Hirudinea, Pulmonata, and by spiders. Development within a cocoon shows much the same modifications as that within a hard egg-shell. We often find as complicated genital systems in animals with this type of protection as in those which lay down hard egg-shells.

(iii) *Viviparity*

This, the retention of the embryo within the body of the parent until the end of embryonic life, is another means by which the early developmental stages are protected. It occurs in many nematodes, some scattered species of molluscs, both Gastropoda and Lamellibranchiata, some Crustacea (*Daphnia*, asexual development), most

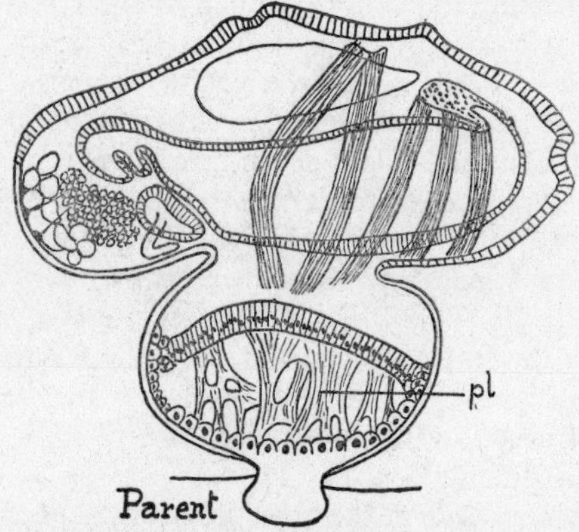

Figure 162. Placentation in *Salpa*.

The developing animal, shown above, is attached to the parent through a placenta (*pl*). (After Salensky.)

species of *Peripatus*, some insects, and in the Salpidæ among the Urochordata. The egg may be retained either in spaces among the parent tissues, or in enclosed external spaces (brood-sacs). In most of these cases of viviparity, the shelled egg is simply retained within the body of the parent until it hatches. This is known as ovoviviparity. Such development does not differ essentially from development in a shelled egg outside the body, except that better protection is given to the embryo. But in the salps (Fig. 162) a true placenta is formed. Tissues of the embryo come into close contact with tissues of the parent and food-material is passed from the parent to the embryo. The provision of a large amount of yolk in the egg is then unnecessary. Among the species of *Peripatus* the development of the egg varies greatly. A few species (*Ooperipatus*, New Zealand, Australia) have large shelled eggs which are laid and not retained in the parent body. Other species with large eggs are ovoviviparous (*e.g. Eoperipatus*, Borneo, Sumatra, etc.). Some species of *Peripatopsis* (S. Africa) have smaller eggs but no placenta; the eggs absorb food secreted from the uterine wall of the parent. Finally in many species of *Peripatus* (S. and C. America) a true placenta is formed, and the eggs are very small (50μ).

As in the mammals, the development of a placenta in invertebrates probably serves as a means by which many other physiological needs of the embryo besides the need for food are satisfied. Excretory and respiratory substances as well as food are probably exchanged across the placenta.

(b) *The Larva as a Locomotory Stage*

In many life-histories the larva is the chief locomotory phase. Thus, the larval stages of many aquatic animals are planktonic, while the adult stages are bottom-living or even sessile. Such planktonic larvæ occur in almost all marine invertebrate groups; they are much rarer among freshwater invertebrates but they occur in a few forms (Polyzoa and *Dreissena*, a lamellibranch). Among marine larvæ, annelid trochophores, molluscan veligers and the plutei and other larvæ of echinoderms are typical examples. Barnacles and tunicates are examples of sessile animals with planktonic larvæ. In parasitic animals the larval stage is often free and locomotory, and it is at this stage that the animal passes from one host to another (p. 382). The larvæ of marine parasitic animals are often planktonic (Sacculina, Copepoda).

All these larvæ show typical planktonic adaptations. Their bodies are often transparent; they frequently have long extensions of the body which increase its surface and make slower its rate of falling through the water; their skeleton, if any is present, is light, and so on. Although, as in all planktonic animals, the distribution of these larva is governed by the currents of the environment and not by their own powers of locomotion, the larvæ usually possess locomotory organs. These organs are often in the form of lines or bands of cilia and are used to control the vertical distribution of the larvæ in the environment (p. 390). The cilia are often used for the collection of food as well as for locomotion. When this is so, the method of food collection is that of vortical currents such as we found many Protista and the Rotifera to use (p. 210). Both trochophores and echinoderm larvæ feed in this way.

(c) *The Larva as a Feeding Stage*

In contrast to the locomotory larvæ we have just discussed we find that in some animals, of which the insects are the best example, the larval stage is one in which the animal feeds actively and most, or all, of the growth occurs, and the adult stage is locomotory and reproductive.

Here again the difference in habit leads to very great differences in structure. A caterpillar or dipterous maggot is clearly adapted for a life of which the main function is to absorb food and build a larger body.

5. *Metamorphosis*

Since adaptation of a larva to some way of life different from that of the adult necessarily means specialisation of the organs along lines which will not lead directly to the structure of the adult organs, we must expect that in forms with highly adapted larvæ there will be great alteration of structure at the stage at which the animal passes to the adult way of life. The change in the habit is often sudden, and it is therefore not surprising that the change of structure is also often sudden.

Such a sudden change of structure during the course of a development is called a *metamorphosis*. It will usually be accompanied by loss of the specialisation of the organs which have previously been acquired in adaptation to the larval habits.

Metamorphosis is of many grades of suddenness. It is said to be more or less *extreme*. The change-over from one type of adaptation to another may require only somewhat rapid growth of certain organs and reduction of others by resorption. This is so, for instance, in the metamorphosis of the amphibian tadpole, and that of many marine planktonic larvæ. Thus, in the metamorphosis of a trochophore into an annelid worm there is resorption of the prototroch and other organs and rapid outgrowth of the tail, but the metamorphosis is no more than this. On the other hand, in the more extreme forms of metamorphosis, *e.g.* in holometabolous insects and many echinoderms, almost all the larval tissues are lost, and the adult tissues are formed by new growth from special rapidly growing tissues, the "imaginal buds" (p. 143) of the insects and the "adult rudiment" of the echinoderms.

The manner in which such extreme forms of metamorphosis may have been evolved can be well seen by comparing the various types of metamorphosis which occur in different insect orders. But in making this comparison it must be emphasised that these forms of metamorphosis occur in evolutionary lines—the insect orders—which have in general evolved in parallel with each other by radiation (p. 386), so that the types of metamorphosis we observe cannot be regarded as ancestral to each other. These types of metamorphosis are not stages in a single evolutionary process; rather, the insect orders have evolved varying distances along the path to extreme metamorphosis. Nevertheless the forms of metamorphosis we find in the various orders do give us some idea of the manner in which the extreme metamorphosis of the holometabolous orders may have evolved.

We find the following types of development among the insects:

(*a*) Orthoptera, Hemiptera, etc. The larva (*nymph*) is hatched in a form very like that of the adult except that it is smaller and the gonads and wings are undeveloped. There is very little difference in mode of life between larva and adult, except that the adult is reproductive and sometimes flies. The change in structure from larva to adult is gradual and extends over several instars. There is here no true metamorphosis in the sense in which we have used the term.

(*b*) Odonata, Ephemeroptera. The larva is aquatic and the adult aerial. There is great adaptation of the larva to its aquatic mode of life, and great change of structure at the moult which leads to the adult instar. The structural change is due to rapid change of form and size in the various organs. But this last moult differs from the other moults only in the different form which the animal takes on after it. There is here a true metamorphosis, but one brought about solely by rapid positive and negative growth of organs during and immediately after the last moult.

(*c*) Holometabola. Here a pupal period is developed, *i.e.* a period between the larval and adult phases in which the animal is inactive and the change in structure goes on. In the simpler types (Neuroptera, etc.) the change of structure is mainly by differential growth, but this is largely replaced in the more extreme forms of metamorphosis by destruction of larval tissue and re-growth from imaginal buds. In the series from the Neuroptera to the Diptera there is continual increase in the proportion of the larval tissues replaced.

Though these are not stages in a single evolutionary process, there can be no doubt that the most extreme metamorphoses of the Holometabola must have been evolved along some such line as that which this series suggests. However this may be, it is clear that an extreme form of metamorphosis is always a highly modified form of development. Indeed, we must regard all metamorphosis as non-primitive. Metamorphosis never occurs unless the larva has great adaptation to some mode of life which is not that of the adult; it only occurs in life-histories where there is a sudden change from one type of adaptation to another. Such a life-history can never be primitive. Metamorphosis is also non-primitive in the rapidity of the change of structure which occurs in it. It is true that even in direct life-histories changes in the speed of development at certain stages of development seem to have occurred in evolution. Certain stages of development have frequently been quickened—this is so, for instance, of the early stages of development in the life-histories of many of the more complex animals—but this also is never a primitive feature. The primitive development must have been gradual.

The pupal period is a peculiarity of the metamorphosis of the insects, but in other respects the metamorphosis of the echinoderms, which is one of the most extreme metamorphoses in any animal outside the insects, shows considerable resemblance to that of the holometabolous insects. In both types of metamorphosis there is destruction of by far the greater part of the larval tissues and replacement of them by new growth.* Also the change of structure is as extreme and rapid in the echinoderms as in the insects. In echinoderms there is the further complication that the symmetry of the body is altered at metamorphosis. And in some echinoderm metamorphoses (*Echinus*) larval tissues are not merely resorbed but die and are consumed by phagocytes, just as they are in the pupa of some insects (Diptera). The metamorphosis of the pilidium into the adult nemertine is as extreme as those of the insects and echinoderms. In that metamorphosis large parts of the larval body are thrown off and discarded. Many invertebrate metamorphoses are far less extreme. Most of them are much more like that of the trochophore into an annelid worm (p. 397).

* In larvæ of *Echinus* it has been shown that treatment with very dilute H_gCl_2 ($2/10^6$ M) initiates metamorphosis. The larval tissues are less active and more sensitive to the poison, which is not concentrated enough to kill the more active tissues of the adult rudiment. The latter therefore grow, whereas the larval tissues decay (J. S. Huxley, *Amer. Nat.*, **62**, 363, 1928).

CHAPTER XXI

THE BEHAVIOUR OF THE INVERTEBRATE METAZOAN

THERE can be no doubt that the study of behaviour is the branch of animal biology in which there is the greatest temptation to anthropomorphism, that is to say to interpretation of the facts in terms of our own experience rather than by the objective methods which we should use in dealing with scientific facts. We must therefore be more than usually careful to avoid this mistake in discussing the subject. It may be that the temptation is greatest when the behaviour of the higher vertebrates is being discussed, but it is present in all discussions of animal behaviour and certainly in discussions of the complex behaviour of such invertebrates as the insects.

The simplest types of animal behaviour are those least like our own. They are therefore the types of behaviour which it is easiest to discuss objectively. For this reason it will be best to start our discussion by considering these simple types of behaviour in multicellular animals. We will compare them with the behaviour of the Protista which we have already considered (ch. V). We will then pass on to more complicated invertebrate behaviour, trying throughout the discussion to interpret as much as possible of the behaviour of each animal in terms of the simpler behaviour we shall have previously considered. Higher mental functions must never be postulated in an animal unless the facts of the behaviour force us to do so. But it must be remembered that the opposite mistake—to neglect and disregard animal behaviour for no other reason than that it seems to demand the higher mental functions—is equally unscientific.

1. PROTISTAN BEHAVIOUR AND THE BEHAVIOUR OF MULTICELLULAR ANIMALS

In discussing protistan behaviour (ch. V) * we found that the behaviour of each species consists of the continuous actions of the animal and of a few well-defined types of reaction, and that the type of each reaction is determined by the specific characters of the

* We defined an animal's behaviour as the sum of its actions, both continuous and non-continuous, and not only as the changes in these actions (the reactions) which follow stimulation.

animal and not by the nature of the stimulation. Different stimuli sometimes produce different reactions in a protistan—*Paramecium* will respond to very strong stimulation with explosion of the trichocysts and to weaker stimulation with its shock reaction—but the same reaction may very often be produced by stimuli of many kinds. Chemical stimuli, heat, pressure, and vibration will all cause the shock reaction in *Paramecium.* A reaction is initiated by the stimulus, but its nature is determined by the specific characters of the animal.

Further, the reactions of a protistan are almost always reactions of the whole organism and not local reactions of a part of the organism. This is obviously true of much protistan behaviour—no one will question it, for instance, of the shock reaction of *Paramecium*—but it is not true of every example of behaviour in the Protista. *Amœba* in catching its food puts out pseudopodia from parts of its surface. This behaviour consists of local reactions of parts of the animal.

Finally, the behaviour of a protistan may alter with the physiological condition of the organism. We found an example of this in the series of reactions by which *Stentor rœselii* reacts to the stimulus of carmine particles introduced into its feeding current.

The sponges (Parazoa) differ from the Metazoa as widely in their behaviour as in other features of their biology. Sponge behaviour has been discussed to some extent in ch. XIX and we need not repeat the discussion here. It may be said, however, that the behaviour of sponges differs in no essential character from that of colonial protistans such as *Volvox* (p. 94). In the sponge, as in the Protista, the number of reactions of which the animal is capable are few. As in colonial Protista, the cells of the sponge react independently to stimulation. The behaviour of the whole sponge is built up of these independent reactions of the cells.

The behaviour of the simpler Metazoa is also in many ways similar to that of the Protista. Metazoan behaviour, like that of the Protista, consists of continuous activity and of reactions determined in nature for the species of the animal. These reactions are very often initiated by external stimulation, but they may, as we shall see, arise automatically in the organism. As in the Protista, many different types of stimulation may produce the same reaction. But, in the Metazoa, the number of types of reaction of which the animal is capable is much greater than in the Protista, and the number increases very rapidly as we pass up the series of Metazoa to the more complicated forms.

Metazoan behaviour also agrees with that of the Protista in that it varies with the general physiological condition of the animal. In one condition the animal will behave in certain ways, and in other conditions it behaves entirely differently—animals may be active or inactive, sensitive or insensitive. In fact an animal's behaviour at any moment, if this is defined as the sum of its actions and not merely as its reactions to stimulation, is best regarded as an expression of the physiological condition of the animal at that moment. If so, the behaviour will alter with changes of any kind in the physiological condition. One type of these changes occurs when a stimulus reaches the animal. The physiological condition is altered by the changes in the nervous system resulting from the impact of the stimulus, and the change in the behaviour, the reaction of the animal, is the result of this change in the physiological condition. It is only because the changes of behaviour due to stimulation are more obvious than those produced by other kinds of physiological change that we think of the animal as reacting only to stimulation. We should remember (1) that reactions are changes in behaviour not the total behaviour, and (2) that the nature of the whole behaviour is determined by the physiological condition of the animal, this condition being itself determined by the whole external and internal conditions in which the animal is living.

In one character the behaviour of the simpler Metazoa differs fundamentally from the greater part of protistan behaviour. Much of simple metazoan behaviour consists of local reactions of parts of the body and not of centralised reactions of the whole organism. It is therefore more similar to the behaviour of *Amœba* in chasing food than to the greater part of protistan behaviour. In the more complex Metazoa this uncentralised behaviour is replaced to a greater and greater extent by centralised behaviour of the whole organism, until in the highest invertebrates, such as the insects, the behaviour has become almost as perfectly centralised as it is in such a protistan as *Paramecium*. In this and all its other features the behaviour of the metazoan is necessarily correlated with the structural organisation within the body on which the performance of the behaviour depends, *i.e.* with the structure of the receptor, co-ordinating and effector systems. We have seen in ch. XVI that there is a gradual centralisation of the co-ordinating system as we pass up the invertebrates. We will now consider how far the development of centralised behaviour proceeds in parallel with this development of centralisation in the organs.

2. THE EVOLUTION OF BEHAVIOUR AND THE DEVELOPMENT OF CENTRAL CONTROL IN THE INVERTEBRATES

(a) *Cœlenterata*

In most cœlenterates we have no evidence that the nerve-net has any other functions beyond that of conducting impulses about the body. Also, in most of the group there is no evidence of centralised behaviour. In the cœlenterate, weak stimulation at a point of the nerve-net produces reactions of the neighbouring effector organs only—the reactions are, in fact, entirely local. If a small piece of food is placed on a tentacle of a sea-anemone, that tentacle bends towards the mouth. If the stimulation is greater, the reaction may spread to other tentacles, which also bend towards the mouth. The reaction is still local though it spreads over a greater part of the body. Sometimes the stimulation may spread over the whole body. We see an example of this in the contraction of a *Hydra* when it is touched. The reaction is then one of the whole body, but there is, so far as we know, no central control of the reaction. The nerve-net here still acts as a conducting system and as nothing more.

Certain other types of behaviour occur in some cœlenterates. We have seen that impulses may arise automatically in the nerve-net—in the neurogenic rhythm of the beat of a medusa (p. 243). Such impulses may give rise to actions of the whole organism, as they do in the swimming of a medusa. We have no knowledge of the manner in which this initiation of behaviour occurs in the nerve-net. But, however it arises, it forms a very simple type of control of the behaviour so that it is unified in the whole organism. It may perhaps be regarded as a simple form of central control. The behaviour which results from this control, the swimming of the medusa, is very like the centralised behaviour of more complex animals.

In a few cœlenterates complicated acts may be carried out. Some sea-anemones divide by constriction across the middle of the disc. This is apparently produced by the two halves of the body moving apart, so that the body is pulled asunder. Later, reorganisation of the body takes place by differential growth of the parts. This behaviour is apparently initiated within the body, but it does not necessarily demand any type of central control beyond that demanded by other types of automatic behaviour in the cœlenterates, such as the swimming of a medusa.

Hydra may show very complicated behaviour in its movements from one place to another. These movements take place in more than one manner. One type of this behaviour consists of a series of actions (Fig. 163) in which (1) the body is bent so that the mouth is brought into contact with the substratum, (2) the mouth is attached, (3) the tail is released and the body swung over the mouth until the tail is again brought into contact with the substratum, and (4) the tail is attached in the new position, the mouth released and the body straightened. So far as we know this behaviour is initiated automatically in the nervous system of the polyp. Its initiation is not more difficult to understand than that of the swimming movements of a medusa. But the behaviour is itself complicated. The simplest interpretation that can be given of this series of actions is to suppose that each act is initiated by stimulation provided by the performance of the previous acts. Thus, the release of the tail and the swinging over of the body would be initiated by stimuli produced by the attachment of the mouth and the initial bending of the body. We have here an example of a type of behaviour, *chain behaviour*, which we shall discuss in more detail later.

Whether, or not, we may regard the neurogenic initiation of impulses in the nerve-net as a very simple form of central control of behaviour, the cœlenterates differ from most other Metazoa in possessing no differentiated part of the nervous system which we may regard as the seat of this control—no part comparable to the "brain" of the higher Metazoa. The echinoderms resemble the cœlenterates in having no clearly recognisable "brain," * and their behaviour is, like that of the cœlenterates, very largely localised. They also resemble the cœlenterates in their radial symmetry. It is when we come to the

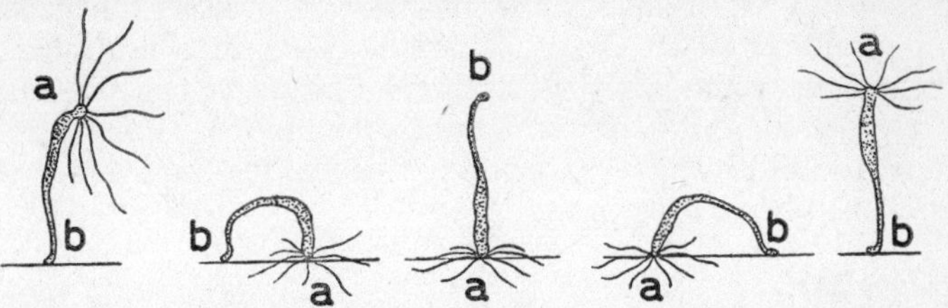

Figure 163. Walking movements of *Hydra*. (After Trembley.)

bilaterally symmetrical animals that we find a "brain." But in the simplest Metazoa which possess such an organ—the planarians, for example—this organ has few of the controlling functions it possesses in the higher animals.

(b) *Planarians*

We have seen (p. 251) that the "brain" of a planarian is mainly a receptive centre for impulses coming from the sense organs of the head region, but that it is also necessary for the co-ordination of more complicated types of behaviour which the animal can carry out *e.g.* the looping progression which occurs in some planarians (p. 252). It is probable that this behaviour can be initiated in the nervous system.

Reactions of the whole organism form a much greater part of the behaviour of the planarians than of the cœlenterates. As a rule, when a planarian is stimulated, the stimulation is carried over the whole body; local responses of parts of the body are comparatively rare.

* See J. E. Smith, *Biol. Rev.*, **20**, 29, 1945, for evidence of control of echinoderm behaviour; Kerkut, *Behaviour*, **6**, 206, 1954; **8**, 112, 1955.

This is due to the better transmission of stimulation in the planarian body, made possible by the development of the nerve cords of the inner nervous system. Also, the planarian nervous system, besides being more efficient than that of the cœlenterate, has one function in addition to those which the nerve-net is known to serve—we shall see that learning occurs in the planarian body. We know almost nothing of any structural basis on which the capacity for learning depends, but its development is correlated with the evolution of the nervous system and it is presumably a function of that system.

We have no evidence that the brain of a planarian has any functions different in type from those of the rest of the nervous system. Because the head region contains the greatest concentration of receptor organs, it is the most sensitive part of the body and initiation of behaviour by external stimuli most often occurs there. The control of behaviour by the brain is probably entirely due to its structure as a part of the nervous system through which many nervous paths go. It is probably for this reason that the brain is necessary for the more complicated behaviour of the planarians. The greater centralisation of behaviour in this group is, in fact, so far as we can see, almost entirely due to the better structural organisation of the nervous system. In this organisation the elaboration of the brain as a central part of the system is important.

(c) *Annelida*

The behaviour of the annelids is not essentially different in most of its features from that of the planarians, but the control exerted over the rest of the body by the head region and its ganglia, the "brain" of this group, is better developed. In an annelid the brain can initiate behaviour, and it also controls the tone of the muscles and the sensitivity in other parts of the body (p. 254). These last are new types of central control, types which become much more developed in higher animals.

In spite of the greater central control of behaviour in the annelids, local reactions still persist and are important in the behaviour. Much of the behaviour is, in fact, built up of such reactions which are transmitted from one part of the body to another. The conduction of a wave of contraction from segment to segment takes place in this way (p. 255). So, also, does the swimming of polychætes such as *Nereis* and many other examples of annelid behaviour.

(d) *Arthropods*

In some of the arthropod groups, the Crustacea, Arachnida and, above all, the insects, we find animals with behaviour immensely more complicated than anything we have so far considered. This complex behaviour is not characteristic of all arthropods. The behaviour of *Peripatus* and the myriapods is much simpler, and probably not very different in type from annelid behaviour.

As we have seen (ch. XVII), the receptor system of the higher arthropods is much more highly developed than that of any other invertebrates, with the possible exception of the cephalopods. In these arthropods the "brain" (the supra- and subœsophageal ganglia), which is, as in most other invertebrates, the main receptor centre of the body, is far more elaborate in structure, and more different from the other ganglia of the body in size, than in the annelids from which the arthropods have been evolved. Also, the nervous system of the arthropods has more widely spaced synapses than that of the annelid, and is therefore able to conduct impulses between the two ends of the body much more quickly. We thus have in the arthropods the structural basis for quicker response and more active behaviour than that of the annelid, and also for greater central control.

That the central control in the higher arthropods is greater than in the annelids is evident from observation of their behaviour. In almost all its typical behaviour such an arthropod as an insect reacts as a single organism. Local reactions are not evident in the normal behaviour. They do, however, occur in the arthropod body. We have seen (p. 260) that a headless insect can run and that a brainless crab can turn over. These actions are complex, being composed of numerous simpler reactions. But the reactions are restricted to the segments in which the legs, the effector organs concerned in them, lie—they are local reactions of these segments. In the normal behaviour of the animal these actions are co-ordinated with those of other parts of the body and built up into the centralised behaviour of the organism.

The manner in which this co-ordination takes place is illustrated by the results of some experiments on egg-laying in the silk-worm moth (*Bombyx mori*). The female of this moth normally lays its eggs on mulberry leaves in regular rows. A moth from which the head had been removed was found to be unable to choose a mulberry leaf on which to lay its eggs. This failure was clearly due to removal of the receptor organs necessary for the normal behaviour, and of the normal control which produces choice of the site for the eggs. But a headless moth could lay eggs and showed the movements of the legs which occur in egg-laying, so that the eggs were laid in rows. Even an abdomen separated from the thorax could still lay eggs, but it would only do so when it was stimulated by touch. It then showed the co-ordinated abdominal movements associated with egg-laying and deposited the eggs, but not in the normal rows. The co-ordination of these abdominal movements was more and more disturbed when the connections between the abdominal ganglia were cut one by one from the front. Their co-ordination was therefore due to impulses passing between these ganglia.

It appears from these results that the complex behaviour of egg-laying in this moth is based on numerous local reactions. Many of these are restricted to small parts of the body, and can occur in separated parts, but to produce the normal and complete behaviour they must be co-ordinated under the influence of sense stimuli. Local co-ordination between the ganglia of the body behind the head plays a part in the co-ordination of the behaviour, but the brain is always necessary if the behaviour of the arthropod is to be adapted to the animal's needs. Arthropod behaviour is probably always based upon local reactions co-ordinated in this way.

We have seen (p. 260) that in the arthropod the brain also controls —to a much greater extent than in the annelid—the tone of all the muscles and the sensitivity of the whole body. This is another type of central control of behaviour which is more highly developed in the arthropod.

We have now reached a type of behaviour which is almost perfectly centralised in the normal life of the animal. But the behaviour still shows its origin from the non-centralised behaviour of the simplest Metazoa in the occurrence of local reactions and in the fact that these local reactions still form the basal behaviour on which the central control is imposed.

The behaviour of the many groups of invertebrates which have not been mentioned in this discussion shows varying degrees of complexity and of the development of central control. Even within some of the invertebrate phyla the variations are great. We have seen that this is so in the arthropods. In the molluscs we find the very simple behaviour of the lamellibranchs and the complex and centralised behaviour of the cephalopods.

3. ORIENTATION

By orientation we mean determination of an animal's direction of movement by some character of the stimulation. Orientation is usually either positive or negative, the animal moves either directly towards or away from the source of stimulation.

In the Protista we found that orientation is brought about in either of two ways (pp. 92–4). It often results from a series of shock reactions which occur whenever the animal is unfavourably stimulated. By these shock reactions the animal is *in the end* brought into the part of the environment where the reactions do not occur and is forced to remain there. This is the way in which *Paramecium* and many flagellates become orientated. Secondly, in a few Protista, true directive behaviour occurs—the direction of the animal's movement after the response to a stimulus is determined by the direction from which the stimulation comes. Thus, the orientation is an *immediate* result of the direction of the stimulation. The behaviour of *Amœba* in chasing and catching its prey is an example of directive behaviour.

In multicellular animals directive behaviour is much commoner than among the Protista. A planarian, for instance, when it comes into a region in which dissolved substances are diffusing outwards from a piece of food, will turn its head so that it is more nearly in

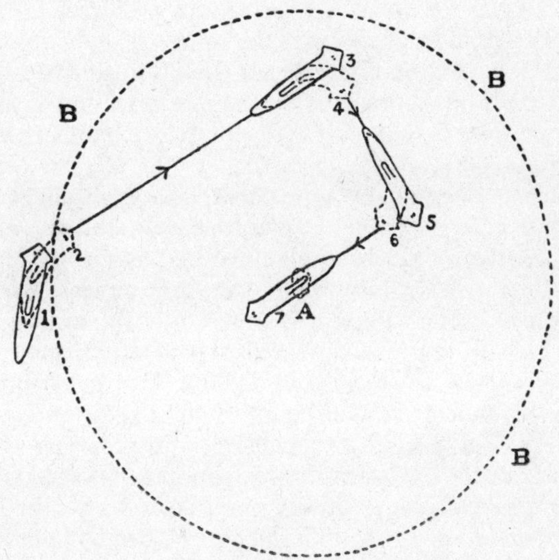

Figure 164. Feeding reactions of a planarian.

Substances diffusing from food at A outwards through the circle B cause successive reactions 1–2, 3–4, 5–6 by which the animal finally reaches the food. (After Pearl.)

the direction of the food and will then proceed in the new direction of the head (Fig. 164). This reaction is repeated until the animal is brought into contact with the food. Although the earlier of these reactions usually do not bring the animal directly to the food, this is still directive behaviour for the direction in which the head is turned is determined by the direction of the stimulation arising from the food.

We must ask how such behaviour is brought about. The actively moving, multicellular animals which show this behaviour are bilaterally symmetrical, and their receptor organs are symmetrically arranged on the two sides of the body. Their structure is therefore suitable for reactions such as those which the local action theory of tropisms (p. 97) postulates. If the interpretation suggested by this theory is correct, the sense organs on one side of the planarian body are stimulated more strongly by the substances diffusing from the food than those on the other side, and this unequal stimulation is transmitted from the sense organs on the two sides directly to the effector organs on the same sides. The muscles on the side towards the food would be supposed to be stimulated to contract more strongly, and the head therefore turned in that direction. This theory gives the simplest and perhaps the most probable interpretation of such simple reactions as the one we are discussing. It may be, indeed, that many similar reactions in invertebrates are forced movements of this type. Orientation away from the source of the stimulus—negative orientation—may be interpreted equally readily on these lines. The contraction of the muscles on the side most strongly stimulated must then be weaker than that of the muscles on the other side.

Even in complex invertebrates such as the insects forced movements which may be of this type occur. The spiral flight of a moth towards a candle may be so interpreted. In insects, evidence in favour of the theory has been obtained by obscuring one eye of the animal. If the insect is phototaxic (*i.e.* if its movements are controlled by the stimulus of light) and it is exposed to diffuse (*i.e.* non-directional) light with one eye obscured, it will often carry out circus movements, continually turning to one side. This behaviour is clearly due to the permanent lack of equilibrium in the stimulation of the two eyes, the darkened eye being unstimulated. The insect turns continuously either towards or away from the darkened side according as it is negatively or positively phototaxic. Later, the insect may *learn* to avoid these circus movements so that its course becomes straight. We shall discuss learning below.

Not all orientation in multicellular animals is due to these forced movements. At least in complex animals such as the insects, the behaviour is probably always complicated by less simple reactions. Even in the simpler invertebrates other types of orientation occur. If planarians are placed in a vessel which is illuminated from directly above but with a gradient of intensity of illumination from one end of the vessel to the other, they will be found to collect in the end of the vessel where the illumination is least. They are negatively phototaxic and would therefore move away from light in the plane of their movement, but in this experiment the light is at right angles to their plane of movement and therefore cannot cause any simple phototaxic movement. It has been shown that the orientation of the animals towards the region of least illumination is the result of an increase in the frequency of turning movements when the illumination of the animals is increasing. The animals' direction of movement alters from time to time in all circumstances, but it alters more frequently when they are moving towards a region of higher illumination. Thus, their movement is straight for longer periods when they are moving down the illumination gradient in the experimental vessel. This results in all the animals moving a greater distance in this direction and therefore ultimately collecting in the least illuminated part of the vessel.

This behaviour is in some ways parallel to the orientation of *Paramecium* which is produced by an indefinite number of shock reactions. The turning movements of the planarians, like the shock reactions of *Paramecium*, are random in direction and therefore do not each separately lead to orientation, though a series of the reactions does so. As in *Paramecium*, the behaviour is continued until the orientation is attained. The increased frequency of turning when the illumination is increasing may, in fact, be regarded as a shock reaction in the planarian.

Much of the orientation of insects cannot in any way be attributed to the types of orientation we have so far considered. A bee will return to its hive after a foraging expedition, or to a flower it has already visited. Many other insects that need to find their way back to a nest behave similarly. This behaviour clearly implies orientation towards the goal, but there is not necessarily any stimulation from the point to which the movement is directed. A bee will find its way back to the hive from points at which the hive is invisible and cannot be supposed to supply any stimulation.* This behaviour forces us to postulate learning from previous experience in the insects. It can in fact be shown that bees learn the features of the surroundings of their hive and use this experience in homing. Young bees are lost if they are taken a short distance from the hive, older bees return from distances of several miles. Presumably the bee is orientated by the stimuli which it receives from the surrounding objects during its flight, the orientating power of these stimuli being due to the previous experience, *i.e.* learning (p. 358).

We know almost nothing of the causes which determine differences in the orientation of animals. Thus, we do not know why some animals are positively and others negatively phototaxic. It has, however, been shown that the sign of orientation reactions may alter with changes in the physiological condition of the animals, as well as with the strength of stimulus. Changes of temperature and of the chemical constituents of the external environment, when this is aquatic, have been found to alter the orientation reactions of animals, and sometimes to reverse the sign of the orientation.

* Some types of orientation resulting from series of shock reactions share this feature, *e.g.* the behaviour of planarians just discussed. But the orientation of the bee is not interpretable as a series of shock reactions.

A typical example of change of phototaxic sign and the part it plays in the behaviour of an animal occurs in the larva of a moth, *Porthesia chrysorrhœa*. The eggs of this moth are laid on trees, and the larvæ when they first hatch are positively phototaxic and therefore move up the branches to their tips. There they find, and feed on, the new shoots which have just opened at the time that the eggs hatch. After feeding the larvæ cease to be positively phototaxic and wander down the branches, where they feed on the shoots which come out later. There is here not only change in phototaxy with physiological condition but also correlation of the behaviour and its changes with the needs of the larva. If the larvæ were not positively phototaxic when they hatch, they would not find their first food, the early shoots; if they remained so, they would starve by failing to find the later shoots.

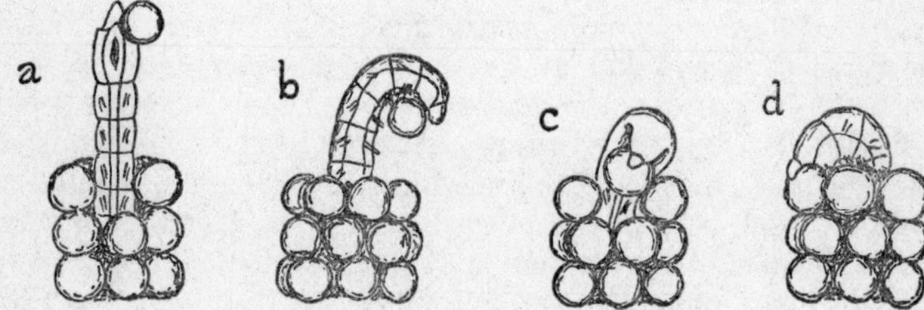

Figure 165. *a–d*, chain behaviour in *Aulophorus*.
Successive acts by which a spore is added to the tube. (After Carter and Beadle.)

4. CHAIN BEHAVIOUR

Chain behaviour consists of a series of actions each stimulated by the performance of the previous actions. We have met a simple example of this type of behaviour in the walking of a *Hydra*. A great part of invertebrate behaviour is composed of these chains of actions. The looping progression of a leech, for example, is chain behaviour which is exactly the same in type as the walking of *Hydra*. The attachment of each sucker stimulates sense organs in the sucker, and impulses from these sense organs initiate release of the other sucker and contraction or relaxation of the muscles by which the shape of the body is altered and its movements produced.

An example of somewhat more complex chain behaviour occurs in a small oligochæte (a species of *Aulophorus*). This worm lives in the surface layer of certain tropical swamps and makes for itself a tube of the spores of the water-ferns, *Azolla* and *Salvinia*, which are very plentiful at the surface of the swamp. The behaviour by which a spore is added to the tube is as follows (Fig. 165). The worm extends its head from the opening of the tube and waves it round until the prostomium comes into contact with a spore (*a*). The head is then bent and the spore is passed to the mouth and rotated there, perhaps by cilia (*b*). While being rotated it is probably covered with a sticky secretion. After this, the animal retracts into the tube with the head still bent and by this movement the spore is brought into contact with the top of the wall of the tube (*c*, *d*). It is held in this position for a short time (about 30 secs.), during which time it adheres to the wall. The head of the animal then straightens and the behaviour is complete.

This is clearly chain behaviour. The easiest interpretation is that performance of each action of the series is automatically stimulated as a result of the occurrence of the earlier actions. Some of the actions of the series are not single acts but are actions continued for a certain time.

In the arthropods chain behaviour forms a considerable proportion of the whole behaviour of the animal and is often very complex, especially in the insects. We will consider as an example of behaviour of this type the nest-building habits of solitary wasps. Many solitary wasps dig nests in the ground, fill them with food which will be eaten by the young after it hatches, lay an egg on the food and close the nest, often carefully hiding it. The nature of the food varies with the species; it is often caterpillars or spiders. The food is usually stung and paralysed but not killed.

We may consider in rather more detail the behaviour of a solitary wasp, *Ammophila campestris*, that has been carefully observed.* The wasp chooses a site for the nest in a sandy spot and digs until the nest is complete. It then seals the nest, hunts, catches, and stings a caterpillar, brings it to the nest, opens the nest, places the caterpillar in it and lays an egg. After sealing the nest, she leaves it for one or two days.

During this interval she starts a second nest in the same way as she started the first. Thereafter she returns to the first nest, opens and inspects it. If the egg has not yet hatched, she seals the nest and does no more to it for a day or two when she returns again. But if the egg is hatched she brings 1–3 more caterpillars and places them in the nest. After each visit she seals the nest. After the last of these visits she leaves this nest and provisions the second nest in the same way.

Thereafter, the wasp again returns to the first nest and provisions it with 3–7 more caterpillars. Finally, she seals it with much more than the usual care and goes to provision the second nest in the

* G. P. Baerends, *Tijdschr. voor Entom.*, **84**, 1, 1941; *Proc. Nederl. Akad. Wetensch.*, **44**, 1, 1941.

same way. This completes her work on these two nests, and she may then start two more.

This, again, is chain behaviour, and a very complex example of this type of behaviour. It can be clearly shown to be such by interrupting the chain. In general, in insect behaviour of this type, the succession in the chain cannot be modified. Either the chain is continued or it must be started again *de novo*. The behaviour differs in some features from the chain behaviour we have so far discussed. The occurrence of each action is not strictly determined in time. The seizing and stinging the prey, for instance, occur only when the prey is found, which may be sooner or later. And in dragging the prey to the nest the behaviour is not entirely stereotyped. Obstacles are avoided or overcome as they are met. What is determined is that the main behaviour types in the chain should follow one another in a fixed series. Search for prey follows the digging of the nest, and this succession is determined in the normal behaviour. The chain is not one of simple reflexes as are those in the behaviour of *Hydra* and the leech; it is rather a chain of complex behaviour patterns determined in the insect's central nervous system. Within these broad divisions of the behaviour, the separate acts appear to be stimulated by external stimuli. The wasp seizes the prey when it has found it and has come into close contact with it. It stings it when it has seized it and is in the correct position for doing so.

The change-over from one of the main behaviour types in a chain to the next is also frequently determined by external stimulation. This appears to be so at some steps in the wasp's behaviour. Digging of the nest continues until the nest is complete, which may take a longer or a shorter time. The change to hunting prey seems to be caused by stimuli provided by the complete nest. This aspect of insect chain behaviour is well illustrated by Fabre's experiment with processional caterpillars. These caterpillars migrate from one food plant to another in processions in which each caterpillar holds the tail of the one next in front of it, the first caterpillar of the procession leading the way. Fabre led a procession of these caterpillars up a stick on to the rim of a flower-pot, round which the procession proceeded to walk. When the first caterpillar had walked round the rim, he removed the part of the procession which had not reached the rim. The first caterpillar, finding itself behind another caterpillar, attached itself to its tail, so that a complete circle of caterpillars on the rim of the flower-pot was produced. The point of interest to us here is that this circle of caterpillars continued to walk round the flower-pot for many hours and only ceased to do so when they became so fatigued that they fell off. In the normal life of the caterpillar the walking would have ceased when the procession reached a new food plant, presumably as the result of stimulation provided by their arrival. In the experiment the stimulation which would have caused a change to another type of behaviour never took place, and the first type of behaviour continued indefinitely.

On the other hand, in some examples of insect chain behaviour the succession of the types of behaviour in the chain seems to be determined automatically, and not to depend on external stimulation. The following behaviour illustrates this point. Some mason wasps make nests of clay, often shaped as vases, on walls and other supports, and fill these nest with caterpillars (Fig. 166). In two species the experiment of breaking away the side or bottom of the nest soon after it was completed has been carried out, so that the prey fell out of the nest when it was put in by the wasp. The wasp of one species was observed to put in the correct number of caterpillars. In general—but *cf.* pp. 365–6—it then proceeded to seal the nest, although the caterpillars had fallen out and the nest was empty. That of the other species continued more or less indefinitely to bring caterpillars and put them in the nest. In the one species the number of hunting trips was fixed, in the other the change from hunting to the next type of behaviour was apparently determined by stimulation provided by a full nest.

Figure 166. Nest of a mason wasp.

Behaviour such as that of the wasp in forming its nest and filling it may justifiably be called "*instinctive*," but the term *instinct* has been used in so many senses that, if it is used, it should be carefully defined. Shortly, instinct may be defined as "*an inherited psycho-physical disposition.*" * The wasp has a complex instinct to form its nest, and this instinct is built up of the less-complex instincts of the behaviour of digging, filling the nest, laying the egg, and so on. It should be noted, however, that in complex behaviour such as this many of the details of the behaviour are determined by the external stimulation of the moment and are not instinctive. The wasp's actions in bringing the prey to the nest are in detail determined by the circumstances in which it finds itself, and are not controlled by the inherited instincts. The whole behaviour consists of an instinctive core associated with much detailed behaviour elicited by external stimulation. Instinctive behaviour in animals is almost always of this nature.†

One other characteristic of the automatic behaviour of animals deserves mention. This is that an instinctive activity is very often called into action by a very simple stimulus. Often animals, even the

* W. H. Thorpe, *Brit. J. Psychol.*, 33, 220, 1943. Other definitions of instinct are "an inborn movement form" (Lorenz), or "a fixed pattern of behaviour" (Tinbergen).

† W. H. Thorpe, *Bull. anim. Behaviour*, No. 7, Feb., 1948.

most complex animals, react not to the whole situation but to some quite simple feature of it. A robin in its territory is stimulated to fight another male robin by seeing the red feathers of its breast, and will so attack a patch of red feathers even though they are not on another robin. Insects behave in the same way. A wasp that provisions its nest with bees has been shown to recognise them as bees by their smell, and by this feature alone. It will take and sting other flying insects if they are made to smell like bees.* These simple stimuli are called the *releasers* of the instincts that they call up. Realisation of their simplicity is one of the most striking results of recent study of animal behaviour.

There is much more of interest in the wasp behaviour than we have here discussed, but our discussion will at least have made clear the fundamental characters of the behaviour.

5. LEARNING

All the types of behaviour we have so far considered are composed of behaviour patterns which are completely determined in the animal, presumably in its hereditary constitution. The behaviour patterns are very often, as we have just seen in chain behaviour, caused to occur by external stimulation, but the pattern of the behaviour is determined and, in the behaviour we have so far considered, not modifiable during the life of the animal.

There is, however, one type of modifiable behaviour which must without question be attributed to the invertebrates. This is the ability to vary behaviour by learning. As the result of experience, the pattern of the behaviour is altered—modification has occurred during the life of the animal. The modifications consist in changes in the association of stimulus and response; the responses initiated by stimulation are altered.†

It can be shown that comparatively simple invertebrates are capable of learning. A planarian (*Leptoplana*) has been found to possess this faculty. This animal starts to move actively when it is brought from the dark into the light. In some experiments a *Leptoplana* was brought into the light and stimulated by a touch at the front end as soon as it started to move. The touch inhibited the movement, but at first this movement started again after a short interval. Whenever this happened the stimulation was repeated, and, in the first experiment, it was found that the movement did not cease permanently until the animal had been stimulated 150 times. The animal was then replaced in the dark and the experiment was repeated

* N. Tinbergen, *Z. vergl. Physiol.*, **16**, 305, 1932; **21**, 699, 1935. *Cf.* E. S. Russell, *Proc. Linn. Soc.*, *London*, 1941–2, p. 195.

† Learning is sometimes restricted to *adaptive* modifications of behaviour (Thorpe, *Brit. J. Psychol.*, 33, 220, 1943).

after it had again become adapted to the absence of light. It was found in a series of these experiments on the same animal that the number of stimulations needed to produce permanent inhibition of the movement decreased, until a condition was finally reached in which the animal did not begin to move at all when brought into the light. The animal had "learnt" not to move when it was brought into the light. The association of the stimulus of light with the response of movement had been inhibited. This learning in the planarian has been shown to be retained to some extent, though not completely, for a considerable time (10 hours). It fades out, but the fading is slow.*

We have already seen (p. 344) that the behaviour of animals may be altered by changes in the general physiological condition of the body. This occurs both in Protista (*Stentor rœselii*, pp. 95–6) and in multicellular animals (*e.g.* changes in the sign of orientation, pp. 353–4). But the learning phenomena we are here discussing are different from these changes. We have no reason to suppose any *general* physiological change in the *Leptoplana* as the result of the series of experiments. It is very difficult to believe in any such general change that could persist for a considerable time. Clearly the change of behaviour in learning is due to some change in the conditions within the body (p. 345), but it seems much more probable that the learning is due to some change or changes within the nervous system of the animal, changes much more like those which follow the arrival of a stimulus (pp. 344 f.) than any more general physiological change. Certainly, they are changes that can survive change of almost any other kind in the body. Learning has for instance been found to survive metamorphosis in insects.† Whatever the structural basis of learning may be, it is undoubtedly a process by which the behaviour of animals can be modified during their life, and it occurs in animals as simple as the planarians.

Learning can be shown to occur in many other invertebrates. An earthworm, for instance, can be taught the T problem. If it is placed in the longer arm of a T-shaped tube and exposed to light, it is stimulated by the light to move forwards and will in time reach the branching of the T, where it can turn in either direction. If it receives some unpleasant stimulus every time it turns in one direction, it will, after a number of trials, always turn in the other direction. This is typical *conditioned* behaviour in which the association of an action with the stimuli which produce it has been learnt and is not given in the hereditary constitution of the animal. The worm has *learnt* to

* G. Humphrey (*Psych. Forschr.*, **13**, 1930) gives an even simpler example of learning in the snail.

† A. C. Crombie, *J. exp. Biol.*, **20**, 166, 1944.

turn in the one direction when it receives the stimulus of reaching the branching of the T. It has been shown that this learning is retained in an earthworm after removal of the head and its ganglia. An earthworm from which the anterior five segments had been removed was found to retain the learnt habit. Learning has also been observed in molluscs (snails) and crustacea (crabs.)

In the behaviour of the insects learning is probably of much greater importance than in that of the less complex invertebrates. Insects can learn much more quickly than simpler animals, and learned reactions are much more frequent in their behaviour. Visual stimuli play a very large part in this as in other features of insect behaviour. A bee, for instance, can be conditioned to search for food on a background of a certain colour. The phenomena in insects that seem at first sight to demand "memory" are learning phenomena, but the learning is often acquired after few repetitions of the stimulus. The homing of bees (p. 353), and also of ants and many other insects, is behaviour of this type. It is conditioned by previous stimuli, probably mainly visual, proceeding from the surroundings of the insects in journeys to and from the nest. We shall see immediately that this is not to say that the insects recognise objects from their past experience called up in remembered mental images, as we do (*cf.* below, p. 362).*

6. THE HIGHEST TYPES OF INVERTEBRATE BEHAVIOUR

It can be maintained that all the behaviour of the simpler invertebrates is covered by the account which has been given.† Behaviour in many of these animals may be modified by learning, and the importance of the phenomena of learning in the behaviour of the animal increases as we pass up the series of invertebrates. The behaviour may originate automatically in the nervous system, or be initiated by stimulation. Always the type of behaviour which occurs is determined by the hereditary constitution of the species. Learning may alter the responses to stimulation; but no new types of behaviour are originated during the animal's life.

We must now ask whether this description covers all invertebrate behaviour. Do any, even the most complex, invertebrates show that they possess any faculties in control of their behaviour more like our own mental faculties? The most complex invertebrate behaviour is

* For a fuller discussion of learning and of its various types, see W. H. Thorpe, *Brit. J. Psychol.*, 33, 220, 1943, and *Proc. Linn. Soc., London*, 1943–4, p. 70; also in *Symposium of Soc. Exp. Biol.*, Cambridge, 1949. *Cf.* also G. Humphrey, *The Nature of Learning*, Kegan Paul, 1933.

† *Cf.* Thorpe, *Learning and Instinct in Animals*, for other views.

that of insects, and if any higher mental faculties are to be found in invertebrates it is among the insects that we may expect to find them. We shall therefore consider only the insects in the discussion of these questions.

It must first be noted that many features of insect behaviour have not yet been considered.

1. In much of insect behaviour it is clear that the animal is reacting to a *situation*, *i.e.* to the whole complex of stimuli reaching the animal at any one time and not to the stimuli separately and independently. A bee or an ant returning to the nest is clearly doing so; the animal is orientated by the whole situation in which it finds itself during its flight.* We have seen (p. 344) that all animal behaviour should accurately be regarded as determined by the whole physiological condition of the animal and never by the arrival of a single stimulus. A reaction is merely a change in behaviour due to the change in physiological condition produced by the stimulus. In animals with such complex receptor systems as those of the insects, the stimuli are much more numerous than in the simpler animals, and many reach the animal simultaneously. It is the effect of these numerous stimuli, *i.e.* of the whole situation in which the animal finds itself, that modifies the condition of the animal and therefore produces the changes in its behaviour. This feature of insect behaviour is, however, no more than an elaboration of the reactive system. It demands no new mental faculties.

2. Insects may be able to appreciate *pattern* in the stimuli they receive. If a bee, which has been trained to collect food from pieces of paper, is given the choice between pieces of simple shapes such as squares or circles, and pieces similar in other respects but of complex shapes more or less resembling the flowers from which it is accustomed in its normal life to collect its food, it will choose the complex shapes. These and other experiments show that bees are able to appreciate pattern. The structure of the compound eye is well adapted for this purpose.

That insects have this power of recognising pattern is of great interest, for it makes it possible that they react to their surroundings as composed of *objects* and not as complexes of varying stimuli (*e.g.* different shades of light) and nothing more. We appreciate our surroundings in this way and the behaviour of the higher vertebrates shows that they also do. The power of reacting to objects is clearly a large step forward in the reactions of an animal to the outside world. It is impossible to any animal which has not an eye capable of

* This *may* imply a higher faculty, "insight"—"the grasping of relevant or essential relations between the features or objects entering into a total situation" (MacDougall). It does not necessarily imply insight.

forming an image, for without such an eye the animal cannot recognise the pattern which represents the object.

It must be emphasised, however, that this power of reacting to objects does not necessitate any *conscious* realisation of the objects in a mental image, such as the mental images we ourselves have. All that we need to postulate is that the animals react to the pattern of stimuli coming from the object. Nor does it imply any recognition of the objects as solid bodies in a 3-dimensional world.*

Reaction to objects requires no higher mental faculty than appreciation of a situation. It is an elaboration of the system of reaction. Stimuli are here recognised by the patterns they form.

3. Insects and other invertebrates are able to continue on a course of behaviour for a considerable time when the behaviour has once been started. They can then be diverted from this behaviour only with difficulty. In ourselves we should describe this as "concentrating the attention" on the actions in hand. But in animals such as insects all that this necessarily implies is that in an animal carrying out some action (or series of actions in chain behaviour) a large stimulus is required to cause an alteration to another type of behaviour. At such a time the animal's sensitivity is lowered to stimuli except those associated with the course of behaviour it is performing. This requires differentiation between groups of stimuli and alterations in sensitivity from time to time, but these again do not require any higher faculties in control of the behaviour than those we have discussed.

4. The occurrence of communal behaviour in the insects must be mentioned, though we have not space to discuss it in any detail. Insects often live together in communities and their behaviour towards other members of the same community is different from that towards outsiders. In insect communities a very large body of behaviour becomes built up round the life of the community. We shall discuss below whether any of this, or other, insect behaviour is non-automatic, but in so far as it is automatic this behaviour demands no higher mental functions than the automatic behaviour of non-social insects. The life of the community is the situation in which the social insect lives, a complex situation but one which is not different in its essential characters from those in which other insects live. Here again we are dealing with specialisations of the receptor system. Often it appears that the threshold of stimulation is lower towards stimuli from members of the same community than towards other stimuli. But often the reactions within the community may be entirely different from those to stimulation coming from outside it—a

* Nevertheless, homing in bees and other insects implies appreciation of a 3-dimensional world and of distance.

stranger ant is killed or thrown out of the nest, a member of the same nest is not.

So far we have been able to interpret invertebrate behaviour as resulting from elaborations of the simple systems of automatic reactions from which we started. We have not found it necessary to postulate any type of self-consciousness; so far we have considered the animal as no more than an automatic reacting system. As we shall see, by far the greater part of even the complex behaviour of an insect can be accounted for on these lines. It should be realised how far the mental life required by an animal capable of no other types of behaviour is from our own. It may be able to carry out very complicated behaviour patterns but it will not be able to modify them except by learning. It need not be able to realise its own existence, nor the existence of the objects of the outside world by which it is surrounded. It is hard for us to imagine what the life of such an animal will be like.

We can now return to the question whether it is necessary to postulate any higher mental function in the interpretation of insect behaviour. We may first ask what are the types of control that we should expect to be first evolved in an animal which was passing beyond the behaviour we have already discussed? All types of behaviour higher than those we have discussed are without doubt in the field of psychology rather than of zoology, and it is outside the scheme of this book to discuss them in detail. We may, however, discuss whether there is any evidence for these higher systems of behaviour-control in invertebrates and especially in the insects.

Below the psychological level, learning is probably the only manner in which behaviour can be modified during the animal's life. All other types of modifiable behaviour demand the presence of a conscious mental life, however ill-developed it may be. We must therefore ask how consciousness would first show itself in the evolution of animals.

It is probable that consciousness would first appear in an animal as the ability to think about objects and situations not present at the time of thought. But we cannot investigate whether animals possess such a mental life—there is no way in which we can get evidence on the point. Only an animal's behaviour can be investigated, never its mental life whether conscious or unconscious. We must therefore pass to the psychological phenomenon which is likely to arise next in evolution. This will probably be a realisation of the end to which behaviour is directed, *i.e.* appreciation of a future situation ("foresight"). This implies thought of a non-present situation, for it is only in such thought that a future situation can be appreciated. We can investigate whether animals have this faculty. We can find out whether their behaviour is such that we are forced to believe that they realise the end towards which they are acting.*

We have therefore to ask (1) whether any insect behaviour, in addition to the phenomena of learning, must be interpreted as modifiable—for, if not, no higher mental functions are required—and (2) whether, if there is any such behaviour, insects realise the end towards which they are acting.

There cannot be the least doubt that by far the greater part of even the most complex insect behaviour can be interpreted without any demand for higher mental faculties. Let us take a typical example of insect behaviour and see how far this is true of it. We will choose an example which has been investigated to some extent.†

When foraging, an ant finds a large piece of food, the whole of which it is not able to carry back to the nest. It is "excited" by its find, that is to say its activity is increased and its behaviour is altered in other ways. It returns to the nest carrying a part of the food and guided by its previous experience of the way. In the nest it meets other ants. It is the usual behaviour that ants of the same nest, when they meet, should "communicate" by touching their antennæ together. In this communication the excited state of the first ant is handed on to the second. There is no evidence for any more detailed communication. An "antennal code" has often been postulated, *i.e.*, it has been supposed that complex messages may be passed, but there is not the least proof that this occurs. The state of excitement so communicated is associated with the foraging, for many of the stimulated ants leave the nest and go in search of the food which the first ant has found. It has been shown that they find the way to the food by following a trail, presumably chemical, laid down by the first ant. The laying of this trail is apparently associated, probably quite automatically, with the state of excitement; the first ant automatically lays it down as it returns to the nest. The trail is, however, certainly complex. It has been shown to be different in its various parts, probably graded from the food to the nest. This is proved by the following experiment. The ant that finds the food is made to cross a piece of paper in returning to the nest. This paper is turned round before the following ants reach it, so that the trail is in the same line as before but reversed in direction. It is found that these ants are much disturbed when they come to the paper and have difficulty in following the trail across it.

* Behaviour so directed to an aim may justifiably be called *intelligent*, another of the many psychological terms that are used in many senses. The term intelligent is best restricted to behaviour of this type, behaviour in which the animal appreciates its aims. Certainly, it should not be used to apply to all forms of learning.

† Thorpe, *Learning and Instinct in Animals*, 1956, pp. 213 ff.; Carthy, *Animal Navigation*, 1956, pp. 18 ff.

When the following ants reach the food, they are excited, as the first ant was, and behave in the same way as it did. Thus, the supply of ants foraging the food is kept up until the food is exhausted.

The behaviour is in fact much more complicated than this. It contains many reactions which have not been mentioned. But in all this behaviour there is nothing to force us to demand for the ants any of the higher faculties we have been discussing. Learning enters the behaviour in the return of the original ant to the nest. Apart from this the whole behaviour seems to be composed of automatic reactions, either succeeding each other in chains of behaviour or initiated by appropriate stimulation. This is as true of the parts of the behaviour which have not been mentioned as of those we have discussed. The whole behaviour is very closely adapted to the needs of the life of the ants. It varies much between species.

All *typical* insect behaviour, even the most complicated, such as the use of aphids as cows by ants, or the cultivation of fungi by the harvesting ants, can, so far as we can see, be wholly interpreted on these lines. Typical insect behaviour is complicated because the reactions which compose it are numerous, and because many long chains of behaviour patterns occur in it, but not for any other reasons. It is, so far as we can see, entirely automatic and modifiable only by learning.*

Nevertheless, insect behaviour which seems at first sight to require higher mental faculties is occasionally observed. Such observations are not frequent, and it may be thought doubtful whether they really force us to postulate these faculties in the insect. We will take only two examples of these observations.

In the experiments on the mason wasps mentioned above (p. 357) the wasp usually continued the normal chain of behaviour after the bottom of the nest had been broken. This was to be expected if the behaviour was automatic, for the chain of behaviour-patterns is normally determined in order. On one occasion, however, the wasp, after having brought some caterpillars which fell out of the nest, found the hole and was much disturbed. It then repaired the hole by building a new part of the wall over it. In doing this it returned to the behaviour of building the nest, and thus disturbed the normal sequence of its chain behaviour. On another occasion a wasp brought caterpillars to the broken nest, and one of these did not completely fall out of the nest but remained hanging half out of the hole. The

* The very elaborate behaviour of bees by which they direct other members of the hive to sources of honey is probably explicable on the same lines, though here the difficulties of the explanation may be greater. (K. von Frisch, transltd. by W. H. Thorpe, *Bull. Anim. Behaviour*, No. 5, 1947, No. 9, 1951; see also *Nature*, **164**, 11, 1949.)

wasp then brought more caterpillars and placed them in the nest, but later she examined the hanging caterpillar, pushed it back into the nest and sealed the hole.

At first sight these observations seem to require that the wasp in both cases realised the position and took steps to put it right. If so, she must have very high mental faculties. She must at least be able to realise the end to which her behaviour is proceeding. But it is doubtful whether the observations require these conclusions. In the second case it seems more probable that the wasp, having found the caterpillar hanging out of the nest and being therefore in the same situation as she is in when she puts caterpillars into the nest in the normal course of her behaviour, acted as she would normally act in these circumstances. She pushed the caterpillar into the nest. She had trouble in doing so, as she would have when she was putting a caterpillar into a nearly full nest. So she sealed the hole, as she normally seals the hole through which she has filled the nest. Similarly, in the first case, the wasp, being in the presence of an incomplete nest when she found the hole, carried out the behaviour normal to these circumstances; she completed the building. We must suppose that she acted thus in both cases in spite of the fact that the circumstances were not entirely normal. The hole, for instance, was at the bottom of the nest and not at the top as in normal building. But we know that animals will often carry out their normal behaviour in abnormal conditions—a hen will brood and hatch duck's eggs.

What these observations show us very clearly is that insect chain behaviour is not irrevocably determined in the sequence of its behaviour types. We have seen that in the normal behaviour the change from one type of behaviour to the next is often instigated by external stimulation (p. 356). We find here that when the animal receives stimulation appropriate to some part of the behaviour chain which it is not carrying out at the moment of stimulation, the stimulation may occasionally instigate the behaviour which normally follows it, even though this disturbs the sequence of the chain behaviour. When the wasp finds a hole in the nest, she is in contact with an incomplete nest and therefore starts to build. When she finds a caterpillar half out of the nest, she behaves as she does normally to caterpillars so placed. In both cases, the sequence of the chain behaviour is disturbed.

We cannot discuss here whether such interpretations as these will cover all the observations of insect behaviour which seem at first sight to require the presence of higher mental faculties in the insects. There are other facts in insect behaviour, in the use of objects as tools, in some features of ant-behaviour, and especially in the facts of insight-learning (*i.e.* learning that seems to require insight), that have been thought to imply that the animal can realise its aim.* It can only be said that many biologists do not at present regard the evidence for the existence of any of the higher faculties in any invertebrate as conclusive. At least it is clear that we should be extremely cautious before attributing such faculties to invertebrates. We should make every effort to interpret the behaviour on simpler lines, even if the interpretation is difficult and perhaps seems forced. Probably we ought not to accept the presence of these faculties until we know much more of the simpler types of behaviour and of the modifications of which these types of behaviour are capable. Even then we should accept their existence only if the accumulation of evidence makes it impossible to avoid doing so. Nevertheless, it is true that observations which make difficult interpretation of all insect behaviour as purely automatic have been accumulating in recent years.

* See the papers by Thorpe previously cited, p. 360.

CHAPTER XXII

HABITS OF LIFE IN THE INVERTEBRATES

WHEN we come to consider the life of invertebrate animals in their environments, we reach an unusually complex and detailed subject, an even more difficult subject than the similar study of the Protista which we have already discussed (ch. V). The species of the invertebrates are extremely numerous and each has its own range and its own interactions with the environment, both physical and biological. Also, the environments in which invertebrates live are often small, and investigation of the conditions in such environments is difficult. Since invertebrates, like other animals, are frequently sensitive to very small changes in these conditions, it will be clear that determination of the conditions on which their life depends will often be difficult or even impossible. We have a large and detailed knowledge of invertebrate ecology, but it is not a subject from which general conclusions can be easily drawn, and certainly not a subject which can be summarised in a single chapter.

We will therefore confine our discussion to a single aspect of invertebrate ecology, the distinction between the three chief types of habit of life in invertebrate (and other) animals. These habits of life are those of the free-living and motile animal, the sessile animal, and the parasite, habits which lead to systems of organisation and physiology so different from each other that there can be no doubt that the distinction between these habits is the primary classification into which the life of animals should be divided.

Free life is the primitive habit for at least the great majority of invertebrate Metazoa. This is so in spite of the fact that the simplest Metazoa living to-day, the cœlenterates, are typically sessile, at least for large parts of their life-histories, and have the type of organisation, radial symmetry, which is, as we shall see, usually associated with the sessile habit. But all sessile Metazoa except the cœlenterates give clear evidence of being descended from free-living ancestors (ch. XXIII). We do not know whether the cœlenterates also are secondarily sessile, but if not they stand apart from all other invertebrate Metazoa in this respect. The reverse change, from sessile to free life, is rare; it has certainly occurred in one only of the major invertebrate groups, the echinoderms.

We know very little of the evolutionary history of the sponges. We cannot say whether they should be considered primitively sessile. They have free-living larvæ and may have been descended from free-living ancestors, or, perhaps, from a sessile protistan group.

Further evidence that free life is primitive to invertebrates is the fact that this type of life is characteristic of the great majority of animal species at all stages of evolution, among the Protista as well as among the Metazoa. It is the typical mode of life of animals, and it is unlikely to have been lost in the ancestors of the Metazoa and then to have been regained in the majority of them.

Parasitism is still more clearly a secondary and non-primitive mode of life. Only where we know nothing of the evolutionary history of parasitic animals (*e.g.* in the nematodes) can their descent from free-living, or occasionally sessile (Rhizocephala), forms be doubted. A few parasites may have returned to free life—the free-living nematodes are a possible example—but this is no evidence against the belief that the parasitic habit itself is secondary.

The early invertebrate must have been aquatic as well as free-living. A simple animal can survive only in an aquatic environment, for in all other environments greater adaptation is required for active life than is compatible with simple organisation. In the simpler invertebrates, as in the Protista (p. 100), only protected and inactive stages can live in non-aquatic environments.

We can make one other statement about the mode of life of the earliest invertebrates. The animal body is always heavier than water, unless it has special adaptations such as oil-drops, air-bladders, etc., which will enable it to float. It is unlikely that a primitive animal would have these adaptations, and, if not, it could only keep itself above the bottom of its environment by its own activity. It is true that a large proportion of the Protista are not bottom-living forms; many of them swim freely in aquatic environments. But, as we have seen (pp. 48, 104), increase in size above that of the Protista is a characteristic feature of multicellular animals, and the larger an animal is the more rapidly it will sink and the more energy will be required to keep it afloat. The early metazoan was probably larger than most of the Protista and, with its simple organisation, is not likely to have been free-swimming.

We must think then of the early invertebrate as a free-living animal inhabiting the bottom of an aquatic environment. That this was its mode of life is confirmed by the fact that almost all invertebrates, that are not sessile or parasitic, possess bilateral symmetry, which is characteristic of animals living such a life as this. The larvæ of these early invertebrates, so long as they were small enough, may well have been planktonic (ch. XXIII).

1. FREE LIFE

There are several characters which are general in the organisation of free-living animals. We will discuss these in turn.

(a) *Bilateral Symmetry*

The early metazoan, living a free-moving life on a surface at the bottom of an aquatic environment would be in an environment which was differentiated between the regions above and below its body. We should expect that this would result in evolution of dorso-ventral differentiation in the animal. Also, in the animal's free movement it is to be expected that one end would normally go in front, and this we should expect to result in anterior-posterior differentiation of the body. With the differentiations of these two axes the animal necessarily becomes bilaterally symmetrical.

We may therefore conclude that bilateral symmetry was evolved in an early bottom-living metazoan. The cœlenterates alone among the metazoan groups may not have had such a bilateral ancestor.

Bilateral symmetry is not to-day confined to bottom-living animals. Many other environments are as clearly differentiated between upper and lower as life on the bottom of an aquatic environment. This is true of all types of aerial environment, of free-swimming life in water, of life at the surface of water, and so on. We should therefore expect that this type of symmetry would be retained when an actively moving animal invaded these other environments, and we find that this is so; most free-living animals in these environments have bilateral symmetry. It is only when the movements due to an animal's own activities become unimportant for its life that another type of symmetry begins to appear. Thus, many floating animals, especially among the marine plankton, show a tendency towards radial symmetry (Radiolaria and some Foraminifera—Fig. 23, Plate V—among the Protista, many metazoan larvæ, Fig. 169, p. 391, etc.). For such floating animals, so long as they are not themselves actively motile, there is no differentiation in the environment on their different sides, though there is differentiation between upper and lower. Such conditions naturally lead to radial symmetry—we shall see that the very similar conditions of sessile life also lead to this type of symmetry. Nevertheless, the radial symmetry of planktonic animals is hardly ever complete, nor is the tendency towards this type of symmetry universal in planktonic animals. It could not be expected that it should be so, for many planktonic animals, though their horizontal distribution is determined by currents and not by their own movements, are still motile and make use of their movements for such purposes as controlling their vertical distribution, capture of food, and so on. When they do so, we should expect differentiation of two axes in their bodies, one correlated with their own movements and one with the conditions of the environment. They should be bilaterally and not radially symmetrical animals.

(b) *Cephalisation*

The tendency for increased differentiation, as evolution proceeds, of the front end of the body, the head, for its special functions is to be found in most invertebrate phyla. The chief functions of this part of the body are reception of stimulation from the environment and capture of food. We find therefore greater development of the nervous system and sense organs in the head than in other parts of the body, and also development of organs around the mouth which are used in food-capture. This differentiation of the head is known as *cephalisation*—the animal acquires a better and more highly organised head. We have already discussed the part which this region of the body and the nervous organs contained in it play in the control of the behaviour of the animal (chs. XVI, XXI).

In many invertebrate groups other parts of the body become specialised for certain special functions—the thorax of the arthropods is mainly concerned with locomotion and the abdomen contains the greater part of the nutritive organs—but, in invertebrates as a whole, there is no such general specialisation of parts of the body behind the head as there is of the head. These other specialisations cannot therefore be considered direct results of the conditions of free life, and we will not consider them here.

(c) *Locomotory Organs, etc.*

The need for rapid movement in the free-living animal, in order that it may capture its food, escape from its enemies and so on, naturally leads to evolution of complexity and efficiency in the locomotory organs. We find this evolution in many groups of free-living animals. But in the animal body evolution in one system of organs necessarily leads to parallel evolution in other systems. The locomotory organs cannot become complex without corresponding increase in the complexity of the nervous system by which their movements are controlled, of the circulatory system and so on. We may indeed regard the need for rapid movement in the free-living animal as one of the chief causes of the evolution of complex structure in multicellular animals, and also, perhaps, of the increase of size which we have seen to be general in evolution (p. 46), for the larger an animal is, the more easy rapid movement is for it. Rapid movement is one of the ways in which animals acquire greater isolation from environmental changes (p. 49).

(d) *Metameric Segmentation*

This type of organisation, internal division of the body by transverse septa, is not general among free-living animals. But it seems to be a direct result of one type of free movement and may for this reason be considered here. It occurs in the annelids, and the arthropods which are descended from them, and in the chordates. It should be clearly distinguished from the segmentation which results from incomplete separation of the bodies of distinct individual animals, as in platyhelminthes which form chains of buds (*Planaria* or *Stenostomum*, pp. 136, 144), and probably in adult tapeworms. In metameric segmentation the divisions are within a single body.

The annelids and the chordates also agree in having the same type of locomotory organ, a body moved rhythmically by the passing of alternate contractions down the muscles on its two sides. Few other large groups of animals have either of these characters. Nevertheless, the annelids and chordates are, as we shall see (ch. XXIII), by no means closely related; the occurrence of this type of locomotion and of metameric segmentation in association in these two groups cannot be due to any close evolutionary relatedness of the groups. There must be some functional reason for it.

It is easy to see what is the functional reason why the type of locomotion which the annelids and chordates possess should be associated with metameric segmentation. The passage of a rhythm of contraction up or down a body demands contraction of the muscles successively at one point after the next as we pass along the body. Clearly such a rhythm would be most easily brought about if the muscles were divided transversely into small groups each of which could be stimulated to contract as a unit. Each unit could then be made to contract in turn either through the nervous system or in response to stimulation provided by the contraction of the units adjacent to it (pp. 255–6). But this division into units means that the muscles would become transversely segmented, and the nervous system by which the muscles were controlled would also tend to become segmented. It is not improbable that the segmentation would spread from these two systems to the other organs of the body, and that so the whole body would become metamerically segmented. We must, in fact, regard metameric segmentation as an adaptation to effective use of this type of locomotion.

This seems to have been the probable origin of metameric segmentation and to explain its occurrence in two distantly related groups of animals, but it is not necessary that all animals which have this type of locomotion should be metamerically segmented. In fact, we find that not all such animals are so segmented. Among the chordates, the urochordates are without obvious metameric segmentation, although the tail is used in the tadpole larva and in the Larvacea for swimming in the normal chordate manner. Many nemertines can also swim in this way though their bodies are not segmented.* The swimming of some planarians by rhythms of contraction along the sides of the body (p. 252) is also locomotion of this type and it occurs in bodies which are not segmented. Metameric segmentation seems to be an adaptation to the more effective use of this type of movement; it is not essential that all animals that swim in this way should have it.

2. THE SESSILE HABIT

In evolution, so long as an animal remains free-living, the fundamental features of its organisation are unaltered, although enormous modifications of the details of their structure may take place. Thus, in its basic arrangement the organisation of the body is identical in the annelid and the highest arthropods; and the organisation of the highest vertebrates is identical with that of *Amphioxus*. There has been no reorganisation of the fundamental plan of the body in either of these two long evolutionary lines. But when a group of animals passes from free-moving life to a sessile habit or to parasitism we find that the organisation of their bodies becomes greatly altered in plan, and these alterations may occur in relatively small groups of animals, such as the barnacles or urochordates. Among the copepods, parasitic groups as small as families show complete loss of the typical crustacean organisation which families closely related to them possess.

These facts emphasise, first, the strictness of the control which the conditions of free-moving life must have exerted in evolution over the organisation of an animal; and the similarity of these conditions in all types of such life, for we find examples of almost every type of free life between the annelid and the insect or between *Amphioxus* and the mammal. Secondly, they show us that these conditions are greatly and fundamentally altered whenever the animal ceases to be free-living and becomes either sessile or parasitic.

A very marked feature of the organisation of sessile animals is that they tend to lose the bilateral symmetry of the free-living animal. This tendency is almost general in sessile animals. Only few sessile groups retain bilateral symmetry completely (Lamellibranchiata); in many others, such as the barnacles and the urochordates, some features of bilateral symmetry are retained, and in some—*e.g.* the adult echinoderm, the structure of which is believed to be due to sessility even though many of them have become secondarily free—

* The repetition of some organs along the nemertine body may indicate incomplete metameric segmentation.

all or almost all traces of bilateral symmetry are absent. This type of symmetry is, indeed, replaced by another, radial symmetry, which is typical of sessile animals. Even where the body is not completely radial, there is usually a tendency in sessile animals towards the assumption of this type of symmetry (Rotifera, Polyzoa, etc.).

Radial symmetry is clearly appropriate for a sessile animal. To such an animal there is still differentiation between the substratum and the medium above, and this axis, that between the free and attached ends of the body, therefore, becomes differentiated. But around this axis the environment is for a sessile animal more or less the same in all directions, just as it is for a planktonic animal leading an inactive, floating life in an aquatic environment (p. 370). We should therefore expect that the body of a sessile animal would become radially arranged around the axis between its free and attached ends, *i.e.* that the animal would have radial symmetry around this axis. This, in fact, is what we find. Usually the mouth comes to be at the free end of the animal although this was not necessarily the anterior end before the animal became sessile. In the echinoderms the axis of radial symmetry is frequently at an angle to the anterior-posterior axis of the bilateral larva, which we must suppose to represent an earlier bilateral stage in the evolution of the group (ch. XXIII).

There are other features which are typical of sessile animals. One of the most obvious of these is the frequency with which such animals have developed some method of filter-feeding. This, also, is a natural result of the conditions of sessile life. The ability to move allows the free-living animal to seek and chase its food, which will usually be in pieces of relatively large size compared with the size of its own body. The sessile animal can obtain food only by waiting for it to strike its body, or by some device, such as a current set up by its own activity, which will bring the food to it. We find the first of these methods employed in the tentacles of the sea-anemone or *Hydra*, and the second, together with some form of trap or filter to capture the food when it has been brought within range, in the various other forms of filter-feeding apparatus (pp. 210–19). Nevertheless it must be remembered, as has been already mentioned (p. 210), that filter-feeding is not restricted to sessile animals. Many free-living forms feed in this way.

So long as it is sessile and fixed, the animal is unable to move to new habitats. Even slow movement is often of value to an animal in enabling it to escape from unfavourable conditions. Thus, we find some power of movement retained by many animals which are almost completely sessile. Many lamellibranchs can move, either by flapping the valves rapidly together (the scallop, *Pecten*, the cockle, *Cardium*, etc.), or by other means (*e.g.* by attaching a byssus to the substratum and pulling themselves up on this attachment—*Mytilus*, the mussel). Anemones can glide over the rock to which they are attached, though very slowly.

Movement is also necessary for the distribution of sessile animals throughout their habitats. Very often we find that animals which are sessile as adults have free-living larvæ, and that the distribution of the animals is provided for at these stages of their life-histories. This is so in the echinoderms, tunicates, polyzoa, and many other groups. Often these larvæ are planktonic and their distribution is controlled not by their own movements but by the currents in the medium, a method of distribution which is necessarily extravagant since many larvæ must reach unfavourable environments. In many cœlenterates the larvæ are free-living, but the medusa phase is responsible for the greater part of the distribution in those groups in which it occurs.

Other characters of sessile animals are the loss of locomotory organs, development of rapid powers of contraction and of efficient sense-organs, and so on.

There are certain other modes of life in which the animal is almost or quite completely immotile, if not sessile. The habit of living in tubes is one of these. In animals with this habit there is a tendency for the outward bilateral symmetry of the body to be lost, so that the body tends to become cylindrical (many tube-living polychætes), and in some parts the body may become almost entirely radial in its symmetry (branchiæ of polychætes such as *Sabella*, *Spirorbis*, etc.). Movement being usually slight, we find filter-feeding frequent. Burrowing animals also have slight powers of movement and cylindrical bodies, and some feed by filtering methods (*Chætopterus* and some burrowing molluscs, *e.g.* the burrowing clams, *Tridacna*); others feed on the soil or other material in which they burrow (*Arenicola*, earthworms on soil; the ship-worm, *Teredo*, and termites on wood). The burrowing and tube-living habits lead to some modifications which do not occur in animals sessile in the open environment. The oxygen supply is often deficient in burrows and tubes, and we find considerable development of the respiratory organs in these animals, usually in the form of gills on the outer surface of the body. Adaptations for the maintenance of currents of water along the tube or burrows are also frequent. These adaptations may also serve for the removal of excreta.

3. THE PARASITIC HABIT

This is itself a very large subject which we can discuss only very briefly here. We must first try to define as exactly as possible what we mean by parasitism, for the term is often loosely used. It is easy to define a term in any sense we prefer and then to use it consistently in that sense, but, if the term is in general use outside zoology—as parasitism is—it is clear that to give a definition which disagrees with the common use must always lead to confusion. When a term which is commonly used is taken over into scientific use, its meaning in science should be kept as close as possible to the common meaning. The function of the scientific definition should be to define more accurately the sense in which the term is commonly used, not to give the term a new meaning.

Clearly, dependence of the parasite on the host for the satisfaction of some of its needs is an essential element in common meaning of the term parasitism. Clearly, also, the dependence must be one-sided, for an association in which both members benefit is not regarded as parasitic, but is called a *symbiotic* association. But not all such relationships are parasitic. A holozoic animal feeding on other organisms is dependent on other organisms for its food but it is not parasitic on these organisms—carnivorous animals are not parasitic on their prey. This also excludes, as a complete definition of the term, the statement, which is frequently made, that parasitism is an association of two animals in which one of the animals gains all the advantage and the other none. But there is more in the common idea of parasitism than the simple dependence of one animal upon another. It cannot be questioned that there is in the common use of the term some conception of degeneration resulting from the parasitic association. However, when we examine parasitic animals we find that they are in no true sense degenerate. They are often very closely adapted to their own parasitic environments and often very successful in these environments. They are as efficient living organisms as any free-living animal. Nevertheless the parasite, in becoming adapted to its own peculiar parasitic environment, has almost always lost some, and often many, of the adaptations which are necessary for a free-living animal. *So far as free life is concerned*—with which it is no longer concerned—the parasite may be said to be degenerate. This is true even of such slightly modified external parasites as the louse or the flea, for they are adapted only to life on the surface of the host's body and their powers of movement are correspondingly restricted.

It is probably this loss of the adaptations suited for free life which is responsible for the conception of degeneration present in the layman's idea of parasitism. To the non-scientific observer the typical animal is a free-living organism, and organisms which have lost the power of free life are "degenerate." If this is so, it seems that the truest definition that we can give to parasitism is to say that it is an association of animals of such a kind that one, the parasite, alone benefits by depending on the other for satisfaction of some of its vital needs and has become restricted in its power of free life when separated from the host. Even internal parasites which simply feed on the tissues of the host (often called "internal predators") are included in this definition. They are confined to life in the body of the host.

The parasitic association may take many different forms but for a first classification we may separate *ectoparasitism*, in which the parasite remains outside the body of the host, from *endoparasitism*, in which the parasite has penetrated the body of the host and lives within it. We will consider these two types of parasitism separately.

(a) *Ectoparasitism*

It is not necessary in a parasitic association that the parasite should be always in contact with the body of the host. The cuckoo is truly parasitic on the various species of birds in whose nests the eggs are laid, for its distribution is restricted by this habit. In social insects many similar instances of parasitism occur. In more than one species of ants it has been found that the female of one species enters the nest of another and lays its eggs there, sometimes killing the original queen. The larvæ which hatch from the eggs of the parasitic species are then tended by the host species. This again is true parasitism. Such social parasites are sometimes called *inquilines*. On the other hand, the ants which capture aphids and use them as cows, or the other ants (*e.g.* the British *Formica sanguinea*) which use workers of other species as slaves, are no more parasitic than the carnivorous animal is on its prey, except in so far as they lose freedom by so doing.

Nevertheless, in by far the greater number of cases of parasitism the parasite is definitely confined in its movements to close contact with the body of the host. But, again, not all such associations are parasitic. In most symbiotic associations there is also this close contact of the two members of the association, even when one symbiont is not within the body of the other (as in the association of fungus and alga to form a lichen, or of many animals with green algal cells—cœlenterates, *Hydra*, corals; turbellaria, *Convoluta*; lamellibranchs, *Tridacna*; etc.). Examples of external association of symbionts are very numerous; that of the hermit-crab with a sea-anemone (*Adamsia*) so often attached to its shell is typical. The hermit-crab probably receives advantages from the protection provided by the nematocysts of the anemone, and the latter probably obtains a larger food supply owing to the movements of the crab.

The least specialised form of true ectoparasitism is that in which the parasite is free-moving except in so far as it is restricted to the surface of the host's body. A simple example of this relationship is the association of the ciliate *Trichodina* with *Hydra*. This ciliate is to be found moving over the surface of the *Hydra*, but not so far as can be seen, having any closer relationship with it. The advantage of this habitat to the parasite is not clear. Other examples are given by many of the associations known as *commensalism*, in which the parasite feeds on the food supply of the host, but gets no other parasitic advantage from its neighbourhood to the host, except, perhaps, some protection. A polychæte, *Nereis fucata*, lives in the shell of the hermit-crab and feeds on the food captured by the crab. Another polychæte, *Acholoë astericola*, lives in the ambulacral grooves of the oral face of the starfish *Astropecten* and probably feeds on the food supply of the starfish. Since in these cases the food is usually collected by only one member of the association, the relationship is truly parasitic. So far as we know, this member of the association obtains no benefit.

The next advance in ectoparasitism is in one or both of two directions. Either the parasite becomes attached to a position on the host's body and ceases to move over its surface; or the parasite becomes adapted to feed on the body of the host by the development of some organs by which the surface is pierced.

Many parasites are attached to the host body but do not feed on its tissues. The Temnocephala, for instance, are a group of platyhelminths which live attached by suckers to the gills of crabs and feed on food brought past the gills by the respiratory current. They have no means of absorbing food from the tissues of the host's body. The advantage to the parasite of attachment to the host is less clear when the parasite is situated on the outer surface of the host's body and not in contact with the respiratory current. Probably there is some advantage in a greater supply of food provided by the movements of the host. However this may be, many parasites are so situated (suctorians on many types of Crustacea, the endoproct polyzoan *Loxosoma* on many invertebrates, etc.). The growth of hydroids (*Hydractinia*) on the shells of hermit-crabs is an example of a similar type of ectoparasitism. Here there can hardly be any symbiotic relationship as there is said to be in the association of the hermit-crab with the sea-anemone *Adamsia*, and as there certainly is in its association with a sponge *Suberites*. The latter covers the shell in which the young crab is living and then grows continually. It forms a covering which is always large enough for the growing crab. The crab is thus relieved of the necessity of changing its covering each time it grows too big for its shell. This is a time of danger for the soft-bodied crab, and the association is therefore truly symbiotic.

Thus, in the group of animals which live associated with hermit-crabs we find one case of commensal parasitism (*Nereis*), one of non-commensal parasitism (*Hydractinia*) and two of symbiosis (*Suberites* and *Adamsia*).

Many ectoparasites are able to absorb food from the tissues of the host, usually by means of some organ by which the skin is pierced. Some of these are not permanently attached to a point of its body. The fleas and lice are in this group. Others are both attached and absorb food from the host's body. These are very numerous and belong to a large number of phyla. The Copepoda, perhaps, give the

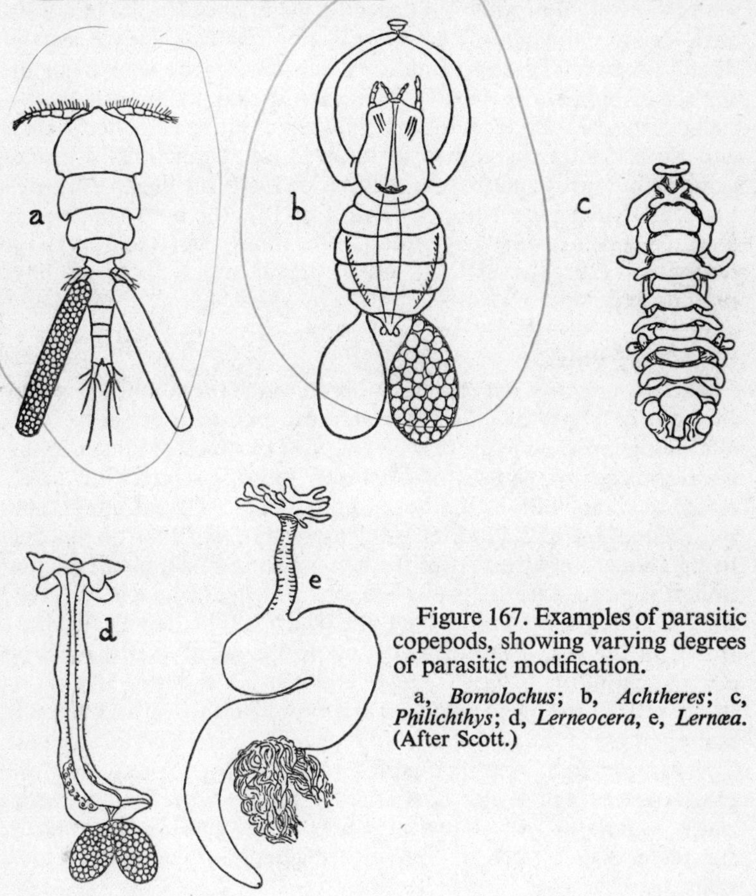

Figure 167. Examples of parasitic copepods, showing varying degrees of parasitic modification.

a, *Bomolochus*; b, *Achtheres*; c, *Philichthys*; d, *Lerneocera*, e, *Lernæa*. (After Scott.)

best series of parasitic forms of this type (Fig. 167). Parasitic habit has been evolved independently many times among the Copepods and the parasitic adaptations have reached varying degrees of development in different families.

Whereas the tendency in sessile animals is, as we have seen, for the body to become radially symmetrical, in parasitic animals the tendency is for all symmetrical organisation in the body to be lost. In ectoparasites this tendency is carried much further in those which are sessile on the host and absorb food from it than in those which move over the surface or feed in some way on the external medium (*e.g.* on food in the respiratory current of the host). When the parasite is sessile and also absorbs food from the host, the only exchanges with the external medium that need be maintained for the life of the parasite are discharge of the reproductive products and passage of dissolved excretory and respiratory substances into and from the surface of the parasite's body. These last exchanges are usually carried out by diffusion from the general surface of the parasite. In these circumstances there seems to be no need for symmetrical organisation, or indeed for any accurately modelled form in the parasite's body. In extreme cases (*e.g. Lernæa*, Fig. 167) the body becomes an almost shapeless sack containing little more than the very large reproductive organs. All the other organs are reduced or have disappeared.

(b) *Endoparasitism*

There is one very important feature in which the conditions within the body of a host are different from those on the surface of its body. Within the host the parasite is surrounded by an environment which is determined by the host; it is entirely out of contact with the external medium. Life in the host's body demands great adaptation, but adaptation of a kind different not only from that of the free-living animal but also that of the ectoparasite. Much of the adaptation of the endoparasite is physiological. The parasite has to defend itself against the attacks of the host, which will be largely chemical. If it is in the gut, it must be immune to the action of the digestive enzymes; if in the tissues, it must be able to resist destructive action by the cells of the host—attempts of amœbocytes to kill and digest it, and attempts of the host tissues to enclose it in an impermeable cyst. The parasite must also be adapted to many other conditions in the environments within the host's body. For instance, gut parasites must be able to live at low pressures of oxygen or anærobically, for there is very little oxygen in the liquids of the gut of most animals.

We know very little of the nature of these physiological adaptations. We have knowledge of a few isolated facts. *Ascaris*, for instance, has been shown to be able to render the digestive enzymes of its hosts innocuous, and it has been shown that some gut parasites can certainly live at low oxygen pressures. Beyond such results we have little knowledge of these adaptations. Nevertheless, they must be both numerous and exact.

Endoparasitic environments are of two kinds. The parasite either lives in liquids included within the body of the host, *e.g.* in those of the gut, the body cavity or the blood system; or it lives among the cells of the tissues. Many endoparasites living in the liquids of the host's body, if they are small compared with the size of the host, retain almost perfectly the structural organisation of a free-living animal (protistans in the cow's stomach or the gut of termites, trypanosomes, etc.). These parasites may be regarded as living a free life in an aquatic medium, although that medium is enclosed in the body of the host. They therefore retain the organisation suitable for free life. When the parasite becomes attached to the wall of the space in which the internal liquid is contained (*e.g.* tapeworms), we find the same loss of many of the organs required for free life that we find in external sessile parasites.

Parasites living in the tissues of the host often show greater modifications of organisation than those of any other type of parasite. Free movement is usually entirely absent and the symmetrical organisation of the body may be entirely lost. Thus, the internal *Sacculina* is a ramifying mass of tissue which shows no trace of the organisation of the Crustacea. The parasite is, in fact, organised in the same way as an internal tissue of the host's body. Some tissue parasites, however, especially those which are in the tissues for only a part of their life-history, may retain bilateral symmetry, *e.g.* nematodes encysted in tissues.

(c) *Parasitic Life-histories*

In the body of a parasite, whatever its type of parasitism, the only system of organs which is generally developed beyond its condition in free-living animals is the reproductive system. The reason for this feature of parasitic organisation is clear. In any parasitic life-history, the parasite must be able, if its species is to survive, to find a new host from time to time. Unless the parasite can be carried over from the parent host to its egg (some bacteria, etc.), this must occur at least once in each generation of the host. Usually it is the egg or larva of the parasite that enters the new host, and, since the parasitic environment in the host's body is always a very restricted one, only a small proportion of the young of each generation of the parasite will find it. The parasite must therefore produce an immense number of young, and for this a large reproductive system is required. Often this system fills by far the greater part of the parasite's body.

Most of the complexity which we find in parasitic life-histories is related to this same need for transference from one host to another. Broadly, there are two types of parasitic life-history. In the first type, which is more common in ectoparasites, there is a free-living and often actively motile stage in the life-history, and the new host is reached during this stage. The free-living stage is often larval, as it is, for instance, in the parasitic copepods, but it may be any other stage of the life-history. Thus, in many insects the larva is parasitic and the adult free; in nematodes there are species in which all the life-history except the egg is parasitic. Such free-living stages in parasitic life-histories must be clearly adapted for free life. They often retain the bilateral symmetry which has been lost in those parts of the life-history in which the animal is parasitic—the larvæ of parasitic copepods, for instance, are often typical crustacean nauplii, and the same is true of larval cirripedes. It is, indeed, often true that if we had not these free-living stages in parasitic life-histories we should have great difficulty in determining the systematic groups to which many parasites belong.

Such parasitic life-histories give us good examples of adaptation to different modes of life in different stages of the life-history. Metamorphosis (p. 340) is therefore very common in them, and is indeed one of their characteristic features.

In the second type of parasitic life-history the transference from one host to another is provided by some other animal which is in some way in biological contact with the host. Usually the parasite is parasitic within this second animal as well as in its first host, and we get the double parasitic life-histories which are so common. But accidental transport on the outside of the body of the second animal is not impossible. Some bacterial diseases in man, for instance, are spread by house-flies, the bacteria being merely carried from place to place on the feet of the flies.

The contact between the host and this second species may be of any kind. In the example of the fly and man, the fly need only come into contact with the food of the man, but where the parasite passes a part of its life-history within the second species there is usually closer contact between the two hosts. The second host may feed upon the first, *e.g.* the *Anopheles* mosquito in the life-history of the malarial parasite, or it may be introduced, either as food or accidentally with the food, into the body of the first host, *e.g.* tapeworms, the snail *Limnœa* in the life-history of *Fasciola;* or the second host may be parasitic on the first, *e.g.* lice and fleas as carriers of bacterial diseases. The most complicated parasitic life-histories belong to this group. There may sometimes be three hosts in a single life-history. Some cestodes occur as larvæ in snails, as non-reproductive, sub-adult stages in fish, and as reproductive tapeworms in birds. The life-history is completed by the fish feeding on the snail, and the bird on the fish. The most striking feature of all such life-histories is the close correlation between the behaviour and physiology of the parasite and the biology of each of its hosts. This correlation is necessary if the life-history is to succeed.

Whereas the life-histories of most ectoparasites belong to the first of these two types,* endoparasites may have life-histories of either type. Many endoparasites pass from one host to another by inactive stages which are carried out of the body of the host and remain inactive in the external medium, until they are taken up into a new host (*Monocystis*, many nematodes, etc.). These life-histories belong to the first type. Many other endoparasites have two or more hosts.

One other feature of parasitic life-histories must be mentioned. This is the frequent occurrence in them of asexual reproduction at some stage of the life-history. This is another adaptation to the need for great multiplication that we have seen that a parasitic life-history demands. It occurs very commonly in the life-histories of parasites, and the asexual reproduction may take place more than once in a single life-history, *e.g.* in the life-history of *Fasciola*.

* Fleas carried by rats and other mammals from man to man are an exception.

CHAPTER XXIII

THE EVOLUTION OF THE INVERTEBRATES

THE palæontology and comparative morphology of the vertebrates show us the history of a single animal stock which has given rise during a long course of palæontological evolution to new forms of increasing structural complexity and increasingly efficient organisation. It is a history which we can follow in considerable detail, and one in which there can be no doubt of the common plan of organisation in the whole group—we cannot doubt that the vertebrates are a single stock.

At first sight the comparative zoology of the invertebrates yields a very different story. We find among them a large number of groups of animals, the phyla, in each of which a common plan of organisation is evident. In each phylum we have little difficulty in believing in descent from a single stock, even though, as is often the case, we have no fossil evidence of the course of evolution. But the evolutionary relations of these phyla to each other are much less clear. Often we can, at first sight, see little relationship between the organisation in one phylum and another, and we are left in doubt whether we must regard these phyla as related animal stocks or as entirely unrelated to each other. It is the object of the chapter to show that there is some evidence that the invertebrate phyla are in fact related.

The difficulties we meet in trying to work out how the invertebrate phyla are related to each other are largely the result of the early period at which these phyla became separated. In the earliest fossiliferous rocks, the lower Cambrian, we already find examples of many of the invertebrate phyla, and highly evolved examples of some of them. These rocks contain many molluscs—Lamellibranchiata and Gastropoda—sponges, brachiopods, annelids, trilobites, crustacea—Branchiopoda and Ostracoda—etc. By that time all the larger invertebrate groups were differentiated; their differentiation must have taken place during the long Precambrian period. The rocks of that period have been so altered by heating, crushing, and in other ways that we cannot hope for palæontological evidence from them.

Even within the smaller invertebrate groups there has generally been relatively little fundamental evolution during palæontological time. In some groups, in fact, fossil forms from very early fossiliferous rocks are nearly identical with modern forms. This is true, for instance, of some cœlenterates, annelids and brachiopods (*Lingula*). It is only in some of the more specialised groups that there has been any great evolution since the beginning of the fossiliferous series. The insects have evolved since the Carboniferous period, and some groups of the Cœlenterata may be still more modern.

In the absence of any palæontological evidence of by far the greater part of invertebrate evolution, we are driven to the only other type of evidence which may be used in discussions of the course of evolution. This is the evidence of comparative morphology. We have to ask whether comparative study of the structure of invertebrate animals gives us any clues to their evolutionary affinities. But it should be said at once that any conclusions we can derive from this evidence must necessarily be uncertain and tentative. The events we are discussing took place near the beginning of metazoan evolution, and since that time the changes in the structure and life-histories of animals have very often been enormous. We must expect the record of these evolutionary changes in the organisation of our modern animals to be incomplete. It is surprising rather that the evidence of comparative morphology can give any conclusions on such questions than that the conclusions we can reach are not more certain than they are. Nevertheless, it is worth while to discuss the subject, for without such a discussion the invertebrates remain a collection of isolated and apparently unrelated phyla, and we are left with a large gap in our general picture of the evolution of the animal kingdom. If we can fill this gap, it will be worth while, however many the qualifications we must add to our conclusions.

Since we know more of vertebrate than of invertebrate evolution, and since, in the absence of evidence to the contrary, we may expect the process of evolution to have been similar in its general characters throughout its course, we shall be well advised, before discussing invertebrate evolution, to note the main features of the evolutionary process as they have been displayed by palæontological study of the vertebrates.

If we look at the course of vertebrate evolution as a whole, we find that the evolution of this group of animals has taken the form of repeated alternations between development of new types of vertebrate organisation, and radiation of these types of organisation into large numbers of environments and habits of life as soon as they became successful. We see the radiation most clearly in the mammals and reptiles, where we know most of it. When these types became successful (by the disappearance of earlier groups with which they were previously in competition or for some other reason), the successful group divided, more or less simultaneously, into a large number of smaller groups each of which became adapted to a different environment or habit of life. In this adaptation the structure of each of the smaller groups became differentiated, and this process continued throughout the successful life of the group. The mammals, for instance, became differentiated at the beginning of tertiary times into a large number of adaptational lines, from which the mammalian orders are derived, and the differentiation of these lines has continued since that time. This adaptational differentiation of a successful group is what we mean by radiation.

The second process which we find in vertebrate evolution, the development of new types of vertebrate organisation, is exemplified by the evolution of the mammalian type of organisation from that of a reptile, or the reptilian type from that of an amphibian. In this process we find that one of the successful radiating lines of the earlier group became gradually altered by evolution until the new type of organisation was reached. We see this process most clearly in the evolution of the mammals from the synapsid reptiles. The change from one type of organisation to another must always involve an immense amount of closely correlated change of structure in all parts of the body. It is therefore not surprising that this process is never rapid, as the differentiation of radiating lines appears to have been. It is always slow and gradual. The evolution of the mammalian type of organisation took the greater part of the secondary epoch.

We need not discuss whether these two types of evolutionary change are, or are not, at base the same process. Even if they are, they are certainly distinct in their time-relations and their results—they are certainly very different aspects of this process.

We may now ask whether there is any evidence of similar types of evolutionary change in the evolution of the invertebrates.

It may first be said that there is undoubted evidence of radiation in successful invertebrate groups. We see radiation in those recently evolved groups of invertebrates for which palæontological evidence is available. The insects seem to have evolved by the differentiation of a large number of parallel radiating lines which are represented to-day by the insect orders; and there is palæontological evidence of radiation in the echinoderms. In other groups for which we have no palæontological evidence the systematics of the groups are in accordance with an origin by radiative subdivision.

However, such evidence as this does not help us to relate the larger invertebrate groups to each other. The origin of these larger groups must have been mainly by the other process that occurs in vertebrate evolution, the development of new types of organisation. If they are related at all at the metazoan stage of organisation, the phyla must have arisen either the one from another, or two or more from a common ancestral group. In either case, they must have arisen by the development of new types of organisation.

When we compare the morphology of members of the different phyla, we find that the adult structure is almost always so different in the phyla that it is not possible to deduce any evolutionary relationships between the phyla. At first sight, as has been said, the structure in each phylum seems almost entirely unrelated to that in any other. There are, for instance, very few obvious similarities in adult structure between the annelids, molluscs, and echinoderms. Such resemblances as we can find in several phyla—triploblastic organisation, the presence of a cœlome, etc.—are not enough to allow us to trace the evolutionary connection of the phyla. In only one comparison is this not so—the comparison of the arthropod with the annelid. The arthropod body shows clearly in the whole of its fundamental organisation that its arrangement is identical with that of the annelid body, though more specialised. On this and other grounds there can be no doubt that the arthropods have been evolved from a group of animals which we should call annelids if they were alive to-day.

It is when we compare the larvæ of the various phyla that we find striking resemblances, and the resemblances are greater the earlier the developmental stage we compare. Before we pass on to use the evidence which these resemblances offer us in our attempts to relate the phyla to each other, we must consider what is the meaning of this greater similarity of organisation in larvæ than in adults, and what is its value as evidence of the course of evolution.

The fact that the members of two phyla have similar larvæ can mean only one of two things. Either the similarities between the larvæ have been evolved by parallel evolution, probably in adaptation to similar habits, when these similarities will tell us nothing of the course of evolution; or the phyla must both have been evolved from a group which had a structure similar to that of the larvæ at some time during its life-history. As we shall see, the resemblances between invertebrate larvæ are too many and detailed to allow us to believe in the first of these alternatives. We are therefore forced to accept the second, and this implies that in the evolution of the phyla change from ancestral structure has been greater in the modern adults than in their larvæ. It is in fact found to be frequently true in animal evolution that earlier development stages change in structure less than later stages. We see this, for instance, in the smaller groups the history of which is well known to us, *e.g.* in the mammals—the adults may be of very different structure but the embryos are very similar. Only when the early developmental stages are altered by special secondary adaptations, such as the deposition of large amounts of yolk in the egg, is the principle that larvæ and embryos show greater resemblances than adults untrue.

It was held for many years that this structural similarity between the larvæ of groups in which the adults differed greatly implied that these groups were descended from common *adult ancestors* similar in structure to the larvæ. The larvæ were supposed to represent the structure of the common adult ancestor of these groups, and it was supposed that evolution has proceeded by a lengthening of the development of animals, new developmental stages being added at the end of the development. Thus, the tadpole was supposed to represent the adult fish ancestor of the amphibian, and the evolution from fish to amphibian was thought to take place by the addition of developmental stages in which the structure of the animal changes from that of a fish to that of an amphibian. So, it appeared that the amphibian recapitulated its ancestral history during its development. The theory was therefore known as that of *Recapitulation.*

In recent years this view of the evolution of the life-histories of animals has been very largely discarded. There can be no question that larvæ do very often resemble earlier evolutionary stages—that the structure of a tadpole is more like that of a fish than is the structure of the adult amphibian. But there is no good evidence that the evolution of the life-history has taken place by addition of new developmental stages at its end; to assume that this has occurred generally, or indeed frequently, is unwarranted. Rather, those examples of evolutionary change of which we know most show that change in evolution takes place by modification of structure at all stages of the life-history—greater changes in the later parts of the development, but some change throughout the development. Thus, in the modern Amphibia, anuran tadpoles are much more modified from the fish type than the larvæ of the more primitive Urodela. It is true that development has lengthened during evolution, for the more complex animal takes longer to develop than the less complex. But, so far as we know, this lengthening has in general taken place throughout the life-history, not only at its end, though, again, perhaps to a greater extent in the later parts of development.

The contrast between the two views is expressed in the diagrams of Fig. 168.

On this more recent view * the whole development of the later animal represents the development of the earlier animal; the larva of the later animal represents the larva of the ancestor—not, as on

* The view outlined here is in origin nearly as old as the other (von Baer), but it has recently gained more general acceptance and can therefore be called the modern view. *Cf.* S. J. Holmes, *Quart. Rev. Biol.*, **18**, 819, 1944.

the earlier view, the adult. The tadpole represents the late larva of the fish from which the amphibia are descended, not the adult of this fish.

This view of the evolution of the animal life-history in no way reduces the value of larval resemblance as giving us evidence that animals with similar larvæ are related. That two groups have similar larvæ implies (on this view) that they are descended from an ancestral group with this type of larva. But the structure of the larvæ does not give us evidence of the structure of the adult animals of this ancestral group. To get some idea of the adult structure of these animals we can, in the absence of palæontological evidence, only try to find some structure which might have been a later stage in the life-history of this larva and which by divergent evolution might evolve into the modern adults. When the modern groups are widely different in structure, this is usually by no means easy.

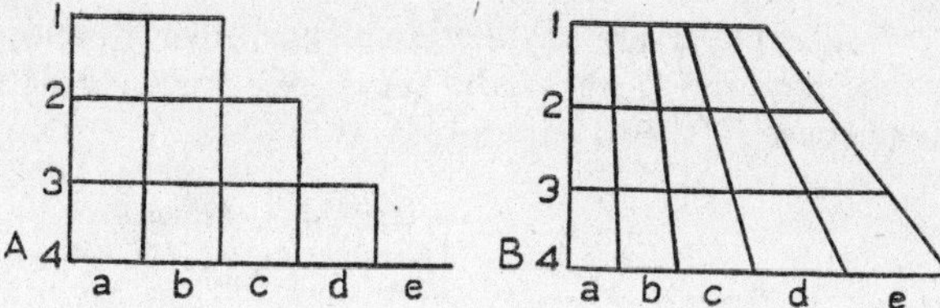

Figure 168. Diagrams illustrating the earlier (A) and the more recent (B) theories of the evolution of the life-history.

1–4, an evolutionary series of life-histories; a–e, successive stages of the life-history.

The fact, then, that many of the invertebrate phyla have similar larvæ is good evidence that these phyla were descended from common ancestors at the remote epoch at which they were first evolved. Only if we may put down the larval resemblances to convergent evolution can this conclusion be avoided. We will now examine the facts of larval resemblance in the invertebrates, and try to determine what evolutionary connections between the phyla these resemblances indicate.

We will leave aside: (1) the sponges (Parazoa) which, as we have seen (p. 311), may probably have had an origin from unicellular organisms independent of that of the Metazoa, and (2) the cœlenterates, the affinities of which to other Metazoa are by no means clear.

All the metazoan phyla except the cœlenterates—and a few phyla in which the structure has become so modified that we are unable to say anything of their affinities—fall into one or other of two large divisions which we may call superphyla. In one of these superphyla, the *annelid superphylum*, a larva of the trochosphere type is very widely disseminated, occurring in some members of all the phyla. To this group belong the annelids, molluscs, Polyzoa (both Ectoprocta and Endoprocta*), Podaxonia (Sipunculoidea and probably Phoronidea) and a few other phyla. In the other superphylum, the *echinoderm superphylum*, are included the echinoderms and the chordates; in this superphylum a larva of a type in many ways different from the trochosphere, the pluteus type, is characteristic. Some platyhelminthes (Polyclada) possess a larva, Müller's larva, which agrees with the trochosphere in many structural features but not in all. They are related to the annelid superphylum, though probably not so closely related to the other phyla of this superphylum as these phyla are to each other. The same is probably true of the nemertines, some of which have a larva, the pilidium, which is of the trochosphere type. The arthropods, being descended from an annelid stock, also belong to this superphylum.

The two superphyla are distinct in some other developmental characters besides the form of the larva. We may tabulate these differences between the two superphyla as follows:

	Annelid superphylum	*Echinoderm superphylum*
1. Type of larva . .	Trochosphere	Pluteus type
2. Segmentation . .	Spiral	Radial
3. Development . .	Mosaic	Equipotential
4. Cœlome . . .	Schizocœlic	Enterocœlic

We will consider these differences in turn.

1. *Type of Larva.* The character in which the trochosphere and pluteus types of larva (Fig. 169) differ most obviously is the position of the ciliated band by which the larva swims. In the early trochosphere this band, the prototroch, forms a transverse ring in front of the mouth; in the early pluteus it forms a ring around the mouth on the ventral side. In both larvæ the beat of the cilia of these bands is also used in feeding. Vortices are formed in the region of the mouth by the beat of the cilia; the food is collected in these vortices and passes on into the mouth. In the later development of both types of larva the ciliated bands may be variously modified, and come to occupy various positions on the body of the larva.

In many features of their organisation the trochosphere and pluteus larvæ agree. Both are more or less spherical in shape, until their shapes are altered by the changes of the later development; but both have clear bilateral symmetry. Also, they are both triploblastic, both

* Hyman (*The Invertebrates*, vol. 3) denies that the endoproct larva is a trochosphere. She regards the group as non-cœlomate and places them near the Platyhelminthes and Rotifera.

have a ventral mouth, a posterior anus, a gut with œsophagus, stomach, and intestine, and an anterior sense-organ.

The Müller's larva of the Platyhelminthes agrees with the trochosphere in the position of its ciliated band and in all these other characters except that it has no differentiated anus, its enteron having only a single opening, and that the mesoderm, although it is formed in the same way as that of the trochosphere, does not develop cœlomic pouches.

The pilidium larva of the nemertines is similar to Müller's larva in these features. It has no anus, although the adult nemertine has one.

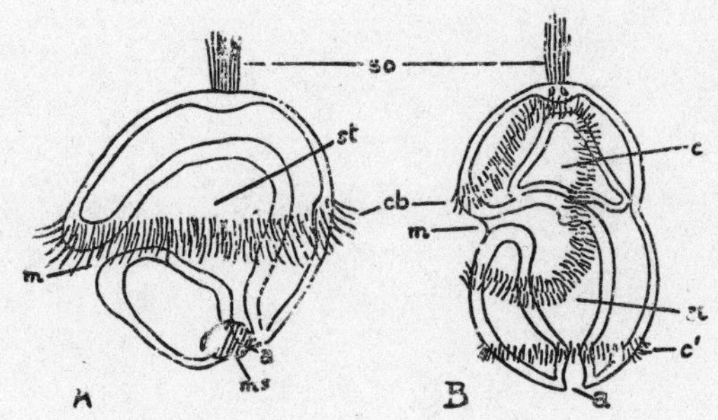

Figure 169. A, Trochosphere larva (*Polygordius*). B, Pluteus type of larva (tornaria larva of *Balanoglossus*).

a, anus; *c*, enterocœlic cœlome; *cb*, ciliated band; *c'*, additional posterior ciliated band (telotroch) in the tornaria; *m*, mouth; *ms*, mesoderm cells which will form the schizocœlic cœlome; *so*, sense organ; *st*, stomach.

2. *Radial and Spiral Segmentation*. The distinction between these two types of segmentation (Fig. 170) lies in the directions of the cleavages in the early segmentation of the egg. In radial segmentation the first four blastomeres are formed by cleavages at right angles to each other passing through the axis of polarity; and the third cleavage is at right angles to the first two and also to the axis of polarity. In spiral segmentation the first four blastomeres are again formed by cleavages at right angles to each other, and these cleavages are parallel to the axis of polarity, if they do not pass through it. From the group of four cells so produced successive quartettes of cells are separated by later cleavages. But these cleavages are not at right angles to the axis of polarity or through it; they are oblique to this axis. It results that the successive quartettes lie alternate to each other around the axis of polarity. So the arrangement of the blastomeres is spiral round the axis.

3. *Mosaic and Equipotential Development*. We have already discussed the difference between these two types of development

(p. 327). We saw that the distinction between them resulted from differences in the time at which the fate of the blastomeres in later development was determined. In mosaic development this determination occurs before the blastomeres are formed by segmentation; in equipotential development somewhat later.

4. *Schizocœlic and Enterocœlic Cœlome.* An enterocœlic cœlome is one which arises as pouches from the cavity of the enteron, the process which occurs in the development of *Amphioxus.* Where the cœlome is schizocœlic, the mesoderm which will form the walls of the cœlomic pouches (*mesothelium*) is separated early in segmentation—typically it arises from one of the cells of the fourth quartette

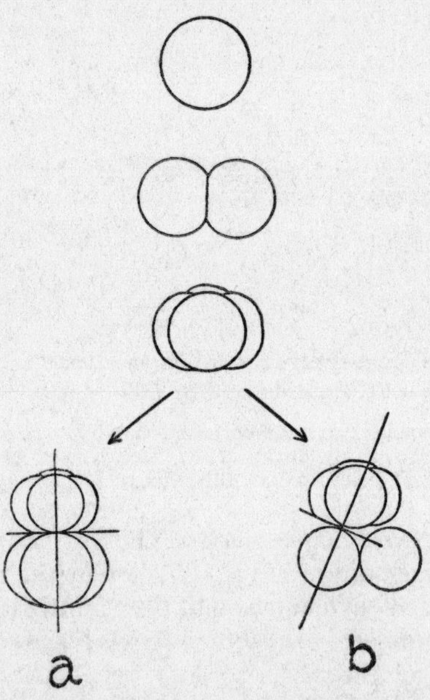

Figure 170. The first three segmentation divisions in (a) radial and (b) spiral segmentation.

of blastomeres to be formed in spiral segmentation. This mesoderm forms solid blocks of tissue in the blastocœle, and the cœlomic cavities are formed as splits in these blocks of tissue. The cœlomic cavities are therefore never in connection with the cavity of the enteron.

These four characters all occur very early in development. They are all fundamental in the development of organisation in the body. They are therefore not characters which we should expect to vary readily in adaptation to different habits. We may for this reason use them with more confidence in trying to work out the relationships of the invertebrate phyla to each other.

In general the phyla of the annelid superphylum differ from those of the echinoderm superphylum in all these characters. But there are many exceptions to the strictness of this discrimination between the phyla of the two superphyla. We sometimes find that one or more of these characters have become altered in the later evolution of a phylum in spite of their fundamental nature. Thus, the vertebrate cœlome does not arise as clearly defined pouches from the gut in the enterocœlic manner, although the vertebrates are chordates and therefore belong to the echinoderm superphylum. In the frog, for instance, the mesothelium arises as solid masses of tissue separating from the endoderm, and the cœlomic pouches are formed as splits in these masses of tissue.* This is not schizocœlic cœlome, for the mesoderm is not formed directly from one of the early blastomeres, but it differs from the typical enterocœlic development. Since such primitive chordates as *Amphioxus* and *Balanoglossus* have true enterocœlic cœlome, we must conclude that the condition in the frog and other vertebrates is secondary.

Again, the Urochordata have a development that is largely mosaic, although most chordates have equipotential development. And the mosaic development of many eggs of the annelid superphylum is not complete. If a blastomere is removed, the larva may form some parts normally formed from this blastomere.

There are other similar divergences from the strict differentiation between the two superphyla. Enterocœlic cœlome occurs, for example, in a few groups which seem to have most affinity with the annelid superphylum (Chætognatha, Phoronidea †). We cannot expect perfect evidence in considering these questions, in view of the great changes in evolution since the time when the phyla were differentiated.

On all the facts, there is no doubt that the balance of the evidence is on the side of accepting the distinction between these superphyla as natural. If so, we must believe, on the modern theory of the evolution of the life-history, that each superphylum is descended from a group of animals with larvæ which had the characters which we now find in the larval development of the superphylum. In the annelid superphylum the Platyhelminthes may represent an offshoot from the

* Also the cells which will form the mesothelium can be recognised in the vertebrate at a much earlier stage of development—in the gastrula stage. We do not know whether this is also true of other types of enterocœlic development. They have not so far been recognised at stages by any means so early as those at which the cells which form the mesothelium in schizocœlic development are separated (the early segmentation stages).

† These phyla have often been placed in the Echinoderm superphylum.

main stock earlier than the origin of the other phyla—before, in fact, an anus and cœlome had been evolved. Or, perhaps equally probably, the absence of these features in the Platyhelminthes is degenerate.

The resemblances between the typical larval forms in these two superphyla are great and numerous. These resemblances have often been put down to convergent evolution. It has been said that many of them—the spherical form, apical sense-organ, posterior anus, etc. —are characters which might be expected to be found in any planktonic larvæ of simple structure, that they are in fact adaptations to a planktonic life. But there are, besides these, many resemblances which we have not discussed. It seems that the resemblances are too detailed and numerous to be due to convergence. Elsewhere, when two or more animals develop functionally similar organs in adaptation to similar modes of life, we rarely find the details of the structure of the organs similar in the various animals; the organs, though functionally similar, differ in their detailed structure, *e.g.* the wings of birds, bats, and pterodactyls. It seems more likely that both trochosphere and pluteus are modifications of a single early metazoan type of larva, and therefore that the two superphyla had a single origin in a very primitive stock of Metazoa. Whether the cœlenterates were also descended from this stock is a question that we cannot here discuss.

If we accept these conclusions, we reach the conception of the evolution of the Metazoa which is shown diagrammatically in Fig. 171. Such a tree must always be provisional and tentative. It is also incomplete. There are several invertebrate phyla, such as the Rotifera and Nematoda, which have not been mentioned in our discussion. Their development is so modified that we cannot at present reach any worthwhile conclusions about their relationships. Other phyla, such as the Chætognatha, give us some evidence of their affinities, but this evidence is so incomplete and doubtful that it seems better at present not to try to place them.

Can we reach any conclusions about the *course* of the evolution by which these phyla became differentiated? The tree drawn in Fig. 171 reminds one very strongly of the trees by which the radiation of successful groups of vertebrates are illustrated. In the annelid superphylum especially we have a number of parallel lines, the phyla, all descended from a common ancestral stock, just as the mammalian orders were differentiated from the original mammalian stock. This suggests the question whether we may think of the separation of the phyla in each superphylum as a radiation. Did very early metazoan groups of animals split up into lines each adapted to different environments and habits of life, and so give rise to the phyla we now have?

This seems a probable view of the origin of the phyla. Since, as we have seen, adaptational change occurs chiefly in the later parts of development, we should expect the changes of structure which took place in such a radiation to be mainly changes in development after the stages of the trochosphere and pluteus larvæ. Now, when we compare the later development in each of the phyla, we find in each, after the stage of the trochosphere or pluteus, a development characteristic of the phylum and different from that in any other phylum. Often this development includes a metamorphosis in which the development is highly modified. Nevertheless, we can in most of the phyla make out how the structure of the adult is derived from that of

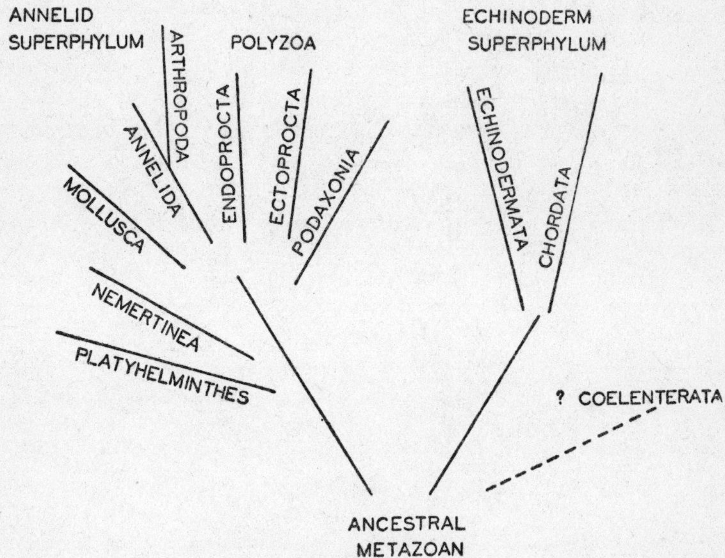

Figure 171. Evolutionary relationships of the invertebrate phyla.

the larva. We can also correlate the course of development in each phylum with the typical habit of life of the more primitive members of the phylum at the present time; we can see how the characteristic organs which are required for the mode of life followed in each phylum are formed in the development. If we do this, it seems that we shall be justified in concluding, however tentatively, that these organs were evolved in the radiation of the phylum, and that this radiation was in adaptation to the mode of life now led by primitive members of the phylum.

We will consider the phyla in turn (Fig. 172), beginning with the phyla of the annelid superphylum.

1. We must first put aside the Nemertea, for those of this phylum which possess a larva of the trochosphere type have so extreme a type

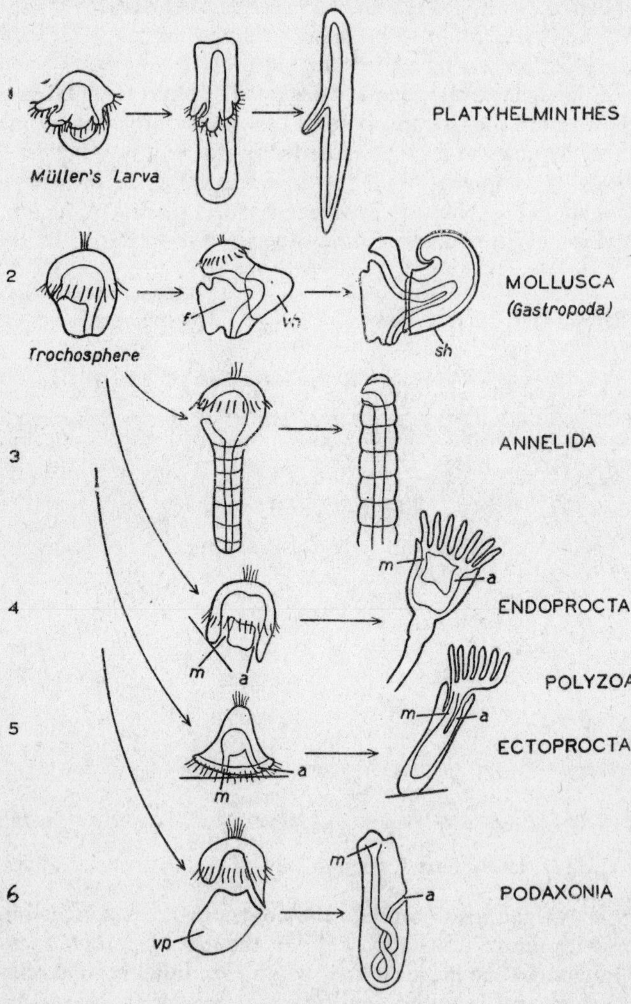

Figure 172. Later development and metamorphosis in the invertebrate phyla.

a, anus; *c*, cœlome; *f*, foot; *m*, mouth; *sh*, shell; *vh*, visceral hump; *vp*, ventral process.

of metamorphosis that it is almost impossible to correlate the structure of the adult and larva. The present-day habit is that of a free-living animal which moves by longitudinal expansion and contraction of the body, or by rhythmical swimming movements like those of an annelid.

2. In the Platyhelminthes the larva develops into the adult by growth in the anterior-posterior direction at both ends of the body, so that the mouth remains central. The prototroch degenerates. The less modified members of the phylum are free-moving animals gliding on the ventral surface (Turbellaria). We must regard the Platyhelminthes as a group which took on the habit of using the whole ventral surface for gliding on a solid substratum, and became flattened dorso-ventrally.

3. In the Annelida, metamorphosis occurs by outgrowth of the posterior part of the larva around the anus, and metameric segmentation of this outgrowth. This segmentation is, as we have seen (p. 372),

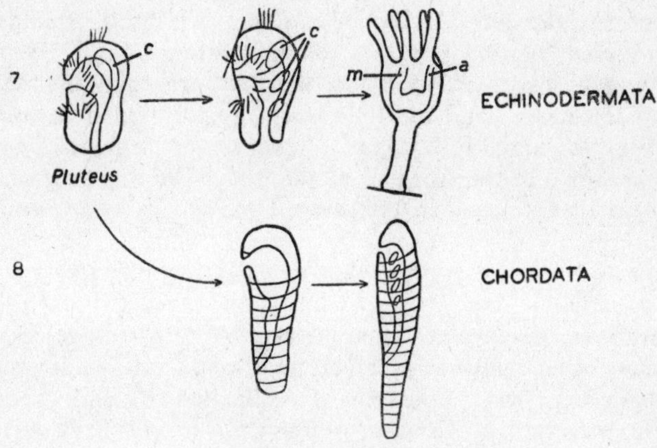

Figure 172 (*continued*).

associated with the annelid mode of locomotion, rhythmical contraction of the muscles. We must regard them as a free-living group which took on the habit of swimming in this way and developed the segmentation. From their typical mode of life they have later radiated in many directions.

The Arthropoda, being derived from the annelid stock after its original separation, do not here concern us.

4. The development of the Mollusca is characterised by the formation of two protuberances from the body of the larva, one ventral, the foot, and one dorsal, the visceral hump. Primitively, the molluscan foot is a locomotory organ on which the animal glides; the visceral hump, protected by the shell, contains most of the viscera. The molluscs seem to have been a group of animals which, like the Platyhelminthes, took to a gliding habit, but to gliding on the

part of the ventral surface behind the mouth, not on the whole ventral surface as the Platyhelminth did. Having developed a dorsal shelled process, the visceral hump, they did not become flattened dorso-ventrally. They also have later radiated very strongly.

5. The Podaxonia (Sipunculoidea and Phoronidea *) are a group which has taken to a tube-living or burrowing habit. In their development a ventral outgrowth between the mouth and anus is formed and develops into the part of the body which lies in the tube. This becomes by far the greater part of the body. We must suppose that they developed a ventral outgrowth in association with the habit of tube-living.

6. The two groups of the Polyzoa (Ectoprocta and Endoprocta *) are distinct lines both of which took on a sessile habit. In their development these two groups have free-swimming trochosphere larvæ which settle down on to a solid substratum by different parts of the ventral surface of the body, the Endoprocta by the region in front of the mouth and the Ectoprocta by the region between the mouth and the anus. In both, as in most sessile animals, the mouth and anus move to the free end of the body. We must regard them as two radiating lines which developed the sessile habit in different ways.

In the echinoderm superphylum we have to consider only two phyla.

1. Both the development and palæontology of the echinoderms show them to be a phylum which became sessile, settling down by the ventral region in front of the mouth,† as the Polyzoa Endoprocta did. In them also mouth and anus moved to the free end. They developed their radial symmetry in association with the sessile habit. Most of the modern forms have become secondarily free, but this is not true of the majority of fossil members of the phylum.

2. The Chordata remained free-living and developed the same type of locomotion as the annelids. In association with this habit they have developed, like the annelids, metameric segmentation. Their tail, however, differs from the body of the annelids in that it is posterior to the anus and not anterior to it. The Hemichordata (*Balanoglossus*) have no tail of the chordate type.

Although we cannot at present give their places in this scheme to some of the invertebrate phyla, it seems that we may regard most at any rate of the phyla as originating as radiating lines from two very early groups of metazoan animals which had larvæ similar in struc-

* The Phoronidea and Endoprocta are sometimes thought to belong to the echinoderm superphylum. See also note on p. 390.

† This is sometimes doubted of the Eleutherozoa.

ture to our present-day trochosphere and pluteus. These groups must have lived long before the beginning of the palæontological series. Probably not all the phyla were differentiated exactly simultaneously. The Platyhelminthes may, as we have seen (p. 394), have separated before the other phyla of the annelid superphylum. So, also, may the Nemertea. Many other points in the scheme must be left undecided. The primitive nature of the cœlome in the annelid superphylum is one of these. In the echinoderm superphylum the cœlome is undoubtedly enterocœlic, but in the annelid superphylum, although most of the phyla have schizocœlic cœlome the Phoronidea are enterocœlic.* It may be that the cœlome was originally enterocœlic in the annelid as well as the echinoderm superphylum, and that the schizocœlic cœlome was evolved from this original condition in the ancestral group of the annelid superphylum. If so, we may suppose that the Phoronidea were separated before the evolution of the schizocœlic cœlome, and therefore earlier than the schizocœlic phyla. We have already noted (p. 390) that there are great structural resemblances as well as differences between the trochosphere and the pluteus. We have seen that, unless we ascribe these resemblances to convergent evolution, we must conclude that both the ancestral groups of the superphyla must have arisen from a single metazoan stock. If so, and if at a still earlier time the cœlenterates arose from this stock, multicellular organisation has arisen at most twice in the evolution of animals, once in the sponges and once in the Metazoa.

It may be asked whether we can form any idea of the structure of the *adult* in these ancestral groups of the Metazoa. The ancestral group of each superphylum must have had the characters which are common to all the phyla of the superphylum descended from it. Both ancestral groups and their common ancestors would have had the characters which both superphyla possess. These include bilateral symmetry, triploblastic organisation, a ventral mouth and an anus. A few characters may be added to these. All these animals would probably have had ectodermal, tubular, excretory organs with either flame-cells or solenocytes, for such organs occur in both superphyla. They would also have had slight but definite cephalisation. And they would have been bottom-living, for we have seen (p. 369) that this was the probable mode of life of the early metazoan. The ancestors of the two superphyla would have differed from each other in the characters which distinguish the superphyla. But all the characters of this kind which we have discussed (p. 390) are characters of the development; there are hardly any adult characters which can be said to be characteristic of one superphylum and not present in the other.

* But see note, p. 398.

We can therefore say nothing of the differences between the adults of the ancestral groups of the two superphyla.

We may conclude that all these early metazoans were simple, soft-bodied, triploblastic, bilaterally symmetrical, unsegmented, bottom-living animals with slight cephalisation, a ventral mouth, an anus, and probably tubular ectodermal excretory organs. Beyond these statements it is not possible to go.

BIBLIOGRAPHY

The following list of books and articles is intended to give suggestions for further reading.

GENERAL TEXT-BOOKS

Morphology

L. A. BORRADAILE AND OTHERS, *The Invertebrata*, Cambridge Univ. Press, 3rd edtn. revised by G. A. Kerkut, 1958.

Physiology

L. E. BAYLISS, *Principles of General Physiology*, Longmans Green, 1960.

E. PONDER, *Essentials of General Physiology*, Longmans Green, 1929.

L. V. HEILBRUNN, *Outlines of General Physiology*, Saunders, Philadelphia, 1937.

P. H. MITCHELL, *Text-book of General Physiology*, McGraw-Hill, 1938.

V. B. WIGGLESWORTH, *The Principles of Insect Physiology*, Methuen, 1939.

CHAPTER II

Protoplasm and the Cell

J. GRAY, *Experimental Cytology*, Cambridge Univ. Press, 1931.

R. CHAMBERS, "Micrurgical Studies of Protoplasm," Biol. Rev., **24**, 246, 1949.

W. SEIFRIZ, *Protoplasm*, McGraw-Hill, 1936.

——, "Permeability," Ann. Rev. Physiol., **7**, 35, 1945.

Mitochondria and Golgi Bodies

G. BOURNE, *Cytology and Cell Physiology*, Clarendon Press, Oxford, 1942.

J. R. BAKER, Quar. J. micr. Sci., **85**, 1, 1944; **87**, 441, 1946; **88**, 463, 1947.

Fixation, etc.

W. B. HARDY, "The Structure of Cell Protoplasm," Jour. Physiol., **24**, 158, 1898.

J. R. BAKER, *Cytological Technique*, Methuen, 1933.

The Microscope

S. H. GAGE, *The Microscope*, Comstock, New York, 1936.

Biochemistry

T. R. PARSONS, *Fundamentals of Biochemistry*, Heffer, 1939.

E. BALDWIN, *An Introduction to Comparative Biochemistry*, Cambridge Univ. Press, 1937.

N. U. MELDRUM, *Cellular Respiration*, Methuen, 1934.

E. HOLMES, *The Metabolism of Living Tissues*, Cambridge Univ. Press, 1937.

CHAPTER III

Essential Structure of the Cell

E. B. Wilson, *The Cell in Development and Heredity*, Macmillan, New York, 1928.

General Cytology, edited by E. V. Cowdry, Chicago Univ. Press, 1924.

C. D. Darlington, *Recent Advances in Cytology*, Churchill, 1938.

——, *The Evolution of Genetic Systems*, Cambridge Univ. Press, 1939.

CHAPTER IV

The Free-living Cell

GENERAL

E. A. Minchin, *An Introduction to the Protozoa*, Arnold, 1917.

C. M. Wenyon, *Protozoology*, Baillière, Tindall and Cox, 1926.

G. N. Calkins, *The Biology of the Protozoa*, Baillière, Tindall and Cox, 1926.

FORM

W. D'Arcy Thompson, *Growth and Form*, Cambridge Univ. Press, 1942.

SIZE

J. B. S. Haldane and J. S. Huxley, *Animal Biology*, Oxford Univ. Press, 1927.

H. G. Wells, J. S. Huxley, and G. P. Wells, *The Science of Life*, Cassell, 1929.

ORGANS OF THE CELLS

J. Gray, *Ciliary Movement*, Cambridge Univ. Press, 1928.

C. F. A. Pantin, on "The Physiology of Amœbid Movement," Jour. mar. biol. Assn., **13**, 24, 1923.

J. A. Kitching, "Contractile Vacuoles," Biol. Reviews, **13**, 403, 1938.

CHAPTER V

Life-histories

G. N. Calkins, *The Biology of the Protozoa*, Baillière, Tindall and Cox, 1926.

H. S. Jennings, *Life and Death, Heredity and Evolution in Unicellular Organs*, Badger, Boston, 1920.

M. Robertson, "Life-cycles in the Protozoa," Biol. Reviews, **4**, 152, 1929.

C. V. Taylor, "Protoplasmic Reorganisation and Animal Life-cycles," Biol. Reviews, **10**, 111, 1935.

J. H. Beale, *The Genetics of Paramecium*, Cambr. Univ. Press, 1954.

Ecology

A. S. Pearse, *Animal Ecology*, McGraw-Hill, New York, 1930.

P. S. Welch, *Limnology*, McGraw-Hill, New York, 1935.

K. E. Carpenter, *Life in Inland Waters*, Sidgwick and Jackson, 1928.

F. S. Russell and C. M. Yonge, *The Seas*, Warne, 1928.

Behaviour

H. S. Jennings, *The Behaviour of the Lower Organisms*, Columbia Univ. Press, 1906.

S. O. MAST, *Light and the Behaviour of Organisms*, John Wiley, New York, 1911.

——, "Factors involved in the Process of Orientation of the Lower Organisms in Light," Biol. Reviews, **13**, 186, 1938.

J. LOEB, *Forced Movements, Tropisms and Animal Conduct*, Lippincott, Philadelphia, 1918.

CHAPTER VI

L. A. BORRADAILE AND OTHERS, *The Invertebrata*, ch. IV, Cambridge Univ. Press, 1935.

J. S. HUXLEY, *The Individual in the Animal Kingdom*, Cambridge Univ. Press, 1912.

CHAPTER VII

Uncontrolled Growth

T. S. P. STRANGEWAYS, *Tissue Culture in Relation to Growth and Differentiation*, Heffer, 1924.

E. N. WILLMER, "Tissue Culture from the Point of View of General Physiology," Biol. Reviews, **3**, 271, 1928.

E. N. WILLMER, *Tissue Culture*, Methuen, 1935.

W. SEIFRIZ, *Protoplasm*, ch. V, McGraw-Hill, 1936.

Dedifferentiation

J. S. HUXLEY AND G. R. DE BEER, *The Elements of Experimental Embryology*, ch. VII, Cambridge Univ. Press, 1934.

J. S. HUXLEY, Quar. J. micr. Sci., **65**, 1921.

Form and Environment

C. WESENBURG-LUND in *A Bathymetrical Survey of Scottish Freshwater Lochs*, Murray and Pullar, Challenger Office, Edinburgh, 1910.

L. A. BORRADAILE, *The Animal and its Environment*, Hodder and Stoughton, 1923.

CHAPTERS VIII, IX

Axial Organisation

C. M. CHILD, *Senescence and Rejuvenescence*, Chicago Univ. Press, 1915.

——, *Individuality in Organisms*, Lippincott, Chicago, 1915.

J. S. HUXLEY AND G. R. DE BEER, *The Elements of Experimental Embryology*, chs. VIII–X, Cambridge Univ. Press, 1934.

Regeneration

T. H. Morgan, *Experimental Embryology*, Columbia Univ. Press, 1927.

N. J. BERRILL, "Regeneration in Sabella and other sabellid worms," J. exp. Zool., **58**, 405, 1931.

Reconstitution

J. S. HUXLEY, "Some Phenomena of Regeneration in Sycon," Phil. Trans. R.S. London, **202B**, 165, 1911.

——, "Further Studies in Reconstitution Bodies and Tissue-culture in Sycon," Quar. J. micr. Sci., **65**, 293, 1921.

" Organisers "

C. H. WADDINGTON, *How Animals Develop*, Allen and Unwin, 1935.

——, *Principles of Embryology*, Allen & Unwin, 1956.

H. SPEMANN, *Embryonic Development and Induction*, Yale Univ. Press, 1938.

CHAPTER X

Growth and Form

J. S. HUXLEY, *Problems of Relative Growth*, Methuen, 1932.

C. CHAMPY, *Sexualité et Hormones*, Doin, Paris, 1924.

G. R. DE BEER, *Growth*, Arnold, 1924.

CHAPTER XII

Diffusion

D. BURNS, *An Introduction to Biophysics*, Churchill, 1921.

A. KROGH, *The Anatomy and Physiology of Capillaries*, Yale Univ. Press, 1922.

J. BARCROFT, *Architecture of Physiological Function*, Cambridge Univ. Press, 1938.

CHAPTER XIII

Respiration

J. S. HALDANE AND J. G. PRIESTLEY, *Respiration*, Oxford Univ. Press, 1935.

J. BARCROFT, *Respiratory Function of the Blood*, I and II, Cambridge Univ. Press, 1925, 1928.

A. KROGH, *Comparative Physiology of Respiration*, Univ. Pennsylvania Press, 1941.

Respiratory Pigments

J. BARCROFT, "The Significance of Hæmoglobin in sub-mammalian forms of life," Physiol. Reviews, **5**, 596, 1925.

A. C. REDFIELD, "The Hæmocyanins," Biol. Reviews, **9**, 175, 1934.

H. M. FOX, "Blood Circulation in Animals possessing Chlorocruorin," Proc. R.S. London, **112B**, 479, 1933.

M. FLORKIN, "La Courbe de Dissociation de l'Oxyhémerythrin dans la liquide cœlomique de Sipunculus," C.R. Acad. Sci., **195**, 832, 1932.

——, *Biochemical Evolution*, translated and augmented by S. Morgulis, Academic Press, New York, 1949.

Anærobiosis

W. K. SLATER, "Anærobic Life in Animals," Biol. Reviews, **3**, 303, 1928.

Tracheal System

V. B. WIGGLESWORTH, *Insect Physiology*, Methuen, 2nd Edn., 1951.

CHAPTER XIV

Food-collection

C. M. YONGE, "Feeding Mechanisms in the Invertebrates," Biol. Reviews, 3, 1, 1928.

H. S. JENNINGS, *Behaviour of the Lower Organisms*, Columbia Univ. Press. 1906.

J. H. ORTON, "The ciliary Mechanism of the Gill and Mode of Feeding in Amphioxus, etc.", J. mar. biol. Assn., U.K., **10**, 19, 1913.

H. G. CANNON, "The Feeding Mechanism of the Branchiopoda," Phil. Trans. R.S. London, **222B**, 1933.

Digestion

C. M. YONGE, "Digestive Processes in Marine Invertebrates and Fishes," J. Cons. Explor. Mér, **6**, 175, 1931.

——, "Evolution and Adaptation in the Digestive System of the Metazoa," Biol. Reviews, **12**, 87, 1937.

Nematocysts

J. MEIXNER, "Über die Kleptokniden von Microstomum lineare," Biol. Centralbl., **43**, 559, 1923.

A. GRAHAM, "The Structure and Function of the Alimentary Canal of Æolid Molluscs with a Discussion of their Nematocysts," Trans. R.S. Edin., **59**, 267, 1938.

CHAPTER XV

Osmotic Control and Excretion

A. KROGH, *Osmotic Regulation in Aquatic Animals*, Cambridge Univ. Press, 1939.

E. BALDWIN, *An Introduction to Comparative Biochemistry*, Cambridge Univ. Press, 1937.

J. NEEDHAM, "Correlation between Uricotelic Metabolism and Habitat in the Phylum Mollusca," Bioch. J., **29**, 238, 1935.

L. E. R. PICKEN, "The Mechanism of Urine Formation in the Invertebrates," Jour. exp. Biol., **13**, 309, **14**, 20, 1936–7.

E. S. GOODRICH, "The Study of Nephridia and Genital Ducts since 1895," Quar. J. micr. Sci., **86**, 113, 303, 1945.

CHAPTER XVI

Co-ordination

NERVOUS

W. H. NEWTON, "Conduction and Excitation in Nerve," in Evans' *Recent Advances in Physiology* (5th edition), Churchill, 1936.

A. D. RITCHIE, "The All-or-None Principle," Biol. Reviews, **7**, 336, 1932.

E. D. ADRIAN, *The Basis of Sensation*, Christophers, 1928.

——, *The Mechanism of Nervous Action*, Oxford Univ. Press, 1935.

C. F. A. PANTIN, "The Nerve-net of the Actinozoa," J. exp. Biol., **12**, 119, 139, 156, 389, 1935.

D. M. HALL AND C. F. A. PANTIN, "The Nerve-net of the Actinozoa," J. exp. Biol., **14**, 71, 1937.

J. GRAY AND H. W. LISSMANN, "Locomotory Reflexes in the Earthworm," J. exp. Biol., **15**, 506, 1938.

J. A. C. NICOL, "Giant Fibres in Annelids," Quar. Rev. Biol., **23**, 219, 1948.

CHEMICAL

B. HANSTRÖM, *Hormones in the Invertebrates*, Oxford, Clarendon Press, 1939.

G. H. Parker, *Humoral Agents in Nervous Activity*, Cambridge Univ. Press, 1932.

——, *Animal Colour Changes*, Cambridge Univ. Press, 1948.

J. S. Huxley, "Chemical Regulation and the Hormone Concept," Biol. Reviews, **10**, 427, 1935.

V. B. Wigglesworth, *The Physiology of Insect Metamorphosis*, Cambr. Univ. Press, 1954.

A. D. Lees, *Diapause in Arthropods*, Cambr. Univ. Press, 1955.

CHAPTER XVII

Receptor Organs

W. von Buddenbrock, *Grundriss der vergl. Physiologie*, Borntraeger, Berlin, 1928.

G. H. Parker, *The Elementary Nervous System*, Lippincott, Philadelphia, 1919.

H. Eltringham, *The Senses of Insects*, Methuen, 1933.

W. von Buddenbrock, "Die Physiologie des Facettenauges," Biol. Rev., **10**, 283, 1935.

R. J. Pumphrey and A. F. Rawdon Smith, "Frequency Discrimination in Insects," Nature, **143**, 806, 1939.

R. J. Pumphrey, "Hearing in Insects," Biol. Reviews, **15**, 107, 1940.

CHAPTER XVIII

Effector Organs

J. Gray, *Ciliary Movement*, Cambridge Univ. Press, 1928.

G. C. Hirsch, "The Theory of Fields of Restitution with Special Reference to Phenomena of Secretion," Biol. Reviews, **6**, 88, 1931.

A. D. Ritchie, *The Comparative Physiology of Muscular Tissues*, Cambridge Univ. Press, 1928.

C. F. A. Pantin, "The Excitation of Crustacean Muscle," J. exp. Biol., **11**, 11, 1934; **13**, 111, 148, 159, 1936.

G. H. Parker, "Chromatophores," Biol. Reviews, **10**, 59, 1930.

E. Newton Harvey, *The Nature of Animal Light*, Lippincott, Philadelphia, 1920.

CHAPTER XIX

The Physiology of Sponges

G. H. Parker, *The Elementary Nervous System*, Lippincott, Philadelphia, 1919.

G. P. Bidder, "The Relation of the Form of a Sponge to its Currents," Quar. J. micr. Sci., **67**, 293, 1923.

——, "The Perfection of Sponges," Proc. Linn. Soc., London, 119, 1936–7.

CHAPTER XX

Life-histories of the Invertebrates

T. H. Morgan, *Experimental Embryology*, Columbia Univ. Press, 1927.

J. Loeb, *The Organism as a Whole*, Putnam, 1916.

A. Dalcq, *Form and Causality in Early Development*, Cambridge Univ. Press, 1938.

G. R. de Beer, *An Introduction to Experimental Embryology*, Oxford, Clarendon Press, 1926.

CHAPTER XXI

Behaviour

H. S. Jennings, *The Behaviour of the Lower Organisms*, Columbia Univ. Press, 1906.

J. Loeb, *Forced Movements, Tropisms and Animal Conduct*, Lippincott, Philadelphia, 1918.

N. R. F. Maier and T. C. Schneirla, *Principles of Animal Psychology*, McGraw-Hill, 1935.

F. Alverdes, *The Psychology of Animals*, Kegan Paul, 1932.

T. B. Barnes, *General Physiology*, Blakiston, Philadelphia, 1937.

E. S. Russell, *The Behaviour of Animals*, Arnold, 1934.

A. D. Imms, *Social Behaviour in Insects*, Methuen, 1931.

G. S. Fraenkel and D. L. Gunn, *The Orientation of Animals*, Oxford Univ. Press, 1940.

W. H. Thorpe, *Learning and Instinct in Animals*, Methuen, 1954.

CHAPTER XXII

Habits of Life

A. S. Pearse, *Animal Ecology*, McGraw-Hill, 1939.

L. A. Borradaile, *The Animal and its Environment*, Hodder and Stoughton, 1923.

CHAPTER XXIII

Evolution

E. W. MacBride, *Text-book of Embryology*, vol. I, Macmillan, 1914.

A. Richards, *An Outline of Comparative Embryology*, Wiley, 1931.

A. K. Wells, *Outline of Historical Geology*, Allen and Unwin, 1938.

INDEX

Arabic figures refer to the pages, roman figures to the plates.